ELEMENTARY LOGIC

ELEMENTARY LOGIC

MICHAEL D. RESNIK

Department of Philosophy
University of North Carolina

McGRAW-HILL BOOK COMPANY

NEW YORK   ST. LOUIS   SAN FRANCISCO
LONDON   SYDNEY   TORONTO
MEXICO   PANAMA

ELEMENTARY LOGIC

Library of Congress Catalog Card Number 69-13613

51897

1234567890   MAMM   7654321069

PREFACE

There are many logic texts — some very excellent. The novelty of this book is that it attempts to provide a complete and technically rigorous treatment of deductive logic which will also be comprehensible to the average undergraduate who has had no previous university training in logic or mathematics. To this end elegance and brevity of style have sometimes given way to pedagogic necessities.

The book covers quantification theory, identity, and descriptions, but elementary portions of the theories of classes and relations are also introduced as applications of quantificational logic. The influence of two of my teachers is evident throughout the book. To Willard Van Orman Quine the book owes its basic organization, its philosophical bent, and its emphasis upon semantics. To Frederic Benton Fitch it owes its subordinate-proof approach to natural deduction. Of my own doing there is an extensive treatment of applications, not only to ordinary language but also to the foundations of both mathematics and electronics.

The Introduction preceding Part One reviews the principles of logic and concepts that are basic to any study of logic. Therefore, the student should prepare for the main body of the text by familiarizing himself with this introductory section.

Part One covers truth-function theory. Truth tables are combined with some of Quine's methods to treat the semantic concepts of validity, implication, and equivalence. The syntactic concepts of proof and derivation are developed via Fitch's method of subordinate proofs. There is also a substantial section on switching and sequential circuits which includes treatments of binary numbers and circuit-design problems.

Part Two develops one-variable quantification theory. This is monadic-quantification theory with one variable, and thus occupies an intermediate position between the full-monadic theory and Quine's uniform-quantification theory. I find that this approach permits the introduction of the basic concepts of quantificational logic without encountering the "engineering problems" that arise when more than one variable is present. It is in the treatment of quantification theory that my chief compromise with rigor occurs. Instead of developing a completely set theoretic semantics, I have used open sentences as a device for interpreting predicate letters. The Fitch method is used for the presentation of universal generalization and existential instantiation. Although this makes the proofs of a few simple schemata rather complex, it does have the theoretical advantage that every derivation is sound in all its lines. I also hope that the pedagogic advantages of this approach will be readily apparent from my exposition. This part concludes with an application of the one-variable theory to the virtual theory of classes.

Part Three presents the remainder of quantification theory. The open-sentence interpretation of predicate letters gives way to a logical-predicate interpretation. In addition, several metatheoretic laws of the semantics of quantification theory are proved.

Part Four covers a variety of extensions and applications of quantificational logic. The book is less thorough here, and the reader and instructor are called upon to supply more of the details: but anyone who has made it this far should find little difficulty in so doing. Identity theory, the theory of descriptions, and the logic of relations are found in this Part. There is also an extensive discussion of formal systems, with the theory of densely ordered sets, group theory, and kinship theory forming examples. This is also the occasion for a treatment of definitions and the contextual definition of definite descriptions.

The Appendix contains soundness and completeness proofs for the rules of inference used in the book. Henkin's approach to this problem has been used since it nicely avoids prenex normal forms.

This book can be used in several courses. I have covered Parts One and Two in a one-semester course for freshman, but one could devote a whole semester to Part One and the relevant sections of the Appendix. The entire book could be used as a one-year undergraduate course or as a brisk one-semester graduate course. There are several other options, however, since one can stop with any single Part and have a fairly complete presentation of the portion of logic covered. Also, several sections dealing with applications can be omitted without any loss of continuity.

I should like to thank the many students who have suffered with drafts of this book for their helpful comments and reactions. Eric Walther used the book in his lectures and has been responsible for several improvements. Of the graduate students who have assisted me in teaching, Kuan T. Fann, Michael Makibe, and James L. Stiver have made an extra effort to make the book a success. Richard C. Jeffrey's valuable criticisms have also led to important changes in the book. I am especially indebted to Nuel D. Belnap, Jr., who read several drafts of the text. His many comments have saved the book from several blunders and have led to as many improvements. At the same time his encouragement made it possible for me to complete these revisions. Of course, the responsibility for any remaining inadequacies is mine.

I would also like to thank my wife Janet for her general encouragement and particular help in preparing the index.

MICHAEL D. RESNIK

CONTENTS

ELEMENTARY LOGIC

INTRODUCTION

Logic is concerned with arguments, inferences, and reasoning. Such concerns are important to all of us, even in everyday life. For we use arguments not only to convince others, we use them also to come to decisions and to determine facts. This can be seen by considering some cases and examples. To persuade someone that he should not drop out of high school, we might argue as follows:

> Only the most menial work is available today to those without a high school education. You desire better work than menial work. So you should complete your high school education.

In deciding whether to go surfing or to the movies, you might reason:

> If I go to the movies, I will have to spend all my money for admission. And if I do this, I will have to go without dinner. But I could not stand that. On the other hand, it will not cost me anything to surf; so I'll go surfing.

The scientist is another logic user. He deduces predictions from his scientific theory and then makes experiments and observations to see if his predictions are true. If they are, he infers that his theory is confirmed, but if they are not, he looks for a mistake in his theory. In weighing evidence a jury reasons and argues as it tries to establish the facts of the case. A murder-trial jury might proceed as follows:

> If the accused was in Rome on July 11, he could not have committed the murder. His attorney has introduced a Roman hotel register with the accused's name on the July 11 entry. The hotel is pretty shady, but it is still probable that the accused signed on July 11. Hence it is probably true that he was in Rome then, and there is a reasonable doubt as to his guilt.

Mathematicians also use logic to prove mathematical theorems; philosophers use it in constructing philosophical arguments. Some theologians used it to try to prove the existence of God. Here is a version of a theological proof known as the ontological argument for the existence of God:

God is the greatest conceivable being. If He did not exist, we could conceive of an even greater being, namely, one who had all God's attributes and also existed. But this would contradict the fact that God is the greatest conceivable being; hence God must exist.

The examples show that the business of logic is at the heart of our practical and theoretical activities.

In recent times logic has been subjected to a mathematical treatment. As a result, modern logicians have been able to achieve important insights into the structure and foundations of mathematics. On the more practical side, they have succeeded in making important contributions to the design and use of electronic computers. Thus the study of logic is well worth the effort of the student of today. This book will develop the basic elements of modern logic, and study arguments and inferences with its aid.

0.1 LOGIC AND PSYCHOLOGY

Logicians are not interested in the hunches, intuitions, or guesses that we use in constructing arguments. They study arguments, but they do not care about the thoughts we may have when we construct an argument. In short, the logician is not interested in psychological causes for our conclusions; rather, he is interested in our rationalizations of these conclusions. Thus Smith may believe that man could not have descended from the apes, because he abhors apes, having been bitten by one as a child. The logician cares not a whit for this, but he is interested in the evidence Smith gives for his belief and the manner in which he argues. In other words, the logician is interested in reasoning, and especially when the reasoner's conclusions and his grounds for them are formulated in written or spoken discourse. The logician is neither a psychologist, a psychoanalyst, nor a mind reader; instead, he concerns himself with written or spoken arguments and attempts to judge their merits.

0.2 ARGUMENTS

The logician's use of the term 'argument' is slightly different from some of its more common uses. One can offer a logical argument without being involved in dispute. Indeed, a person who offers an argument need not have any emotional involvement with the conclusion he attempts to establish. To the logician an argument is not a fight or a dispute, it is merely a certain body of discourse. More exactly, logicians characterize arguments as follows:

An argument *is a sequence of two or more statements, some of which are offered in support of (as evidence for) another.*

This means that every argument contains one statement which the argument is supposed to establish—its conclusion—and one or more other statements which are supposed to support this conclusion.

Notice that not all sequences of statements are arguments. Even the following abstract and highfalutin prose is not an argument:

Some children suffer from the Oedipus complex, while others are orally fixated. The former tend to have difficulties in making marital adjustments. The latter are often very heavy smokers.

There is no argument here because there is no conclusion. Instead, two different types of children are recognized, and something is said about each. On the other hand, the following is an argument:

Oral fixates tend to be heavy smokers. Blake is a heavy smoker. Thus Blake may be an oral fixate.

Here there is a definite conclusion, and statements are offered to support it.

The phrase "offered in support of" contained in the characterization of arguments must be emphasized. Its inclusion allows for the possibility of incorrect arguments. When a person who wants to establish a given conclusion states that conclusion and offers evidence for it, his statements count as an argument even if he does not succeed in establishing his conclusion. Thus, when we examine a piece of discourse to ascertain whether it is an argument or not, its author's intentions are the decisive factor. We classify the discourse as an argument if and only if we decide that it contains a conclusion which its author is attempting to establish. On these grounds the following is an argument, although it certainly is not a good one:

The course is graded on a curve. If the teacher puts on a blindfold and picks the examination papers out of a box and assigns grades according to the order in which the papers are selected, then ghe grades will form a curve. So this is the best way for the teacher to grade on the curve.

This discourse is an argument simply because it contains a conclusion about how to grade the course and reasons, albeit bad ones, for grading it in this way. To show that this discourse contains a bad argument is, of course, an entirely different matter.

Often it is difficult to decide whether a sequence of statements is an argument. This is because most arguments are not presented in the form of simple textbook examples. A conclusion can be buried in the main body of the argument containing it. The presence of extraneous statements can obscure the conclusion and the evidence for it. Or the sequence of statements, of which the argument is composed, may be presented as one big statement. Or finally, the author of an argument may write complicated and unclear prose. Fortunately, languages contain devices which help determine whether something counts as an argument. *Inference words* such as 'hence', 'therefore', 'thus', 'whence', 'so', 'because', and 'since' are among the best linguistic clues to arguments, for they are used to indicate that a conclusion has been drawn. Careful attention to the context in which the discourse occurs is also very useful here. For example, consider the statement

Robinson committed the murder because he was jealous of Jones.

If the district attorney said this to the jury at Robinson's trial, then it would be a condensed version of the argument

Robinson was jealous of Jones. Thus Robinson committed the murder.

On the other hand, if the statement was made in response to a question, "Why did Robinson commit the murder?", then it would simply be a statement with no argument intended. It should also be realized that some discourse is so badly written that it is impossible to determine whether it contains an argument.

0.3 THE ELEMENTS OF AN ARGUMENT

It will be useful to have a method for classifying the statements which compose an argument. The *conclusion* of an argument has already been mentioned. This is the statement which the argument is designed to establish. The statements offered in support of the conclusion are called *premisses*. Thus, consider the argument

(1)   All bad men wear black hats.
(2)   Ringo is a bad man.
(3)   Hence Ringo wears a black hat.

The conclusion is (3), while (1) and (2) are premisses. It goes without saying that the conclusion need not be the last statement of an argument, nor need the premisses be the first. In the next argument the conclusion comes first and the single premiss last:

Most bald men wear hats.
For most bald men prefer to cover their baldness.

When an argument is critically evaluated, it is essential to determine its premisses and conclusion, for the argument is a good one if and only if the premisses provide good reasons for the conclusion.

The same statement can be a premiss of one argument and a conclusion for another, or conversely, it can be the conclusion of one argument and the premiss of another. Consider the arguments

(1)   Some cats are furry.
(2)   Hence some mammals are furry.

(3)   Some mammals are furry.
(4)   If some mammals are furry, no dogs are.
(5)   Thus no dogs are furry.

(6)   Either some dogs are furry or some cats are frisky.
(7)   No dogs are furry.
(8)   Therefore some cats are frisky.

The conclusion of the first argument is also a premiss of the second one, while the conclusion of the second argument is a premiss of the third, (7). This means that a statement is not *simply* a premiss or a conclusion, but rather a premiss or a conclusion *relative to a given* argument.

0.4   DEDUCTIVE VERSUS INDUCTIVE LOGIC

There are two main branches of logic, *deductive* and *inductive* logic. Deductive logic is concerned with the construction of arguments whose conclusions follow *necessarily* from their premisses, while inductive logic is concerned with the construction of arguments whose conclusions are only *probable* relative to their premisses. Both branches of logic are equally important and have their proper functions. Deductive logic has one of its most important applications in mathematics, because mathematical proofs consist solely of deductive arguments. On the other hand, in less abstract subjects, inductive logic is also an essential method of reasoning. Both methods of reasoning can be combined, and where inductive reasoning is used, it is rare to find a deductive reasoning lacking.

The difference between inductive and deductive reasoning can be clarified with an example. Let us suppose that Mr. Smith is a banker and that we want to demonstrate to someone that he is rich. First, let us suppose that we know that all bankers are rich. Then we could argue *deductively*

(1)   Mr. Smith is a banker.
(2)   All bankers are rich.
(3)   Hence Mr. Smith is rich.

Given what we know, Mr. Smith is certainly rich. More generally, the conclusion of a good deductive argument cannot be false if all its premisses are true. Next, let us suppose that we do not know whether all bankers are rich, but we do know that all bankers whom we have met before meeting Mr. Smith are rich. Then we could argue *inductively*

(4) Mr. Smith is a banker.
(5) All other bankers we have known have been rich.
(6) So Mr. Smith is rich.

Given what we are supposed to know in this case, Mr. Smith need not be rich. He could be the first poor banker we have met. Although (4) and (5) confer a high degree of probability on (6), (6) is not a necessary consequence of (4) and (5). They could both be true while (6) is false. In general, the conclusion to an inductive argument is only probable relative to its premisses.

Inductive arguments are (in a sense) weaker than deductive arguments. But this does not mean that it is wrong to use inductive logic. In many cases it is the only logic we can use. For often the information at our disposal is insufficient to support our conclusions deductively, although it does support them inductively. To forgo inductive logic, then, would be to give up the use of rational procedures altogether.

The study of inductive logic presupposes a firm grounding in deductive logic, while deductive logic is presently much more refined and exact than inductive logic. For this reason this book will be devoted almost exclusively to deductive logic.

0.5 LOGIC AS A SCIENCE

Most of you already possess a certain talent for reasoning well. You can construct good arguments and you can successfully criticize bad ones. Nonetheless, logic is still more or less an art for most of you. You still do not possess general principles for assessing and constructing arguments. This is where the logician differs from the layman. He does not have to depend upon insights, intuitions, or feelings. For him the correctness of an argument is an objective matter. He possesses general principles of argumentation and proof, which can be formulated precisely and communicated to others. Anyone who uses these principles will arrive at the same results in assessing and constructing arguments. In this way logic is as objective as physics or mathematics. Furthermore, although the layman may be able to tell us that a particular argument is incorrect, unlike the logician, he cannot state general principles to explain *why* the argument is wrong. Thus the objectivity, generality, and explanatory power of logic, all serve to make it a genuine science.

Logical theory is like many other scientific theories in that it has led to the design of "instruments" for "measuring" logical properties. *Tests* and *procedures* answering the central questions of logic will be presented in this book. These tests and procedures will be *purely mechanical;* that is, in principle, they can be carried out by means of machines. This is no longer just a matter of theory either, for in recent years electronic computers have been programmed to use these tests and procedures, and in many instances they are able to outperform humans. (It is likely that present-day computers could answer almost all the exercises in this book in an hour or so.) Thus one of the aims in this book is the design of "logic machines", that is, mechanical methods for solving logical problems. Most of these "machines" will not be presented in detail, since it will usually be clear that the methods in question are "mechanical".

0.6 STATEMENTS AND SENTENCES

The same form of words can be used by different people to *mean* different things. When, for example, Jones says 'I am hungry', he means that he, Jones, is hungry; but when Robinson says 'I am hungry', he *means* something quite different, namely, that Robinson is hungry. The same form of words can be used by the *same* person to mean different things. If in Honolulu you said 'It never snows here', you would have said something true, but if you uttered the same words in Anchorage, you would have said something false. In the first case you would have meant that it never snows in Honolulu; in the second case that it never snows in Anchorage. Thus not only can a person use the same words to mean different things, he can also use them to say something true on one occasion and something false on another.

According to ordinary high school grammar, a declarative *sentence* is a string of words which expresses a complete thought. Consequently, the term 'sentence' does not refer to complete thoughts themselves (for the sentence expresses these), but rather to forms of words. Let us use the term 'sentence', then, to refer to those forms of words which grammar classified as declarative sentences. The point of the last paragraph can now be restated as follows: The same sentence can be used to mean different things; moreover, the same sentence can be used to mean something true on one occasion and something false on another. (This does not necessarily hold for all sentences, but it certainly holds for the examples given above.)

Variations in the meaning of a sentence can also lead to logical difficulties. An example will illustrate this. Let us suppose that two men, Paul Smith and Paul Robinson, are in love with the same girl. Let us also suppose that the girl loves Paul Smith and has indicated so by responding eagerly to his kisses. Finally, let us suppose that Paul Robinson argues as follows:

(1)　If you responded to Paul's kisses, you love Paul.
(2)　You did respond to Paul's kisses.
(3)　But I am Paul.
(4)　So you love me.

Obviously, this would be a bad joke at best. The strength that the argument *seems* to have derives from an equivocation upon the word 'Paul'. If it is taken to refer to Paul Smith, (1) and (2) are true, but then (3) is false. In any case, the whole argument is a good deductive argument only if 'Paul' retains the same meaning throughout. Only then do the premisses necessitate the conclusion. On the other hand, if the meaning of 'Paul' is fixed so that the conclusion will follow necessarily from the premisses, then at least one of the premisses will be false. And no one has to accept a conclusion drawn from false premisses, even if the chain of reasoning *from these premisses* is perfectly correct. Bad arguments like this one which trade upon various meanings of a word are called *fallacies of equivocation*. They will be encountered again later in the book.

Because of difficulties such as the fallacy of equivocation, many logicians have urged that *statements* must be distinguished from *sentences*. Statements are then taken as the *meanings sentences have at their times of utterance*. Thus, when someone uses the same sentence at different times to mean different things, he has used the same sentence to make different statements. Statements also have the advantage of not changing from true to false or from false to true, or, as the logicians say, statements do not alter their *truth-values*. What someone states on a given occasion, that is, the statement he makes, is true just in case it corresponds to the facts. There is no changing what has been stated or the facts; thus the statement someone makes on a given occasion is either true or false, and its truth-value never changes from true to false or conversely. (A person can retract a statement, that is, admit that he was wrong in making it. Or he can deny making it, but none of this changes the statement or its truth-value.)

By appealing to statements, we can also disregard nuances in the wording of an argument, or even the language (French, German, English, etc.) in which it is expressed. For example, by appealing to statements, we can say that each of the following triads of sentences expresses the same argument:

(1)　Quand il pleut, il neige.
(2)　Il pleut.
(3)　Donc il neige.

(1′)   When it rains, it snows.
(2′)   It rains.
(3′)   Hence it snows.

(1″)   If it rains, it snows.
(2″)   It is raining.
(3″)   So it is snowing.

For although each triad is composed of different sentences, each has the same statements as premises and the same statement as its conclusion.

Although the introduction of statements has its obvious advantages, a number of logicians have argued that there are strong theoretical grounds for denying that there are such things as statements. They urge that the problems, such as differences in meaning, which the introduction of statements is designed to solve can be handled adequately in terms of sentences alone. These problems are too involved to consider in this book. In any case, the issues at stake can be appreciated only after one has an understanding of the topics to be treated here.

Although the issue about statements is rather controversial, it is very convenient to talk *as if* there are statements. This is the way we shall talk in this book. With some effort, however, most of what will be said can be said without talking about statements.

0.7   VALIDITY

One of the most important words in the *technical* vocabulary of logic is the word 'valid'. This is the term which logicians use to characterize *deductive* arguments whose premises necessitate their conclusions. As a term of deductive logic, it is not used with respect to inductive arguments. In fact, even the best arguments of inductive logic are not valid in the technical sense. Most of this book will be devoted to giving a precise description of the class of valid arguments. Since none of the other technical terms of logic have been explained yet, it is not possible to present an exact definition of the term 'valid' now. However, some approximations to the ultimate definition will be useful to consider.

A valid deductive argument is supposed to be one whose premises necessitate its conclusion. This can be rephrased as follows:

A valid *argument is one whose conclusions follow logically from its premises.*

This does not help much, however, because the phrase 'follow logically' still needs to be explained. Since the conclusion of a valid argument follows logically from its premises, the conclusion must be true if the premisses are. This leads to the following description:

A valid *argument is one whose conclusion cannot be false if its premisses are all true.*

This is still not much of an explanation since the word 'cannot' must mean 'cannot on logical grounds', and we still do not know what logical grounds are. But the second description does have an advantage over the first. It shows us that certain arguments are not valid, namely, arguments with premisses which are all true and conclusions which are false. Let us call these arguments 'patently invalid'; that is,

A patently invalid *argument is one whose premisses are all true and whose conclusion is false.*

Clear patently invalid arguments are not valid, for in a valid argument the conclusion must be true if all the premisses are.

The concept of patent invalidity provides a simple method for showing that a limited number of arguments are not valid. One merely points out that each of the premisses is true and that the conclusion is false. Thus, consider the argument

(1)   No woman has been a President of the U.S.A.
(2)   No women are fathers.
(3)   Hence no Presidents of the U.S.A. are fathers.

This argument is obviously not valid since it is patently invalid.

Statements are true or false. Arguments, on the other hand, are valid or invalid, but are neither true nor false. We do not say that an argument is true or false any more than we say that a number is young or old. Good deductive arguments must lead from true premisses to true conclusions. Those with all true premisses and false conclusions obviously fail to do this, and so they have been called patently invalid. But deductive arguments can have one or more false premisses and true or false conclusions and still be valid. Thus we must look a little more closely at the connection between validity and truth.

The logician has a rather indirect interest in truth and facts. He is not so much interested in discovering whether, say, 'Every man has his price' is true or false as he is in discovering what can be *inferred* from its truth or falsity. Logic is an instrument for getting at the truth because it allows us to generate new truths from previously given truths. But how these initial truths are known is a matter of relative indifference to the logician. For all he cares, they could be falsehoods; this is because the logician asks not what is true, but rather, *given* that this and that are true, what else *must be* true. The logician is primarily concerned with the logical relationships between the statements which make up an argument. He is less concerned with their actual truth or falsity.

It should not seem strange, then, for false premisses or conclusions to occur in a valid argument. Indeed, the only case that cannot arise is that of the patent invalidity: the premisses are all true and the conclusion is false. The tenuous relationship between the validity of an argument and the truth of the statements it contains is summarized in the following table.

PREMISSES	CONCLUSION	ARGUMENT
All true	True	Valid or invalid
All true	False	Invalid
Some true, some false	True	Valid or invalid
Some true, some false	False	Valid or invalid
All false	True	Valid or invalid
All false	False	Valid or invalid

It will be noted that a valid argument may have premisses and conclusions having any combination of truth-values except that excluded by patent invalidity. It should also be noted that invalid arguments (except patently invalid ones) may share all the combinations with valid ones. It is easy to construct examples of invalid arguments to answer each line of the table. All one need do is choose two or more statements which are completely unrelated but which are appropriately true or false. Thus the following is an example of an invalid argument with a true and a false premiss and a true conclusion:

(1) $1 + 1 = 2$
(2) The sun never shines in Rome.
(3) Hence all men are mortal.

Since our logical principles are, as yet, few in number, we must rely on our logical "intuitions" to see that there is no logical connection between (1), (2), and (3), so that if (1) and (2) were true, (3) would not have to be. The reader can construct his own examples of invalid arguments for the other entries in the table.

It is more difficult to construct valid arguments; so examples for each position in the table follow. Once again, we must rely on our "intuitions", for we are not yet in a position to establish scientifically the validity of these arguments.

EXAMPLES OF VALID ARGUMENTS

a. True premisses, true conclusion:

All Greeks are men.

All men are mortal.
Hence all Greeks are mortal.

b.   True and false premisses, true conclusion:

Both 2 and 3 are even numbers (*false*).
If x is an even number, so is $x + 2$ (*true*).
$2 + 2 = 4$ (*true*).
Hence 4 is an even number (*true*).

c.   True and false premisses, false conclusion:

Both 2 and 3 are even numbers (*false*).
If x is an even number, so is $x + 2$ (*true*).
$3 + 2 = 5$ (*true*).
Hence 5 is an even number (*false*).

d.   False premisses, true conclusion:

Both 2 and 3 are even numbers (*false*).
Hence 2 is an even number (*true*).

e.   False premisses, false conclusion:

If silver were gold, then everyone would be rich (*false*).
Silver is gold (*false*).
So everyone will be rich (*false*).

Sound arguments are valid arguments whose premisses are all true. It follows that every sound argument is valid. However, not every valid argument is sound, because some valid arguments have one or more false premisses. Since the conclusion of a valid argument must be true if its premisses are, the conclusion of a sound argument must be true. This is why the best strategy is to offer sound arguments to demonstrate truths. An unsound argument is always open to at least one of the two criticisms: its conclusion might not follow logically from its premisses or one or more of its premisses might be false. Of course, it is not always possible to offer sound arguments. When this happens, it is clearly much better to offer a good inductive argument with true premisses than a valid deductive argument with false premisses.

Valid arguments which we know to be unsound or which we do not know to be sound may still be useful. Arguments of the former type may be used to demonstrate that a disputed statement is false. Arguments of the latter type can be used to reduce the question of the falsity of one statement to the question of the falsity of another more easily falsified statement. For example, let us suppose that Brown erroneously believes that every positive even number is the sum of two positive even numbers. Then we could demonstrate Brown's error by arguing

(1) Every positive even number is the sum of two positive even numbers (let us suppose).
(2) 2 is a positive even number.
(3) Hence 2 is the sum of two positive even numbers.

Since the argument is obviously valid — (2) is obviously true and (3) is obviously false — the falsity of (1) would become obvious to Brown. Yet here we should have employed an argument which we knew to be unsound. As another example, consider the case of the cancer researcher who suspects that cancer is not a virus but who reasons:

(4) Cancer is a virus (let us suppose).
(5) If cancer is a virus, then it is contagious.
(6) Therefore cancer is contagious.

Our researcher does not know whether cancer is a virus, and so he does not know whether his argument is sound. But since it is probably easier to show that cancer is not contagious (if this is true) than to show that it is not a virus, his reasoning could lead him to important avenues of research.

Questions of truth and falsity are usually not just questions of logic alone, but rather matters pertaining to the more specialized sciences. For this reason logicians place far less emphasis upon soundness than upon validity. But do not forget about soundness when you apply logic. An argument which is used to establish the *truth* of a statement is no better than its premisses.

0.8   LOGICAL FORM AND VALIDITY

The logician studies mathematical, scientific, theological, and legal arguments with equal ease. This is because he is not concerned with the subject matter of an argument, but only with the reasoning contained in it. Because the same principles of reasoning are applied in every field, logic has a wider range of application than any other discipline and is presupposed by them all. We have already seen that the truth or falsity of the statements in an argument plays a minor role in logic. Now we see that the subject matter of an argument is in the same boat. But if logic is not concerned with these aspects of an argument, then what does concern logic? The answer is: *the structure of an argument.*

The easiest way to understand what the structure of an argument is and why it is so important to logic is to consider some examples. First, look at these three arguments:

All men are mortals.
Socrates is a man.
Hence Socrates is a mortal.

All logic books are boring books.
This is a logic book.
Hence this is a boring book.

All Greeks are brave persons.
Plato is a Greek.
Hence Plato is a brave person.

By now you should have recognized a common pattern in these arguments, and it should be easy for you to invent new ones of the same pattern, say,

All elephants are mammals.
Dumbo is an elephant.
Hence Dumbo is a mammal.

Moreover, it should be clear that these forms of arguments fit this pattern:

All _____ are . . . .
***************** is a _____
Hence ******** is a . . . .

Each of these arguments is valid. Moreover, any argument which satisfies the same form must also be valid; its premises cannot be true and its conclusion false. Let us consider some other valid arguments which fit another pattern:

If Jones promised to pay, then he must pay.
Jones promised to pay.
So Jones must pay.

If $1 + 1 = 2$ then $2 + 2 = 4$
$1 + 1 = 2$
So $2 + 2 = 4$

If the Devil exists, then evil exists.
The Devil exists.
So evil exists.

This time the pattern exhibited is the following:

If _____, then . . . . . .
_____
So . . . .

Again, it is obvious that an argument which fits this pattern must also be valid. It should also be clear that in determining this we were able to disregard both the actual truth or falsity of any of the statements given and the subject matter treated in the examples.

What we have observed is completely general: *the validity of an argument depends upon its form alone.* Thus, to determine whether an argument is valid, we need only examine its form. An important consequence of this is that we can characterize the class of valid arguments by delimiting the forms of valid arguments. Accordingly, a great portion of our studies will be devoted to constructing and testing forms of arguments in order to determine whether they are forms of valid arguments.

0.9 REVEALING THE FORMS OF ARGUMENTS: SCHEMATA

The notion of the form of an argument would be useless if we did not have some clear and precise method for specifying argument forms. The form of an argument is determined by the *logical forms* of the statements which constitute it. Accordingly, the problem of argument forms reduces to the problem of statement forms. This problem, in turn, is handled by means of devices called *schemata* (singular, *schema*), which are used to diagram the logical forms of statements. A schema is related to a statement in the way that a blueprint is related to a building. A trained architect can draw a blueprint and then construct a building from it. He can also look at an existing building and obtain a blueprint of it. Logicians are similarly trained to construct schemata and obtain statements from them and to reverse this process and obtain schemata from statements. This will be one of the things you will learn in this book.

Schemata look a lot like ordinary sentences, but they are composed of symbols instead of words. Because of this, logic today is frequently known as *symbolic logic*, and it has a strong mathematical flavor. But the beginner should not be frightened of symbols or the mathematical atmosphere of logical studies. This book does not assume a mathematical background on the part of the reader, and beginning logic is a lot easier than college mathematics.

In terms of schemata, the assessment of an argument for validity reduces to three major steps:

1 Find schemata which diagram the premisses and conclusion of the argument.
2 Use these to obtain the form of the argument.
3 Perform operations (to be specified later) in order to ascertain whether the argument has a valid form.

0.10 IMPLICIT PREMISSES AND PARAPHRASES

Many arguments encountered in practical life are not readily amenable to the techniques which we shall subsequently develop. First, not all their premisses are explicitly stated. Second, their statements may have to undergo some paraphrasing before they can be diagrammed by schemata. Let us look into the matter of *implicit*, or *suppressed*, premisses first.

Consider the argument

(1) Tabby is a cat.
(2) So Tabby drinks milk.

If we were presented this in an ordinary nonacademic context, we could certainly accept it as convincing and correct. But we have time to be critical now, and a little thought shows that the argument is not valid *as it stands*. The premiss (1) could be true, and the conclusion (2) false. Of course, it is easy to make this argument valid by adding as a new premiss:

(3) All cats drink milk.

Ordinarily, it is completely unnecessary to add this premiss, as it is part of our background knowledge. Premisses such as (3), which are left "understood" but are necessary for an argument to be valid, are called *implicit*, or *suppressed*, premisses. In practice, it is unnecessary to make them explicit, since anyone who understands the arguments they belong to will supply them in his head, so to speak. Moreover, to avoid wordiness, the use of implicit premisses is a practical necessity. A one-page proof in a mathematical journal might run to ten or more pages if it were explicitly spelled out. But there is no need to do this in practice, since the implicit premisses in this case are part of the background knowledge of mathematicians specializing in the field of the journal. Yet, although implicit premisses are a boon in practical life, they can be a bane in applications in logic. For the techniques in logic are applicable to the *explicitly given* forms of arguments, and this means that arguments which have suppressed premisses will not be counted as valid unless these premisses are explicitly supplied. The solution to this problem seems simple enough: before assessing an argument one must be sure to supply all its implicit premisses.

This solution only *looks* simple, however. Let us suppose that we encountered an argument in a book on, say, political theory. We first take it as it stands and find that it is invalid. Would it be fair to conclude that the author's reasoning is faulty? Certainly not, if the argument becomes valid when we add another premiss which the author had obviously assumed implicitly. This might be easy enough. But what if it is not clear whether the author made any implicit assumptions? Since he is probably not available for questioning, our task becomes very difficult. All we can do is make an educated guess. On the other hand, we might realize that the argument depends on suppressed premisses but supply the wrong one. Thus our logical techniques have definite limitations when it comes to suppressed premisses. We may fail to supply any at all or we may supply wrong ones. Fortunately this cuts both ways. Our author, himself, may have been unaware of his implicit assumptions, and these assumptions may be faulty. Then it would be very proper to criticize him for using an argument whose validity depended upon dubious premisses. He might even make a worse mistake: he might implicitly assume the very thing he is trying to prove. Someone who commits this error is said to have *begged the question.* To illustrate this let us consider the argument

(4)   All Marxists are Communists.
(5)   Hence all Socialists are Communists.

This reasoning occurs from time to time in the discussions and writings of Conservatives, and Socialists object to it. They contend that an argument like this makes use of false implicit premisses, namely,

(6)   All Socialists are Marxists.

Socialists point out that Conservatives tacitly equate socialism, communism, and Marxism, and thus tacitly assume the truth of (6). Moreover, since Marxism and communism are almost the same, with the consequence that (5) and (6) are nearly equivalent, Socialists also object that this argument begs the question by tacitly assuming what it is supposed to establish.

This illustrates the complexities that the use of implicit premisses may entail. Similar problems arise when statements are diagrammed by schemata. For schemata are very exact and are like sentences in an artificial language, while most arguments are expressed in ordinary language, which is very flexible. The flexibility of ordinary language, however, also permits statements to be expressed vaguely, ambiguously, or incompletely. Thus, before a statement can be properly diagrammed by a schema, it may be necessary to paraphrase it so that it is expressed more fully and precisely. Sometimes this poses no problems. But sometimes it is not obvious how a statement should be paraphrased, and a thorough logical analysis of the statement may be needed to determine its proper form. To take an example, consider the simple argument

(7)   John married her before she became famous.

(8)   Hence John married her.

It turns out that the form of this argument is best given by paraphrasing (7) and (8) as

(9)   There is a time at which John married her, and this time is before the time at which she became famous.

(10)   Hence there is a time at which John married her.

Of course, now that the correct paraphrases have been presented, it is obvious that they are paraphrases of (7) and (8), but the real problem is that of finding the correct paraphrases.

When the language in which an argument is couched is complex, vague, or ambiguous, the problem of finding correct paraphrases is just as difficult as that of spotting implicit premisses. Instead of guessing at premisses, we shall have to guess at meanings. And mistaken guesses will lead to misrepresentations of an argument and, in turn, to incorrect evaluations of its validity or soundness. A misinterpretation of a premiss or the conclusion might cause us to assign an argument an invalid form when in fact it is valid, while a misinterpretation of a premiss might make us count it as false when in fact it is true.

It is essential to remember these problems connected with implicit premisses and paraphrasing when you use logic as a critical instrument. This is the only way you will be able to give an author a fair hearing. Errors are still possible, but the fault does not lie in *logic*. It is due to the nature of communication, since these errors are due to failures in communication, and such failures are inevitable (although fortunately infrequent). These considerations also point up the need for the author of an argument to express himself as clearly as possible (unless he is trying to mislead his audience).

Earlier it was stated that in this book mechanical tests and procedures will be developed for evaluating arguments. To be more accurate, these tests and procedures will *apply directly only to schemata*. It may be useful to think of these methods as forming an imaginary *logic computer* which is like an ordinary computer except that it handles logical rather than arithmetical problems. Just as the data for ordinary computers must be prepared and specially coded before the computer can handle them, so must the "data" for our logic computer be prepared and coded. Supplying implicit premisses and diagramming the logical forms of statements are parts of the data-preparation stage of logic. Schemata are "sentences" in the code which the logic computer reads. Moreover, data preparation for the logic computer is liable to human errors, just as is data preparation for ordinary computers. In both cases, these errors arise because imprecisely given data must be described in a very precise language.

EXERCISES FOR THE INTRODUCTION

A. Which of the following passages contain arguments? If a passage does contain an argument, specify the premises and conclusion.

   1.   All crows are black. Peeper is a crow. Hence Peeper is black.

   2.   People may be divided into two categories: those who are wide awake in the morning and those who cannot get going until about noon. The former are usually terrible bores; it is the others who are usually interesting.

   3.   Taxes will probably be raised this year. For the economy is going through an inflationary period and raising taxes will be an effective curb on inflation.

   4.   This money will be used to pay off my loan or to buy a new car. If I use it to pay off my loan, I will not have enough left to buy a new boat, and if I use it to buy a new car, I will not be able to go to Europe. So either I will not be able to buy a new boat or else I will not be able to go to Europe.

   5.   Substance is the ultimate stuff of which all material things are composed. It cannot be broken down into nonsubstances.

   6.   There must be simple substances. For compound substances exist and a compound is only a collection of simples.

   7.   It will be assumed that there is an undefined relation which holds between certain ordered pairs of points. If the relation holds between the pairs (A,B) and (C,D), we shall write '$A, B \psi C, D$' and read this as '(A,B) is congruent to (C,D)'.

   8.   All dogs are furry animals, while some dogs have short tails. Consequently, some short-tailed animals are furry.

   9.   Spaniels and beagles have long ears, while boxers and bulldogs have short tails. Long-eared dogs have trouble with ticks, and this problem doubles if the dog also has long hair. Many more beagles than spaniels are found in tick-infested areas.

   10. If St. Paul had a vision, there is a record of it in the New Testament. Thus St. Paul did have a vision. For there is a record of one in the New Testament.

   11. Bentham and Mill both proposed that what is ultimately desirable is the greatest good for the greatest number. However, Bentham made no distinction between qualitatively different pleasures and pains. Mill tried to remedy this in his theory of utilitarianism.

   12. Every statement I have ever made (including this one) is false. Consequently, the last sentence I uttered cannot express a statement. For every statement is either true or false, but not both true and false; and the last sentence expresses a true statement if and only if it expresses a false one.

   13. When and only when two sets A and B have the same members, they are identical. In this case we write '$A = B$'.

   14. When two sets have the same members, they are identical. Sets A and B are

not identical. Hence something must belong to one which does not belong to the other.

15. The fertility of southern soils has been depleted by growing cotton on the same land for many years on end. The fertility of such soils can be increased by growing soybeans or clover on these lands and then plowing under the crop. On the other hand, it is also possible to obtain a temporary increase in fertility by the use of chemical fertilizers. As a result of this, many southern farmers spend a lot on fertilizers and plant some of their fields in soybeans or clover.

B. Which of the following sentences can be used to make different statements?

1. This patient is an emergency case.
2. $1 + 1 = 2$
3. Registration this year will be much simpler.
4. Every person in this room is a woman.
5. Every deductive argument is valid or not.
6. I hope to be a good logic student.
7. If some inductive arguments are valid, then this book is mistaken.
8. This car has been in an accident.
9. Every argument has a conclusion.
10. You have become a very beautiful woman.

C. For each example below produce a patently invalid argument of the same form.

1. If I pay the price, I shall have a ticket. I have a ticket. Hence I paid the price.
2. Some women are blondes, and some are fat. So some women are fat blondes.
3. All dogs are mammals. Some mammals have tails. Hence all dogs have tails.
4. If taxes were raised, teachers would be paid more. But taxes were not raised. So teachers will not be paid more.
5. No fish are mammals. No mammals are birds. Therefore no birds are fish.

D. True or false?

1. Every declarative sentence may be used to make at least one statement, but several sentences may be used to make the same statement.
2. Different arguments must be composed of different statements.
3. An argument with a true conclusion must be valid.
4. A valid argument with a false premiss must have a true conclusion.
5. An argument with a false conclusion cannot be sound.
6. The premises of a valid argument with a false conclusion must all be false.
7. Schemata are true or false.
8. An argument can be known to be valid although the truth of its conclusion is unknown.
9. An argument which uses implicit premisses is valid as it stands.
10. In paraphrasing an argument it is possible to misrepresent its author's intentions.

PART ONE: TRUTH-FUNCTION THEORY

1.1 THE STATEMENT CONNECTIVES

1.1.1 SIMPLE AND COMPOUND STATEMENTS

A statement which contains one or more statements as parts is called a *compound statement*. The statemental parts of a compound statement are its *component statements*. A *simple statement*, on the other hand, is merely one which is not compound. Every statement is thus simple or compound. The difference between the two types of statement will now be illustrated by several examples.

EXAMPLES

Simple Statements:
All cats are carnivorous.
The big brown dog chases the pretty little rabbit.
$2 + 2 = 7 \cdot 4 - 6 \cdot 4$
John is married to Edith.
There is no king of the United States.

Compound Statements: *(The components are underlined.)*
If it is raining, then it is cloudy.
I think that Lee understands logic.
The class was dismissed because there was a fire.
If every number is even, then and only then three is even.
Unless Jones calls you, he will meet you at home.

Quite a bit of logic can be developed by dealing with the structure of compound statements while ignoring the inner structure of simple statements. For example, consider this argument

If Jones paid the bill, then the bank gave him the car.
Jones paid the bill.

So the bank gave him the car.

Its form can be brought out by replacing its simple statements by the letters 'p' and 'q'. This produces

If p, then q.
p
So q.

Now, clearly, this argument is valid: if both 'if p, then q' and 'p' are true, then 'q' *must* be true. Furthermore, any argument of the same form is also valid, which shows that the validity of at least this type of argument derives solely from the form of its compound statements. Since the logic of compound statements is easier for the beginner than the other branches of logic, this is where we shall begin. However, because we shall treat only those compounds known as truth-functional compounds, this beginning portion of logic is called *truth-function theory*.

Compound statements are built from simple ones by using other expressions to connect the simple statements. We can think of these "connecting expressions" as being patterns of words and blanks, with the blanks to be filled by statements. Let us call these connecting expressions *statement connectives*. Then we have

A statement connective is a pattern of words with one or more blanks, such that statements are produced from filling all the blanks by statements.

EXAMPLES
_____ because _____
If _____, then _____
_____ and _____
I think that _____
It is false that _____.

The blanks of a statement connective may be filled by any statement, simple or compound, and *the same statement may be used to fill two or more blanks*.

EXAMPLES
I said it because I believed it.
If I said it, then I said it.

At this point it is useful to introduce the term *truth-value* into the discussion. It is used to refer to the truth or falsity of a statement in such a way that a true statement has the truth-value *true* while a false one has the truth-value *false*. Thus every statement has one and only one truth-value, since every statement is either true or false but none is both true and false. Even when we do not know whether a statement is true or false, we can still speak of its truth-value, and thus avoid lengthier locutions. For example, instead of saying

These statements are both true or both false

we can simply say

These statements have the same truth-value

and thereby save two words. It will also be convenient to use 'T' to stand for the truth-value *true* and 'F' for the truth-value *false*.

The statement connectives which will concern us are all truth-functional statement connectives, that is, statement connectives which always produce compounds whose truth-values are completely determined by the truth-values of the components which fill their blanks. We shall give a more precise characterization of the truth-functional statement connectives later. For the moment it will be more useful to familiarize ourselves with some examples of these statement connectives.

Because this book will deal with only truth-functional statement connectives, it will be convenient to use the shorter term *statement connective* and add the adjective *truth-functional* only when a confusion between truth-functional and non-truth-functional statement connectives might arise. Let us now turn to some of the particular statement connectives which we shall study.

1.1.2   NEGATION
The statement connectives

it is false that _____
it is not the case that _____
not: _____

are used to form compounds which have the opposite truth-values of their components. Since these compounds deny or negate their components, they are called *negations* of these components. In ordinary language there are also simpler ways to deny a statement. For example,

(1)   John is a football star

(2)   All men love steak

may be negated by

(3)   John is not a football star

(4)   Not all men love steak

Of course, they are also negated by

It is false that John is a football star
It is false that all men love steak

but these are too cumbersome for practical purposes. Although the word 'not' is used in (3) and (4) to form negations of (1) and (2), simply using this word is not always sufficient to negate a statement. For example, suppose that someone asserted

(5)   Some men are bald.

To deny this it would *not* suffice to reply

(6)   Some men are not bald

because the two statements need not have opposite truth-values. (In fact, both are true.) A way to deny (5) is to assert

(7)   There are no bald men

or something similar. Unlike (5) and (6), (5) and (7) do have opposite truth-value (one is true, the other false), but in addition, even if they had other truth-values, these values would be opposite. In general, a statement and its negation must have opposite truth-values. It is not just a matter of actually having opposite truth-values. It is a matter of *having to have* opposite truth-values, whatever these may be. This point can be illustrated with a nonsense example. Consider

(8)   All boglies are woglies

(9)   All boglies are not woglies

(10)   Not all boglies are woglies

Since these are nonsense examples, they are not genuine statements and do not have truth-values. But let us assume that they do. The essential thing is that we do not know what these truth-values are. We do know, however, that (8) and (10) must have opposite truth-values. Whatever boglies are, it cannot be that all are woglies and not all are woglies. One of these two (pretend) statements must be true and the other false. By contrast, (8) and (9) need not have opposite truth-values. They could both be false, for instance, since some boglies might be woglies while others might not.

Although a statement and its negation must have opposite truth-values, we shall not call every pair of statements which are so related a statement and its negation. Instead, it will be useful to introduce the term *contradictories* for such pairs. In other words,

Two statements are contradictories if and only if they must have opposite truth-values.

It will turn out that only one of the contradictories of a statement will be its negation. For example, if we start with

(11)   John is a man

and negate it to get

(12)   John is not a man

and then negate this, obtaining

(13)   It is not the case that John is not a man

we arrive at a statement which must have the same truth-value as (11). Hence its negation,

(14)   It is false that it is not the case that John is not a man

must have a truth-value opposite to that of (11). So (11) and (14) are contradictories. However, we shall not call (14) the negation of (11), but rather the triple negation of (11). (Notice, by the way, that the example illustrates that a statement and its double negation must have the same truth-value.) Or to take a less contrived example,

(15)   There are no brown cows

negates

(16)   Some cows are brown

but it happens that (16) and

(17)   All cows are not brown

must have opposite truth-values, and so are contradictories. Despite this, (17) will not count as a negation of (16). Finally, although 'John is not a man' is the negation of 'John is a man', the latter is not the negation of the former. More generally, *the negation of a statement will be one produced by filling in the blanks* of one of

(18)   it is false that _____,   it is not the case that _____.

We shall also count variants such as 'John is not a man' or 'No brown cows exist' as negations of 'John is a man' and 'Some cows are brown', respectively, because there are the same statements as those obtained from the statement connectives of (18). Unfortunately, this raises the question of when two statements are the same, to which there is no satisfactory answer.

In logic these problems are avoided by introducing a special symbol, the dash '—', for negation. It is stipulated that writing '—' in front of a statement produces a new statement which is *the* negation of the first. That is, if S *is a statement*, $-S$ *is the negation of* S. In fact, '—_____' is a statement connective which produces a statement with a truth-value opposite to that of the one filling its blank. (You may read '—_____' as 'not: _____'.) A given statement S has one of two truth-values, true (T) or false (F). If S is true, then $-S$ is false, while if S is false, then $-S$ is true. These facts are summarized in the following table, called the *truth table for negation.*

TRUTH TABLE FOR NEGATION

S	$-S$
T	F
F	T

The new statement connective can be readily used to form negations of statements. The negations of, for example,

John's cow needs milking
The sun shone brightly
$1 + 1 = 2$
If $1 + 1 = 2$, then $6 + 2 = 8$

are simply

$-$(John's cow needs milking)
$-$(The sun shone brightly)
$-(1 + 1 = 2)$
$-$(If $1 + 1 = 2$, then $6 + 2 = 8$)

(Parentheses have been used here for clarity.)

Sometimes it will be useful to write the dash *over* the statement instead of in front of it. For example, when we start representing statements by the letters 'p', 'q', and 'r', it will be easier to write '$\bar{p}$', '$\bar{q}$', and '$\bar{r}$', instead of '$-p$', '$-q$', and '$-r$'. Either notation is acceptable, however, and the reader may suit his taste in this matter.

1.1.3 CONJUNCTION

Someone who wants to assert two statements, say,

(1) The golden mountain does not exist

(2) Beef bulls are less dangerous than dairy bulls

may assert these statements separately, or he may *conjoin* them and assert a single statement to the same effect. Such a statement is called a *conjunction* of the two statements. In English the statement connective '_____ and _____' is commonly used for forming conjunctions. A conjunction of (1) and (2) is thus

(3) The golden mountain does not exist and beef bulls are less dangerous than dairy bulls.

Since the assertion of a conjunction of two statements has the same effect as the assertion of each separately, *a conjunction is true if and only if both its components are true*. Consequently, a conjunction is false if one or both its components are false.

In logic a special symbol, the dot, '·', is used for conjunction, so that writing a dot between two statements yields their conjunction. (You may read '_____ · _____' as '_____ and _____.') If S and W are two statements, then $S \cdot W$ and $W \cdot S$ are conjunctions of them. Moreover, since a conjunction is true just in case all its components are true, conjunction has the following truth table.

TRUTH TABLE FOR CONJUNCTION

S	W	$S \cdot W$
T	T	T
T	F	F
F	T	F
F	F	F

Notice that the four possibilities — both true, S true, W false; S false, W true; both false — are represented here, and only in the first case is the conjunction true. Notice, also, that the conjunction $W \cdot S$ is true under the same conditions that $S \cdot W$ is, that is, when both S and W are true. This means that $S \cdot W$ and $W \cdot S$ always have the same truth-value. The components S and W are called *conjuncts* of the conjunction. Thus we have just seen that the order of the conjuncts is immaterial to the truth-value of the conjunction.

A more mathematical way of expressing this is to say that conjunction is *commutative*.

EXAMPLES.   The truth-value of each conjunction follows it. Check this value by means of the truth table.

a. $(1 + 1 = 2) \cdot (6 + 2 = 8)$ *T*
b. $-(1 + 1 = 2) \cdot (6 + 2 = 8)$ *F*
c. (The Earth is a planet) $\cdot$ (Lincoln was the first U.S. President)   *F*
d. $-$(The Earth is a planet) $\cdot$ $(1 + 1 = 2)$ *F*

1.1.4   DISJUNCTION

On many occasions we are unwilling to commit ourselves to the truth of either of two statements, although we are confident that at least one of them is true. For example, suppose that, after examining a patient, a physician concludes that the symptoms indicate a severe intestinal virus or an appendicitis, although not clearly deciding between the two. Then he would be unwilling to assert either of

(1)   The patient has a severe intestinal virus.

(2)   The patient has an appendicitis.

So instead he might disjoin the two statements and assert their *disjunction*:

(3)   The patient has a severe intestinal virus or he has an appendicitis.

This statement is true if at least one of (1) or (2) is true. (So the physician would protect himself.) More generally, when two statements are compounded by the statement connective '_____ or _____', the disjunction of the two statements is formed. The statements compounded are called the *disjuncts* of the disjunction.

There are two types of disjunction. When the person asserting a disjunction intends to exclude the possibility that both disjuncts are true, then the disjunction is an *exclusive* disjunction. The disjoining word 'or' is used in its exclusive sense here, that is, to mean 'either _____ or _____ but not both'. A shopkeeper, for example, might use this sense of 'or' when offering one free sample from a group: 'One is yours for free — the plate or the bowl'. The word 'or' also has a *nonexclusive* sense, the sense of the legal word 'and/or' and of 'either _____ or _____ and possibly both', which is used to form *nonexclusive disjunctions*. For example, a marriage-license clerk with a poor memory, when asked why the consent of a parent was not on an application, might reply

The applicant is over 21 or a female over 18.

By using 'or' nonexclusively, our clerk would avoid the embarrassment of having the applicant turn out to be both over 21 and a female.

An exclusive disjunction is true if and only if exactly one of its disjuncts is true, while a nonexclusive disjunction is true if and only if one or both disjuncts are true. In logic the wedge symbol 'V' is used for *nonexclusive* disjunctions, while a circled wedge 'Ⓥ' may be used for exclusive disjunctions. (Read '_____ V _____' as '_____ or _____' and '_____ Ⓥ _____' as '_____ exclusive-or _____'.) Thus the two truth tables for these statement connectives are as follows:

TRUTH TABLE FOR NONEXCLUSIVE DISJUNCTION

S	W	$S \lor W$
T	T	T
T	F	T
F	T	T
F	F	F

TRUTH TABLE FOR EXCLUSIVE DISJUNCTION

S	W	$S Ⓥ W$
T	T	F
T	F	T
F	T	T
F	F	F

Notice that the two tables differ only in the first row.

It is common to think that when the two disjuncts in a disjunction (expressed in ordinary language) cannot both be true, as in 'win or lose', 'boy or girl', 'vegetable or mineral', and 'positive or negative', then the disjunction must be exclusive. Actually, here there is no difference in truth-value between the two disjunctions. The only way they could differ in truth-value would be for both disjuncts to be true, but this case has been excluded by hypothesis. It not only makes no difference whether the disjunction is taken as exclusive or as nonexclusive, but there is little ground for making either interpretation. (Of course, if the logical notation is used, then the type of disjunction is obvious, but again, in the case under consideration, there is no difference in truth-value between the two.) There is also a presumption in English that, unless the context of an utterance explicitly indicates otherwise, the word 'or' is used in the nonexclusive sense. For this reason, it will be convenient to interpret all disjunctions with incompatible disjuncts as nonexclusive.

Nonexclusive disjunction is also the primary disjunction of mathematics.

In addition, exclusive disjunctions can always be reexpressed in terms of negation, conjunction, and nonexclusive disjunction; for $S \textcircled{V} W$ has the same truth-value as $(S \vee W) \cdot -(S \cdot W)$, that is, S or W, and not both S and W. For these reasons little attention will be paid to exclusive disjunction and the circled wedge. Henceforth, *in this book the word 'disjunction' will mean 'nonexclusive disjunction' and the word 'or' should be interpreted nonexclusively,* unless, of course, these words are accompanied by an explicit waiver of this rule.

EXAMPLES

a. $(1 + 1 = 2) \vee (2 + 3 = 6)$ T
b. $(4 + 2 = 1) \vee (2 + 3 = 6)$ F
c. $-(2 + 3 = 6) \vee$ The Sun is a star T
d. $(7 + 2 = 10) \vee -(2 + 3 = 6)$ T

1.1.5   THE CONDITIONAL
Conditionals are if-then statements such as

If Jones fed the meter, then he did not receive a ticket.
If it was hot yesterday, then the beaches were crowded.
If Rosie loved John, she would let him know it.

The 'if' clause is called the *antecedent* of the conditional, while the 'then' clause is called the *consequent*. The compound of the two clauses is the conditional *between* the antecedent and the consequent. We shall use the horseshoe symbol '$\supset$' to express the *truth-functional conditional*. (Read '_____ $\supset$ _____' as 'if _____, then _____'.) (There are other types of conditionals, which will be discussed shortly.)

   If a conditional has a true antecedent and a false consequent, then it must be false. For a conditional states that if one thing holds, then so does something else. But in the case under consideration, the first thing does hold while the other does not. More concretely, if James loves Mary but Mary does not love James, then the conditional

If James loves Mary, then Mary loves James

is false. Thus the conditional $S \supset W$ is false if S is true and W is false.
   When is $S \supset W$ true? Ordinary usage does not guide us very well here. If the antecedent of the conditional is *known* to be false, then the whole conditional often loses its point, and the question of its truth-value drops. In this respect, conditionals in ordinary language are like conditional bets,

such as 'if it rains, then I bet that Holly's Folly will not win'. If the condition of the bet — it is raining — is not satisfied, then the bet lapses. Similarly, it seems somewhat pointless to ask about the truth-value of, say,

(1)   If the Earth is not a planet, then the Moon is not a star

because we know that its antecedent is false. Besides, it is often impossible to do anything but arbitrarily assign a truth-value to such conditionals. Is (1) true or false? Either answer seems equally disconcerting. The reason for this behavior of conditionals with false antecedents is that, ordinarily, we do not affirm a conditional unless we feel that there is some connection between the antecedent and the consequent. And then the reason for affirming the conditional usually is that we do not know the truth-value of either the antecedent or the consequent, but believe that if the antecedent is true, then so is the consequent. A physician, for instance, would sound pretty silly if he said

If the child's temperature is not normal, then he has measles

having already stated that the child had measles.

We have introduced

————————— $\supset$ —————————

as a truth-functional statement connective. As such, the truth-value of any compound formed by filling its blanks with statements must be determined by the truth-values of its components. Accordingly, we shall *stipulate* that *truth-functional* conditionals with false antecedents are true. Thus $S \supset W$ is true if S is false no matter what the truth-value of W is. This is quite a departure from ordinary language, but it leads to a much simpler logical theory. No harm can come from this departure so long as we remember that the horseshoe is at best an approximation to the conditionals of ordinary language.

We still have to consider the case in which both antecedent and consequent are true. So long as we do not consider bizarre examples in which the antecedent and consequent have no apparent connection, then ordinary usage tends to count conditionals with true antecedents and consequents as true. We shall extrapolate on this and stipulate that a truth-functional conditional with a true antecedent and a true consequent is true.

This discussion can be summarized by presenting the truth table for the conditional. (From now on we can drop the adjective "truth-functional".)

TRUTH TABLE FOR THE CONDITIONAL

S	W	$S \supset W$
T	T	T
T	F	F
F	T	T
F	F	T

Notice that there is only one case when $S \supset W$ is false, that is, when S is true and W is false. Also notice that $S \supset W$ is true when W is true regardless of S, and it is also true when S is false regardless of W.

EXAMPLES

a. $(1 + 1 = 2) \supset (1 + 1 = 2)$ T
b. $-(6 + 2 = 8) \supset$ The United States is in North America T
c. $(4 + 8 = 5) \supset (6 + 8 = 6)$ T
d. $(4 + 4 = 8) \supset (6 + 6 = 11)$ F

1.1.6   THE BICONDITIONAL

Our final statement connective is the biconditional. This is a two-way conditional and is used to form "if and only if" statements such as

This student will pass if and only if his performance on the final examination is satisfactory.

There are various types of biconditionals, just as there are various types of conditionals, but this section concerns the truth-functional biconditional. The triple-bar symbol '$\equiv$' is used for this statement connective. (Read '_____ $\equiv$ _____' as '_____ if and only if _____'.) Since $S \equiv W$ is a two-way conditional, asserting it amounts to asserting $(S \supset W)$ $\cdot (W \supset S)$, that is, the conjunction of two conditionals. Consequently, we can stipulate that $S \equiv W$ is to behave just as this conjunction does, and this will fully determine the truth-value of $S \equiv W$.

Let us see how this comes out. If both S and W are true, then both $S \supset W$ and $W \supset S$ are true; so their conjunction is true. Thus $S \equiv W$ is true if both its components are. If both S and W are false, then $S \supset W$ and $W \supset S$ are again both true; so $S \equiv W$ is true. On the other hand, if one of S and W is true and the other is false, then either $S \supset W$ or $W \supset S$ is false; so $S \equiv W$ is false. Thus we have the following truth table for the (truth-functional) biconditional.

TRUTH TABLE FOR THE BICONDITIONAL

S	W	$S \equiv W$
T	T	T
T	F	F
F	T	F
F	F	T

Notice that this shows that a biconditional is true just in case its components have the same truth-value.

EXAMPLES

a. $(1 + 1 = 2) \equiv (1 + 2 = 3)$ T
b. $(4 + 3 = 7) \equiv (7 + 5 = 11)$ F
c. $(4 + 3 = 7) \equiv (4 + 3 = 7)$ T
d. $(4 + 8 = 13) = (4 + 8 = 12)$ F

1.1.7 PARENTHESES

Parentheses, brackets, or like devices are needed to preclude the ambiguities that may arise when more than one of our statement connectives is used in the same statement. Without additional punctuation,

(1) John will call us ∨ He will visit us ⊃ We shall visit him

is hopelessly ambiguous. For it does not clearly mean either that we shall visit John if he visits or calls or that John will call us or else we shall visit him if he visits us. But the ambiguity is easily cleared up by parentheses:

(2) (John will call us ∨ He will visit us) ⊃ We shall visit him

(3) John will call us ∨ (He will visit us ⊃ We shall visit him)

Not only do (2) and (3) differ in meaning, but they will also differ in truth-value if John calls us and neither we visit him nor he visits us. Then (3) is true, while (2) is false.

    This problem is not confined to the use of two different statement connectives either. For

(4) I love her ⊃ She loves me ⊃ The world is happy

could mean either that if I love her, then the world is happy if she loves me, or else that if she loves me if I love her, then the world is happy. The difference is then between

(5) I love her ⊃ (She loves me ⊃ The world is happy)

(6) (I love her ⊃ She loves me) ⊃ The world is happy

If I do not love her, she loves me and the world is not happy, then (5) is true while (6) is false.

It is easy enough to avoid these problems by using parentheses and brackets when constructing compounds. Naturally, a complicated compound will be rather densely populated with parentheses, and this does not make for easy reading. Shortly, we shall take measures to avoid this pressure. For the time being, let us stipulate that negation is to have the shortest scope that parentheses and grammar allow. This means that

(7) $-(1 + 1 = 2) \cdot (6 + 6 = 12)$

is to be taken as

(8) $[-(1 + 1 = 2) \cdot (6 + 6 = 12)]$

and *not* as

(9) $-[(1 + 1 = 2) \cdot (6 + 6 = 12)]$

Thus (7) is a conjunction with a negation as a conjunct while (9) is the negation of a conjunction. Similarly,

(10) $-(1 + 1 = 2) \supset (6 + 3 = 10)$

is a conditional with a negation as antecedent. To obtain the negation of a conditional, we must use punctuation to lengthen the scope of negation, namely,

(11) $-[(1 + 1 = 2) \supset (6 + 3 = 10)]$

EXERCISES FOR SECS. 1.1.1 TO 1.1.7

A. For each of the following groups of three statements, identify the two which are contradictories.

    1. a. All cats are mammals.
         b. No cats are mammals.
         c. Some cats are not mammals.
    2. a. Some cattle produce milk.
         b. Some cattle do not produce milk.
         c. All cattle produce milk.
    3. a. Jones is at home and Smith is at work.
         b. Jones is not at home or Smith is not at work.
         c. Jones is not at home and Smith is at work.

4. a. It is raining or it is snowing.
    b. It is not raining or it is not snowing.
    c. It is not raining and it is not snowing.

5. a. No men are bald.
    b. Not all men are bald.
    c. All men are bald.

B. Give the truth-values of the following:

1. $-(7 + 5 = 12)$
2. $(7 + 5 = 12) \cdot (1 + 1 = 2)$
3. $(7 + 5 = 12) \lor (6 + 6 = 13)$
4. $(7 + 5 = 12) \supset (6 + 6 = 12)$
5. $(7 + 5 = 12) \supset (6 + 6 = 10)$
6. $(6 + 6 = 12) \equiv (6 + 6 = 13)$
7. $(6 + 6 = 12) \equiv (6 + 7 = 13)$
8. $(6 + 6 = 14) \supset (6 + 6 = 12)$
9. $(1 + 1 = 3) \lor (6 + 6 = 13)$
10. $(7 + 5 = 12) \cdot (6 - 6 = 13)$
11. $(7 + 5 = 14) \equiv (6 + 6 = 13)$
12. $-(7 + 2 = 9) \lor (6 + 6 = 12)$
13. $(7 + 2 = 9) \supset -(1 + 1 = 2)$
14. $((7 + 2 = 9) \cdot (6 + 6 = 13)) \supset (6 + 6 = 12)$
15. $-((6 + 6 = 12) \equiv (6 + 6 = 13))$

C. The sentences presented below are ambiguous. Insert parentheses in each in two different ways so as to obtain a false statement and a true statement from the sentence. Indicate which statement is true.

1. Washington is President $\supset$ Mrs. Washington is the first lady $\cdot$ This is the nineteenth century. (*Note:* The word 'lady' is followed by a dot, and not a period.)

2. Washington was the first U.S. President $\lor$ Lincoln was assassinated $\cdot$ Grant was the second U.S. President. (*Note:* The word 'assassinated' is followed by a dot, and not a period.)

3. Jefferson Davis was the Treasurer of the Confederacy $\supset$ Jefferson Davis was the President of the Confederacy $\supset$ Grant was a Confederate general.

4. $(6 + 6 = 13) \equiv (1 + 1 = 3) \cdot (1 + 2 = 5)$

5. Honolulu is in Japan $\cdot$ Honolulu is in Hawaii $\supset$ Honolulu is in Hawaii. (*Note:* The word 'Japan' is followed by a dot, and not a period.)

1.1.8 TRUTH-FUNCTIONAL STATEMENT CONNECTIVES

The logical statement connectives introduced above are all truth-functional statement connectives; that is, the truth-values of every compound formed from one of them is completely determined by the truth-values of the statements filling the blanks of the connectives in question. Let us make this characterization more exact by avoiding the phrase 'completely determined by' and putting the matter as follows:

A statement connective is truth-functional *if and only if the truth-value of every compound formed by filling its blanks remains unchanged under all alterations of the blank-filling components which preserve the truth-values of these components.*

Thus '_____ ∨ _____' is truth-functional since any compound $S \lor W$ will retain its truth-value under all changes of S and W so long as the statements replacing S (respectively, W) have the same truth-value as S (respectively, W). In a similar way it can also be seen that the other logical statement connectives are truth-functional.

Any compound built from given statements and truth-functional statement connectives will be said to be a *truth-functional compound of these statements*. Thus the compound statement

(1) $(1 + 1 = 2) \supset ((6 + 6 = 10) \lor (1 + 1 = 2))$

is a truth-functional compound of '$1 + 1 = 2$' and '$6 + 6 = 10$'. On the other hand, the compound

(2) $(6 + 1 = 7) \cdot$ (Sea water corrodes silver because sea water contains salt)

while a truth-functional compound of '$6 + 1 = 7$' and 'Sea water corrodes silver because sea water contains salt' is not a truth-functional compound of '$6 + 1 = 7$' and 'Sea water corrodes silver', and 'Sea water contains salt'. This is because the statement connective '_____ because _____' must be used to build (2) from the latter three statements, and it is not truth-functional. As the example illustrates, one compound may be a truth-functional compound of one set of components from which it can be built, but not of a set of simpler components.

We have asserted that '_____ because _____' is not truth-functional. Let us see why this is so. To this it is necessary to consider some compound formed from it, say,

(3)   Sea water corrodes silver because sea water contains salt.

This compound and both its components are true. So if the connective is truth-functional, any replacement of these components by other true statements will produce another true compound. But this is not so; for consider the compound

(4)   Sea water contains salt because sea water corrodes silver

which results from interchanging the components of (3). Its components are both true, but it is false. This replacement technique may be used to show that other statement connectives are not truth-functional. The reader should try it on the connectives 'given that _____ it is probable that _____' and 'it is mathematically true that _____'.

It must always be possible to construct a truth table for a truth-functional statement connective. For the truth-value of every compound formed from the connective is always determined by the values of the components filling the connectives blanks, and a truth table simply describes the relationship between the truth-values of the components and that of the compound. Indeed, a statement connective is truth-functional if and only if it is possible to specify a truth table for it.

In having truth tables truth-functional statement connectives contrast markedly with non-truth-functional ones, and even with their counterparts in English. But there are other ways in which the logical connectives differ from their English counterparts that bear mentioning. Relevance is a major area of difference. In English we do not ordinarily compound two statements unless we feel that there is some relevance between them. In English we do not usually say

(1) $1 + 1 = 2$ or there is life on Mars

(2) If $1 + 1 = 3$, then some cats eat beef

and so the question of the truth-values of such statements does not arise. By contrast, the statements

(3) $(1 + 1 = 2) \lor$ (There is life on Mars)

(4) $(1 + 1 = 3) \supset$ (Some cats eat beef)

do have truth-values (both are true) even though there seems to be no relevance between their components. But this is simply a consequence of the truth-functional nature of '$\lor$' and '$\supset$'; relevance (real or sensed) has no effect upon the truth-value of a truth-functional compound.

There are examples of so-called differences between logical statements and the English counterparts, however, which vanish when the component statements in the examples are fully stated. Take, for instance,

(5) Mary was married and Mary had a baby

(6) Mary had a baby and Mary was married

which seem to show that 'and' is not commutative, although a conjunction is. By indicating the time, however, at which Mary was married and had her baby, commutativity can be restored:

(5′) Mary was married in 1963, and Mary had a baby in 1965.

(6')   Mary had a baby in 1965, and Mary was married in 1963.

Turning to the conditional, however, a marked difference between conditionals of ordinary language and our logical conditional arises which restatement will not eliminate. Consider, for example, these conditionals:

(7)   If Paul had been a Roman, he would not have been a saint.

(8)   If Paul had been a Roman, he would have been a pagan.

(9)   If Paul had been a Roman, he would have been a saint.

Since St. Paul was not a Roman, the antecedents of each of these conditionals is false. Thus, if they are interpreted as truth-functional, each conditional is true. But it seems quite obvious that some of these are not true. In particular, (7) and (9) could not both be true. Thus we must conclude that these conditionals are not truth-functional. In fact, they are what are known as *counterfactual conditionals*. Anyone who affirms a counterfactual is convinced that the antecedent is false—contrary to the facts—but still wants to tell us what things would have been like if the facts were different. (This is why these conditionals are often phrased in the subjunctive mood.) Counterfactuals are not only used for speculating about alterations of the past, they are also used for speculating about events which one thinks will never happen, for example,

(10)   If I jumped off the Empire State Building, I should be killed.

(11)   If I jumped off the Empire State Building, I should fly to the moon.

(12)   If this $100 bill were set on fire, it would be destroyed.

(13)   If this $100 bill were set on fire, it would change into two $100 bills.

Of course, (10) and (12) are true while (11) and (13) are false—at least this is what ordinary usage prescribes. On the other hand, a truth-functional interpretation of these statements would count all of them as true, since their antecedents are false and a truth-functional conditional with a false antecedent is true.

Counterfactuals also appear to have an important role in science. To say, for example, that something is soluble in water is to say that *if* it were placed in water, then it would dissolve. Every lump of sugar is soluble in water, but not every lump of sugar will be placed in water. Thus, certainly, some statements about the solubility of certain lumps of sugar are tantamount to counterfactual conditionals about these lumps. Many other *disposition terms* (-*ible* or -*able* terms) are important in science (malleable, irritable, fissionable, etc.), and so philosophers of science are concerned about the proper analysis of counterfactuals. Unfortunately, no easy treatment of them is known, and the issues are too complex to be studied here.

Despite its inability to handle counterfactuals, the truth-functional conditional can be used quite successfully in treating problems in deductive logic. This will become evident as the book develops.

1.1.9 COMPUTING TRUTH-VALUES

Let us suppose that we start with one or more statements whose truth-values are known to us and compound them truth-functionally. Then, of course, the truth-values of the compounds can be computed from the truth tables given before. Thus we may assume that the truth-values of the compounds are known to us, too. Consequently, if we also truth-functionally compound these compounds, the truth-values of the new compounds can be computed, too. For example, if we start with

(1) $1 + 1 = 2$

(2) $1 + 3 = 5$

then we can form, say,

(3) $(1 + 1 = 2) \lor (1 + 2 = 5)$

(4) $-(1 + 1 = 2)$

We can next form, say,

(5) $-[(1 + 1 = 2) \lor (1 + 3 = 5)]$

(6) $-(1 + 1 = 2) \supset 1 + 1 = 2$

and since (3) is true and (4) is false, we know that (5) is false and (6) is true. Clearly, any number of iterations of this procedure will yield compounds whose truth-values can be computed from the truth-values of our initial statements and the truth tables for our statement connectives. More generally, *any compound built from a given group of initial statements and our logical statement connectives will be a truth-function of these initial statements.* If the truth-values of the initial statements are known, then the truth-value of the compound may be computed by means of the truth tables.

In carrying out these computations it is best to start with the simplest compounds contained in a complex compound statement and work up from these. For example, let A and B be true statements, and X and Y false ones. Then, in order to compute the truth-value of

$$[(X \equiv Y) \lor (-X \cdot A)] \supset -B$$

first obtain the truth-values of

$-X$	T
$-B$	F
$X \equiv Y$	T

and then of

$-X \cdot A$	T

and next of

$(X \equiv Y) \lor (-X \cdot A)$	T

and then, finally, of

$[(X \equiv Y) \lor (-X \cdot A)] \supset -B$	F

1.1.10 TRUTH-FUNCTIONAL SCHEMATA

Schemata, you will recall, are diagrams of the logical forms of statements. A special type of schema, truth-functional schemata (TFS, for short), will be used to diagram the truth-functional forms of statements. As a starting point, simple statements (or any statement which we wish to treat as simple) will be represented by the letters 'p', 'q', 'r', and 's'. These are called *statement letters*, and they are the simplest kind of TFS. Since we may want to represent more than four different simple statements at the same time, the same letters with numerical subscripts attached to them will also count as statement letters. Thus we are assured of an inexhaustible supply of statement letters, namely,

$$p,q,r,s,p_1,q_1,s_1,p_2,q_2,r_s,s_2,\ldots$$

Consider the simple statement

(1) Boston is north of Washington.

If we represent it by 'p', then its negation

(2) $-$(Boston is north of Washington)

can be represented by '$-p$' or '$\bar{p}$'. Next let us represent

(3) St. Louis is west of New York

by 'q'. Then the conjunction of (1) and (3) can be represented by '$p \cdot q$', the disjunction between them by '$p \lor q$', the conditional by '$p \supset q$', and the biconditional by '$p \equiv q$'. Notice that the conditional *between* (3) *and* (1) is now represented by '$q \supset p$'. Because these diagrams reflect the mode of statement composition used in building these statements, this method can clearly be extended to more complex statements. For example,

(—(Boston is north of Washington) ∨ St. Louis is west of New York) ⊃ St. Louis is west of New York

is diagrammed by '$(\bar{p} \vee q) \supset q$'. As these examples illustrate, TFS look exactly like truth-functionally compounded statements except that the places occupied by simple statements are now occupied by statement letters.

Nonetheless, neither statement letters nor the compounds built from them are statements. They are diagrams of statements; they do not state anything; they are neither true nor false. They give rise to statements when their statement letters are replaced by statements, but these statements must not be confused with schemata. It is essential to keep the difference between schemata and statements clearly in mind; otherwise many of the subsequent developments will remain unclear and confusing.

Now we shall present precise rules for constructing TFS. To begin with, any statement letter counts as a TFS. These are building blocks for forming further TFS. If we take a statement letter and put a '—' in front of it (or over it), we get a new TFS. More generally, prefixing a '—' to any TFS yields another TFS. Thus 'p', '$\bar{p}$', '$\bar{\bar{p}}$', and '$\bar{\bar{\bar{p}}}$' are all TFS. Reflecting our other modes of statement composition, we may also build TFS by taking two (not necessarily different) TFS and placing '·', '∨', '⊃', '≡' between them and *enclosing the result in parentheses*. (These parentheses are necessary to avoid ambiguities. However, as they are used with '·', '∨', '⊃', or '≡', they need not be used with '—'.)

The construction of a TFS by means of these rules can be analyzed by means of a *tree diagram*, where the TFS itself is the "root", its TFS parts the "branches", and the statement letters, the "tips of branches". For example, the construction of

$(-(\bar{p} \vee q) \supset ((p \equiv \bar{r}) \vee q))$

may be pictured as follows:

A compound expression is a TFS just in case it has been properly constructed from *shorter* TFS statement connectives and parentheses. A simple expression, of course, is a TFS if and only if it is a statement letter. For this reason most of the TFS with which we shall deal can be recognized as TFS at a single glance. However, there is also a purely mechanical test for determining whether an arbitrary expression is a TFS. For our purposes the test has more theoretical than practical interest, but in order that the reader may see what a purely mechanical test is like, it will now be described in some detail.

TEST FOR RECOGNIZING TFS. In this test it is assumed that negation signs are not written above expressions.

Step 1   Determine whether the expression to be tested begins with a statement letter (if so, go to step 2), a '—' (if so, go to step 3), or a '(' (if so, go to step 4). If it begins with none of these, it is not a TFS.

Step 2   The expression is a TFS if and only if it is a statement letter standing alone.

Step 3   Cross off the initial '—' and return to step 1 and test the remainder. The original expression is a TFS if and only if the remainder is.

Step 4   [This step isolates the left component (if any) of a conjunction, disjunction, conditional or biconditional.] Count the parentheses in the expression, counting +1 for each left parenthesis and —1 for each right parenthesis; for example, the count on '—(—(*p* ∨ *q*)))—))' is 1,2,1,0,—1,—2,—3; on '((*p* ∨ *q*))((((——))' it is 1,2,1,0,1,2,3,4,3,2. (Neither expression is a TFS.) When the count of 1 falls on a *right* parenthesis or else on a *left parenthesis followed by a plain statement letter or one negated any number of times*, then mark the symbol which follows the right parenthesis (or the statement letter, as the case may be). If no symbol is marked (because the count is never right) or if the marked symbol is not a '·', '∨', '⊃', '⊃', or '≡', then the expression is not a TFS. Otherwise continue with step 5.

Step 5   Take the total expression which occurs to the left of the marked symbol. Cross off its leftmost parenthesis and test the resulting expression by returning to step 1. If this expression is not a TFS, then neither is the original expression. Otherwise, continue with step 6.

Step 6   Now take the total expression to the right of the marked symbol and cross off its last symbol. (If the original expression is a TFS, this will be a ')'.) Then return to step 1 and test the resulting expression. The original expression is a TFS if and only if this expression is.

EXAMPLES

a.   Expression to be tested: ∨
   Test: Not a TFS. Step 1 failed.

b. Expression to be tested: $---p$
    Test: Passes step 1. Applying step 2 three times yields 'p'. By step 1 this
    is a TFS; thus, so are '$-p$', '$--p$', and '$---p$'.

c. Expression to be tested: $(p \lor q) \supset r$'
    Test: Passes step 1. Step 2 tells us to go to step 3.
    The count is 1 on '(', and this is followed by a statement letter; so '$\lor$' is
    marked and we go to step 5. This says test 'p', and this is a TFS by step 1.
    So we go to step 6. This says test '$q) \supset r$', which fails to be a TFS at
    step 2. So the whole expression tested is not a TFS. [Later '$(p \lor q) \supset r$'
    will abbreviate the TFS '$((p \lor q) \supset r)$'.]

The test is inefficient for us to use, since it involves reading an expression
one symbol at a time; but since it involves only this and crossing out symbols,
it can be easily carried out by a machine. Thus there is a mechanical test
procedure for recognizing TFS, or as logicians put it, there is a *decision procedure* for TFS.

1.1.11 DISCOURSE ABOUT EXPRESSIONS
From now on we shall speak frequently about TFS and the way in which they
are constructed; so it will be useful to have a convenient notation for doing
this. Our current talk of expressions has been burdened with such locutions
as

(4) The result of writing a '$\supset$' between two expressions and enclosing this
     in parentheses

which are cumbersome. The load can be lightened by using capital letters
S, W, and E to represent arbitrary expressions. Then (4) can be written as

(5) the result of writing a '$\supset$' between S and W.

However, a much greater simplification can be obtained by replacing (5) by
a "picture", that is,

(6) $(S \supset W)$

Notice that (6) is not a TFS, since S and W are not TFS. It is really a diagram
of any expression we can obtain by replacing S and W by expressions, that
is, a shorthand description of what we obtain by taking an expression (S)
and then an expression (W) (which does not have to be a new expression)
and writing '$\supset$' between them and enclosing the result in parentheses.
Similarly, $-S$ is a shorthand description of the result of prefixing a '$-$' to an
expression.

If we use this device, the rules for constructing TFS are easily restated. For they may now be put as follows:

a.   Every statement letter is a TFS.
b.   If S and W are TFS, so are $-S$, $(S \cdot W)$, $(S \lor W)$, $(S \supset W)$, $(S \equiv W)$.
c.   An expression is a TFS if and only if its being so follows from (a) and (b).

This type of specification is known as an *inductive definition*. Such definitions consist of three clauses. a *basis clause*, an *inductive clause*, and an *extremal clause*. The basis clause provides an initial supply of things to build from [clause (a)]. The inductive clause states how new things may be constructed from things already obtained [clause (b)], while the extremal clause states that only things obtained via the first two clauses belong to the class defined [clause (c)]. (The word 'inductive' used here has no connection with inductive logic. The terminology derives instead from mathematics.)

The notation introduced above is to be used for formulating general statements about all expressions. Another device will be used to speak about particular expressions. It consists in simply enclosing the expression to be mentioned in single quotation marks. Thus, to refer to, say, the first letter of the alphabet, we may name it by quoting it. This is done, for example, in the sentence "His name ends with an '*a*'". The same device applies to logical symbols; for example, "Disjunction is symbolized by '$\lor$'". Single quotation marks are used for talking about expressions, that is, mentioning them, and this must not be confused with *using* these expressions. Thus the expression 'New York' is *used* to name a city, but when we say "The expression 'New York' contains seven letters", we do not *use* the name of a city; we *mention* it and say something about its spelling. Here are some additional examples illustrating the difference between use and mention:

a.   New York is a large city.
b.   New York is north of Washington.
c.   How do you spell 'New York'?
d.   I could not read the word completely, but I think it was 'New York'.

In (a) and (b) 'New York' has been *used*; in (c) and (d) it has been mentioned. (Where else has it been mentioned in this paragraph?)

1.1.12   ABBREVIATIONS OF TFS
Abbreviations which dispense with certain parentheses will now be introduced so that the task of reading and writing TFS can be made easier. The first is that *the outermost pair of parentheses surrounding a TFS may be omitted.* (This does not apply to negations.)

EXAMPLES

Abbreviated TFS	Unabbreviated TFS
$(p \supset q) \cdot (\bar{p} \lor q)$	$((p \supset q) \cdot (\bar{p} \lor q))$
$p \equiv (p \lor q)$	$(p \equiv (p \lor q))$
$\bar{p} \supset (q \cdot r)$	$(\bar{p} \supset (q \cdot r))$
$p \lor -(p \lor q)$	$(p \lor -(p \lor q))$

This convention applies only to the outermost pair of parentheses; so it may not be used to abbreviate, for example, '$p \equiv (p \lor q)$' as '$p \equiv p \lor q$' or '$(p \supset q) \cdot p$' as '$p \supset q \cdot p$'. It is also easy to see that the convention does not introduce any ambiguities into our symbolism, since an unabbreviated TFS may be immediately recovered by enclosing its abbreviation in parentheses.

The next two conventions deal with conjunctions and disjunctions. They may be stated as follows:

> *We may omit the pair of parentheses containing a conjunction which is itself the left component of a conjunction; and we may omit the pair of parentheses containing a disjunction which is itself the left component of a disjunction.*

This allows us to abbreviate TFS of the form $(S \cdot W) \cdot E$ as $S \cdot W \cdot E$, and those of the form $(S \lor W) \lor E$ as $S \lor W \lor E$. The rules also apply to conjunctions which occur within other schemata, such as '$p \supset ((p \lor q) \lor r)$', which may be abbreviated as '$p \supset (p \lor q \lor r)$'. Furthermore, the rule may be applied several times to the same TFS, so that '$((p \cdot q) \cdot r) \cdot s$' may be abbreviated first as '$(p \cdot q) \cdot r \cdot s$' and then as '$p \cdot q \cdot r \cdot s$'.

EXAMPLES

Abbreviated TFS	Unabbreviated TFS
$(p \lor q \lor r) \equiv (s \cdot p \cdot q)$	$(((p \lor q) \lor r) \equiv ((s \cdot p) \cdot q))$
$(p \cdot q \cdot r \cdot) \lor (p \lor q \lor r)$	$(((p \cdot q) \cdot r) \lor ((p \lor q) \lor r))$
$(p \lor q \lor r \lor s) \supset ((p \cdot q) \lor r)$	$((((p \lor q) \lor r) \lor s) \supset ((p \cdot q) \lor r))$

Note that the two rules do not apply to disjunctions which are components of conjunctions; so that '$(p \lor q) \cdot r$' is not abbreviated as '$p \lor q \cdot r$'.

The rules do not apply to conjunctions or disjunctions which are not *left* components of conjunctions or disjunctions. This means that '$p \lor (q \lor r)$' is *not* abbreviated as '$p \lor q \lor r$' and that '$(p \lor q) \lor (r \lor s)$' is not abbreviated as '$p \lor q \lor r \lor s$'. This prevents the use of one and the same abbreviation for two distinct TFS and guarantees that from every abbreviated TFS an unabbreviated one may be uniquely obtained. It happens, however, that for most purposes '$p \lor (q \lor r)$' and '$p \lor (q \lor r)$', '$(p \cdot q) \cdot r$' and '$p \cdot (q \cdot r)$', '$((p \lor q) \lor r) \lor s$' and '$p \lor (q \lor (r \lor s))$', etc., are interchangeable. So, ordinarily, we can write conjunctions and disjunctions which have any number of components, without worrying about parentheses. When parentheses are called for, our convention ensures that they will be restored in exactly one way, that is, by grouping to the left.

Our final convention concerns *conjunctions* which are components of disjunctions, conditionals, or biconditionals. We shall think of '∨', '⊃', and '≡' as marking a "greater break" than '·' in a TFS just as '.', ';', and ':' mark greater breaks than ',' in sentences. Then

> *We may omit the pair of parentheses containing a conjunction which is a component of a disjunction, conditional, or biconditional.*

Thus $(S \cdot W) \vee E$, $E \vee (S \cdot W)$, $(S \cdot W) \supset E$, $E \supset (S \cdot W)$, $(S \cdot W) \equiv E$, $E \equiv (S \cdot W)$ are abbreviated, respectively, as $S \cdot W \vee E, E \vee S \cdot W, S \cdot W \supset E, E \supset S \cdot W, S \cdot W \equiv E$, and $E \equiv S \cdot W$. Notice that, once again, parentheses can be uniquely restored to an abbreviated schema.

EXAMPLES.   The following TFS will be abbreviated in stages, using all the rules:

$((((p \cdot q) \vee r) \vee s) \equiv ((p \cdot q) \cdot r))$
$(((p \cdot q) \vee r) \vee s) \equiv ((p \cdot q) \cdot r)$
$((p \cdot q) \vee r \vee s) \equiv ((p \cdot q) \cdot r)$
$(p \cdot q \vee r \vee s) \equiv ((p \cdot q) \cdot r)$
$(p \cdot q \vee r \vee s) \equiv (p \cdot q \cdot r)$
$(p \cdot q \vee r \vee s) \equiv p \cdot q \cdot r$

Parentheses will be restored in stages to this abbreviated TFS:

$p \cdot q \supset (r \vee s \vee p \cdot q) \cdot (p \cdot q \cdot r \equiv s)$
$(p \cdot q) \supset (r \vee s \vee p \cdot q) \cdot (p \cdot q \cdot r \equiv s)$
$(p \cdot q) \supset ((r \vee s \vee p \cdot q) \cdot (p \cdot q \cdot r \equiv s))$
$(p \cdot q) \supset ((r \vee s \vee (p \cdot q)) \cdot (p \cdot q \cdot r \equiv s))$
$(p \cdot q) \supset (((r \vee s) \vee (p \cdot q)) \cdot (p \cdot q \cdot r \equiv s))$
$(p \cdot q) \supset (((r \vee s) \vee (p \cdot q)) \cdot ((p \cdot q) \cdot r \equiv s))$
$(p \cdot q) \supset (((r \vee s) \vee (p \cdot q)) \cdot (((p \cdot q) \cdot r) \equiv s))$
$((p \cdot q) \supset (((r \vee s) \vee (p \cdot q)) \cdot (((p \cdot q) \cdot r) \equiv s)))$

Negation still has the shortest scope possible. (This is a feature of our rules for constructing TFS.) We cannot, therefore, omit the pair of parentheses surrounding an expression which has a '−' prefixed to it. For example, we cannot write '−$(p \supset q)$' as '−$p \supset q$', for the first schema diagrams the negation of a conditional statement, while the second diagrams a conditional with a negation as an antecedent. Of course, we can always write the negation sign above the schema negated, as in

'$\overline{p}$' '$\overline{(p \vee q)}$',   '$\overline{(p \cdot q)}$',   and   '$\overline{(p \supset q)}$'

and anyone who used this notation extensively could abbreviate these nega-
tions as $\overline{p \lor q}$, $\overline{p \cdot q}$, and $\overline{p \supset q}$. But this course will not be adopted in this
book.

EXERCISES FOR SECS. 1.1.8 TO 1.1.12

A. Which of the following statement connectives are truth-functional?
1. _____ and _____
2. _____ because _____
3. it is true that _____
4. it is known that _____
5. that _____ is a consequence of _____
6. it is mathematically true that _____
7. (_____ $\lor$ _____) $\supset$ _____
8. if it were the case that _____, then it would be the case that
_____
9. that _____ is the reason that _____
10. not both _____ and _____

B. Where A and B stand for true statements and X and Y stand for false ones, compute the truth-values of the following:
1. $(X \cdot A) \equiv A$
2. $-A \lor X$
3. $-(A \supset X)$
4. $A \cdot (B \supset -X)$
5. $(X \equiv A) \lor -B$
6. $-(X \supset A) \equiv (B \lor Y)$
7. $((X \cdot Y) \lor (A \cdot B)) \supset X$
8. $-((X \supset Y) \supset (A \supset X))$
9. $(A \lor (X \lor Y)) \equiv (A \cdot -B)$
10. $(A \equiv B) \equiv A$
11. $(X \equiv Y) \equiv X$
12. $(X \cdot A) \supset (X \equiv A)$
13. $-((A \cdot B) \lor (B \supset X))$
14. $-(A \supset B) \cdot -(X \supset Y)$
15. $(-A \lor B) \cdot (-X \equiv (A \cdot X))$
16. $((A \equiv B) \lor (X \equiv -Y)) \lor -A$
17. $-((-A \lor --A) \supset (X \equiv --X))$
18. $X \supset ((A \cdot B) \lor -(X \equiv Y))$
19. $(X \equiv A) \lor (B \supset (A \equiv B))$
20. $-((B \supset (B \supset B)) \lor (X \cdot A))$

C. Which of the following expressions are genuine TFS?
1. $P \lor Q$
2. $(p \cdot (q \lor r))$
3. $(p \equiv q)$
4. $(S \lor W)$
5. if p, then q
6. $-p \supset q \supset r$
7. $p \cdot (q \lor r)$
8. $(p \cdot q \cdot r)$
9. $-((p \supset q) \equiv r)$

D. Abbreviate these TFS as much as possible by applying the three rules for omitting parentheses.
1. $(((p \cdot q) \lor r) \lor s)$
2. $(p \supset (q \cdot r))$
3. $(q \cdot ((r \lor s) \lor p))$
4. $(((p \cdot q) \cdot r) \lor (p \cdot (q \cdot r)))$
5. $(((p \cdot q) \supset (p \lor q)) \supset -(p \cdot q))$
6. $(((p \cdot q) \lor ((r \cdot p) \cdot s)) \lor r)$
7. $(((r \lor s) \lor p) \lor ((p \lor s) \lor q))$
8. $(((p \cdot q) \supset ((p \cdot q) \cdot r)) \cdot (p \cdot q))$

E. Obtain unabbreviated TFS from these abbreviated ones.
1. $p \cdot q \cdot r$
2. $p \lor q \cdot r$
3. $p \cdot q \lor r \lor s$
4. $p \cdot q \supset (r \lor s \lor p)$
5. $p \equiv q \cdot \bar{s} \cdot r$
6. $p \cdot q \cdot r \supset (r \cdot s \lor -p \cdot q)$
7. $p \cdot (q \cdot r) \supset (p \lor q \lor r) \cdot (s \cdot p \equiv p)$
8. $p \cdot q \cdot r \equiv (p \cdot q \lor (r \equiv s) \lor p)$

F. In which of the following is the expression 'Red Rover' used?
1. Red Rover is a game.
2. 'Red Rover' is a name of a game.
3. 'Red Rover' is an expression.
4. Let us play Red Rover.

G. Translate this into plain English: If S and W are TFS, so is $-(S \lor W)$.

1.2 TFS AND THEIR INTERPRETATIONS
1.2.1 INTERPRETING TRUTH-FUNCTIONAL SCHEMATA
A TFS is, by itself, a meaningless form which is neither true nor false. However, when the statement letters of a TFS are replaced by statements, a

meaningful statement is produced. Since this replacement assigns meaning, so to speak, to the TFS, it is natural to speak of this operation as *interpreting* the TFS. The statement produced by interpreting a TFS is, naturally, true or false. Consequently, we say that a TFS *comes out* true or false when it is interpreted, although a TFS is never *simply* true or false. When a TFS is so interpreted that it comes out true (that is, the statement produced is true), then it has received a *true interpretation;* when it comes out false, it has received a *false interpretation.* Since different statements may be substituted for each statement letter in a TFS, every TFS has more than one interpretation. In addition, a schema may behave differently for different interpretations by coming out true under some and false under others.

EXAMPLES. The following are interpretations of '$p \supset p \cdot q$':

a. $(1 + 1 = 2) \supset (1 + 1 = 2) \cdot (2 + 2 = 4)$
b. $(3 + 5 = 8) \supset (3 + 5 = 8) \cdot (2 + 3 = 0)$
c. $(2 + 3 = 0) \supset (2 + 3 = 0) \cdot (3 + 5 = 8)$
d. $(2 + 2 = 7) \supset (2 + 2 = 7) \cdot (2 + 2 = 7)$

Notice that while all occurrences of a statement letter must be replaced by the same statement, two statement letters may be replaced by the same statement [as in (d)]. The true interpretations of '$p \supset p \cdot q$' are (a), (c), and (d).

Suppose that we interpret the TFS '$p \supset (p \supset q)$' by replacing 'p' by '$1 + 1 = 2$' and 'q' by '$6 + 6 = 12$'. Then we obtain the true statement

(1) $(1 + 1 = 2) \supset ((1 + 2 = 2) \supset (6 + 6 = 12))$

which is a truth-functional compound of '$1 + 1 = 2$' and '$6 + 6 = 12$'. Therefore, if either '$1 + 1 = 2$' or '$6 + 6 = 12$' is replaced by other true statements, other true interpretations of the TFS will be produced. Similarly, if we obtain a false interpretation of our TFS, say,

(2) $(1 + 1 = 2) \supset ((1 + 1 = 2) \supset (1 + 1 = 3))$

then any replacements of '$1 + 1 = 2$' and '$1 + 1 = 3$' which have the same truth-values will produce another false interpretation. More generally,

> *The truth-value of the interpretation of a* TFS *is determined by the truth-values of the statements replacing its statement letters.*

For every interpretation of a TFS is a truth-functional compound of the statements replacing its statement letters.

The notion of interpretation is one of the most fundamental notions of logic, and by its means the important concept of validity can be defined. In using the notion of interpretation, however, we shall not be concerned with the *actual* statement produced by interpreting a schema, but rather with the *truth-value* of that statement. Since this truth-value is uniquely determined by the truth-values of the statements replacing the schema's statement letters, it will be simpler to forget about statements altogether and think of TFS as being interpreted by assigning truth-values to their statement letters. More precisely,

> *A statement letter is interpreted by assigning one (and only one) truth-value to it. A* TFS *is interpreted by interpreting its statement letters.*

The truth-values assigned to the statement letters of a TFS are its *interpretation*, and different interpretations of a TFS are obtained by assigning different truth-values to its statements letters. The TFS has a *true interpretation* (comes out true) if the computed truth-value for its interpretation is true; otherwise it has a false interpretation. This constitutes our "official" definition of the interpretation of a TFS.

EXAMPLES.   The following are interpretations of $'p \equiv (q \lor r \cdot p)'$:

a. $T \equiv (F \lor F \cdot T)$ $p : T,$ $q : F, r : F$
b. $F \equiv (F \lor F \cdot F)$ $p : F,$ $q : F, r : F$
c. $F \equiv (T \lor T \cdot F)$ $p : F,$ $q : T, r : T$
d. $T \equiv (F \lor T \cdot T)$ $p : T,$ $q : F, r : T$

The assignments are indicated on the right. The true interpretations are (b) and (d).

1.2.1.1   RULES OF RESOLUTION
The process of computing the truth-value of an interpretation of a TFS can be simplified considerably by employing the following *rules of resolution:*

RULES FOR NEGATION:

1   Replace '$-T$' by 'F'.
2   Replace '$-F$' by 'T'.

RULES FOR CONJUNCTION:

3   Replace a conjunction with 'F' as a component by 'F'.
4   Drop 'T' as a component of a conjunction.

RULES FOR DISJUNCTION:

5   Replace a disjunction with 'T' as a component by 'T'.
6   Drop 'F' as a component of a disjunction.

RULES FOR THE CONDITIONAL:

7   Replace a conditional with 'T' as a consequent by 'T'.

8   Drop 'T' as an antecedent of a conditional.

9   Replace a conditional with 'F' as an antecedent by 'T'.

10   Drop 'F' as a consequent of a conditional and negate its antecedent.

RULES FOR THE BICONDITIONAL: 11   Drop 'T' as a component of a biconditional.

12   Drop 'F' as a component of a biconditional and negate the other component.

EXAMPLES

a. $(-F \lor F) \equiv T$

   $-F \lor F$ by (11)

     $-F$ by (6)

      T by (2)

b. $T \supset (F \lor T)$

    $F \lor T$ by (8)

      T by (5)

c. $(F \cdot T \equiv T) \supset F$

  $-(F \cdot T \equiv T)$ by (10)

    $-(F \equiv T)$ by (3)

      $-F$ by (11)

       T by (2)

d. $(T \lor (F \equiv T)) \supset F$

    $T \supset F$ by (5)

     F by (8)

e. $(T \equiv F) \cdot (F \equiv F) \supset T$

     T by (7)

Since the rules can be applied in any order, the selection of one rule to apply first may produce a computation which is much simpler than one produced by applying some other rule first. This is illustrated in examples (d) and (e).

A word of justification for the rules is in order. It is clear that Rules 1 and 2 always produce correct computations. Rule 3 is correct because every conjunction with a false component is false. On the other hand, the correctness of Rule 4 follows from the fact that the truth-value of a conjunction with a true component hinges upon the values of its other components. Similar comments apply to Rules 5 and 6. Turning to Rules 7 and 9, since conditionals with false antecedents and true consequents are true, they are correct. The motivation for Rules 8 and 10 is more complex. A conditional with a true antecedent is true if its consequent is; otherwise it is false; so everything depends upon the truth-value of the consequent. Thus we may ignore the antecedent and compute the value of the consequent. If and only if we obtain a T is the whole conditional true. Thus Rule 8 is correct. On the other hand, a conditional with a false consequent is true if and only if its antecedent is false. If we ignore the consequent and *simply* compute the antecedent, then getting a T will mean that the conditional is *false*. But we want to end with the real truth-value of the conditional. This is ensured by computing the negation of the antecedent. Thus Rule 10 is correct. Similar comments apply to Rules 11 and 12.

1.2.1.2   THE NUMBER OF INTERPRETATIONS OF A TFS
Every TFS has a limited number of statement letters, and there are only so many ways to assign truth-values to these statement letters. Hence every TFS has a limited number of distinct interpretations. Now if we consider schemata which contain only one statement letter, say, 'p' or '$(p \equiv p) \lor \bar{p}$' or '$q \supset q \cdot q$', we notice immediately that they have exactly two interpretations. One is obtained by assigning the single statement letter the value *true*, the other by assigning it the value *false*. Turning to TFS which contain two statement letters, we see that four interpretations exist. For consider any TFS containing only the two letters 'p' and 'q'. The letter 'p' may be assigned T or F. Suppose that it is assigned T. Then we may continue and assign T or F to 'q'. This accounts for two interpretations (T to 'p' and T or F to 'q'). Similarly, when 'p' is assigned F, 'q' may be assigned T or F, which yields two more interpretations. But this is all that is possible. So a TFS with two statement letters has exactly four different interpretations. Let us represent these interpretations by means of the following diagram:

p:

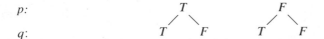

q:

Here the first line represents the two possible interpretations of 'p' while the second line represents the "continuing" assignments to 'q'. The diagram may be naturally extended to cases of three or more statement letters by simply adding additional lines and branching with each new line, namely,

p:

q:

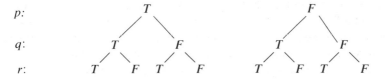

r:

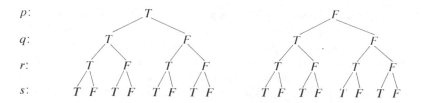

Each diagram consists of two inverted "trees", and a path through either tree represents an assignment of truth-values to the statement letters in question. There are just as many assignments as there are paths; so a TFS with 4 statement letters has 16 interpretations. Let us turn to the general case and consider a TFS with n statement letters, where n is any positive whole number. By ordering the statement letters so that one is first, another second, etc., we may construct a diagram such as those given above. Since each new statement letter (each new row) doubles the total number of branches in the whole diagram, a diagram with n statement letters has $2 \times 2 \times \ldots \times 2$, that is, 2^n branches. This means that a TFS which contains

$\underbrace{}$
n times

exactly n statement letters has exactly 2^n distinct interpretations. This fact will play an important role in the next section.

1.2.2   TRUTH-VALUE ANALYSIS

Since a TFS has only finitely many interpretations, it is theoretically possible to investigate systematically the behavior of a TFS for each of its interpretations. Such an investigation will be called a *truth-value analysis* of the TFS, and its results will be summarized in a *truth table* for the TFS. Since many of the important properties of TFS can be studied by means of truth-value analyses and truth tables, it will be worth our while to study the construction of truth tables.

Let us begin by looking at a simple example:

p	q	$p \cdot (q \equiv p) \supset \bar{p}$
T	T	F
T	F	T
F	T	T
F	F	T

The schema's statement letters head the two left-hand columns. These are called the *reference columns* of the truth table. The schema itself heads the right (third) column of the table, which is called the *main column* of the table. This column is written under the *main connective* of the schema, that is, the last connective used in constructing the schema. Each row of the table displays an interpretation (presented in the reference columns) and the value of the TFS for the interpretation (presented in the main column). The value in the main column is simply computed from the values in the reference columns. ("Scratch paper" may be necessary in performing the computation.)

The truth table for every TFS has a main column (headed by the TFS) and a reference column for each statement letter. [Let us order statement letters as follows:

$$p,q,r,s,p_1,r_1,s_1,p_2,q_2,r_2,s_2,\ldots.$$

Then we can stipulate that the earliest statement letter in this ordering is to head the first reference column; the next is to head the second reference column; etc. Thus the reference columns of the table for '$(s \vee p) \supset q_2$' are headed by 'p', 's', and 'q_2', taken in that order.] A truth table has just as many rows as the TFS to which it belongs has interpretations. Thus the truth table for a TFS with n statement letters has 2^n rows.

Truth tables are constructed so that schemata with the same number of statement letters have identical entries in the reference columns of their truth tables. For example, the reference columns of all truth tables of all TFS with just two statement letters are filled as follows:

T	T
T	F
F	T
F	F

(Of course, the main column of each truth table varies from schemata to schemata, since its entries depend upon the behavior of the schema under each interpretation.) These standardized reference columns are a consequence of abiding by the following method for filling in reference columns (here it is assumed that the truth table has 2^n rows):

1. Fill the upper half of the first (that is, left) column with 2^{n-1} T's; fill the lower half with 2^{n-1} F's.
2. Fill the upper quarter of the second column with 2^{n-2} T's, the next quarter with 2^{n-2} T's, the next quarter with 2^{n-2} F's, the next with 2^{n-2} T's, and the last with 2^{n-2} F's.
3. Fill the upper eighth of the third column with 2^{n-3} T's, the next eighth with 2^{n-3} F's, etc.

When there are more than three reference columns, smaller blocks of T's and F's are used for filling the addition column, but the size of each block is always half of those used in the preceding columns. This means that, by the time the last row is reached, T's and F's are simply alternated. (Note that $2^{n-n} = 2^0 = 1$.) This procedure, which mimics our tree diagrams, guarantees that each interpretation is represented by one and only one row of a TFS.

EXAMPLES

8 {	T						
	T	4 {	T	2 {	T	1 {	T
	T		T		T	1 {	F
	T		T	2 {	F		T
	T		T		F		F
	T		F		T		T
	T	4 {	F		T		F
	T		F		F		T
	T		F		F		F
8 {	F		T		T		T
	F		T		T		F
	F		T		F		T
	F		T		F		F
	F		F		T		T
	F		F		T		F
	F		F		F		T
	F		F		F		F

$n = 4$,	$2^n = 16$,	$2^{n-1} = 8$	$2^{n-2} = 4$	$2^{n-3} = 2$	$2^{n-4} = 1$

After the reference columns have been filled in, the main column is filled row by row. The entry for a row is obtained by computing the value of the TFS for the interpretation represented in the reference columns of that row.

EXAMPLE.   The truth table for '$-(p \cdot q \equiv (p \lor q))$'

Step-by-step Construction:
1   Setting up the reference columns

a.

p	q	$-(p \cdot q \equiv (p \lor q))$
T		
T		
F		
F		

b.

p	q	$-(p \cdot q \equiv (p \lor q))$
T	T	
T	F	
F	T	
F	F	

2   Filling out the main column

a.

p	q	$-(p \cdot q \equiv (p \lor q))$
T	T	F
T	F	
F	T	
F	F	

b.

p	q	$-(p \cdot q \equiv (p \lor q))$
T	T	F
T	F	T
F	T	
F	F	

c.	p	q	$-(p \cdot q \equiv (p \lor q))$
	T	T	F
	T	F	T
	F	T	T
	F	F	

d.	p	q	$-(p \cdot q \equiv (p \lor q))$
	T	T	F
	T	F	T
	F	T	T
	F	F	F

1.2.3   TRUTH-FUNCTIONAL VALIDITY AND CONSISTENCY

A TFS which comes out true under *every* interpretation is said to be *truth-functionally valid* (or simply, valid, for short). Truth-value analysis will quickly determine whether a TFS is valid or not, since a TFS is valid if and only if the main column of its truth table contains only T's. Here are some examples of valid TFS:

a. $p \lor \bar{p}$
b. $p \supset p$
c. $p \equiv \bar{\bar{p}}$
d. $(p \lor q) \equiv (q \lor p)$
e. $-(p \cdot \bar{p})$

The reader may easily verify that these TFS are indeed valid. As an example, the validity of (a) is established by means of its truth table.

EXAMPLE.   Truth table for '$p \lor \bar{p}$'

p	$p \lor \bar{p}$
T	T
F	T

    Truth-functionally consistent (or simply, consistent) TFS are TFS with *one or more* true interpretations. Truth-value analysis also may be used to determine consistency since a consistent TFS has at least one T in the main column of its truth table. Some examples of consistent TFS now follow:

a. p
b. $p \cdot q$
c. $p \lor \bar{p}$
d. $p \supset q$
e. $\bar{p} \supset (p \equiv q)$

Notice that (c) is an example of a TFS which is both valid and consistent. This is simply because a TFS which is true under *every* interpretation must be true under *at least one* interpretation. Thus *every valid TFS is consistent*.

But not every consistent TFS is valid, as the other examples of consistent TFS show.

A schema which is not (truth-functionally) valid will be called (truth-functionally) *invalid*. One which is not (truth-functionally) consistent will be called (truth-functionally) *inconsistent*. Invalid TFS have truth tables with *one or more F*'s in the main column, while inconsistent TFS have truth tables with only *F*'s in the main column. Consequently, *every inconsistent TFS is invalid*. The converse is not the case, as may be gathered from examples (a) and (b) below.

EXAMPLES

Invalid TFS:
a. $p \lor q$
b. $p \equiv q$
c. $p \cdot \bar{p}$ (also inconsistent)

Inconsistent TFS:
d. $p \cdot \bar{p}$
e. $p = \bar{p}$
f. $-(p \lor \bar{p})$

No schema is both valid and inconsistent, although some schemata are both consistent and invalid. This situation may be pictured as follows:

Observe that the consistent and invalid regions overlap, but that the valid and inconsistent regions are totally separate.

Schemata resemble statements, and validity resembles truth. This resemblance must not be pressed far, however. For while every statement is either true or false, some schemata are neither valid nor inconsistent. Moreover, while a statement or its negation must be true, a TFS or its negation need not be valid. An example is '*p*'; this TFS and its negation '$\bar{p}$' are both consistent and invalid. The following relationships between schemata and the negations do hold:

1   A schema S is *valid* if and only if its negation $-S$ is *inconsistent*.
2   A schema S is *invalid* if and only if its negation $-S$ is *consistent*.

Let us see why (1) is true. If S is valid, then it is true under every interpretation. Hence its negation $-S$ is false under every interpretation and is inconsistent. Conversely, if $-S$ is inconsistent, and so false under every interpretation,

S must be true under every interpretation, and so valid. This establishes (1). The reader may establish (2).

If the statement letters of a *valid* TFS are replaced by statements, then a *true* statement must be produced. For the statements replacing the statement letters interpret these letters, and a valid TFS is true under every interpretation. (It is assumed, to be sure, that the same statement replaces *all* occurrence of a statement letter in a TFS.) Similarly, statements produced by replacing the statement letters in inconsistent schemata must be false. Statements thus produced from valid TFS are known as *tautologically true statements* (or tautologies), while those obtainable from inconsistent TFS are known as *contradictory statements* (or contradictions).

EXAMPLES

Tautologies:
a. $(1 + 1 = 2) \lor -(1 + 1 = 2)$
b. (It rains) $\supset$ (It rains)
c. (John loves Jane) $\cdot$ (Jane loves Bill) $\supset$ (Jane loves Bill)

Contradictions:
d. $(1 + 1 = 2) \cdot -(1 + 1 = 2)$
e. (Joe likes ice cream) $\equiv$ $-$(Joe likes ice cream)

Tautologies and contradictions have attracted the attention of philosophers, since their truth-values seem to be determined solely by their logical structures and not by empirical circumstances. One might say that tautologies are true in every possible world, while contradictions are false in every possible world. Consequently, tautologies and contradictions convey no genuine information about this world; they are bound to have the truth-values they have, no matter what the circumstances may be. Other statements, by contrast, derive their truth-values from actual circumstances. Since their truth or falsity is dependent upon these circumstances, they are known as *contingent statements*. For instance, the statement

The moon will explode in the year 2001

is neither a tautology nor a contradiction, and (if true) it conveys very important information. These philosophical questions are beyond the scope of this book, however.

One final but important point about truth-functional validity: there is a mechanical test to determine whether a TFS is valid. For clearly, the truth table for any TFS can be mechanically constructed (computers have already done this), and once this is done, the validity of the TFS can be decided by reading the truth table. Thus *there is a decision procedure for truth-functional validity.*

EXAMPLES

a. '$p \equiv (p \lor p \cdot q)$' is valid.
    Test:

p	q	$p \equiv (p \lor p \cdot q)$
T	T	T
T	F	T
F	T	T
F	F	T

b. '$(p \lor q) \supset p$' is not valid.
    Test:

p	q	$(p \lor q) \supset p$
T	T	T
T	F	T
F	T	F
F	F	T

Since the invalidity, consistency, and inconsistency of a TFS can also be determined by truth-value analysis, truth-functional invalidity, consistency, and inconsistency have decision procedures too.

EXERCISES FOR SECS. 1.2.1 TO 1.2.3

A. Apply the rules of resolution to these expressions so as to obtain 'T' or 'F'.
1. $(T \lor T) \supset T$
2. $-T \supset T \cdot F$
3. $T = (T \supset F)$
4. $-(T \lor (T = T))$
5. $T \supset p \cdot F$
6. $(T \lor (p \equiv q)) \equiv -T$
7. $p \supset (T \lor q)$
8. $p \cdot F \equiv (T \supset -T)$
9. $-(p \cdot q \supset (T \equiv -(q \cdot F)))$
10. $p \cdot (q \cdot F \lor r \cdot -(T \supset T))$

B. Apply the rules of resolution to these expressions so as to obtain a TFS.
1. $F \lor p$
2. $T \supset (p \cdot q \cdot T)$
3. $T = (q \lor (T \supset p \cdot F))$
4. $(p \supset q) \supset (T \supset r)$
5. $(T \cdot q \equiv T \cdot r) \lor F \cdot q$

C. Construct truth tables for these TFS.
1. $p \equiv (p \lor \bar{p})$
2. $p \cdot q \supset (p \equiv \bar{q})$

3. $p \lor q \cdot p$
4. $r \supset (p \equiv r)$
5. $p \cdot q \supset (p \equiv (q \lor r))$
6. $(s \supset (p \lor q)) \cdot -(p \cdot q)$
7. $-((s \equiv r) \lor p \cdot s)$
8. $(p \lor q) \supset (q \lor p)$
9. $p \supset ((q \cdot r) \equiv s)$
10. $p \cdot (r \lor s) \lor q$

D. Test the following TFS for consistency and validity.
   1. $p \supset (q \lor \bar{q})$
   2. $p \equiv p \cdot p$
   3. $p \equiv p \cdot q$
   4. $(p \supset q) \lor \bar{q}$
   5. $(p \equiv \bar{p}) \cdot (q \lor \bar{q})$
   6. $p \cdot q \supset (p \lor r)$
   7. $p \cdot \bar{p} \lor -(q \equiv q \cdot q)$
   8. $((p \lor q) \lor r)$
   9. $((p \lor q) \lor r) \equiv (p \lor (q \lor r))$
   10. $(p \equiv q) \equiv (p \equiv \bar{q})$

E. Determine whether the following are tautologies, contradictions, or neither of these.
   1. The large cow broke her leg $\lor$ −(The moon is blue)
   2. The large cow broke her leg $\cdot$ −(The moon is blue) $\cdot$ The moon is blue
   3. The moon is made of cheese $\supset$ (A cow jumped over the moon $\lor$ −(A cow jumped over the moon))
   4. An election is held $\supset$ (The government will lose $\equiv$ The government is unpopular)
   5. I sent the letter $\equiv$ (−(I sent the letter) $\lor$ −(I sent the letter) $\cdot$ (Someone read it))

F. True or false?
   1. A valid TFS must contain at least one statement connective.
   2. A valid TFS must contain more than one statement connective.
   3. Any conjunction of two consistent TFS is always consistent.
   4. The disjunction of two consistent TFS is always consistent.
   5. A conditional with a valid consequent is valid.
   6. The conjunction of two valid TFS is valid.

1.2.4 TRUTH-FUNCTIONAL IMPLICATION

Logic in its role as an instrument of criticism and proof relies heavily upon the concept of *implication*. The reason for this is evident enough: a statement follows logically from one or more statements, just in case it is implied by them. As a consequence, an argument is valid if and only if its premisses imply its conclusion. Thus, to arrive at a characterization of valid arguments, we must study statemental implication. This in turn requires us to discuss implication between schemata.

First, let us introduce the notion of a *simultaneous interpretation* of two or more TFS. This is simply an assignment of truth-values to all the statement letters that appear in any of the TFS in question. Thus a simultaneous interpretation of several TFS interprets each TFS. In addition, any statement letter which appears in more than one of the TFS is given the same assignment for each appearance. For example, to simultaneously interpret '$p \equiv q$' and '$p \supset r$', we must make assignments to 'p', 'q', and 'r'. If all three are assigned T, then both TFS come out true for the simultaneous interpretation. This can be represented as follows:

p	q	r	$p \equiv q$	$p \equiv r$
T	T	T	T	T

This leads in turn to a generalized type of truth table which will summarize the behavior of several simultaneously interpreted schemata. Let us call such truth tables *extended truth tables*. An extended truth table for two or more TFS may be constructed by using all the letters that occur in these TFS to head its "reference columns", and the TFS themselves to head the "main columns". The entries under the reference columns are filled by treating those columns as if they were columns of a regular truth table. The main columns are filled by referring to the reference columns in the usual way.

EXAMPLE. An extended truth table for '$p \lor \bar{q}$', '$q \supset r$', and '$p \supset \bar{q} \cdot r$'

p	q	r	$p \lor \bar{q}$	$q \equiv r$	$p \equiv \bar{q} \cdot r$
T	T	T	T	T	F
T	T	F	T	F	F
T	F	T	T	F	T
T	F	F	T	T	F
F	T	T	F	T	T
F	T	F	F	F	T
F	F	T	T	F	F
F	F	F	T	T	T

The notion of simultaneous interpretation may now be used to define truth-functional implication.

A TFS *S* truth-functionally implies *a* TFS *W if and only if every simultaneous interpretation of the two which makes S true also makes W true.*

Thus *S* implies *W* if and only if, in the extended truth table for *S* and *W*, every '*T*' under *S* is matched by a '*T*' under *W*. (If there are no *T*'s under *S*, then *S* also implies *W*.)

EXAMPLE.   That '*p*' implies '*p* ∨ *q*' is shown by the following extended truth table:

p	*q*	*p*	*p* ∨ *q*
T	*T*	*T*	*T*
T	*F*	*T*	*T*
F	*T*	*F*	*T*
F	*F*	*F*	*F*

Suppose that *S* implies *W*, and consider their extended truth table. A regular truth table for *S* ⊃ *W* may be obtained from this extended truth table by simply putting a '⊃' between *S* and *W* (and perhaps adding some parentheses) and then filling in the column under the '⊃'. Since, in the extended truth table, there is never a '*T*' under *S* matched by an '*F*' under *W*, the column under the '⊃' will contain only *T*'s. Thus, if *S* implies *W*, *S* ⊃ *W* is valid. Next, suppose that *S* ⊃ *W* is valid, and consider its truth table. By first erasing the '⊃' and the main column and then filling in the columns under *S* and *W*, we shall obtain an extended truth table for *S* and *W*. But since *S* ⊃ *W* is valid, there can never be a '*T*' under *S* which is matched by an '*F*' under *W*. So if *S* ⊃ *W* is valid, then *S* implies *W*. In sum, *S implies W if and only if S ⊃ W is valid.*

Exercise: Construct a truth table for '*p* ⊃ (*p* ∨ *q*)' from the extended truth table for '*p*' and '*p* ∨ *q*' given above.

As a TFS *S* implies a TFS *W* just in case every *T* in the column under *S* in the extended truth table for *S* and *W* is matched by a *T* under *W*, the table may be used to test the implication between *S* and *W*. Since this truth-table test is purely mechanical, *there is a decision procedure for truth-functional implication.*

EXAMPLES

a.   '*p* · *q*' implies '*p* ∨ *q*'.
      Test:

p	*q*	*p* · *q*	*p* ∨ *q*
T	*T*	*T*	*T*
T	*F*	*F*	*T*
F	*T*	*F*	*T*
F	*F*	*F*	*F*

b. '$p \lor q$' does not imply 'p'.
   Test:

p	q	$p \lor q$	p
T	T	T	T
T	F	T	T
F	T	T	F
F	F	F	F

Besides the truth-table test for implication, there are two shortcut tests which, although not always applicable, will save us a lot of time and energy. The tests, which are called the *left-right* and *right-left tests*, will be presented in recipe fashion and justified afterward.

THE LEFT-RIGHT TEST

Question Answered: Does S imply W?
Precondition for Application: S must have *exactly one true* interpretation.
Examples of such TFS: 'p', '$p \cdot q$', '$\bar{p}$', '$p \cdot (p \supset q)$'
Method: 1   Find *the* assignment which makes S true. A truth-value analysis of S can be used to do this if necessary.
   2   If S and W share any statement letters, then assign truth-values to the occurrences of these letters in W as prescribed by step 1. Note that this may not completely interpret W. Apply the rules of resolution as far as possible. If this produces T or a valid TFS, then S implies W; otherwise it does not.
   3   If S and W do not share statement letters, then test W for validity. In this case S implies W just in case W is valid.

EXAMPLES

a.   'p' implies '$q \supset p$'.
   Test: 1   'p' has exactly one true interpretation, namely, when it is assigned T.
   2   We assign T to 'p' in '$q \supset p$'. This yields '$q \supset T$'. Resolution (Rule 7) produces T.

b.   '$p \cdot q$' implies '$r \lor \bar{r}$'.
   Test: 1   '$p \cdot q$' has exactly one true interpretation.
   2   Step 3 of the method applies and '$r \lor \bar{r}$' is valid; so the implication holds.

c.   'p' does not imply '$p \cdot q$'.
   Test: 1   'p' has only one true interpretation.

      2   Applying step 2 of the method, we resolve '$T \cdot q$'. This pro-
          duces (Rule 4) 'q', and this is not valid.

d. '$p \cdot (p \supset q)$' does not imply '$\bar{q}$'.
     Test: 1 '$p \cdot (p \supset q)$' has exactly one true interpretation, namely, when
               both 'p' and 'q' are T.
           2 Applying step 2 to '$\bar{q}$' produces F.

Now that the left-right test has been stated and illustrated, its correctness should be demonstrated. To do this let us assume that we are given two TFS, S and W, and want to use the test to determine whether S implies W. We must assume, of course, that the test is applicable. Thus let us assume that S has exactly one true interpretation, and consider any simultaneous interpretation of S and W which makes S true. This, of course, brings the one true interpretation of S under consideration. If S and W share statement letters, then these letters are interpreted alike in both TFS. Moreover, step 2 of the method applies. Now step 2 will result in T, or a valid TFS, if and only if the interpretation of the letters which both S and W share is bound to make W come out true *no matter how the other letters* (if any) *of W may be interpreted.* Thus step 2 produces T, or a valid schema, if and only if S implies W. So step 2 (if applicable) is correct. Next suppose that S and W share no statement letters. Then they may be interpreted independently even when interpreted simultaneously. Since S has a true interpretation, S will imply W if and only if W has no false interpretations, that is, if and only if W is valid. So step 3 (if applicable) is also correct.

We turn next to the right-left test.

THE RIGHT-LEFT TEST

Question Answered: Does S imply W?
Precondition for Application: W must have exactly one *false* interpretation.
Examples of TFS with Exactly One False Interpretation:
$p, \bar{p}, p \lor q, p \supset q, p \supset (q \supset r)$
Method: 1 Find the assignment to W which makes it false.
           2 If S and W share any statement letters, then assign truth-values
               to their occurrences in S as prescribed by step 1. Apply the
               rules of resolution. If this produces F or an inconsistent TFS,
               then S implies W; otherwise it does not.
           3 If S and W share no statement letters, then test S for consist-
               ency. S implies W in this case if and only if S is inconsistent.

EXAMPLES

a. '$p \cdot q$' implies 'p'.
     Test: 1 'p' has exactly one false interpretation.

2 By step 2 we resolve '$F \cdot q$' and obtain the value F.
(Note that the left-right test can be applied to this example too.)

b. '$p \lor q$' does not imply '$\bar{p} \supset s$'.
    Test: 1 '$\bar{p} \supset s$' has exactly one false interpretation, namely, when 'p' is
    false and 's' is false.
    2 Resolving '$F \lor q$' according to step 2 yields 'q', which is consistent.

c. '$p \cdot \bar{p}$' implies '$q \supset r$'.
    Test: 1 '$q \supset r$' has exactly one false interpretation.
    2 Step 3 applies, and '$p \cdot \bar{p}$' is inconsistent.

d. '$p \lor q$' does not imply '$p \supset \bar{r}$'.
    Test: 1 '$p \supset \bar{r}$' has exactly one false interpretation, namely, when 'p' is
    T and 'r' is T.
    2 Resolving '$T \lor \bar{q}$' according to step 2 produces T.

These two tests are used to obtain answers to *the same question*: Does
S imply W? The left-right test focuses on S and its one true interpretation and
determines whether W must have a true interpretation when S does. The
right-left test works in the opposite direction by focusing on W and its one
false interpretation and determining whether S must be false. Clearly, the
justification of the right-left will be quite similar to that given for the left-
right test. However, let us sketch it out for the sake of completeness. Suppose
that the right-left may be applied to W. If S and W share statement letters,
then step 2 applies. Step 2 will produce F or an inconsistent schema if and
only if S is bound to be false when W is simultaneously interpreted as false.
But this means that step 2 produces F or an inconsistent schema if and only
if S implies W. If step 3 applies, then S and W may be interpreted independently, and S will be false whenever W is, if and only if it is inconsistent.
So step 3 is correct.

Finally, observe that some questions may be answered by either test. The
question

Does '$p \cdot q$' imply '$p \lor q$'?

for instance, can be answered by either test. Some questions can be answered by only one of the tests. For example, only the left-right test applies
to the question

Does '$p \cdot q$' imply '$p \cdot q \cdot r$'?

while only the right-left test applies to the question

Does '$p \lor q$' imply '$p \supset q$'?

Then there are questions to which neither test is applicable, for example,

Does '$p \equiv q$' imply '$q \equiv p$'?

(Both TFS have two false and two true interpretations.) But then we can always apply the extended truth-table test to these TFS. This longer test, while always applicable, is often far less efficient than the left-right or right-left tests. This is illustrated by the next example.

EXAMPLE.   Does 'p' imply '$p \lor (q \supset r)$'?

Left-right Test: 1   'p' has exactly one true interpretation.
2   Resolving '$T \lor (q \supset r)$' yields T; so the implication holds.

Long Test:

p	q	r	p	$p \lor (q \supset r)$
T	T	T	T	T
T	T	F	T	T
T	F	T	T	T
T	F	F	T	T
F	T	T	F	T
F	T	F	F	F
F	F	T	F	T
F	F	F	F	T

At this point it will be useful to list and justify several fairly obvious laws of implication. If you have understood the two shortcut tests, several of these laws should be immediately apparent to you.

LAW 1   Any TFS implies itself (*reflexive law*).
Justification: Any interpretation of a TFS which makes it true always makes it true.

LAW 2   If S implies W and W implies E, then S implies E (*transitive law*).
Justification: Assume that S implies W and that W implies E. Next consider any simultaneous interpretation of S and E which makes S true. We want to show that E must be true. Since W may not be interpreted yet (because it may contain statement letters which appear in neither S nor E), assign the uninterpreted letters (if any) any values; for example, make them all T. Then S, W, and E are simultaneously interpreted. Since S is already true, W must be true because S implies W. But then E must be true because W implies E. But as E must be true whenever S is, S implies E.

LAW 3   a.   Valid TFS are implied by all TFS.
         b.   Valid TFS imply only valid TFS.

        Justification: a. Let W be a valid TFS and S any TFS. Whenever they are interpreted simultaneously, W must be true; so W is true under every simultaneous interpretation which makes S true.

                 b. Let S be a valid TFS and W be any TFS which S implies. We want to show that W must be valid. Consider all the simultaneous interpretations of S and W. These interpretations include all interpretations of both TFS. All make S true since it is valid. But since S implies W, all of them make W true too. Hence W is valid.

LAW 4   a.   Inconsistent schemata imply every schema.
         b.   Inconsistent schemata are implied by inconsistent schemata only.

The task of justifying Law 4 is left to the reader.

1.2.5   STATEMENT IMPLICATION AND THE TRUTH-FUNCTIONAL VALIDITY OF ARGUMENTS

We shall say that

> *A statement A implies a statement B truth-functionally if and only if there are TFS S and W such that S implies W and A can be obtained from S, and B from W, by replacing their statement letters by statements.*

In replacing the statement letters of S and W by statements, it is essential that a statement letter which occurs in both TFS be replaced by the same statement. Otherwise we could arrive at the absurd result that every statement implies every other statement. For 'p' implies 'p', and every statement may be obtained from 'p' by replacing 'p' by it. Thus, if we took 'p' as both S and W, we would find that A implies B for any two statements A and B.

  Our definition really reduces the problem of statement implication to two other problems: implication between schemata and simultaneous diagramming statements via schemata.† For the best way to find TFS S and W which satisfy the definition of statement implication is to simultaneously diagram A and B by schemata. Indeed, statement implication can be roughly characterized as follows:

---

†In a simultaneous diagramming of several schemata, any statement that they share is represented in the same manner in the several diagrams.

The statement A implies the statement B (truth-functionally) if and only if there is a simultaneous diagramming of A and B such that the schema diagramming A implies the one diagramming B.

(We shall study the problem of diagramming statements later in some detail, but this study will not be necessary for comprehending the present section.) In addition, a statement A implies a statement B just in case $A \supset B$ is a tautology. For a TFS diagramming A implies one diagramming B if and only if the conditional between them is valid and $A \supset B$ can be obtained from this conditional by replacing its statement letters by statements.

EXAMPLES

a. 'If it rains, the game is canceled' implies 'If the game is not canceled, it does not rain'.

> *Test:* 1 '$p \supset q$' diagrams the first statement; '$\bar{q} \supset \bar{p}$' diagrams the second.
>
> 2 Applying the right-left test establishes that '$p \supset q$' implies '$\bar{q} \supset \bar{p}$'.

b. 'John is at school and George is at home' implies 'It is not the case that either John is not at school or George is not at home'.

> *Test:* 1 The first statement is diagrammed by '$p \cdot q$', the second by '$-(\bar{p} \lor \bar{q})$'.
>
> 2 Applying the left-right test establishes that '$p \cdot q$' implies '$-(\bar{p} \lor \bar{q})$'.

The laws of implication established above for TFS have versions which hold for statements:

LAW 1   Every statement implies itself.

LAW 2   If statement A implies statement B and statement B implies statement C, then statement A implies statement C.

LAW 3   a. Tautologies are implied by every statement.
        b. Tautologies imply tautologies only.

LAW 4   a. Contradictions imply every statement.
        b. Contradictions are implied by contradictions only.

The justification of these laws is left to the reader as an exercise. This task can be made fairly simple by bringing to bear the corresponding laws for the TFS diagramming the statements in question.

When the conjunction of two or more statements (or schemata) implies another statement (schema), we shall simply say that these statements (schemata) *imply* the other statement (schema). For example, the two statements

John loves Mary
If John loves Mary, John will marry her

imply the statement

John will marry her

because their conjunction implies this statement. By the same token '$\bar{p}$' and '$p \lor q$' imply 'q'. We are speaking now of the *joint* implication of a schema (statement) by several schemata (statements). When there is any danger of confusing this with the separate implication of a schema (statement) by each of several schemata (statements), we shall make the distinction explicit by saying that such and such schemata (statements) *jointly imply* a given schema (statement). For example, 'p' is (separately) implied by '$\bar{\bar{p}}$' and '$p \cdot q$', but it is jointly implied by 'q' and '$q \supset p$'.

We are now prepared to characterize the truth-functionally valid arguments. In later chapters we shall be able to specify other kinds of valid arguments, but the apparatus required to do this is not available now. Here is our long-awaited definition:

> *An argument is (truth-functionally) valid if and only if its premisses jointly imply (truth-functionally) its conclusion.*

EXAMPLES OF VALID ARGUMENTS

a. It will rain tomorrow or it will snow. But it cannot snow. So it will rain. ('$p \lor q$' and '$\bar{q}$' imply 'p'.)

b. Every number is even if and only if every number is divisible by 2. Not every number is even. Hence not every number is divisible by 2. ('$p \equiv q$' and 'p' imply '$\bar{q}$'.)

c. If I love her, she will not love me. So either I do not love her or she will not love me. ('$p \supset \bar{q}$' implies '$\bar{p} \lor \bar{q}$'.)

An argument which is truth-functionally valid will be valid in the pre-systematic sense of validity discussed in the introduction. For a truth-functionally valid argument must have a true conclusion if its premisses are true. Let us see why. If an argument is truth-functionally valid, there must be a TFS which diagrams its conclusion and which is implied by the TFS diagramming the argument's premisses. If the premisses could be true and the conclusion false, then there would be a simultaneous interpretation of the TFS diagramming the premisses and conclusion, which would make the former come out true and the latter come out false. But this is impossible if the former imply the latter.

We have already seen that the implication between TFS is mechanically decidable. Accordingly, our "logic computer" will be able to determine whether one TFS implies another. Its abilities do not extend to statements, however. For it does not seem possible to mechanize completely the task of diagramming statements by schemata. There are, we shall learn later, just too many linguistic nuances involved for a machine to handle. Although it is possible to design machines which can handle simple diagramming problems, they are incapable of tackling problems which are moderately difficult for the average student. (Future developments in computer technology may make these statements false, or at least misleading.) This means that we cannot build a logic machine which can cope with the total task of determining the truth-functional validity of an argument which is formulated in a natural language such as English, French, or German. (Machines can cope with arguments formulated in certain highly restricted artificial languages.) However, we can do this: we can assign the process of diagramming arguments to the data-preparation stage and then let the logic machine take over from there. It will tell us whether the argument, *as we have diagrammed it*, is truth-functionally valid; this because its task is now one of deciding whether certain TFS jointly imply another TFS, which is, of course, mechanically decidable. But the burden of supplying these TFS to the machine lies with us, and as was emphasized in the introduction, supplying implicit premisses and paraphrasing are two sources of human error in this instance. So, like all machines, our logic machine remains no better than its human users.

1.2.6 TRUTH-FUNCTIONAL EQUIVALENCE

Two TFS are *(truth-functionally) equivalent* if and only if they take on the same truth-value under every simultaneous interpretation. The TFS 'p' and '$\bar{\bar{p}}$', for example, are equivalent because both are true when 'p' is true and both are false when 'p' is false. If two TFS, S and W, are equivalent, then $S \equiv W$ must be true under every interpretation, because every interpretation results in $T \equiv T$ or $F \equiv F$. Thus if two TFS are equivalent, their biconditional is valid. Conversely, if the biconditional between two TFS is valid, then they must agree in point of truth-value under every interpretation. Hence

Two TFS *are equivalent if and only if the biconditional between them is valid.*

There is a decision procedure for equivalence because we can use an extended truth table to determine whether two TFS agree under every simultaneous interpretation.

EXAMPLE. 'p' is equivalent to '$p \lor p \cdot q$'.

Test:

p	q	p	$p \lor p \cdot q$
T	T	T	T
T	F	T	T
F	T	F	F
F	F	F	F

The biconditional between two equivalent S and W, $S \equiv W$, has the same truth-value under every interpretation, as does $(S \supset W) \cdot (W \supset S)$. Thus S is equivalent to W if and only if $(S \supset W) \cdot (W \supset S)$ is valid. But this is valid in turn if and only if both $S \supset W$ and $W \supset S$ are valid. (Why?) Consequently,

Two **TFS** *are equivalent if and only if they imply each other.*

For this reason, the left-right and right-left tests may be used to test for equivalence by testing for mutual implication. Two tests are needed (at least to *establish* an equivalence), and either test may be left-right or right-left.

EXAMPLES

A. 'p' is equivalent to '$p \lor p \cdot q$'.
    Test: 1 'p' implies '$p \lor p \cdot q$'.
            Test: a. 'p' is true under only one interpretation.
                    b. Using a left-right test, '$T \lor T \cdot q$' reduces to 'T'.
            2 '$p \lor p \cdot q$' implies 'p'.
                    a. 'p' is false under only one interpretation.
                    b. Using a right-left test, '$F \lor F \cdot q$' reduces to 'F'.

B. '$\bar{p} \lor q$' is equivalent to '$p \supset q$'.
    Test: 1 '$\bar{p} \lor q$' implies '$p \supset q$'.
            Test: a. '$p \supset q$' is false under exactly one interpretation.
                    b. Using a right-left test, '$\bar{T} \lor F$' reduces to 'F'.
            2 '$p \supset q$' implies '$\bar{p} \lor q$'.
                    Test: a. '$\bar{p} \lor q$' is false under exactly one interpretation.
                            b. Using a right-left test, '$T \supset F$' reduces to 'F'.

C. '$p \supset q$' is not equivalent to '$p \lor q$'.
    Test: '$p \lor q$' does not imply '$p \supset q$'.   (Use right-left test.)

Notice that although two tests are needed to *establish* an equivalence, one

negative test is sufficient to refute a putative equivalence. It should be re-
membered that, since the left-right and right-left tests are not always applicable as tests for implication, these tests are also not always applicable
as tests for equivalence. The TFS '$p \equiv q$' and '$q \equiv p$', for instance, are
equivalent, but the short tests cannot be used to show it. Similarly, the short
tests cannot be used to demonstrate that '$p \equiv q$' and '$p \equiv \bar{q}$' are not
equivalent.

Since equivalence amounts to mutual implication, the following laws of
equivalence must hold:

LAW 1   Every TFS is equivalent to itself (*reflexive law*).

LAW 2   If S is equivalent to W and W is equivalent to E, then S is equivalent
to E (*transitive law*).

LAW 3   If S is equivalent to W, then W is equivalent to S (*symmetric law*).

LAW 4   Valid schemata are equivalent to each other and to each other only.

LAW 5   Inconsistent schemata are equivalent to each other and to each
other only.

In addition to these five laws, two important laws for interchanging equivalent TFS hold. Suppose that the TFS S is part of the TFS E. Then we say that
W has been interchanged with S within E when one or more (possibly all) occurrences of S within E are replaced by occurrences of W. (S and E may also
be the same.)

EXAMPLES

a. $E : p \lor (p \supset q),   S : p,   W : r$
Result of interchanging (one occurrence): $r \lor (p \supset q)$
Result of interchanging (the other occurrence): $p \lor (r \supset \bar{q})$
Result of interchanging (both occurrences): $r \lor (r \supset \bar{q})$

b. $E : p \supset q \cdot r,   S : q \cdot r,   W : p \lor \bar{q}$
Result of interchanging: $p \supset (p \lor \bar{q})$

c. $E : p \lor q,   S : p \lor q,   W : r \equiv q$
Result of interchanging: $r \equiv q$

The *first law of interchange* is stated as follows:

*Let N be the result of interchanging W with S within E. Then if S and W are
equivalent, so are N and E.*

Let us see why this law must hold. Consider any simultaneous interpretation
of N and E. This also interprets S and W. Suppose that they are equivalent.
Then they have the same truth-value under this interpretation. But N and E

are truth-functional compounds of S and W, and N differs from E only in that some places occupied by S in E are occupied by W in N. Since these places have the same truth-values accruing to them, they have the same effect upon the interpretations of N and E; that is, N and E must take on the same truth-value. Thus N and E are equivalent.

EXAMPLE. $E : p \vee (p \supset q)$, $S : p$, $W : \bar{p}$, $N : \bar{p} \vee (p \vee q)$

Interpretations:

p	q	$p \vee (p \supset q)$	$\bar{p} \vee (p \supset q)$
T	T	$T\ T\ \ T$	$T\ T\ \ T$
T	F	$T\ T\ \ T$	$T\ T\ \ T$
F	T	$F\ T\ \ F$	$F\ T\ \ F$
F	F	$F\ T\ \ F$	$F\ T\ \ F$

Notice that the columns under 'p' and '$\bar{p}$' have the same entries.

The first law of interchange says that *interchanging equivalent TFS produces equivalent results.* It does not imply that interchanging nonequivalents will always produce equivalent results. Indeed, the next example shows that this is not so.

EXAMPLE. $E : p \supset (p \equiv q)$, $S : p$, $W : \bar{p}$, $N : \bar{p} \supset (\bar{p} \equiv q)$

Test for Equivalence:

p	q	$p \supset (p \equiv q)$	$\bar{p} \supset (\bar{p} \equiv q)$
T	T	T	T
T	F	F	T
F	T	T	T
F	F	T	F

The next law states that interchanging equivalents preserves all the important logical properties we have studied.

Second law of interchange: *Let N be the result of interchanging W with S within E. Suppose that S and W are equivalent, then:*

   a. *If E is valid, so is N.*
   b. *If E is invalid, so is N.*
   c. *If E is consistent, so is N.*
   d. *If E is inconsistent, so is N.*

e.   *If E implies (or is implied by) a schema, so does (is) N.*
f.   *If E is equivalent to a schema, so is N.*

Let us see why (a), (c), and (f) are true. First suppose that S and W are equivalent. Then, by the first law of interchange, N and E are equivalent. So, by the fourth law of equivalence, if one is valid, so is the other. This shows that (a) holds. If E has a true interpretation, then so must N (since they are equivalent). Thus (c) holds. Finally, by the second law of equivalence, if N is equivalent to a schema, so is N (since it is equivalent to E). Thus (f) holds. The reader is left with the exercise of establishing that the other parts of the law hold.

Many TFS may be converted to simpler TFS by interchanging some of their parts with simpler equivalents.

For example, the TFS

(1) $(\bar{\bar{p}} \vee (p \cdot q \vee \bar{\bar{q}})) \equiv (p \supset (r \vee \bar{r}))$

may be simplified to

(2) $(p \vee (p \cdot q \vee q)) \equiv (p \supset (r \vee \bar{r}))$

since 'p' and '$\bar{\bar{p}}$' and 'q' and '$\bar{\bar{q}}$' are pairs of equivalent TFS. Then, since 'q' is equivalent to '$p \cdot q \vee q$', (2) may be simplified as

(3) $(p \vee q) \equiv (p \supset (r \vee \bar{r}))$

Lastly, since '$p \supset (r \vee \bar{r})$' is equivalent to '$r \vee \bar{r}$' (both are valid), (3) may be simplified to

(4) $(p \vee q) \equiv (r \vee \bar{r})$

If we wanted to test (1) for, say, validity, then the two laws of interchange tell us that we can test (4) instead. For (1) and (4) are equivalent; so one is valid if and only if the other is. For the benefit of the reader and for the purposes of exercises, a list of *useful equivalences* will now be presented.

USEFUL EQUIVALENCES

1   S is equivalent to: a. $\bar{\bar{S}}$
                            b. $S \cdot S$
                            c. $S \vee S$
                            d. $S \vee S \cdot W$
                            e. $S \cdot (S \vee W)$
                            f. $S \cdot W \vee S \cdot \overline{W}$
                            g. $(S \vee W) \cdot (S \vee \overline{W})$
2   $S \cdot W$ is equivalent to $W \cdot S$.
3   $(S \cdot W) \cdot E$ is equivalent to $S \cdot (W \cdot E)$.
4   $S \vee W$ is equivalent to $W \vee S$.

5   $S \vee (W \vee E)$ is equivalent to $(S \vee W) \vee E$.
6   $S \cdot W$ is equivalent to $-(\bar{S} \vee \bar{W})$.
7   $S \vee W$ is equivalent to $-(\bar{S} \cdot \bar{W})$.
8   $-(S \cdot W)$ is equivalent to $\bar{S} \vee \bar{W}$.   *De Morgan's laws*
9   $-(S \vee W)$ is equivalent to $\bar{S} \cdot \bar{W}$.
10 $S \supset W$ is equivalent to: a. $\bar{S} \vee W$
                                       b. $-(S \cdot \bar{W})$
11 $S \equiv W$ is equivalent to: a. $(S \supset W) \cdot (W \supset S)$
                                  b. $S \cdot W \vee \bar{S} \cdot \bar{W}$
                                  c. $(\bar{S} \vee W) \cdot (S \vee \bar{W})$
12 $S \cdot (W \vee E)$ is equivalent to $S \cdot W \vee S \cdot E$

EXAMPLE.   Find an equivalent of

$$-((p \supset q) \vee \bar{p} \cdot r)$$

in which only statement letters are negated.

Solution Step-by-step:
a. $-((p \supset q) \vee \bar{p} \cdot r)$
b. $-(p \supset q) \cdot -(\bar{p} \cdot r))$ by (9)
c. $-(\bar{p} \vee q) \cdot -(\bar{p} \cdot r)$ by (10)
d. $\bar{\bar{p}} \cdot \bar{q} \cdot -(\bar{p} \cdot r)$ by (9)
e. $p \cdot \bar{q} \cdot -(\bar{p} \cdot r)$ by (1) (a)
f. $p \cdot \bar{q} \cdot (\bar{\bar{p}} \vee \bar{r})$ by (8)
g. $p \cdot \bar{q} \cdot (p \vee \bar{r})$ by (1) (a)
h. $\bar{q} \cdot p \cdot (p \vee \bar{r})$ by (2)
i. $\bar{q} \cdot (p \cdot (p \vee \bar{r}))$ by (4)   Optional further simplifications.
j. $\bar{q} \cdot p$ by (1) (e)

Let us turn now to equivalence between statements.

> *The statement A is truth-functionally equivalent to the statement B if and only if there are TFS S and W such that S is equivalent to W, and A and B can be obtained from S and W by replacing statement letters by statements.*

Lest it happen that all statements are equivalent, it must be required (as was the case in implication) that any statement letter which occurs in both S and W be replaced by the same statement. In particular, if A and B are different, both cannot be obtained from 'p'. This reduces the problem of statement equivalence to that of diagramming statements and that of equivalence between schemata. Thus

> *The Statement A is equivalent to the statement B if and only if there is a simultaneous diagramming of A and B such that the schema diagramming A is equivalent to the one diagramming B.*

Also notice that A is equivalent to B just in case $A \equiv B$ is a tautology. For $A \equiv B$ is a tautology if and only if it can be obtained from a valid TFS $S \equiv W$ by replacing statement letters by statements. Then and only then are there equivalent TFS which diagram A and B.

EXAMPLES

a.   'Either the dictator will resign or both the dictator will resign and the army will take over' is equivalent to 'The dictator will resign'.
   Test: 1   The statements may be diagrammed by '$p \lor p \cdot q$' and 'p', respectively.
             2   '$p \lor p \cdot q$' is equivalent to 'p'.

b.   'If I go to the movies, then I will be broke' is equivalent to 'If I will not be broke, then I will not go to the movies'.
   Test: 1   The two statements may be diagrammed by '$p \supset q$' and '$\bar{q} \supset \bar{p}$', respectively.
             2   '$p \supset q$' and '$\bar{q} \supset \bar{p}$' are equivalent.

The laws of equivalence stated above for schemata also have versions which hold for statements. Thus, for example, interchanging equivalent statements will produce equivalent results. Moreover, since equivalent statements imply and are implied by the same statements, interchanging equivalent statements within an argument will have no effect upon the validity of that argument. In short, equivalent statements have the same logical import. Thus, in applying logic, there is no need to rest with a particular statement if an equivalent one is at hand which is simpler or more convenient for the given application.

EXAMPLE.   Suppose that we want to determine whether the statement

a.   It is not the case that either the Moon is a planet or the Moon is a star

implies both

b.   If the Sun is a star, then the Moon is not a planet.

c.   The Moon is not a star or the Earth is not a planet.

Now we could proceed straightforwardly to determine whether (a) implies (b) and whether (a) implies (c). But, on the other hand, (a) is equivalent to the simpler statement

d.   The Moon is not a planet and the Moon is not a star.

Now (d) has the form '$\bar{p} \cdot \bar{q}$'; (b) has the form '$r \supset \bar{p}$'; and (c) has the form '$\bar{q} \lor \bar{s}$'. But '$\bar{p}$' implies '$r \supset \bar{p}$' (use a left-right test), and '$\bar{p} \cdot \bar{q}$' implies '$\bar{p}$'; so by the transitive law of implication, '$\bar{p} \cdot \bar{q}$' implies '$r \supset \bar{p}$' and (d) [and also (a)] implies (b). Similarly, '$\bar{p} \cdot \bar{q}$' implies '$\bar{q}$', which in turn implies '$\bar{q} \vee \bar{s}$'; so (a) implies (c).

EXERCISES FOR SECS. 1.2.4 TO 1.2.6

A. Using extended truth tables, determine which implications and equivalences hold between the members of the following lists of TFS.

1. p, $p \vee q$, $p \cdot q$, $-(p \supset q)$
2. $\bar{\bar{p}}$, $p \supset (q \supset p)$, $q \supset p$, $p \equiv q$
3. $p \equiv \bar{q}$, $\bar{q} \equiv p$, $\bar{p} \supset \bar{q}$, $p \cdot q \vee \bar{p} \cdot \bar{q}$
4. $(p \equiv q) \equiv r$, $r \equiv (p \equiv q)$, $p \equiv (q \equiv r)$
5. $p \supset q$, $p \cdot q \vee \bar{p} \cdot \bar{q}$, $p \cdot q \vee \bar{p} \cdot q \vee \bar{p} \cdot \bar{q}$

B. Use left-right or right-left tests to determine whether

1. 'p' implies '$p \cdot (\bar{\bar{p}} \supset p)$'.
2. 'p' implies '$p \equiv (q \vee r)$'.
3. 'p' implies '$p \equiv (q \vee \bar{q})$'.
4. '$p \cdot \bar{q}$' implies '$p \supset (q \vee r)$'.
5. '$p \supset q$' implies '$q \vee p$'.
6. '$p \cdot (q \supset r)$' implies '$\bar{p} \vee q$'.
7. '$r \vee s$' implies '$s \supset p$'.
8. '$-(p \vee \bar{q})$' implies '$s \cdot (s \equiv p)$'.
9. '$(p \supset q) \supset p$' implies 'p'.
10. '$\bar{p} \cdot (\bar{p} \equiv r)$' implies '$r \cdot (q \cdot \bar{q}) \vee s$'.
11. 'p' is equivalent to '$(p \vee q) \cdot (p \vee \bar{q})$'.
12. '$q \equiv (p \vee \bar{p})$' is equivalent to '$p \supset q$'.
13. '$p \supset q$' is equivalent to '$\bar{q} \supset p$'.
14. '$p \cdot q$' is equivalent to '$-(\bar{p} \vee \bar{q}) \cdot p$'.
15. '$p \supset (q \supset r)$' is equivalent to '$q \cdot p \supset r$'.

C. Determine which implication relations hold among the members of the following lists of statements.

1. a. The game is over, and our team lost.
   b. If the game is not over, then our team did not lose.
   c. Our team lost or did not lose the game.
2. a. If Jackson owns a car and Jones brought a gun, the job will not be troublesome.
   b. If the job is troublesome, then either Jackson does not own a car or Jones did bring a gun.
   c. The job will not be troublesome or Jones brought a gun.
3. a. The hunt will be over if and only if the fox is killed.
   b. The fox will be killed or the hunt will be over.
   c. If the hunt is over, then the fox has been killed or the dogs were lost.
4. a. If I am lying, then my statements are false.
   b. My statements are false, and I am not lying.
   c. My statements are true if and only if my statements are not true.

5. a.   If there is a fight, then I will or will not lose.
    b.   If I will not lose, then there will be a fight and I will lose.
    c.   It is false that both there will be a fight and I will lose.

D.   Determine the validity of the following arguments.

1.   The old king is dead; and if the old king is dead, the prince is the king now. Hence the prince is king now and the old king is dead.

2.   If price controls are not initiated, inflation will not cease. If inflation ceases, I shall be able to make ends meet. Thus, if price controls are initiated, I shall be able to make ends meet.

3.   If price controls are initiated, then inflation will cease and I shall make a budget. If I make a budget or inflation ceases, then I shall be able to make ends meet. Therefore if price controls are initiated, then I shall be able to make ends meet.

4.   That horse bucks if you whip him. If that horse bucks, you will be thrown; and if you are thrown, you will be sore. So if you whip that horse, you will be sore.

5.   If you do not whip him, that horse does not buck. If you are thrown then he will have bucked. If that horse bucks and you are thrown, you will be sore. So if you are sore, you will have whipped that horse.

E.   Using the "useful equivalences" presented in the text, find as simple equivalents as possible of these TFS.

1. $--(p \cdot \bar{\bar{p}})$

2. $(\bar{\bar{p}} \supset q) \cdot -(p \cdot \bar{q})$

3. $((p \lor p \cdot q) \cdot (\bar{p} \lor \bar{\bar{p}} \cdot (r \supset s)) \lor p) \lor p \cdot q$

4. $-(\bar{r} \lor \bar{s}) \supset \bar{s}$

5. $(p \equiv q) \lor -(\bar{p} \equiv q) \lor p$

6. $(p \supset \bar{q}) \cdot (\bar{p} \supset q)$

7. $p \cdot q \lor p \cdot \bar{q} \lor \bar{p} \cdot \bar{q}$

8. $(\bar{p} \supset \bar{\bar{p}} \cdot q) \cdot (p \lor (r \equiv s))$

9. $-((p \lor q) \lor (p \supset q))$

10. $(p \supset (q \supset \bar{p})) \cdot (p \supset \bar{q})$

F.   Establish the following:

1.   A tautology is implied by all statements.

2.   All contradictions are equivalent.

3.   If each of two TFS implies a third, then so does their conjunction.

4.   If statement A implies statement B and statement B implies statement C, then A implies C.

5.   If S and W are neither valid nor inconsistent and share no statement letters, then S does not imply W and W does not imply S.

1.3   APPLICATIONS TO ARGUMENTS IN ORDINARY LANGUAGE

The techniques we have learned for testing validity, implication, and equivalence apply directly only to schemata. In order to test arguments for validity and statements for implication and equivalence, we must first diagram the statements involved by schemata. In a few cases, doing this is very simple. For example, it is easily seen that the statement

(1)   John likes fish and Jane likes meat

can be diagrammed by the schema

(2) $p \cdot q$

On the other hand, most statements expressed in ordinary language are more difficult to diagram. Often it is necessary to paraphrase them in a form of words more closely resembling symbolic notation. As an example, consider the statement

(3)   Although John either sails or swims and skis, he is not much of an athlete; indeed, he detests sports.

A little reflection shows that (3) may be rephrased as

(4)   Either John sails or both John swims and John skis, and John is not much of an athlete; and John detests sports.

Although (4) is barbarous and cumbersome, it is far easier to diagram. As the semicolon and comma in (4) mark its greatest and next-greatest breaks, respectively, it can be diagrammed by

(5) $((p \lor q \cdot r) \cdot s) \cdot p_1$

or dropping parentheses, more simply by

(6) $(p \lor q \cdot r) \cdot s \cdot p_1$

Perhaps the passage from (3) to (4), and thence from (4) to (5), seems dubious to you. To the beginning student such things are not always clear, and for this reason this section will be devoted to a detailed discussion of the difficulties and techniques involved in diagramming statements expressed in ordinary language. You will note that the step from (4) to (5) involves three major substeps:

a.   The statement connectives of ordinary language are replaced by logical symbols.
b.   The devices in ordinary language for indicating grouping are replaced by parentheses.
c.   The statements are replaced by statement letters.

Each of these steps and the methods for carrying them out will be discussed separately. But before we turn to this, a word of warning: Diagramming statements in ordinary language is not a purely mechanical procedure. There are no hard-and-fast rules. Each statement must be considered in its own right, and careful attention must be paid to its context and to its author's intent. Frequently, preliminary paraphrasing requiring careful thought and critical analysis will be needed. Consequently, the procedures offered in this section should be regarded only as rough rules which hold for a large number of examples but which also admit frequent exceptions.

1.3.1 SYMBOLIZING STATEMENT CONNECTIVES

The first rules we shall discuss are used to symbolize those English statement connectives which are used to form negations, conjunctions, disjunctions, conditionals, and biconditionals. When these rules are applied to an English statement, a symbolic statement is produced. Since some of our logical symbols differ in meaning from their English counterparts, the symbolic statement is not a complete translation of the English statement. Yet the symbolic statement may be viewed as an *idealization* of the English statement in which certain features of the English statement have been ignored for the purpose of solving logical problems.

Logicians have found that, for the most part, a symbolic idealization of an argument will do complete justice to its original English version. Unfortunately, there are exceptions to this, and a symbolized argument may turn out to be valid, while the English version of it seems intuitively incorrect. As an example, consider the argument

It is not the case that if there was a flood in the Sahara then Rome would have been submerged.

Hence there was a flood in the Sahara.

This argument surely seems incorrect. However, symbolizing it yields the valid argument

$-$(There is a flood in the Sahara $\supset$ Rome is submerged) $\therefore$ There is a flood in the Sahara.†

[$'-(p \supset q)'$ implies $'p'$.]   How are we to explain this surprising result? An observant reader will have noticed that the premiss of the English argument is the negation of a counterfactual conditional. So he might suggest that we simply forgo symbolizing arguments that contain counterfactuals. However, since many other arguments involving counterfactuals can be symbolized with impunity, this solution seems rather drastic. Unfortunately, no satisfactory solution is known today. Logicians have not succeeded in completely determining which arguments can be treated by truth-functional

---

†The symbol '$\therefore$' may be read as 'therefore'.

logic and which cannot. This does not undermine truth-functional logic, however, because there are many arguments which pose no problems for truth-functional techniques. The reader may draw solace from the fact that in this text he will not be asked to deal with problematic arguments.

1.3.1.1 NEGATIONS

There are many words and phrases in English which are used to negate statements. Armed with a list of these clue words, the task of symbolizing negation comes down to extracting the original statement negated. For instance, clearly, 'I am by no means pleased' negates 'I am pleased'; so the former may be paraphrased as '—(I am pleased)'. It is not always so easy, of course. The statement

(1)   No one is at home

is clearly a negation of some statement because it contains the word 'no'. But is it the negation of

(2)   Everyone is at home

or

(3)   Someone is at home?

Of these candidates, (3) is the only choice, because a statement and its negation must have opposite truth-values.

The technique for symbolizing negations which was used in the last example can be stated more generally as follows: First, look for clue words which are indicative of negation. Second, when you find a suspected negation, use your knowledge of English grammar to guess at the statement negated. Third, confirm your guess, and weed out alternatives by applying the principle that a statement and its negation must have opposite truth-values. If A is the original statement and B is the statement which you decide has been negated, then A may be symbolized as $-B$. Here is a list of some clues to English negations:

it is false that	not
it is not the case that	no
no means	in no wise
nowhere	no one
none	not in the least

The list is by no means complete, and is meant only as an aid to help you start tracking down negations. With some practice you will be able to recognize negations which do not use the clue words on this list.

EXAMPLES. Here are pairs of English and symbolic negations:

a.   John never met Jane: —(John met Jane)

b.   The lamb was nowhere to be found: —(The lamb was found)

c.   You are not in the least welcome: —(You are welcome)

d.   Nobody loves me: —(Somebody loves me)

The technique can also be applied to the suspected negations of compound statements, but here it is important to be sure that you are dealing with a negated component.

For example, the statement

(4)   John does not sing and Mary does not act

must not be confused with

(5)   —(John sings and Mary acts)

since statement (4) is not a negation but rather the conjunction of two negations. On the other hand, an English version of (5) is

(6)   It is not the case that both John sings and Mary acts.

1.3.1.2 CONJUNCTIONS

With conjunction the clue words are the essential thing; for once the clue word has been spotted, the conjoined statements are usually simply the statements which flank the clue word. Here is a list of some of the expressions used for conjunction:

but	in spite of
although	despite
however	notwithstanding
nonetheless	while
moreover	whereas
still	yet

It might seem strange to you that words such as 'although', 'but', and 'however' are used to express conjunction. Perhaps an example will explain why. The statements

(7)   Although John was late, his mother gave him dinner

(8)   John was late but his mother gave him dinner

are both compounds; moreover, both are true if and only if John was late *and* his mother gave him dinner. Thus both (7) and (8) may be symbolized as

(9)   (John was late) · (His mother gave him dinner)

Of course, (7) and (8) differ *rhetorically* from each other and (9). Someone might utter (7), for example, if John's mother had laid down a rule that no one who is late will get dinner, while uttering (9) would not emphasize [as do (7) and (8)] that an exception to the rule had been made. But such subtleties do not affect the truth-values of (7), (8), and (9), and so logic ignores them.

   Notice that in (7) the clue word 'although' is not flanked by the conjoined components. Nevertheless, it is usually fairly easy to identify the conjoined components even when they are arranged unusually.

EXAMPLES.   English and symbolic conjunctions are paired.

a.   John married Jane although her father opposed this:
     (John married Jane) · (Her father opposed this)

b.   While Jack held the robber at bay, his brother called the police:
     (Jack held the robber at bay) · (His brother called the police)

c.   Peter went to college, whereas Jack was kept at home:
     (Peter went to college) · (Jack was kept at home)

   Some of our clue words are not always used as statement connectives, and this is something to beware of. In the next three statements neither 'yet', 'and', nor 'still' is a statement connective:

Jill is not home yet.
Jack and Jill went up the hill *together*.
Jack and Jill are still up on the hill.

   Punctuation marks, especially the comma and semicolon, are often symptomatic of conjunction. Here are some examples of this:

Jane runs, Jim plays golf, and Steve sails.
Although Jane runs and Jim plays, Steve sails; all three are athletic.
I came, I saw, I conquered.

Naturally many occurrences of commas and semicolons do not mark conjunction. In the following statement, for example, the comma indicates disjunction:

The burglar either jumped the wall, went out through the cellar, or walked out the front door.

In the next sentence the semicolon even has a non-truth-functional use:

We cannot go to the movies tonight; for all the theaters are closed for the holiday.

The truth of the last statement does not depend upon the truth-values of its components alone; for it is true only if the *reason* why we cannot go to the movies tonight is that all the theaters are closed for the holiday. Conjunction also combines with negation in words such as 'nor' and 'without'.

The statements

Paul does not eat oysters, nor does he eat crabs
Paul left without paying his bill

can be symbolized as

—(Paul eats oysters) · —(Paul eats crabs)
(Paul left) · —(Paul paid his bill)

As a consequence 'neither . . . nor . . .' translates as '—(. . .) · —(. . .)', so that we may symbolize

Robinson neither sails nor swims

as

—(Robinson sails) · —(Robinson swims)

[Observe that '$\bar{p} \cdot \bar{q}$' is equivalent to '—$(p \lor q)$', so that 'neither p nor q' may also be symbolized as '—$(p \lor q)$'.]

1.3.1.3   DISJUNCTION
The following words are used to express disjunction:

or   either . . . or
or else   unless

Of these, only 'unless' poses a problem for the beginner. Why should it be taken as a clue to disjunction? To answer this, recall that a disjunction is a compound which is true just in case at least one of its components is true. Now consider the following statement:

(10)   Pierpont is on his boat, unless he is counting his money.

If Pierpont is not on his boat and not counting his money, then (10) is false. On the other hand, (10) would be true if Pierpont was on his boat or if he was counting his money. So (10) behaves like a disjunction and can be symbolized as

(Pierpont is on his boat) $\lor$ (Pierpont is counting his money)

We must remember not to translate occurrences of exclusive, 'or' as '$\lor$'. In the following statement, for example, 'or' has an exclusive sense:

(11)   Taxpayers must file exactly one return, but it may be a single or a joint return.

Since (11) would be false if a taxpayer could file both single and joint returns, the occurrence of 'or' in (11) must be construed as an exclusive 'or'. There are a variety of ways in which the exclusive 'or', itself, may be symbolized since 'p or q, but not both' may be expressed as '$(p \lor q) \cdot -(p \cdot q)$', which is in turn equivalent to '$(p \lor q) \cdot (\bar{p} \lor \bar{q})$' and '$p \equiv \bar{q}$'. Thus (11) could be symbolized as

(Taxpayers must file exactly one return) $\cdot$ ((The return is a single return) $\equiv -$(The return is a joint return))

EXAMPLES.   English and symbolic disjunctions are paired.

a.   Either the moon rose or lightning struck: (The moon rose) $\lor$ (lightning struck)

b.   Unless the bridge is out, traffic is light: (The bridge is out) $\lor$ (traffic is light)

c.   I shall be there, unless my mother will keep me at home: (I shall be there) $\lor$ (My mother will keep me at home)

1.3.1.4   CONDITIONAL

Many of the clue expressions for conditionals will be found in the following list:

if p, then q	p only if q	provided that p, q
if p, q	p only when q	q provided that p
when p, q	q if p	q in case p

All these expressions are to be symbolized as '$p \supset q$', even those in which 'q' appears first. These examples might convince you of this:

(12)   I shall come if I am invited.

(13)   I shall come in case I am invited.

(14)   I shall come provided that I am invited.

Does not each of these statements affirm that if I am invited I shall come? So cannot each be symbolized as

(15)   (I am invited) $\supset$ (I shall come)

That 'p only if q' can be symbolized as '$p \supset q$' is a stumbling block for many students. However, perhaps the next example will help remove this obstacle:

(16)   You will pass the course only if you take the exam.

Now this is *not* a promise that you will pass if you take the exam; rather it is a threat to fail you if you do not take it. In other words, (16) means

(17)   If you pass the course, then you will have taken the exam.

So both (16) and (17) have the form '$p \supset q$'. However, the frequent reluctance of the beginning student to accept the symbolization of 'p only if q' as '$p \supset q$' is not entirely unfounded. First, although the symbolization is quite accurate with respect to mathematical and scientific discourses, there are cases in everyday discourse when the meaning of 'p only if q' is closer to 'if q, then p' or 'p if and only if q'. For example, the most likely interpretations of

(18)   I will ask Jones only if everyone else refuses

are either that, if everyone else refuses, then I will ask Jones, or that I will ask Jones if and only if everyone else refuses. Second, 'only if p, q' is best symbolized as '$q \supset p$'. For 'only if p, q' also means '$\bar{q}$ unless p', that is, '$\bar{q} \lor p$', and this is equivalent to '$q \supset p$'. (Observe that 'p only if q' could be put as '$\bar{p}$ unless q', and this in turn as '$\bar{p} \lor q$', which is equivalent to '$p \supset q$'.) The moral is, once again, that there are no hard-and-fast rules in this business of symbolization. It is an operation which requires much thought and the careful application of analytical skills.

EXAMPLES.   English and symbolic conditionals are paired.

a.   The bells ring if there is a fire: (There is a fire) $\supset$ (The bells ring)

b.   Provided that the gate is open, the horse will be able to get water: (The gate is open) $\supset$ (The horse will be able to get water)

c.   Only if he calls, will you meet him at the station: (You will meet him at the station) $\supset$ (He will have called)

d.   School will open tomorrow provided that the teachers do not strike: $-$(The teachers strike) $\supset$ (School will open tomorrow)

1.3.1.5   BICONDITIONALS

The standard phrase for the biconditional is 'if and only if', but in addition, these expressions are often used for the same job:

if and only if p, q	p when and only when q
if p and only then q	in case p, q and only then
provided that and only provided that p, q	p just in case q

EXAMPLES.   English and symbolic biconditionals are paired.

a. You can come if and only if you pay your dues: (You can come) ≡ (You pay your dues)

b. A conjunction is true just in case both its components are: (A conjunction is true) ≡ (Both its components are true)

c. If you work hard and only then will you have a chance to graduate: (You work hard) ≡ (You will have a chance to graduate)

1.3.1.6 NECESSARY AND SUFFICIENT CONDITIONS

In scientific and mathematical writings the terms 'necessary', 'sufficient', and 'necessary and sufficient' are frequently used to form conditional and bi-conditional statements. For example, the statement

(1) A sufficient condition for the conjunction '$p \cdot q$' to be false is that 'p' be false

Simply means

(2) If 'p' is false, the conjunction '$p \cdot q$' is false.

On the other hand,

(3) For '$p \cdot q$' to be true, it is necessary that 'p' and 'q' both be true means

(4) If '$p \cdot q$' is true, then 'p' and 'q' are both true.

In general,

p is a necessary condition for q
p is necessary for q
for q, p is necessary
a necessary condition for q is p

can all be symbolized by '$q \supset p$'; while

p is a sufficient condition for q
p is sufficient for q
for q, p is sufficient
a sufficient condition for q is p

are all rendered by '$p \supset q$'. The intuitive reasoning behind this is as follows: To say that doing A is sufficient to bring about B is to say that *if* you do A, *then* B will happen. Thus 'To make that horse buck, it is sufficient to kick him' means 'If you kick that horse, he will buck'. On the other hand, to say that doing A is necessary for bringing about B is to say that B will not come about unless A is done; that is, if B comes about, then A will have been done. Thus someone who says 'For you to sleep, it is necessary that you relax first' means 'If you sleep, then you will have relaxed first', or equivalently, 'If you do not relax first, you will not sleep.' ('$p \supset q$' is equivalent to '$\bar{q} \supset \bar{p}$'.)

Scientists also speak of necessary, sufficient, and necessary and sufficient causes. For example, 'A sufficient cause of death is the cessation of heart action' means in part 'If the heart action stops, death will ensue'. On the other hand, 'A necessary cause of fire is an adequate oxygen supply' means in part 'If there is a fire, then the oxygen supply is adequate'. As the examples show, if the sufficient cause is present, the effect must come out. (If you stop a man's heart action, he must die.) Yet the effect need not come about in the presence of a necessary cause, although it will not come about without it. (You cannot have a fire without an adequate oxygen supply, but many things remain in the presence of enough oxygen to sustain a fire without catching on fire.) Finally, a necessary and sufficient cause is one whose presence will bring out the effect and without which the effect could not be. For example, the sun's rays are the necessary and sufficient cause of the earth's daylight.

As the last example shows, 'necessary and sufficient' can be symbolized by '$\equiv$'. Thus '$\equiv$' symbolizes all the following:

p is necessary and sufficient for q.
p is a necessary and sufficient condition for q.
A necessary and sufficient condition for p is q.

You will have noticed, no doubt, that the terms 'necessary' and 'sufficient' were not discussed along with the other readings of '$\supset$', such as 'if', 'only if', 'provided that', etc. This is because reading '$p \supset q$' as 'p is sufficient for q' or 'q is necessary for p' leads to some slightly odd results. For if we read '$\supset$' in this way, it follows that a true statement is a necessary condition for every statement and that a false statement is sufficient for every statement. However, it is not being recommended that '$p \supset q$' be read as 'p is sufficient for q'; all that is being suggested here is that sometimes 'p is sufficient for q' can be symbolized as '$p \supset q$'. The passage from '$\supset$' to 'sufficient' is not licensed, and the passage from 'sufficient' to '$\supset$' is permitted only with reservations. Similar remarks apply to 'necessary' and 'necessary and sufficient'.

EXERCISES FOR SEC. 1.3.1
Paraphrase the following so as to replace English statement connectives by their symbolic counterparts. Insert necessary parentheses.
1. Jones is by no means pleased.
2. You will pass, but he will not pass.

3. You will pass if you study hard.
4. I have no bananas, yet I do have pears.
5. Unless he pays me, I shall have to sue him.
6. I shall sue him only if he does not pay me.
7. I did not invite him, nor did I urge him not to come.
8. Peter and John share the car with James, although none of them is happy about it.
9. Provided that my expenses are paid, I shall do the job.
10. I shall do the job or I shall get someone else to do it, provided that my expenses are paid.
11. You will get along well with him if you meet him halfway.
12. So long as you meet him halfway, you will get along well with him.
13. This bell rings just in case that cord is pulled.
14. When and only when the door is open, the goat tries to get out.
15. In order for you to pass, it is necessary for you to study.
16. For you to fail, it is sufficient for you not to study.
17. Although John passed without studying, a necessary and sufficient condition for your passing is your studying.
18. In case I am late, my assistant will take over; however, neither am I late nor will my assistant take over.
19. It is not the case that he visits her only when he is sober.
20. This story is in no way true; nonetheless it is interesting.
21. While this conjunction has two components, that one has three components.
22. In spite of the fact that his past behavior was not up to par, he was admitted.
23. Although I am still awaiting his reply, I shall write him if he writes me.
24. His reply is late; still, provided that he writes me, I shall write him.
25. John will be nowhere to be found, unless he is careless.
26. I shall not help you in case you refuse to help me; moreover, I shall help you only if you have helped me.
27. Neither is his act justified nor is it legal; however, he will not be punished, provided that he is found insane.
28. I looked, I listened; but I did not see him, nor did I hear her.
29. If you take a course in philosophy, you will find a previous course in logic quite helpful provided that you studied and retained what you learned.
30. Neither all will pass nor all will fail, but you will pass just in case John does.

1.3.2 GROUPING

Ordinary language has many subtle ways of indicating the grouping of components in compound statements. Unfortunately, once the statement connectives from ordinary language have been replaced by logical symbols, many of these devices are no longer in effect. Their role is taken over by parentheses, naturally; but a statement can be diagrammed correctly only if its grouping is mirrored in the schema diagramming it, and this will happen only if parentheses are correctly placed in the schema.

For example, the statement

(1)   If John went to school, then John went to the beach or John took a swim

is unambiguous. Yet if we replace its statement connectives by logical symbols, the statement we get,

(2)   John went to school $\supset$ John went to the beach $\lor$ John took a swim

is ambiguous between the forms '$p \supset (q \lor r)$' and '$(p \supset q) \lor r$'. A little reflection on the grammatical structure of (1) shows that it has the form '$p \supset (q \lor r)$'. To avoid this kind of ambiguity, it is necessary to supply parentheses in passing from (1) to (2). How to do it is the subject of the present section. Once again, it is impossible to give hard-and-fast rules, but it is possible to call your attention to devices in ordinary language and let you take it from there.

1.3.2.1   'IF . . . THEN', 'BOTH . . . AND', 'EITHER . . . OR', AND 'NEITHER . . . NOR'

The grammatical requirements on constructions involving expressions such as 'if . . . then' or 'both . . . and' are valuable aids to discerning grouping. For example, grammar demands that a clause which begins a sentence and starts with 'if' be followed by a 'then' or a comma or semicolon. Thus the portion between the 'if' and the first 'then', comma, or semicolon marks the antecedent of a conditional. For example,

If p or q then r

cannot have the form '$p \lor (q \supset r)$', because the 'if' would be left dangling. Again,

if p only if q, r

has the form '$(p \supset q) \supset r$', and not '$p \supset (q \supset r)$'. This device, however, only helps to determine the antecedent of a conditional, and does not apply to its consequent. Thus

if p then q or r

is ambiguous between '$p \supset (p \lor r)$' and '$(p \supset q) \lor r$'. Placing a comma before the 'then' will give it the first form. Yet it can be given the second form by exploiting another grammatical requirement and writing it as

either if p then q or r.

Here the construction 'either . . . or' serves to mark the boundaries of the left-hand component of the disjunction. It is not necessary to go into the grammatical details of this and other relevant constructions here. Indeed, the way in which they work is made sufficiently clear in the following table of constructions and schemata.

CONSTRUCTION	SCHEMA
if p then either q or r	$p \supset (q \lor r)$
either if p then q or r	$(p \supset q) \lor r$
either p or if q then r	$p \lor (q \supset r)$
if p then both q and r	$p \supset q \cdot r$
both if p then q and r	$(p \supset q) \cdot r$
if p and q then r	$p \cdot q \supset r$
if p, then q only if r	$p \supset (q \supset r)$
if p only if q then r	$(p \supset q) \supset r$
both p or q and r	$(p \lor q) \cdot r$
p or both q and r	$p \lor q \cdot r$
neither both p and q nor r	$-(p \cdot q) \cdot -r$
both neither p nor q and r	$\bar{p} \cdot \bar{q} \cdot r$
it is false that both p and q	$-(p \cdot q)$
both it is false that p and q	$\bar{p} \cdot q$

This table is far from complete, but it illustrates some of the many constructions which ordinary language uses to avoid ambiguities of grouping.

1.3.2.2 EMPHASIZING STATEMENT CONNECTIVES AND TELESCOPING CLAUSES
Ordinary language also indicates grouping by emphasizing one connective in order to show that it marks a greater break in a sentence than another. For example, the occurrence of 'or else' in

John must pay his bills and Harry must return the car or else John will go to jail

shows that this statement has the form '$p \cdot q \lor r$'. To convert this to the form '$p \cdot (q \lor r)$' it is sufficient to play down 'or' and emphasize 'and', as in

John must pay his bills and, furthermore, Harry must return the car or John will go to jail.

Another device for emphasizing connectives is the 'case that' construction. Thus 'it is the case that p or q and that r' has the form '$(p \lor q) \cdot r$', whereas 'it is the case that p or else that q and r' has the form '$p \lor q \cdot r$'.

Another method used in ordinary language to bring out grouping is the *telescoping of clauses*. When we write, for example, 'John will sing and play', we telescope the two clauses 'John will sing' and 'John will play' into one.

Moreover, expanding the telescoped sentence must yield 'John will sing and John will play', for both 'will sing' and 'will play' need a subject and the word 'John' is the only appropriate one. This tells us that the grouping of

John will sing and play or he will be sent home

takes the form '$p \cdot q \vee r$'. Telescoping with respect to 'or' produces the other grouping: the statement

John will sing and he will play or be sent home

has the form '$p \cdot (q \vee r)$'.

EXAMPLES.   Telescoping as a device for grouping is illustrated in the following statements, each of which is accompanied by an appropriate diagram.

a.   If John sings or plays, then he will have a good time.

$(p \vee q) \supset r$

b.   The market will drop and close early if the President dies or declares war.

$(r \vee s) \supset p \cdot q$

c.   Only if Anderson is promoted and given tenure or Jones is fired will peace in the department be restored.

$s \supset (p \cdot q \vee r)$

d.   Jackson fled the scene but left his address if no witness saw him.

$r \supset p \cdot q$

EXERCISES FOR SEC. 1.3.2
Paraphrase the following so as to replace English statement connectives by their symbolic counterparts. Insert necessary parentheses.

1. If he gets the grant or someone gives him a fellowship, then he will go to Europe.
2. If both John gets married and Sarah goes to college, then we shall be able to sell this house.
3. Either the police will handle it or both the fire department will come and the army will be called in.
4. Neither shall I accept if nominated nor shall I seek the nomination.
5. Both the college will close if no funds are available and the town will die in case the college closes.
6. Both John will be here or one of his friends will be and we shall extend our welcome.
7. If we get the contract, then we can build the road if we are not behind schedule.

8. Provided that the building is open, we shall be able to go into the office in case this key opens it.

9. The police will collect the tickets and direct traffic if we give them a share of the proceeds.

10. The police will collect the tickets, and if we give them a share of the proceeds, they will direct traffic.

11. If Jones phones or writes and Smith gets the message, then the shipment will be made.

12. I cannot buy the car unless it is in good condition and reasonably priced.

13. John will sue you or Jane will divorce you and, moreover, your friends will reject you.

14. Jackson will be fired, but he will appeal it, or else no one will mention the incident.

15. There was a witness only if John was shot but also brought to the hospital in time to save his life.

16. If the university neither recognizes the organization nor accedes to its demands, then there will be a riot; moreover, the trustees will give up the project and fire the president in case there is a riot or a student strike.

17. The building will be completed and the club can start operations provided that the zoning change is approved, funds are available, and the members are ready to proceed.

18. If the army suppresses the uprising and if the populace cooperates, then the government will win the election and carry out its programs.

19. Unless both something is done for the poor and race relations improve, there will be a major riot; and if the police use violent methods, then many innocent people will be killed.

20. It is the case that Jones or Smith is president and that Jackson or Lewis is vice-president, but neither is Jones vice-president nor is Jackson president.

21. If it snows, the streets are plowed, and traffic is tied up; then the county will have to raise taxes, or both the sanitation department and the police force will have to take pay cuts.

22. If you see a yellow dog, take another drink; however, you are not drunk if you do not see one or if you are still depressed.

23. If you marry my daughter without obtaining my permission, I shall shoot you; but if you get my permission or give me some money, then I shall welcome you.

24. Provided that the butler shuts the door or the cook puts the cookies away, we shall have a rat-free evening and enjoy ourselves.

25. If Robinson sells, the deal will go through only if it is the case that Washington was informed and that the necessary papers are available.

1.3.3 IDENTIFYING STATEMENTS

1.3.3.7 THE FORMS OF A STATEMENT

The last step in diagramming a statement by means of a TFS consists in replacing its component statements by statement letters. In the examples in this section we shall replace only those components which themselves are *not* truth-functional compounds of further components. In other words, the statements replaced by statement letters will not be subject to further truth-functional analysis. This will cause our diagrams to reveal the complete truth-functional structure of a statement. This completeness, while pedagogically useful, is not always necessary. For example, the statement

(John loves Mary ⊃ Mary loves John) ∨ −(John loves Mary ⊃ Mary loves John)

is a tautology. It can be obtained from the valid TFS '$(p ⊃ q) ∨ −(p ⊃ q)$' by substituting 'John loves Mary' for 'p' and 'Mary loves John' for 'q'. While '$(p ⊃ q) ∨ −(p ⊃ q)$' does reveal the complete truth-functional structure of the statement, the schema '$r ∨ \bar{r}$' can also be used to show that the statement is a tautology by substituting 'John loves Mary ⊃ Mary loves John' for 'r'. While '$r ∨ \bar{r}$' reveals less structure than '$(p ⊃ q) ∨ −(p ⊃ q)$', it surely provides the more efficient solution to the problem. On the other hand, revealing the complete truth-functional structure of a statement guarantees that it gets the fullest hearing possible. For instance, suppose that the statement

$$(1 + 1 = 2) \cdot (2 + 3 = 5) ⊃ −(−(1 + 1 = 2) ∨ −(2 + 3 = 5))$$

were diagrammed as simply '$p ⊃ q$'. Then it would not be counted as a tautology. Yet it is one, as can be shown by revealing its complete truth-functional structure by means of '$p \cdot q ⊃ −(\bar{p} ∨ \bar{q})$'. This is why we shall pay less attention to the question of efficiency in this section. However, any reader who can save an exercise problem by not revealing the complete truth-functional structure of the statements involved is welcome to do so. It is often possible to show that a statement is a tautology or a contradiction or that one statement implies or is equivalent to another by revealing less than the complete structure of the statements involved. On the other hand, the complete structure is necessary to establish that a statement is not a tautology or a contradiction or that one statement does not imply or is not equivalent to another.

We shall also speak of *the* form of a statement, although, strictly speaking, no statement has a unique form. There are two reasons for this. First, given any statement, there may be more logical structure in it than our techniques can reveal. The statement, for instance,

No logic book is easy

must now be treated by us as simply of the form 'p', but in later chapters we shall be able to expose more of its logical structure. Second, many statements can be obtained from several nonequivalent TFS by replacing their statement letters by statements. Every statement can be obtained in this way from 'p'. Yet the statement

(It is raining) $\vee$ (It is snowing)

can also be obtained from '$p \vee q$'. Thus, when we speak of *the* form of a statement in this section, what we really mean is a TFS from which the statement can be obtained by substituting statements for statement letters and which reveals the complete truth-functional structure of the statement.

To obtain the form of a statement we must replace all repetitions of the same simple statement by the same statement letter and distinguish different simple statements by using different statement letters for them.

For example, it would surely be a mistake to diagram

(1)   If David kills Goliath, Israel will be saved

by '$p \supset p$', because then we should count (1) as logically true, which it most definitely is not. The mistake here consists in replacing different statements by the same letter. On the other hand, we could err in the other direction by counting

(2)   David did or did not kill Goliath

as contingent, when it is in fact logically true. This would happen if we mistakenly diagrammed (2) as '$p \vee \bar{q}$' or '$p \vee q$'. In the case of (2), replacing repetitions of the same statement by the same statement letter yields the valid schema '$p \vee \bar{p}$'. Recognizing and distinguishing statements requires linguistic and critical skills, but attention to grammar helps once again. For example, consider the argument

(3)   Joe is guilty of murder or bigamy. If the former is the case, he should be hanged, but if the latter is true, he should be imprisoned. Thus Joe should be hanged or imprisoned.

It is diagrammed by '$p \vee q, (p \supset r) \cdot (q \supset s) \therefore r \vee s$'.† Seeing this, however, requires us to find the antecedents of 'the former' and 'the latter' in (3). As another example, consider

(4)   Dmitri killed the Cossack, but if he did that, then he cleaned his knife. So he cleaned his knife.

This has the form '$p \cdot (p \supset q) \therefore q$', but in order to understand why this is so, we must recognize that the word 'that' in 'he did that' refers to Dmitri's killing the Cossack and that 'he' in all its occurrences refers to Dmitri. In the next argument the important pronoun is 'the latter':

†The symbol '$\therefore$' may be read 'therefore'.

(5)   Alexander the Great was a great general or a magnificent lover. The
latter is not the case. So he was a magnificent lover.

This argument is *not* valid because it has the form '$p \vee q, \bar{q} \therefore q$'. The words
'the latter' refer to the second alternative and not the former. If we replace
'the latter' by 'the former', then we should have a valid argument; it would
have the form '$p \vee q, \bar{p} \therefore q$'.

Differences in tense need not be counted as marking different statements.
Consider the argument

(6)   If John gets the grant, he will go to Oxford.
He will get the grant. Hence he will go to Oxford.

It contains 'John gets the grant' and 'John will get the grant', but as the
context shows, both may be represented by 'p'. This valid argument has the
form '$p \supset q, p \therefore q$'.

1.3.3.2   THE FALLACY OF EQUIVOCATION
The discussion of tenses and pronouns has been aimed at getting you to
recognize statements as the same even when they are expressed in different forms of words. On the other hand, it is just as important to recognize
that distinct statements can be expressed via the same form of words. This
point was recognized and illustrated in the discussion of the difference between sentences and statements. (See the Introduction.) Failure to recognize it now can lead to mistaken assessments of validity, logical truth, and
contingency. For example,

(7)   King ate rice and was still hungry, but he ate hash and was no longer
hungry

might be diagrammed as '$p \cdot q \cdot r \cdot \bar{q}$', and thus count as logically false. But
this would be a mistake: If 'King was still hungry' and 'King was no longer
hungry' were uttered with reference to the same occasion, then it would be
proper to diagram them by 'q' and '$\bar{q}$'. However, in (7), these two sentences do
not refer to the same occasion: the first refers to the time when King ate
rice, the second to when he ate hash. Thus (7) could be expanded to

(8)   King ate rice at a time t and was still hungry at the time t, but he ate hash
at a time t' and was no longer hungry at the time t'.

This has the form '$p \cdot q \cdot r \cdot \bar{s}$' and therefore is contingent.

Sameness of expression coupled with difference of meaning is illustrated
again in the following *invalid* argument:

(9)   Jones is an unreliable stockbroker, and if he sells again, he will hear
from me.

(10)   Thus, if he does not hear from me, he will not sell.

This argument superficially resembles the following *valid* argument:

(11)   Jones is my teacher, and if he gives me an A, he will pass me.

(12)   So if he does not pass me, he will not give me an A.

This argument has the form '$p \cdot (q \supset r) \therefore \bar{r} \supset \bar{q}$', and consequently it is valid. The first argument, however, only seems to have this form. It really has the form '$p \cdot (q \supset r) \therefore \bar{s} \supset \bar{q}$'. This is because the meaning of the expression 'hear from' differs from (9) to (10). Jones's unreliability indicates that the phrase 'will hear from me' means 'will be reprimanded by me', in (9), and that in (10) the same phrase means 'is restrained by me'.

Expressions which have more than one meaning are called *equivocal*. A very simple example of an equivocal word is the word 'even'. Some of its different meanings are illustrated in the following sentences:

Now we are even.
Two is an even number.
John even kissed Jane.

Equivocacy is no villain in itself, but sometimes it results in misunderstandings (due to *ambiguities*) or invalid arguments called *fallacies of equivocation*.

If a sentence is open to more than one interpretation, then the sentence is ambiguous. For example, the sentence

(13)   John was so green

is ambiguous because it could mean

(14)   John was so green in color

or

(15)   John was so inexperienced.

Of course, (13) is ambiguous only because we have considered it in isolation from both linguistic and situational contexts. When we speak to each other, the situation in which our sentences are uttered or the linguistic context surrounding them usually prevents such ambiguities. If, for example, (13) was part of a story about John's seasickness, it would probably have the sense of (14); but if (13) was part of a discussion about new employees, then it would probably have the sense of (15). Again, if some one utters 'She's a bitch' and points to a dog, he has said something acceptable in "polite society"; but if he utters the same thing while pointing to a woman, he may get his face slapped. (Here linguistic surroundings do not avoid ambiguity, but the situation does.)

Of course, sometimes situation and linguistic contexts are not sufficient to determine a unique interpretation of an utterance. Then we try to resolve the resulting ambiguity by questioning the speaker. Or if he is not present, we can try to follow the consequences of the possible interpretations in order to see which is more likely. If this fails to produce positive results, we may have to count the utterance as hopelessly ambiguous and give up trying to understand it. This type of difficulty can arise, especially in written works, since no one speaks or writes with complete clarity all the time. Here are some examples which illustrate these cases:

Ambiguity Resolved by Questioning:

"Get me a compass". "Do you mean one for drawing circles?" "No, I want a navigator's compass".

Ambiguity Resolved by Following Consequences:

Mr. James once said, "No rule can be long." This could mean that no method can have a lengthy statement or that no reign can have a long duration, but since James was a political scientist, he probably meant the latter.

Hopelessly Ambiguous:

He wrote me that my point was a nice one, but since it was a minor point, I could never decide whether he was complimenting me or merely remarking on the subtlety of my criticism.

By playing upon the meanings of equivocal expressions, one can also construct invalid arguments which, at first sight, appear to be valid. No one is likely to be fooled for long by the arguments (9)-(10), but such changes of meaning in midargument can lead to more subtle invalid arguments. For this reason invalid arguments of this type have been given extra attention by logicians and the special name, fallacies of equivocation. From the point of view of truth-functional logic, such fallacies usually arise when someone treats different statements as if they were the same. This is illustrated in the following example:

(16)   You will attain the end of your life if you are elected.

(17)   If you attain the end of your life, you will be dead.

(18)   So if you are elected, you will be dead.

Now, assuming that your *goal in life* is to be elected and that when you *reach the last moment of your life* you will die, then (16) and (17) are true. But then 'You attain the end of your life' must have a different meaning in (16) and (17). Thus the argument has the form '$p \supset q, r \supset s \therefore p \supset s$' and is invalid. On the other hand, if 'you attain the end of your life' is interpreted as the same in both premisses, then of course the argument will have the valid form '$p \supset q, q \supset r \therefore p \supset r$'. In this case, however, one or the other of its premisses would clearly be false, and the argument (though valid) would not be sound.

Now we can see why people try to use fallacies of equivocation to convince their opponents. By playing on one meaning of an expression, they manage to make all their premisses true. Then, by changing this expression's meaning, they cast the argument in a valid form. But of course they cannot have it both ways. The argument will be valid if and only if *its premisses* imply *its* conclusion. Changing one's statements by means of equivocation amounts to changing one's premisses or conclusion, and thus to changing one's argument.

EXAMPLES OF FALLACIES OF EQUIVOCATION.   The fallacy of equivocation is committed in each of the following arguments. The expressions equivocated upon are underlined, and each argument is followed by diagrams of both its apparent (and valid) form and its real (but invalid) form.

a. If that act was a departure from law, it should be punished.
    If it happened by chance, it was a departure from law.
    So if that act happened by chance, it should be punished.

    Apparent form: $p \supset q, r \supset p \therefore r \supset q$
    Real form: $p \supset q, r \supset s \therefore r \supset q$

b. If James is only five feet tall, he is a small man, and if he is a small man, then he will be difficult to manage. We shall not hire him unless he is not difficult to manage. So if James is only five feet tall, we shall not hire him.

    Apparent form: $(p \supset q) \cdot (q \supset r), \bar{s} \vee \bar{r} \therefore p \supset \bar{s}$
    Real form: $(p \supset q) \cdot (q_1 \supset r), \bar{s} \vee \bar{r} \therefore p \supset \bar{s}$

c. Hugo's error is apparent or concealed. If it is concealed, we shall not discover his error. Yet if it is only apparent, then it is not an error at all, and we shall not discover his error. So in any case, we shall not discover his error.

    Apparent form: $p \vee q, (q \supset \bar{r}), (p \supset \bar{s} \cdot \bar{r}) \therefore \bar{r}$
    Real form: $(p \vee q), (q \supset \bar{r}), (p_1 \supset \bar{s} \cdot \bar{r}) \therefore \bar{r}$

d. James is a groom if and only if he takes care of horses. But he is also a groom just in case he has just been married. So James takes care of horses if and only if he has just been married.

    Apparent form: $(p \equiv q), (p \equiv r) \therefore (q \equiv r)$
    Real form: $(p \equiv q), (s \equiv r) \therefore (q \equiv r)$

e.   If Kant's theories are difficult to understand, he is an <u>obscure</u> philosopher. But Kant is not an <u>obscure</u> philosopher; he is recognized as one of the greatest philosophers. So his theories cannot be difficult to understand.

Apparent form: $p \supset q, \bar{q} \cdot r \therefore \bar{p}$
Real form: $p \supset q, \bar{s} \cdot r \therefore \bar{p}$

1.3.4   DIAGRAMMING STATEMENTS: EXAMPLES COMPLETELY WORKED OUT

In this section several statements will be diagrammed and discussed in detail. This will both help tie together the more abstract discussion of the previous sections and provide additional illustrations of the problems and techniques mentioned.

Let us start with a few simple examples:

(1)   If the train has arrived and the baggage has been unloaded, James will bring the car and Jackson will take Miss Susie's trunk.

(2)   Peter calls the police or the fire department only if an emergency arises.

(3)   Provided that Carlton promised Lydia everything but gave her Arpège, he had a wonderful date.

As the first step toward diagramming these statements, let us replace their truth-functional statement connectives by logical symbols. When this is done, of course, some of the devices for indicating grouping will be lost; so we must also add parentheses at this step if the need for them arises. In (1) the word 'if' occurs once and the word 'and' occurs twice. All three are used as statement connectives too. In (2) we find 'or' and 'only if', while in (3) we have 'but' and 'provided that'. If you recall that 'p only if q' is translated as '$p \supset q$', 'p but q' as '$p \cdot q$', and 'provided p, q' as '$p \supset q$', then you will see that (1), (2), and (3) may be transformed as follows:

(1')   The train has arrived · The baggage has been unloaded $\supset$ James will bring the car · Jackson will take Miss Susie's trunk.

(2')   (Peter calls the police $\vee$ Peter calls the fire department) $\supset$ An emergency has arisen.

(3')   Carlton promised Lydia everything · He gave her Arpège $\supset$ He had a wonderful date.

Notice that in passing from (2) to (2') we had to un-telescope the clause 'Peter calls the police or the fire department'. To preserve the sense of (2), it was also necessary to change the tense of its last clause.

Diagrams (1) to (3) are now easily obtained from (1') to (3') by replacing the component simple statements of the latter by statement letters. It is obvious that no statement is repeated in these examples and that all the components are to be replaced by distinct statement letters. This yields the following diagrams of (1) to (3), respectively:

(1") $p \cdot q \supset r \cdot s$

(2") $(p \lor q) \supset r$

(3") $p \cdot q \supset r$

As these three schemata illustrate, it is convenient to replace the first, that is, leftmost, statement in a given example by 'p', the next by 'q', the next by 'r', and so on. Statements (1), (2), and (3) are three *separate* examples, although they are under simultaneous discussion, and therefore there is no objection to reusing 'p' in both (2) and (3). If, on the other hand, (1), (2), and (3) had been presented in the same example, say, as elements of an argument to be tested for validity, then it would be wrong to reuse 'p', 'q', and 'r' in diagramming them. For this would be a case in which a simultaneous diagramming would be needed, and in such a case, all the statements involved would be treated as if they were a single statement. To take a concrete case, '$(p \lor q) \supset r$' implies '$p \cdot q \supset r$', as a right-left test shows, but it is intuitively clear that (2) does not imply (3). Hence, if we were attempting to determine whether (2) implies (3), it would be wrong to diagram them as they have been diagrammed above. Instead, we should have to diagram them simultaneously by, say, '$(p \lor q) \supset r$' and '$s \cdot p_1 \supset q_1$', respectively. A right-left test now shows that the first schema does not imply the second, and accordingly (2) does not imply (3).

Misrepetition of statement letters can have amusingly paradoxical consequences. For example, someone might argue that all simple statements are equivalent, because (as long as we reveal no structure) they can all be diagrammed by 'p', and 'p' is equivalent to itself. Or someone might argue that any two statements having the same logical form are equivalent since they can be diagrammed by the same schema. The mistake behind these claims should now be clear: If the statements in question are taken as separate examples, then of course they can be diagrammed by the same schema; but if the statements are being tested for equivalence, then it will almost always be erroneous to use the same schema to diagram them.

Let us now turn to a more complicated example:

(4) If price controls or excess profit taxes are instituted, then, unless interest rates are lowered, the stock market will fall and a depression will follow.

Although it is not difficult to recognize the truth-functions in (4), it is hard to determine its grouping at a glance. Accordingly, let us break (4) into several components and work on these separately. This can be done by *paraphrasing inward*, that is, by first picking out the main connective of (4), then by identifying the main connective of its immediate components, and so on. The first comma and the 'if . . . then' construction used in (4) show that (4) is a conditional. Thus it can be transformed as

(4a) (Price controls or excess profit taxes are instituted) ⊃ (Unless interest rates are lowered, the stock market will fall and a depression will follow)

Now let us turn to the antecedent of (4a). Telescoping shows that it can be paraphrased as

(4b) Price controls are instituted ∨ Excess profit taxes are instituted

and this possesses no further problems. The consequent of (4a) is more intricate, however. Since 'unless' is translated as '∨', the comma tells us that the consequent of (4a) can be paraphrased as

(4c) Interest rates are lowered ∨ (The stock market will fall and a depression will follow)

which in turn becomes

(4d) Interest rates are lowered ∨ (The stock market will fall · A depression will follow)

Then, by combining (4b) and (4d), we get

(4e) (Price controls are instituted ∨ Excess profit taxes are instituted) ⊃ (Interest rates are lowered ∨ The stock market will fall · A depression will follow)

And from (4e) we see that (4) has the form '$(p \lor q) \supset (r \lor s \cdot p_1)$'. [Note that none of the simple components of (4e) have any repetitions.]

Next let us do an example in which both grouping and statement identification pose problems:

(5) The movie will be banned unless the risqué scenes are eliminated or redone, but if this is done, then it will be boring if someone does not come up with a better idea.

This sentence contains two commas, and the second one precedes an occurrence of 'then'. The 'if' that goes with this 'then' only governs the clause 'this is done'; so the second comma cannot mark the greatest break in (5). Thus the main connective in (5) is 'but', and (5) may be rewritten

(5a)   (The movie will be banned unless the risqué scenes are eliminated or redone) · (If this is done, then it will be boring if someone does not come up with a better idea)

Breaking (5a) into components and making a few of the (by now) obvious translations, we obtain:

(5b)   The movie is banned ∨ (The risqué scenes are eliminated ∨ The risqué scenes are redone)

(5c)   This is done ⊃ (It will be boring if someone does not come up with a better idea)

[In (5b) telescoped clauses have been expanded. The comma is responsible for the grouping of (5c).]
   While (5b) needs no further analysis, (5c) requires careful attention. The phrase 'this is done' is not a complete statement by itself; it refers to some action. To make sense of (5), we must interpret it as referring to the elimination or revision of the risqué scenes. Thus 'This is done' can be expanded to

(5d)   The risqué scenes are eliminated ∨ The risqué scenes are redone

Turning now to the consequent of (5e), we supply the antecedent of the pronoun 'it' and write

(5e)   Someone does not come up with a better idea ⊃ The movie will be boring

Then we make the use of negation explicit and obtain

(5f)   −(Someone comes up with a better idea) ⊃ The movie will be boring

Now combining (5b), (5d), and (5f), we get the following paraphrase of (5):

(5g)   [The movie is banned ∨ (The risqué scenes are eliminated ∨ The risqué scenes are redone)] · [(The risqué scenes are eliminated ∨ The risqué scenes are redone) ⊃ (−(Someone comes up with a better idea) ⊃ The movie will be boring)]

This can now be diagrammed by the following schema:

$$[p \lor (q \lor r)] \cdot [(q \lor r) \supset (\bar{s} \supset p_1)]$$

Of course, it is quite obvious that statements are repeated in (5g). Yet this was not immediately apparent in the case of (5). Thus it can be quite useful to paraphrase a compound statement in a more transparent form before diagramming it. One can now see readily that (5) implies

(6) If someone does not come up with a better idea, the movie will be banned or boring.

All the work on (5) has facilitated the diagramming of (6); for we can dispense with the intermediate steps and go immediately to the diagram ' $\bar{s} \supset (p \lor p_1)$ '. It is necessary to comment on the choice of our statement letters. Since we test (5) and (6) for implication, we must look for statements which (5) and (6) have in common. Since these statements have already been represented by statement letters in the diagram of (5), we have to be faithful to this representation in diagramming (6). Thus ' s ' stands for 'Someone comes up with a better idea', ' p ' for 'The movie is banned', and ' p_1 ' for 'The movie is boring'.

Now that you have seen several examples worked out, your own sensitivity to the logical structure of statements in ordinary language should be heightened. And with this heightened sensitivity, the task of diagramming statements should become much easier. Of course, it can never become completely trivial, because this is not a mechanical matter, such as a truth-value analysis. Indeed, even the most skilled and experienced logician can be stymied by an intricate argument or statement from ordinary language. On the other hand, you need not be pessimistic; for no really new skills have been imparted in these sections: if you are able to speak, write, and comprehend the ordinary language of the educated layman, you should already have the skills needed to diagram statements.

EXERCISES FOR SECS. 1.3.3 AND 1.3.4

A. Diagram the statements given in the exercises presented at the end of secs. 1.3.1.6 and 1.3.2.2. Reveal as much truth-functional structure as possible.

B. Diagram these statements. Reveal as much truth-functional structure as possible.

1. Smith will be elected, but if that does not happen, I will pay you $1.

2. Peter or Mary is at home; however, if he is at home, watch out, while you will be welcome if she is there.

3. Jackson and Jones are both officers, but the former and not the latter is the one who can sign for this.

4. The new model will contain additional features just in case the design department finishes the project this month; however, if all that is the case, then it is not the best policy to buy a new model.

5. The Smiths went to Honolulu and returned healthy, but they went to India and returned sick.

6. If Smith runs for the Senate, he will be elected, but if he runs for the Presidency, he will not be elected.

7. If it rains, the picnic will be canceled; moreover, it will rain and the picnic will be canceled.

8. Unless I talk to him first, he will plow the field, but it is false that if he does not plow the field, then I will talk to him afterward.

9. While Jackson tends the horses or Smith cares for the goats, the first does not do what the second does.

10. The butler committed the murder, but if that is so, he cannot be trusted; moreover, if that is also true, no one can be trusted.

C. Determine the validity of these arguments.

1. Either John or I will meet you, but if John does, he will bring the truck. On the other hand, I will bring the car in case that I meet you. So I will bring the car, or else John will meet you and he will bring the truck.

2. If you want to be healthy, then you will go to bed earlier and rise earlier. If you do the former, you will miss the sunset, while if you do the latter, you will see the sun rise. So if you do not see the sun rise, you do not want to be healthy unless you miss the sunset.

3. If she comes closer, she will seem even more beautiful. Provided that she marries you, she will seem even more beautiful. Hence if she does not marry you, she will not come closer.

4. I will not pass the course if I do not take the test, while if I take the test, then I will answer only half the questions. Answering only half the questions is sufficient for not passing the course. Therefore I will not pass the course.

5. The table is made of pine or walnut. If it is made of pine, then it will scratch easily, but it does not. So unless I am mistaken, the table is made of walnut.

6. If he has ten children, then that character will be written on his face. If his character is written on his face, he cannot deceive us. So either he cannot deceive us or he does not have ten children.

7. If he is late, there is no reason for it. He will be late; and although he will try to prevent it, his car will break down, thereby causing a delay. So there will be no reason for his being late.

8. The owner will shoe the horse or hire someone to do it if the horse loses a shoe. Unless the owner does not shoe the horse, the owner will have a sore back. The race will be canceled if the owner has a sore back. Hence, if the horse loses a shoe, the owner will not hire someone to shoe him only if the race is canceled.

9. I am mistaken just in case that man is not my uncle, but he is my uncle if and only if you are not my aunt. On the other hand, you are not my aunt if I am not mistaken, although you are my aunt unless I am not mistaken. Therefore I am mistaken and a fool.

10. It is not the case that John will leave without telling his mother. His mother will let us know if he tells her, although there is no action for us to take unless she lets us know. So there is no action for us to take provided that John leaves.

11. If you are convicted of manslaughter or of drunken driving, your license will be revoked. But you have not been convicted of manslaughter. Therefore, if your license has been revoked, you were convicted of being drunk in a public place.

12. Had Franklin D. Roosevelt been a Socialist, he would have been willing to nationalize industries and would have done so in the thirties. But no industries were nationalized by Roosevelt in the thirties. So he must not have been a Socialist.

13. If the rudder does not break and the fuel holds out, the ship will get safely to port and no one will drown. If the fuel holds out but the rudder breaks, then the ship can be steered by means of its propellers, and if that is true, it will get safely to port. If the rudder does not break, the fuel will hold out. Therefore the ship will get safely to port.

14. He can have many friends only if he respects them as individuals; but if he respects them as individuals, he cannot expect them all to behave alike. He does have many friends. Hence he does not expect them all to behave alike.

15. If the first disjunct is true, the disjunction is true; but this is also the case if the second disjunct is true. Hence, if the disjunction is false, both disjuncts are false.

16. To pass Professor Black's course it is sufficient to take the final; moreover, you cannot pass his course without taking the final. So taking the final is both necessary and sufficient for passing his course.

17. The truck will pull this stump out if it does not have a taproot and provided that we cut its lateral roots first. The tractor will pull this stump out so long as we cut its lateral roots first. So, as long as we cut the lateral roots first, the truck or tractor will pull the stump out, and we shall not need a bulldozer.

18. If the intellectuals take over, business will suffer but the poor will benefit. The poor will benefit only if they obtain better housing—which they will not. Hence the intellectuals will not take over.

19. When duty and desire conflict, one must do his duty. But duty and desire conflict only when something pleasurable is forbidden. Hence one must do his duty only when something pleasurable is forbidden.

20. If you plow, you must disk; yet you must plant if you disk. Although you disked, you did not plow. So you cannot plant unless it is not the case that you must disk when you plow.

1.4   TRUTH-FUNCTION THEORY AND ELECTRONIC-CIRCUIT THEORY

One of the most dramatic and important applications of logic concerns the simplest branch of logic—truth-function theory. Truth-functional principles have been applied in the study and design of electric circuits, and even the circuits which computers use to "add", "subtract", etc., may be studied by truth-functional methods. Thus today truth-function theory is an essential tool in the design of electronic computers. We shall investigate computer circuits, but first let us look at simpler ones, namely, two-terminal switching circuits.

1.4.1   TWO-TERMINAL SWITCHING CIRCUITS

A two-terminal switching circuit is a network of wires and switches with one wire leading in to the network and another leading out. Let us use the letters

'p', 'q', 'r', etc., to represent switches. Then here are diagrams of some simple two-terminal switching circuits:

a.

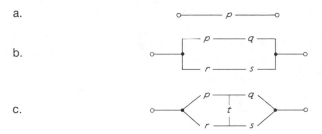

b.

c.

The switches can be open or closed, but the current flows through them only
when they are closed. Some switches are controlled by a "bigger switch".
For example, in many modern living rooms all the lamps may be turned on
by operating a single switch at the door. In such cases it is often convenient
to use the same letter to represent all the switches which are linked together.
Thus we can have such diagrams as

d.

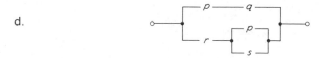

Here all the positions labeled 'p' are controlled by a single switch. Other
switches are linked in such a way that one is closed if and only if the other
is open. Then it is useful to let one of the switches be represented by a negated letter; thus, if one switch is represented by 'p', the other is represented
by 'p̄'. This leads to diagrams such as

e.

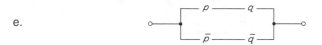

A two-terminal switching circuit whose branches (if any) only take the
forms

is called a *series-parallel circuit*. Thus all the examples given so far, except for (c) are examples of series-parallel circuits. When switches follow one another as in

they are said to be arranged serially, but when they are placed as in

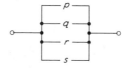

they are said to be parallel.

1.4.1.1 CIRCUITS AND TFS

Current will flow through a series circuit if and only if all the switches are closed. On the other hand, current will flow through a parallel circuit just in case one or more of the switches are closed. Thus a series connection functions like conjunction, and a parallel connection like disjunction. Indeed, given any series-parallel circuit, we can write a TFS corresponding to the circuit. To do this we represent

by '$p \cdot q$' and

by '$p \lor q$'. Analogously, we represent

by '$p \cdot q \cdot r \cdot s$' and

by '$p \lor q \lor r \lor s$'. Thus the circuit

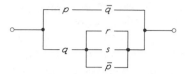

is represented by the TFS '$p \cdot \bar{q} \vee q \cdot (r \vee s \vee \bar{p})$' (here "top to bottom" corresponds with "left to right"). Conversely, given a TFS composed of only '∨', '·', '−', and statement letters, in which '−' appears over statement letters only, a corresponding series-parallel circuit can be easily obtained. Thus the TFS '$r \vee p \cdot (\bar{p} \vee q \cdot \bar{r})$' corresponds to

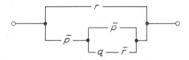

One of the chief questions that can be asked about a switching circuit is "What positions must the switches be in, in order for current to flow through the circuit?" In the case of series-parallel circuits, this question may be answered by applying very simple truth-functional techniques. Let us represent closed switches and circuits by T's and open ones by F's. Then, whether or not current will flow through a given circuit when its switches are in given positions can be viewed as a truth-function of the positions of the switches. Indeed, the truth-function is represented by the TFS corresponding to the circuit. Let us check this with an example. Let the circuit be

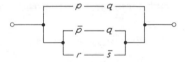

Then the corresponding TFS is '$p \cdot q \vee (\bar{p} \cdot q \vee r \cdot \bar{s})$'. Suppose that p is closed, q is open, r is closed, and s is open. Then current cannot get through the top branch because q is open. It cannot get through the middle branch because $\bar{p}$ is open. But it can get through the lowest branch since both r and $\bar{s}$ are closed. Alternatively, if 'p' is assigned T, 'q' F, 'r' T, and 's' F, then '$p \cdot q \vee (\bar{p} \cdot q \vee r \cdot \bar{s})$' comes out T.

1.4.1.2   CIRCUIT DESIGN
It should now be clear that a truth-value analysis of the TFS corresponding to a series-parallel circuit will reveal the complete behavior of the circuit for

the various positions of its switches. Furthermore, this behavior can be "read off" the truth table for the TFS. By reversing this procedure, that is, by writing a truth table first and then a TFS and finally a circuit, one can design circuits which will behave in a predetermined manner. For example, suppose that two men have the power of life and death in a given community, but they must act with unanimity. They obtain an electric chair, and anyone they are to pass judgment upon must be strapped into the chair. While each has a switch for the chair, the chair electrocutes its victim if and only if both men close their switches. The situation may be pictured as follows:

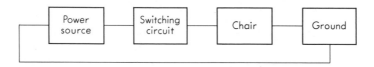

The problem is to design a switching circuit for operating this electric chair. The behavior of the circuit may be represented by the following truth table:

SWITCHES		CIRCUIT
p	q	
T	T	T
T	F	F
F	T	F
F	F	F

The TFS '$p \cdot q$' has this truth table; so the required circuit is

$$\circ\!\!-\!\!-\!\!-\, p \,-\!\!-\, q \,-\!\!-\!\!-\!\!\circ$$

Now let us (perversely) alter the story and have the victim electrocuted if and only if the two judges disagree! Then the truth table is

p	q	CIRCUIT
T	T	F
T	F	T
F	T	T
F	F	F

A TFS which has this truth table is '$p \cdot \bar{q} \vee \bar{p} \cdot q$'; thus the following circuit will do:

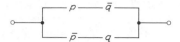

Let us turn to a more mundane example — a light switch for a room with two doors. Here we want to be able to turn the light on or off by using either switch without having to alter the position of the other switch. We must first choose a combination of the switches which will turn the light off. Any combination will do, and we can think of this as the way the switches will be when the light is connected to the circuit. Let us suppose that the switches are both open (off). When we enter the room and turn on switch p, say, then we want the lights to go on. Similarly if we enter and turn on switch q. Thus, when one switch is off and the other on, the light is on. On the other hand, if we had turned the light on at switch p, we want to be able to turn it off at switch q without returning to switch p, and similarly if we had turned the light on at switch q. Thus, when both switches are *on*, the light is *off*. Finally, if we had turned the light on at switch p, we can turn it off at switch p by turning the switch off. The same holds for switch q. Thus the light is on if and only if the switches are in opposite positions. This leads us to the same truth table as that just given for the electric chair, and thus to the same circuit.

As the preceding discussion indicates, finding a truth table that will describe the behavior of a proposed circuit can be a nontrivial problem. Once we have the truth table, however, it is easy to find a circuit; for there is a mechanical method for finding a schema having the truth table, and a circuit can be obtained from this schema. We shall indicate the method by means of an example. Let us suppose that the circuit is to have three switches, p, q, and r. (The method works for any number of switches.) If the circuit is always to be open, so that our truth table contains all F's in its main column, then the schema we want is '$p \cdot \bar{p} \cdot q \cdot r$'. (Why?) In every other case the truth table will have one or more T's in its main column. For example, suppose that the truth table is

p	q	r		
T	T	T	T	✔
T	T	F	T	✔
T	F	T	F	
T	F	F	F	
F	T	T	F	
F	T	F	T	✔
F	F	T	F	
F	F	F	T	✔

We put a check beside each 'T' in the main column. For each checked row we obtain a conjunction whose components are 'p', 'q', and 'r' with or without negation signs. This is done by looking at the entry under 'p', 'q', and 'r', respectively, for the row. If it is 'T', the letter in question is not negated; if it is 'F', the letter is negated. Thus, in our particular examples, the conjunctions we obtain are

$$p \cdot q \cdot r, \qquad p \cdot q \cdot \bar{r}, \qquad \bar{p} \cdot q \cdot \bar{r}, \qquad \bar{p} \cdot \bar{q} \cdot \bar{r}$$

(Here the order from left to right corresponds to top to bottom.) Notice that each conjunction comes out true under just the interpretation given by the row from which it is obtained. For example, '$\bar{p} \cdot q \cdot \bar{r}$' comes out true if and only if '$\bar{p}$', 'q', and '$\bar{r}$' all come out true. And these jointly come out true if and only if 'p' is false, 'q' is true, and 'r' is false. Once we have obtained conjunctions for each checked row, a schema having the truth table in question is simply the disjunction of all these conjunctions. Thus, for the truth table given above, the schema we want is

$$p \cdot q \cdot r \cdot \vee p \cdot q \cdot \bar{r} \vee \bar{p} \cdot q \cdot \bar{r} \vee \bar{p} \cdot \bar{q} \cdot \bar{r}$$

Notice that this schema (and any schema obtained by the same method) has to come out true under just those interpretations which correspond to checked rows. For when the schema is interpreted as indicated by a checked row, one of its conjunctions comes out true. But when it is interpreted as indicated by an unchecked row, none of its conjunctions comes out true. The schema we have obtained corresponds to a series-parallel circuit, and clearly, any schema obtained by the same method will correspond to a series-parallel circuit.

The method always produces a circuit, but it does not always produce a very simple one. For example, suppose that we start with the truth table

p	q		
T	T	T	✔
T	F	F	
F	T	T	✔
F	F	T	✔

(This is the table for '$p \supset q$'.) The method yields the schema '$p \cdot q \vee \bar{p} \cdot q \vee \bar{p} \cdot \bar{q}$', and thus the circuit

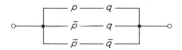

Yet '$\bar{p} \lor q$' has the same truth table, so that the simpler circuit

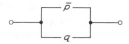

will serve as well. Indeed, let us return to the schema '$p \cdot q \cdot r \lor p \cdot q \cdot \bar{r} \lor \bar{p} \cdot q \cdot \bar{r} \lor \bar{p} \cdot \bar{q} \cdot \bar{r}$', which gives rise to the circuit

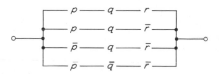

The schema is equivalent to

$p \cdot q \cdot (r \lor \bar{r}) \lor \bar{p} \cdot \bar{r} \cdot (q \lor \bar{q})$

which in turn is equivalent to

$p \cdot q \lor \bar{p} \cdot \bar{r}$

This yields the simpler circuit

The notion of a simpler circuit is ambiguous. Any circuit which is a "simpler" version of a given circuit must have a TFS which is equivalent to the one corresponding to the more complex circuit. But what is to be meant by a simpler circuit besides this will depend to a large degree upon practical considerations. If, for example, one wants to minimize the number of series connections used, then the circuit

will be considered simpler than the circuit

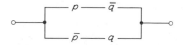

For the first puts two parallel circuits in a series, while the second puts two series circuits in parallel. On the other hand, if one wants to minimize parallel connections, the second circuit will be considered simpler. In addition, one might be willing to drop out *redundant* switches, that is, switches which make no difference to the state of the circuit as a whole. Then, for example, the circuit

can be replaced, simply by

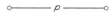

Notice that in this case the two circuits will not only have different switches, but also different truth tables. But since the switch q has no function in the first circuit—current will pass through so long as p is closed—for many purposes the two circuits will have the same function. (But to return to the electric-chair example, if one of the judges was to be given the illusion of power, he would need a switch, and the first circuit would be an appropriate one.)

A simpler circuit is, of course, cheaper to build, and it may even be more reliable than a more complex circuit. Thus electrical engineers have devoted a great deal of attention to methods for simplifying circuits. Because these methods are rather complex and because the exercises to be given in this book can be done very easily without them, they will not be discussed here.

EXERCISES FOR SEC. 1.4.1

A.   Obtain TFS which represent these circuits. Which circuits are closed when p is closed?

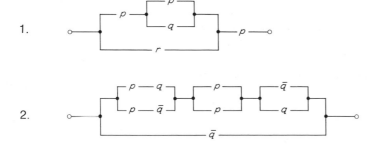

1.

2.

3.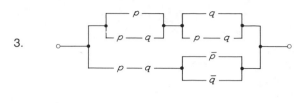

4.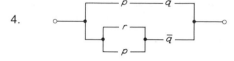

5.

6.

7.

8.

9.

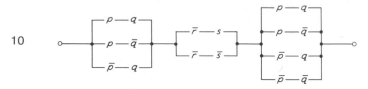

10

B. For each of these TFS, obtain an equivalent which does not contain '⊃' or '≡' and in which '−' governs only statement letters. Then obtain a circuit from the equivalent.

   1. $p \supset q$

   2. $p \equiv q$

   3. $-(p \equiv q)$

   4. $(p \supset q) \supset p$

   5. $-(p \vee q) \cdot (r \supset p)$

   6. $(p \equiv q) \supset r \cdot s$

   7. $-(p \cdot q) \supset (r \vee s)$

   8. $(r \vee q) \supset p \cdot -(p \supset q)$

   9. $((r \supset q) \vee (p \supset q)) \cdot p$

 10. $(r \equiv \bar{q}) \cdot (p \supset q) \vee r$

C. Obtain as simple equivalents as possible of the circuits given in A. (You need not retain all the switches p, q, r, etc.)

D. Circuit-design problems

   1.   Design a circuit to control a light having two switches, which is on when both switches are on or when one but not both are off.

   2.   Design a circuit for controlling a light, which has three switches p, q, and r but which is on just in case p is on.

   3.   Design a circuit for a burglar alarm, which has a master switch p and a door switch q and a window switch r and which rings just in case the master switch is on and the door or window is opened.

   4.   Design a circuit for controlling a voting indicator, which lights just in case two or three of the voters p, q, and r vote *yes*.

   5.   Design a circuit for controlling a voting indicator, which lights just in case two or three of the voters p, q, and r agree in voting *yes* or in voting *no*.

   6.   Design a circuit for controlling a light with three switches, which changes from on to off or off to on just in case the position of any single switch is changed. (Assume that the light is off when all three switches are off.)

1.4.2 BASIC COMPUTER CIRCUITS

1.4.2.1 BINARY NUMBERS

The next circuits we shall consider are those used in modern electronic computers to "add" and "subtract". Because computers operate with electrical impulses, addition and subtraction for computers consist in taking two electrical impulses—the "numbers" to be added or subtracted—and producing a third. Fortunately, one can translate ordinary numbers into computer numbers, and conversely. Thus, before we can discuss computer circuits, we must discuss computer numbers.

Computers use the *binary-number system*. Our own number system is the *decimal-number system*. We use *ten* symbols to represent each number. Starting from 0 we can go to 9; then we have to add an extra column of symbols to get 10; and then another to get 100; and then another to get 1,000; and so on. Each time we add a new column (digit), we can represent 10 times the amount of numbers we could represent before. Thus, with our basic 10 symbols, we can represent the first 10 numbers (starting with zero); with two digits we can represent the first 100 numbers; etc. Thus the number 376 is $300 + 70 + 6$, or $3 \times 10^2 + 7 \times 10^1 + 6 \times 10^0$, since $10^0 = 1$. In general, an $n + 1 =$ digit decimal number

$$a_n \, a_{n-1} \cdots a_1 \, a_0$$

equals

$$a_n \times 10^n + a_{n-1} \times 10^{n-1} + \cdots + a_1 \times 10^1 + a_0 \times 10^0$$

In the binary-number system, however, we use only two basic symbols, '0' and '1'. This means that we must add new digits more frequently since each new digit only doubles the amount of numbers we can represent. The first 11 numbers are given in binary notation by the following table:

DECIMAL	BINARY	TRANSLATION EXPRESSION
0	0	0×2^0
1	1	1×2^0
2	10	$1 \times 2^1 + 0 \times 2^0$
3	11	$1 \times 2^1 + 1 \times 2^0$
4	100	$1 \times 2^2 + 0 \times 2^1 + 0 \times 2^0$
5	101	$1 \times 2^2 + 0 \times 2^1 + 1 \times 2^0$
6	110	$1 \times 2^2 + 1 \times 2^1 + 0 \times 2^0$
7	111	$1 \times 2^2 + 1 \times 2^1 + 1 \times 2^0$
8	1000	$1 \times 2^3 + 0 \times 2^2 + 0 \times 2^1 + 0 \times 2^0$
9	1001	$1 \times 2^3 + 0 \times 2^2 + 0 \times 2^1 + 1 \times 2^0$
10	1010	$1 \times 2^3 + 0 \times 2^2 + 1 \times 2^1 + 0 \times 2^0$

Given a number in $n + 1$-digit binary notation $a_n \, a_{n-1} \cdots a_1 \, a_0$—that is, a string of 0's and 1's of length $n + 1$—one can obtain its decimal equivalent by evaluating the translation formula

$$a_n \times 2^n + a_{n-1} \times 2^{n-1} + \cdots + a_1 \times 2^1 + a_0 \times 2^0$$

Thus, 100110 is $1 \times 2^5 + 0 \times 2^4 + 0 \times 2^3 + 1 \times 2^2 + 1 \times 2^1 + 0 \times 2^0$; that is, $32 + 0 + 0 + 4 + 2 + 0$, or 38.

It is more difficult to go from decimal to binary notation. But a procedure is available which is based upon the fact that a number can be expressed in one and only one way as a sum of the powers of 2, that is, as a sum of one or more of 1, 2, 4, 8, 16, 32, 64, ... Then, in the binary notation, digits '1' mark the powers of 2 that occur in the sum, while digits '0' mark the missing powers. For example, when the number 10 is expressed as $8 + 2$, we have

Powers of 2:   8   4   2   1

Binary digits: 1   0   1   0

Thus '1' and '0' are the only digits needed, since each power of 2 occurs only once, if at all, in such a sum. The following algorithm routinizes the process of discovering such a sum and the binary representation of a number.

1   Determine the highest power, k, of 2 which is not greater than the number.
2   Divide the number by 2^k. The quotient a_k is the first digit; the remainder r_1 is used in step 3.
3   a.   If r_1 is larger than or equal to 2^{k-1}, divide r_1 by 2^{k-1} to obtain a_{k-1}, the second digit. The remainder r_2 is used in step 4.
    b.   If r_1 is smaller than 2^{k-1}, the second digit is 0 and r_1 is used in step 4.
4   Repeat step 3 with the result of (a) or (b) and continue until all powers of 2 less than k have been used. (Note that in the repetitions of step 3 the word 'second' is replaced by 'third', 'fourth', etc.)
5   Once the digits a_n, a_{n-1}, $\cdots$, a_0 have been obtained, the binary number is simply $a_n a_{n-1} \cdots a_1 a_0$

EXAMPLES

a.   To represent 25 in binary notation. k is 4 since $2^4 = 16$ and $2^5 = 32$. $25 \div 16 = 1 + 9/16$. So $a_4 = 1$, $r_1 = 9$. $2^3 < 9$ and $9 \div 8 = 1 + 1/8$; so $a_3 = 1$ and $r_2 = 1$. $1 < 2^2$; so $a_2 = 0$. $1 < 2^1$; so $a_1 = 0$. $1 = 2^0$; so $a_0 = 1 \div 1 = 1$.

   Thus the binary representation of 25 is 11001.

b.   To represent 32 in binary notation. $2^5 = 32$; so $k = 5$. $32 \div 32 = 1$; so $a_5 = 1$. $0 < 2^4$; so $a_4 = 0$. $0 < 2^3$; so $a_3 = 0$. $0 < 2^2$; so $a_2 = 0$. $0 < 2^1$; so $a_1 = 0$. Finally, $0 < 2^0$; so $a_0 = 0$, and the binary representation of 32 is 100000.

   The binary numbers themselves can be viewed as a code for representing sequences of impulses in the computer. Most computers are designed so that only two sorts of impulses flow through their circuits. By letting one of these correspond to 0 and the other correspond to 1, every sequence of impulses can be represented by a binary number. Indeed, it is quite easy to design an electrical printer which will print a '0' when given one impulse and a '1' when given another. Thus it is quite easy for a computer to "communicate" with us, at least in a binary notation. Similarly, we can represent 0 and 1 by punching two different holes on a punch card and read binary numbers into the computer. But these are problems which would take us into the study of the mechanical aspects of computers. Let us turn instead to their circuits.

1.4.2.2 SEQUENTIAL CIRCUITS

Two-terminal switching circuits allow current to flow through them in either direction. Computer circuits, which are also called *sequential circuits*, however, allow current to flow in only one direction. Thus the circuits have one or more *input* leads and one or more *output* leads. The number of inputs and outputs may differ. Impulses of current are sent through the inputs and received at the outputs. Thus the typical computer circuit can be conceived diagrammatically as follows:

Inputs   Circuit   Outputs

Let us use statement letters to label inputs. (The reason for this will soon be clear.) Then let us label each output by means of a symbol such as '$f(p,q,r)$' to indicate that the output is a function of the inputs. Thus, given a circuit with three inputs p,q, and r and two outputs, the outputs could be labeled '$f(p,q,r)$' and '$g(p,q,r)$'.

Our computer circuits are composed of wires and *gates*. There are three types of gates which will concern us. First, there are NOT gates, which convert 0 impulses to 1 impulses and 1 impulses to 0 impulses. These we can represent by

Second, there are AND gates, two inputs and one output. They convert a pair of 0 impulses into a 0 impulse and convert any two other impulses into a 1 impulse. These gates are represented as

Finally, we have OR gates, which also have two inputs and one output. These convert a pair of 1 impulses into a 1 impulse and convert any two other impulses into a 0 impulse. These gates are represented by

Wires in circuits built with these gates as components may also branch or pass over one another. Thus a typical circuit looks like this:†

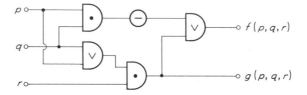

By tracing the paths from an output back to the inputs, we can express the output as a truth-function of the inputs to which it may be traced. The negation sign '−' is used to represent NOT gates, the conjunction sign '·' to represent AND gates, and the disjunction sign '∨' to represent OR gates. We obtain a TFS for each output by taking as the main connective of the TFS the representation of the first gate tracing back brings us to, as the main connective(s) of the component(s), the representations of the next gates, and so on, until we reach the inputs which are represented as statement letters. Notice that the branches and crosses of the wires are *not* represented in the TFS. Thus $f(p,q,r)$ in the last example may be represented by the TFS '$-(p \cdot q) \vee (q \vee p) \cdot r$' and $g(p,q,r)$ by '$(q \vee p) \cdot r$'. In this way the whole circuit can be represented by one or more "equations" whose left sides are output labels and whose right sides are TFS. In our example the equations are

$$f(p,q,r) = -(p \cdot q) \vee (q \vee p) \cdot r$$
$$g(p,q,r) = (q \vee p) \cdot r$$

Given one or more equations of this sort, one can easily find a circuit whose inputs correspond to the statement letters of the TFS involved and whose outputs correspond to the TFS. (The TFS cannot contain '⊃' or '≡', *but* '−' need not be restricted to statement letters.) Many equivalent circuits are possible because the wiring patterns are not represented. These patterns have no effect on the behavior of the outputs as a function of the inputs either. Indeed, we can always find separate circuits for each equation and tie the common inputs together. Thus suppose that our equations are

$$f(p) = p \cdot (p \vee p)$$
$$g(p,q) = p \vee \bar{q}$$
$$h(p,q,r) = (p \vee q) \cdot r$$

†A bump where two wires cross indicates that there is no contact between them.

Then we can obtain these three circuits:

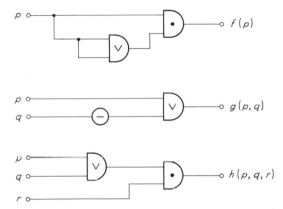

We can then put these together as follows:

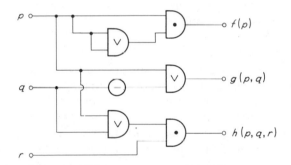

However, any circuit which can be represented by the same three equations will do, and a clever person may be able to draw one which is more compact than that given. For example, the two equations

$$f(p,q) = (p \lor q) \cdot \bar{q}$$
$$g(p,q) = (p \lor q) \cdot q$$

give rise to this circuit if one simply connects two circuits together:

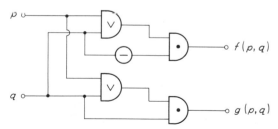

On the other hand, the following more compact circuit also satisfies the two equations:

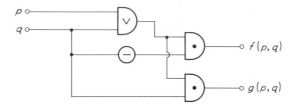

Once circuits are expressed as schemata, it is easy to study their behavior by means of truth-functional methods. For we can let 0 correspond to T and 1 to F and compute the output for given inputs by means of truth tables. Indeed, by performing truth-value analyses on the TFS which express the outputs of a circuit, we can determine the outputs for all possible inputs. The reader may verify, for example, that when $p = 0$ and $q = 1$, then in the circuit just given, $f(p,q) = 0$ and $g(p,q) = 1$.

1.4.2.3 CIRCUIT DESIGN

Since sequential circuits may be represented by one or more equations which present outputs as truth-functions of inputs, these circuits may also be designed by constructing "truth tables", with the inputs as reference columns and the outputs as main columns. Then TFS can be found for the truth tables, and circuits obtained from the TFS. As a first example of a circuit-design problem, let us design a circuit with two inputs and an output which is 1 if the inputs are the same and 0 otherwise. The "truth table" for this is

p	q	$f(p,q)$
0	0	1
0	1	0
1	0	0
1	1	1

Thus an equation satisfying this table is

$$f(p,q) = p \cdot \bar{q} \lor \bar{p} \cdot q$$

and a circuit is

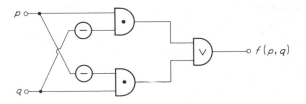

Next, let us design a circuit for determining whether two binary numbers are the same. Generally, a binary number, unless it is 0 or 1, is not a single input, but must be viewed as a *sequence of inputs*. The first input is the last digit of the number, so that the binary number 1101, for example, would be viewed as the sequence 1,0,1,1, the earlier members of the sequence being the earlier inputs. Our circuit will compare two sequences of inputs to see whether they are identical. If they are identical, the sequence of outputs will be a sequence of 0's; otherwise it will be a sequence that ends with a 1. (So we need only look at the last output to see if the numbers are the same.) The two numbers 110 and 111, for example, differ only in their last digits. Since these digits would form the first two inputs for our circuit, it will have to "remember" this difference. Thus our circuit will need a *memory*, that is, a device which can receive an impulse and repeat it at a later moment. As a result our circuit will have *two* outputs: one that tells us whether the numbers are the same, and one that goes to the memory. It will have *three* inputs: two for the two numbers, and one from the memory. The memory will need to be synchronized with the elements producing the other inputs so that the three impulses will arrive at the circuit simultaneously. These are electronic problems, however, beyond the scope of this book. Nonetheless, the present discussion shows that our circuit can be pictured as follows:

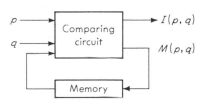

If the inputs p and q are the same *and* no previous inputs for p and q have differed, then the output $I(p,q)$ is supposed to be 0. The output $M(p,q)$ is supposed to indicate to the memory whether $I(p,q)$ was 0 or 1. So we let

$M(p,q)$ be the same as $I(p,q)$. Also, if the memory input is 0 and $p = q$, then $I(p,q)$ is 0. On the other hand, if the memory input is 1 *or* $p \neq q$, then $I(p,q)$ is 1. (The first input from the memory will be 0.) These considerations lead to the following table for $I(p,q)$ and $M(p,q)$:

p	q	MEMORY	$I(p,q)$	$M(p,q)$
0	0	0	0	0
0	0	1	1	1
0	1	0	1	1
0	1	1	1	1
1	0	0	1	1
1	0	1	1	1
1	1	0	0	0
1	1	1	1	1

As in the section on switching circuits, TFS can be obtained from this table, and so we obtain the equations

$I(p,q) = p \cdot q \cdot \text{memory} \lor \bar{p} \cdot \bar{q} \cdot \text{memory}$
$M(p,q) = p \cdot q \cdot \text{memory} \lor \bar{p} \cdot \bar{q} \cdot \text{memory}$

Simplifying, we get

$I(p,q) = M(p,q) = (p \cdot q \lor \bar{p} \cdot \bar{q}) \cdot \text{memory}$

And this leads to the following circuit:

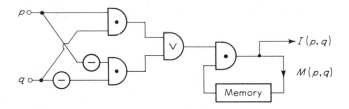

The last example made use of a memory device because the two binary numbers to be compared are represented as sequences of inputs. It is possible to dispense with memory devices, nonetheless, by increasing the number of inputs so that each digit of a binary number corresponds to a unique input. This is illustrated in the problem of designing a circuit to test binary numbers for evenness or oddness. Let us turn to that now.

A binary number is even just in case its last digit is 0. Thus a circuit for determining whether a binary number is even or odd need only "look at" its last digit and "remember" whether it is 0 or 1. Suppose that our binary number x is of the form

$$x_n\, x_{n-1}\, \cdots\, x_1\, x_0$$

Then, instead of using a memory element, we can use a "cascading" circuit that looks like this:

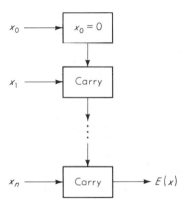

In the first box the circuit determines whether x_0 is 0. If x_0 is 0, then its output is 0; otherwise it is 1. The subsequent boxes simply "carry" this 0 or 1 through the circuit until it reaches the last box and is produced as the output $E(x)$. (As in the last example, we are equating a yes answer to a yes-or-no question with 0.)

Our problem now reduces to one of designing the component circuits for the boxes. The table for the first box is, simply;

x_0	$E(x_0)$
0	0
1	1

[Here $E(x_0)$ is the output of the first box.] Thus the equation for the first box is just

$$E(x_0) = x_0$$

Thus we can simply feed x_0 directly to the first carry box. The carry boxes have this table:

x_i	l	$E(x_i,l)$
0	0	0
0	1	1
1	0	0
1	1	1

[$E(x_i,l)$ is the output, l is the input, from the previous box, and x_i is the ith input to the circuit.] An equation for $E(x_i,l)$ is

$$E(x_i,l) = x_i \cdot l \vee \bar{x}_i \cdot l$$
$$= l \cdot (x_i \vee \bar{x}_i)$$

Thus the circuit for our problem can be drawn as follows:

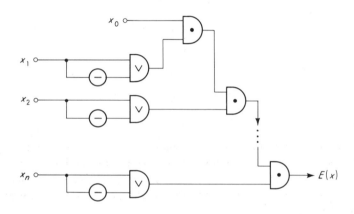

1.4.2.4   ADDERS AND SUBTRACTORS

We are now in a position to examine circuits for adding and subtracting binary numbers. Let us start with a simple example, namely, a circuit for adding 1 to a binary number. Some examples of this on "paper" will introduce us to the problem:

10	1	101	11
+1	+1	+1	+1
11	10	110	100

You will notice that when 1 is added to 1 there is a carry of 1. Consequently, our circuit will need a provision for carrying 1. We shall use a cascading circuit for this, and it will look like this:

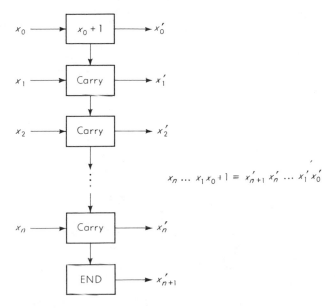

$$x_n \cdots x_1 x_0 + 1 = x'_{n+1} x'_n \cdots x'_1 x'_0$$

Suppose that the number to be added is $x_n \cdots x_1 x_0$. Then the inputs for the circuit are the digits $x_0, x_1, \ldots, x_n$. The first box adds 1 to x_0; that is, if x_0 is 0, x_0' is 1, and the carry to the next box is 0, while if x_0 is 1 x_0' is 0, and the carry to the next box is 1. The subsequent boxes add the carry to their inputs. The END box is needed in case a carry of 1 is added to x_n. The sequence of outputs $x_0', x_1', \ldots, x_n', x_{n+1}'$ constitutes the sequence of the digits in $x_n \cdots x_1 x_0 + 1$.

To complete our problem we need only design circuits for the three types of boxes. This can be done by obtaining TFS for these three tables.

a.

x_0	x_0'	C_{out}
0	1	0
1	0	1

b.

x_i	C_{in}	x_i'	C_{out}	$(0 < i \le n)$
0	0	0	0	
0	1	1	0	
1	0	1	0	
1	1	0	1	

c.

C_{in}	x_{n+1}'
0	0
1	1

(Here 'C_{out}' stands for the carry out of a box and 'C_{in}' for the carry into it.) These tables yield the following equations:

(a) $x_0' = \bar{x}_0$
      $C_{out} = x_0$

(b) $x_i' = C_{in} \cdot x_i \vee \overline{C}_{in} \cdot \bar{x}_i$
      $C_{out} = C_{in} \vee x_i$

(c) $x_{n+1}' = C_{in}$

Thus our complete circuit looks like this:

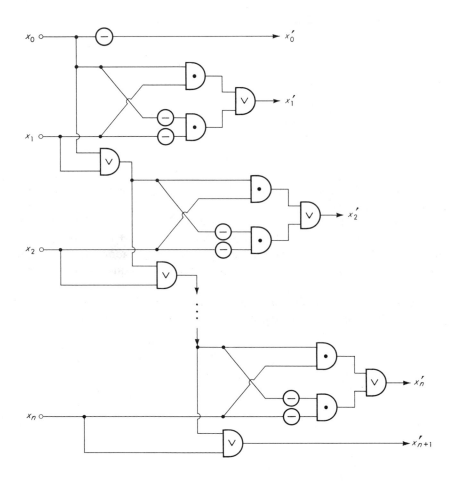

Similar ideas can be used to construct a circuit for adding any two binary numbers. An immediate problem arises, however, because the numbers may not be of the same length. This can be overcome by adding extra 0 digits to the shorter number. Thus we can assume that the two numbers to be added are

$$x_n \cdots x_1 x_0$$
$$y_n \cdots y_1 y_0$$

and that their sum is

$$z_{n+1} z_n \cdots z_1 z_0$$

The extra digit, z_{n+1}, represents a carry from the addition of x_n and y_n. This carry might be 0. Our circuit will look like this:

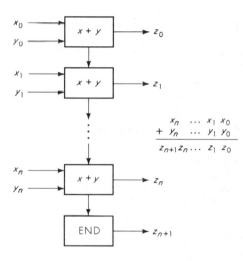

We need three tables since the first and last boxes differ from each other and the middle ones. These tables are as follows:

a.

x_0	y_0	z_0	C_{out}
0	0	0	0
0	1	1	0
0	0	1	0
1	1	0	1

b.

x_i	y_i	C_{in}	z_i	C_{out}	$(0 < I \leqslant n)$
0	0	0	0	0	
0	0	1	1	0	
0	1	0	1	0	
0	1	1	0	1	
1	0	0	1	0	
1	0	1	0	1	
1	1	0	0	1	
1	1	1	1	1	

c.

C_{in}	z_{n+1}
0	0
1	1

The entries in table b are determined by merely adding $x_i + y_i + C_{in}$ and entering the last digit of the sum under z_i and the first digit under C_{out}. Notice that $1 + 1 + 1 = 3 = 11$ (binary). The equations for these tables follow:

(a) $\quad z_0 = x_0 \cdot y_0 \vee \bar{x}_0 \cdot \bar{y}_0$
$\quad\quad C_{out} = x_0 \vee y_0$

(b) $\quad z_i = x_i \cdot y_i \cdot C_{in} \vee x_i \cdot \bar{y}_i \cdot \overline{C}_{in} \vee \bar{x}_i \cdot y_i \cdot \overline{C}_{in} \vee \bar{x}_i \cdot \bar{y}_i \cdot C_{in}$
$\quad\quad C_{out} = x_i \cdot y_i \cdot C_{in} \vee x_i \cdot y_i \cdot \overline{C}_{in} \vee x_i \cdot \bar{y}_i \cdot C_{in} \vee \bar{x}_i \cdot y_i \cdot C_{in}$

(c) $\quad z_{n+1} = C_{in}$

The equations in (a) and (b) are, however, equivalent to

(a) $\quad z_0 = (x_0 \equiv y_0)$
$\quad\quad C_{out} = x_0 \vee y_0$

(b) $\quad z_i = ((x_i \equiv y_i) \equiv C_{in})$
$\quad\quad C_{out} = x_i \cdot y_i \vee C_{in} \cdot -(x_i \equiv y_i)$

Thus, if we added IF AND ONLY IF gates to our apparatus, the adding circuit would look like this:

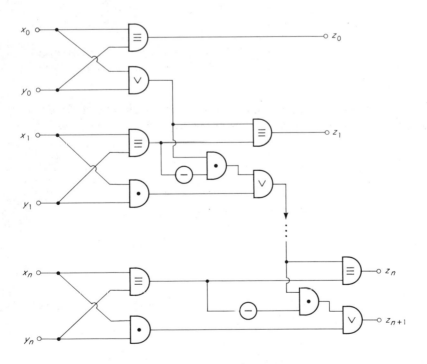

The complete circuit for the adder may be gotten in terms of AND, OR, and NOT gates by replacing each IF AND ONLY IF gate by

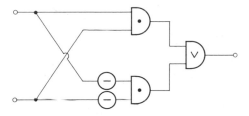

This messy, but straightforward, task is left to the reader.

Cascading circuits such as the last have a definite disadvantage: they can add numbers only of a fixed length. By using a memory unit, however, we can design an adder which can add numbers of any length. This adder has two regular inputs plus an input from memory. It also has a regular output and an output that goes to memory. The regular inputs are the digits of the numbers to be added. The regular outputs are the digits of the sum, while the carries are passed through the memory. Before the two numbers are added, they are "evened up" by adding extra 0 digits to the shortest, and then one additional 0 is added to both numbers in order to handle possible final carries of 1. Thus, if we wanted to add 110 and 10, we should write them first as '0110' and '0010'. The memory is set at 0 initially, since there is no carry in the beginning. Suppose that the numbers to be added are $x_n \cdots x_1 \, x_0$ and $y_n \cdots y_1 \, y_0$, and their sum is $z_{n+1} z_n \cdots z_1 \, z_0$ (z_{n+1} might be 0); then the circuit and its input and output sequences may be pictured as follows:

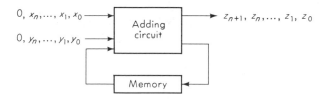

The adding circuit itself has three inputs, x, y, and C_{in}, and two outputs, z and C_{out}. Moreover, it functions in the same way as the middle $x + y$ boxes

of the cascading adder. Thus the adding circuit is simply (using IF AND ONLY IF gates for brevity)

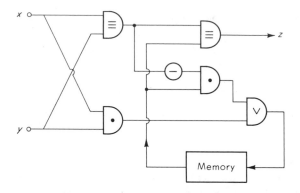

Subtracting circuits work very much like adding circuits except that there is a borrow instead of a carry. Suppose that the number to be subtracted from is $x_n \cdots x_1 x_0$, and the number to be subtracted from it is $y_n \cdots y_1 y_0$, and that the result of subtraction is $z_n \cdots z_1 z_0$. We shall assume that $x_n \cdots x_1 x_0$ is always greater than or equal to $y_n \cdots y_1 \ y_0$, so that there will be no need for a final borrow. Then the cascading subtractor looks like this:

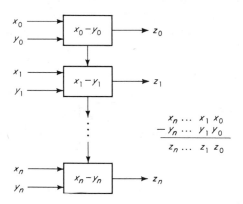

The circuit for the first box is determined by the following table.

x_0	y_0	$x_0 - y_0$	b_{out}
0	0	0	0
0	1	1	1
1	0	1	0
1	1	0	0

Its second row deserves a comment. Here we are subtracting 0 from 1; so we have to borrow 1. Thus we end by subtracting 0 from 10 (that is, 2), and the result is 1. Equations for these circuits are

$$x_0 - y_0 = (x_0 \equiv y_0)$$
$$b_{out} = \bar{x}_0 \vee y_0$$

The other circuits have tables with three reference columns and two main columns. The table for the last circuit has only one main column, but is the same in all other respects. These tables all look like this one:

x_i	y_i	b_{in}	$x_i - y_i$	b_{out}	$(0 < i \leqslant n)$
0	0	0	0	0	
0	0	1	1	1	
0	1	0	1	1	
0	1	1	0	1	
1	0	0	1	0	
1	0	1	0	0	
1	1	0	0	0	
1	1	1	1	1	

The rationale for rows 2, 3, 4, and 8 can be provided by carrying out "on paper" the binary subtraction appropriate to them:

(2)
$$\begin{array}{r} 0 \leftarrow x_i \\ \underline{-0} \leftarrow y_i \\ b_{out} \rightarrow 10 \\ \underline{-1} \leftarrow b_{in} \\ 1 \leftarrow z_i \end{array}$$

(3)
$$\begin{array}{r} 10 \\ \underline{-1} \\ 1 \\ \underline{-0} \\ 1 \end{array}$$

(4)
$$\begin{array}{r} 10 \\ \underline{-1} \\ 1 \\ \underline{-1} \\ 0 \end{array}$$

(8)
$$\begin{array}{r} 1 \\ \underline{-1} \\ 10 \\ \underline{-1} \\ 1 \end{array}$$

Simplified equations for these tables are

$$x_i - y_i = (x \equiv y) \equiv b_{in}$$
$$b_{out} = \bar{x}_i \cdot y_i \vee b_{in} \cdot (x \equiv y)$$

Thus the cascading subtractor looks like this:

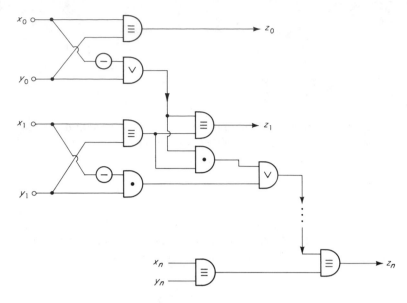

By combining the type of circuit used in the middle boxes with a memory unit, one can easily obtain a noncascading subtractor. This is left as an exercise for the reader.

EXERCISES FOR SEC. 1.4.2

A.   Convert these binary numerals to decimal ones.

1.   1101
2.   1001
3.   11001
4.   101010
5.   1110111

B.   Convert these decimal numerals to binary ones.

1.   6
2.   10
3.   16
4.   17
5.   35
6.   14
7.   15
8.   19
9.   23
10.   29

C. Find "equations" to represent these circuits.

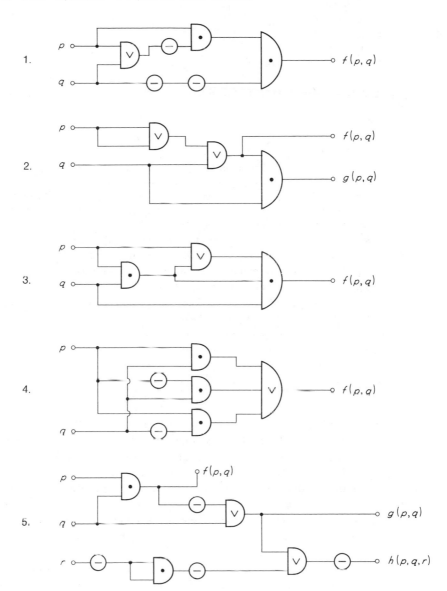

1.

2.

3.

4.

5.

D. Find circuits corresponding to each group of "equations".

1. $f(p,q) = p \cdot q \lor \bar{p}$

2. $f(p,q) = p \cdot q$
    $g(p,q) = p \lor q$

3. $f(p,q) = -(p \cdot q) \vee -(p \vee q)$
   $g(p,q) = p \vee q$

4. $f(p,q,r) = p \vee q \vee r$
   $g(p,q) = p \vee q$
   $h(q,r) = q \cdot r$

5. $f(p,q) = -(p \vee -(p \cdot q)) \cdot q$
   $g(p,q) = (p \vee -(p \cdot q) \cdot \bar{\bar{q}}$

E. Obtain as simple equivalents as possible of the circuits given in C. Retain all inputs.

F. Design problems

   1. $f(p,q,r)$ is 0 when at least two of p,q,r are 0. Design a circuit with inputs $p,q,$ and r and output $f(p,q,r)$.

   2. $f(p,q)$ is 0 when p and q are identical. $g(p,q)$ is 1 when p and q are identical. Design a circuit with inputs p and q and outputs $f(p,q)$ and $g(p,q)$.

   3. Design a circuit for determining whether two binary numerals end with the same digit. (*Hint:* Look at the example in the text of the circuit for determining whether two binary numerals are the same.)

   4. Design a circuit for determining whether a binary number is odd.

   5. Design a circuit for adding 2 (that is, 10) to a binary number.

   6. Design a circuit for subtracting 1 from a binary number greater than 0.

   7. Design a circuit for doubling a binary number.

   8. Design a circuit which converts an odd binary number to an even one and which leaves even numbers unchanged.

   9. Design a noncascading subtracting circuit.

   10. Design a circuit for determining whether one binary number is greater than another.

1.5 AN APPLICATION OF LOGIC IN THE PHILOSOPHY OF SCIENCE

Let us turn from the rather practical applications of logic to circuit design to a rather theoretic application of the logic in the philosophy of science. The problem which will concern us is the testing and refutation of scientific hypotheses. Truth-functional logic will provide a means for obtaining some insight into the issues involved.

Most scientific hypotheses cannot be conclusively demonstrated by merely testing them a large number of times. For if all we have to go on are the tests, then a single contrary test will be sufficient to call the hypothesis into question, and such contrary tests cannot be ruled out in advance. To take a concrete example, an important hypothesis of genetics is that all humans have 48 chromosomes in normal body cells. (The sperm cells and ova have 24 chromosomes.) This hypothesis can be tested very easily by obtaining normal body cells from humans and examining them under a microscope and counting the chromosomes in the nuclei. But no number of these tests alone will provide conclusive evidence for the hypothesis. For, given just the test results, it is always possible that we shall find someone who does not have 48 chromosomes in his normal body cells.

On the other hand, no biologist questions the chromosome-number hypothesis or worries about possible contrary tests. For the hypothesis is not supported by tests *alone*. The rest of genetic theory strengthens the hypothesis. Genetic theory tells us that every normal body cell of every member of a given species must have the same number of chromosomes. Indeed, a biologist would probably not even classify an animal without 48 chromosomes in his normal body cells as a humanoid freak. Thus a biologist would point out that the tests are not used to demonstrate the hypothesis conclusively, but rather to determine how many chromosomes humans have in their normal body cells. Once a few tests have established this number, the rest of genetic theory rules out the possibility of contrary tests. The first few tests determine what chromosome-number hypothesis to adopt. Additional tests will confirm this hypothesis, to be sure, but genetic theory as a whole, not the confirming tests, is what the biologist finds most persuasive.

The situation is quite complicated here. Direct tests do not conclusively demonstrate a hypothesis, but these tests, coupled with other hypotheses, can provide overwhelming evidence in favor of the first hypothesis. Then one naturally asks, "How were the other hypotheses demonstrated?" This leads one to realize that hypotheses are usually not adopted or demonstrated one at a time. Usually, a whole system of hypotheses is proposed, and individual hypotheses of the system are tested and modified until the whole system fits the evidence. The problems surrounding the discovery and demonstration of hypotheses are among the central problems of the philosophy of science, but discussing them any further would take us too far afield.

The problem that interests us here is the *refutation of scientific hypotheses*. There are philosophers of science who argue that, although no amount of testing will demonstrate a hypothesis, a single contrary test will refute a hypothesis. To see their reasoning, we must examine more carefully what testing a hypothesis involves. Let us continue to use the chromosome hypothesis as the focal point of our discussion. The scientist deduces from this hypothesis that, if he takes a sample of normal body cells from a human and examines them, then he will find that each cell has 48 chromosomes. He then proceeds to find a human, takes a sample of his normal body cells, and counts the chromosomes in their nuclei. If he finds this number to be 48, the test is favorable; otherwise the test is not favorable. In other words, the scientist uses the hypothesis to derive a prediction and then tests his prediction. (Not all tests involve predictions, but it will be simpler to pretend that they do.) Let us represent the hypothesis by 'H' and the prediction by 'P'. Then, since the prediction is supposed to follow logically from the hypothesis, the statement

$H \supset P$

is logically true.

Thus the first stage in testing a hypothesis H involves establishing the logical truth of '$H \supset P$' for some prediction P. Suppose that the prediction turns out to be true. Need the hypothesis be true? Clearly not. 'H' can be false, and even logically false, and still imply 'P'. Thus a true prediction does not demonstrate the hypothesis which leads to it, although we do say that it *confirms* the hypothesis. On the other hand, what if the prediction turns out false? Then '$-P$' is true; so we have '$H \supset P$' and '$-P$', and these imply '$-H$'. Thus it seems that an unfavorable test can conclusively falsify a hypothesis. We shall question this shortly, but first let us pass on to a related matter.

Sometimes two incompatible hypotheses are proposed to deal with the same phenomena. For example, someone might have proposed that all humans have 56 chromosomes in normal body cells. If we know that one of the two hypotheses must be true, then it is often possible to test two incompatible hypotheses by means of the same data and thereby determine which one to reject and which to accept. Such tests are called *crucial experiments*. In particular, counting chromosomes would be a crucial experiment for the two chromosome-number hypotheses. More precisely, given two incompatible and exhaustive hypotheses H_1 and H_2 which deal with the same phenomena, a crucial experiment for deciding between them consists in obtaining two incompatible predictions P_1 (from H_1) and P_2 (from H_2) and testing these predictions. The one which turns out false will falsify the hypothesis from which it was obtained and establish the other hypothesis. From the logical point of view, we have the following:

$H_1 \lor H_2$
$H_1 \supset P_1$
$H_2 \supset P_2$
$-(P_1 \cdot P_2)$

Thus we also know that '$P_1 \lor P_2$' must be true. (Why?) If, say, 'P_1' is false, then '$-P_1$' is true; this implies that '$-H_1$' is true, which in turn implies that 'H_2' is true. (If we find that neither P_1 nor P_2 turns out to be true, then '$H_1 \lor H_2$' could not have been true and the test was not a real *crucial experiment*.)

Although some philosophers believe that conclusive refutations of hypotheses and crucial experiments are possible, others reject both these beliefs. This rejection is based upon a more detailed analysis of the arguments used to obtain and test predictions. Thus let us look more closely at the chromosome-number hypothesis. Let us suppose that the tested cells are obtained from a Mr. X. Then the argument proceeds as follows:

1 All humans have 48 chromosomes in normal body cells.
2 Hence, if Mr. X is a human, then Mr. X has 48 chromosomes in normal body cells.
3 Mr. X is a human.
4 Hence, if A is a sample of Mr. X's normal body cells, then each cell in A will have 48 chromosomes.
5 A is a sample of Mr. X's normal body cells.
6 Hence each cell in A has 48 chromosomes.

The prediction which we actually test is (6). Notice, however, that (1) alone does not imply (6), but rather (1), (3), and (5) jointly imply (6). Thus, if we find that some cells in the sample A do not have 48 chromosomes, we need not conclude that (1) is false. All we need conclude is that either (1), (3), or (5) is false. This is because the presence of cells in the sample which do not have 48 chromosomes could be explained in various ways without entailing rejecting (1). For example, the sample slide might have been improperly cleaned and contain cells taken from a fish. Or when the cells were obtained from Mr. X, some of his sperm cells, which have only 24 chromosomes, may have been obtained too. Or Mr. X might be a Martian.

The general point is this: No hypothesis produces a prediction by itself but only when taken in conjunction with other "auxiliary" hypotheses or statements. Thus the true picture is not given by

$H \supset P$

but rather by

$H \cdot A \supset P$

where 'A' represents the auxiliary hypotheses. Therefore, when P turns out to be false, what has been shown is not $-H$, but rather $-(H \cdot A)$, and thus we are free to reject either H or A. Consequently, by rejecting A, we can continue to maintain H.

A similar argument applies to crucial experiments. Here the true picture is given by

$$H_1 \vee H_2$$
$$H_1 \cdot A \supset P_1$$
$$H_2 \cdot A \supset P_2$$
$$-(P_1 \cdot P_2)$$

Thus if, say, P_1 turns out false, we must reject the conjunction $H_1 \cdot A$, but we could continue to maintain H_1 by rejecting A. (Notice that now we no longer have $P_1 \lor P_2$.) Accordingly, the experiment does not conclusively decide between H_1 and H_2, and crucial experiments are not possible.

There is no getting around the logic behind these arguments. They *do* show that we can maintain any hypothesis in the face of so-called contrary evidence so long as we are willing to reject certain auxiliary hypotheses. By the same token, no experiment need be viewed as a crucial experiment. Moreover, in those branches of science which are rather removed from direct observation, such as nuclear physics, the argument makes good scientific sense. For when we deal with very theoretical hypotheses, many hypotheses will be needed in order to arrive at a single prediction. Each of them is likely to be as questionable as any other. Thus contrary evidence will not indicate that some one of the hypotheses is to be rejected, but rather that the whole system of hypotheses must be reexamined.

Nonetheless, to return to the chromosome example, suppose that we had very carefully examined Mr. X to be sure that he is a human being (and not a Martian) and that we had very carefully sampled his cells and prepared and cleaned the slide, etc. Further, suppose that we still found cells which did not contain 48 chromosomes, and so we still might be prepared to reject an auxiliary hypothesis. Yet suppose we continued to test Mr. X's cells and also Mr. Y's and Mr. Z's, and still found that our predictions turned out false. Would it make good scientific sense to continue to hold the chromosome-number hypothesis? Clearly not. For to continue to hold this hypothesis we should have to concoct other very elaborated hypotheses to explain our false predictions. Thus most biologists would accept our false predictions as very good evidence for rejecting the chromosome-number hypothesis and proceed to reexamine the rest of genetic theory. Of course, from the point of view of deductive logic, we can still maintain the hypothesis. But then science is not just a matter of deductive logic.

Similar considerations apply to crucial experiments. If repeated and careful tests showed that Mr. X's cells contained 48 chromosomes, we could always reject our auxiliary hypotheses and refuse to reject the 46-chromosome hypothesis. Nothing in deductive logic would compel us to act differently. But good scientific practice would; and so, from the point of view of the biologist, our tests would constitute a crucial experiment.

We can summarize this discussion as follows: Certain philosophers of science believe that, as a matter of deductive logic, hypotheses can be conclusively refuted by contrary evidence and that crucial experiments are possible. Other philosophers have shown that this belief is mistaken. From the point of view of deductive logic, no hypothesis can be conclusively refuted by contrary evidence, and no crucial experiments are possible. Yet if we appeal to other considerations than deductive ones, then there are cases where contrary evidence *is* sufficient to refute a hypothesis and there are cases where crucial experiments are possible.

1.6 PROOFS AND DERIVATIONS

1.6.1 INTRODUCTION

The techniques presented so far may be used for the recognitions of valid arguments which have already been constructed. However, these techniques do not deal with the construction of new valid arguments. Thus we shall return to the problem of validity, but this time approach it through the concepts of *proof* and *derivation*, and in this way learn about the construction of valid arguments. A schema is valid, it will turn out, just in case it has a proof. Also, a schema is implied by one or more schemata just in case it can be derived from them. (It will be convenient to formulate the concepts of proof and derivation in terms of schemata, although analogous notions can be developed easily for statements.)

Let us first consider the informal notion of proof. When someone tries to prove something informally (or to derive it from previously accepted premisses), then he usually does so in order to convince his audience that what he is trying to prove is unconditionally true (or follows logically from the premisses given).

Ordinarily, such a person wants to convince more than some select group of gullible people; he wants to convince anyone sufficiently educated to read and understand his argument. For this reason he will usually restrict himself to rules of argumentation which are more or less universally accepted. His hope, of course, is that anyone who understands his argument will say to himself, as he reads it: I will grant that, and this follows from that by means of a rule I accept, so I must accept this too; but then I must also admit the next statement, since it follows from what I accept via rules I accept, etc.; until he finds himself accepting the conclusion. A good proof or derivation is thus like a series of moves in a game. Certain initial positions (the premisses) are specified by the rules of the game or admitted for the sake of argument (as in the end-game problems of chess), rules are agreed upon, and further moves are made until a given outcome results. The outcome is also mutually acknowledged, since it resulted from the application of accepted rules. Furthermore, the acceptability of each move can be effectively checked for conformity to the rules. (That is why a successful cheat at games has to be extremely subtle.)

Two features of good argumentation emerge from this comparison with games: (1) the use of accepted rules of inference and (2) the effective verifiability of the applications of these rules in the argument. In other words, an *ideal* argument should proceed according to rules which are agreed upon in advance. Also, it must be possible to check each step in an ideal argument mechanically in order to see whether the step follows from previous steps by means of one of the rules. (The premisses of an argument do not follow from anything.) Arguments in everyday life fall short of this ideal because our everyday rules of inference are more implicit than explicit. They were not set up by convention or legislation, but evolved in some complex way instead. They cannot be learned from a rule book, but must be called from experience, and are part of what a child learns when he learns to speak his native tongue. Consequently, it should be clear that any set of rules which a logician may propose can only be regarded as an approximation to the ones used implicitly by the layman.

Of course, departing from the layman's practice is not an evil in itself, especially if this practice is vague or inefficient. Laying down rules of inference which satisfy the ideal given above may call for a very bold departure from ordinary practice. Indeed, by making a *very* radical departure we could use the next two rules of inference:

Rule 1.   Each valid TFS may be written at any stage of an argument.

Rule 2.   Each TFS may be inferred from any schemata that imply it.

Since an argument is constructed step by step, Rule 1 says that every valid TFS may be written as a new step in an argument, while Rule 2 says that a TFS may be written as a new step provided that it is implied by previous steps. Arguments constructed according to these two rules would satisfy our ideal: first, because the rules have been explicitly stated and, if we accepted them, would be agreed upon in advance; second, because steps according to the rules can be checked mechanically, since there are decision procedures for implication and validity.

Hence we could go through such an argument and mechanically test it to see if each step was a premiss, valid or implied by previous steps. The two rules would also have two other highly desirable properties: they would allow us to infer nothing we do not want to infer, and (at least as far as truth-function theory is concerned) they would allow us to infer everything we do want to infer. This is because the rules allow us to infer a given schema from other schemata if and only if these imply it. We can thus construct all and only valid truth-functional arguments from the rules. When a set of rules of inference permits valid inferences only, it is known as a *sound* set of rules. (This is not to be confused with the soundness of an argument.) When a set of rules of inference allows us to carry out all valid inferences, it is said to be *complete*. Thus, as far as truth-functional logic is concerned, Rules 1 and 2 form a complete and sound set of rules of inference. Because Rules 1 and 2 are explicit, mechanically checkable, and sound and complete, many logicians adopt them as the sole rules for truth-functional logic. A different course, however, is preferable in our introductory studies; for Rules 1 and 2 approximate so little to ordinary practice that they give us little or no insight into everyday arguments and the rules employed therein. For this reason we *shall not* use Rules 1 and 2, but shall use a more complex set of rules which approximate more closely to everyday practice.

Initially, derivations will take the form of finite vertical sequences of schemata; later certain rules will require that we deviate from this form. The sequence making up the derivation will begin with one or more schemata which are taken without proof during the course of the derivation and which are appropriately called the *premisses of the derivation*. (A *proof* is a derivation without premisses, but these will not come until later.) Which schemata are taken as premisses will depend on the problem at hand: when we are trying to derive a schema S from schemata $S_1, S_2, \ldots, S_n$, we take $S_1, S_2, \ldots, S_n$ as the premisses of a derivation and try to obtain S as the last entry in the derivation. Further schemata can be generated (inferred) from the premisses by means of the rules of inference, which will be specified shortly. First, we shall lay down a convention about the style of derivations; it is not, properly speaking, a rule of inference. (It is more like the rules of chess which state what a chessboard must look like.) The convention follows:

Start every derivation by drawing a vertical line, and write the premisses of the derivation in a vertical sequence immediately to the right *of this line. Write a '1' to the* left *of the line and beside the first premiss; write a '2' below this (beside the second premiss); etc. To the right of each premiss write a 'P'. (The 'P' is short for 'premiss'.)*

EXAMPLE. Suppose the premisses of a derivation are 'p', '$p \supset q$', '$r \lor s$'. Then we should write:

$$
\begin{array}{l|ll}
1 & p & \text{P} \\
2 & p \supset q & \text{P} \\
3 & r \lor s & \text{P}
\end{array}
$$

The numerals to the left of the vertical line give the number of each step in the derivation, the schemata are the steps themselves, and the entries in the right-hand column are the "reasons" for each step. The vertical line and the numerals are extended with each succeeding step of the derivation. *Each step in a derivation must have a reason.* Except for premisses, the reason for a given step will be a reference to previous steps and to a rule of inference. Writing derivations in this style greatly simplifies the problem of checking them for correctness. All we have to do is go down the sequence, checking the first steps to see if they are premisses and checking further steps to see if they follow from previous ones via our rules of inference. The reasons given for each step will indicate the step which it is supposed to follow from and the rule which makes this possible. We may turn now to the proper rules of inference.

1.6.2   BASIC RULES OF INFERENCE
1.6.2.1   MODUS PONENS
The first rule of inference we shall consider has been traditionally known as *modus ponens*. It allows us to write down the *consequent* of a conditional schema in a derivation, provided that we already have *both* the *antecedent* and the *conditional schema itself* as steps of the derivation. Schematically, we may represent it as follows:

$$
\begin{array}{ccc}
S & & S \supset W \\
\cdot & & \cdot \\
\cdot & & \cdot \\
\cdot & & \cdot \\
S \supset W & \text{or} & S \\
\cdot & & \cdot \\
\cdot & & \cdot \\
\cdot & & \cdot \\
\therefore W & & \therefore W
\end{array}
$$

The two forms of the rule indicate that the order of S and $S \supset W$ in the derivation is immaterial. The vertical dots indicate that schemata may (or may not) come between S and $S \supset W$ and between these two schemata and W. As the reason for W we write numerals referring back to S and $S \supset W$ followed by 'MP' (for 'modus ponens'.)

EXAMPLES

a.
1	$p \supset (r \lor s)$	P
2	p	P
3	$r \lor s$	1, 2, MP

b.
1	$p \supset q$	P
2	$(p \supset q) \supset r$	P
3	r	1, 2, MP

c.
1	$\bar{p}$	P
2	$q \supset r$	P
3	$\bar{p} \supset q$	P
4	q	1, 3, MP
5	r	4, 2, MP

d.

1	$(p \lor r) \supset s$	P
2	p	P
3	$p \supset \bar{q}$	P
4	$\bar{q} \supset (p \lor r)$	P
5	$\bar{q}$	2, 3, MP
6	$p \lor r$	5, 4, MP
7	s	6, 1, MP

The examples illustrate that the rule may be used to obtain the consequent of any conditional schema and its antecedent. It does not matter whether the antecedent and consequent themselves are statement letters, negations, conjunctions, conditionals, or biconditionals. All that matters is that the three schemata themselves conform to the form of the rule: one must be a conditional, the schema inferred must be its consequent, and the remaining schema must be its antecedent. We can even use modus ponens to obtain 'p' from '$p \supset p$' and 'p'!

Until now most questions that we raised with respect to TFS could be answered by means of mechanical procedures. From now on, however, much greater demands will be placed on our ingenuity. Constructing derivations efficiently requires a certain amount of insight on our part. One helpful technique, however, is that of working backward. Suppose, for example, that we want to derive '$p \equiv q$' from '$\bar{p}$', '$p \supset (p \equiv q)$', '$(p \lor r) \supset p$', and '$\bar{p} \supset (p \lor r)$'. Since the only rule we have at our disposal is modus ponens, matters are simplified; we see that we can obtain '$p \equiv q$' if we first get 'p', and we can get this if we first get '$p \lor r$'. This in turn follows from '$\bar{p}$'. But we have '$\bar{p}$'; so we proceed as follows:

1	$\bar{p}$	P
2	$p \supset (p \equiv q)$	P
3	$(p \lor r) \supset p$	P
4	$\bar{p} \supset (p \lor r)$	P
5	$p \lor r$	4, 1, MP
6	p	5, 3, MP
7	$p \equiv q$	2, 6, MP

This technique can be combined with a technique of working forward: when one sees that a certain schema can be generated from certain previous steps, add it as a new step. This gives us more "information" to work with, even though it may not be used in subsequent steps of the derivation. Remember, as long as each step in a derivation has a legitimate reason, the derivation is correct, although it may be cluttered with unnecessary steps. Here is an example of a cluttered derivation of 'q' from 'p', '$p \supset (p \lor r)$', and '$p \supset q$':

$$
\begin{array}{ll}
1 \mid p & \text{P} \\
2 \mid p \supset (p \lor r) & \text{P} \\
3 \mid p \supset q & \text{P} \\
4 \mid p \lor r & 1, 2, \text{MP} \\
5 \mid q & 1, 3, \text{MP}
\end{array}
$$

Step 4, generated via the technique of working forward, makes no contribution to the derivation of 'q'. The derivation could be shortened by omitting this step completely. Nonetheless, the derivation is a perfectly correct derivation of 'q' from these premisses: every step is either a premiss or follows from previous steps by modus ponens. The techniques of working backward and forward are also useful techniques for working with the other rules of inference we shall use.

1.6.2.2 MODUS TOLLENS

The next rule connects the conditional with negation. *Modus ponens* is a formal version of the informal rule: if that, then this; but that is true; thus so is this. *Modus tollens*, on the other hand, is a formal counterpart of: if that then this, but this is false; thus so is that. Modus tollens permits us to add the *negation* of the *antecedent* of a *conditional* to a derivation, provided that the conditional and the negation of its consequent are already steps of the derivation. Schematically:

$$
\begin{array}{cc}
S \supset W & -W \\
\cdot & \cdot \\
\cdot & \cdot \\
\cdot & \cdot \\
-W & S \supset W \\
\cdot & \cdot \\
\cdot & \cdot \\
\cdot & \cdot \\
\therefore -S & \therefore -S
\end{array}
$$

As the reason for $-S$ we write numerals referring back to $-W$ and $S \supset W$ and 'MT'. Here are some examples:

$$
\begin{array}{lll}
\text{a.} \quad 1 \mid & p \supset q \cdot r & \text{P} \\
2 \mid & -(q \cdot r) & \text{P} \\
3 \mid & r \supset p & \text{P} \\
4 \mid & \bar{p} & 1, 2, \text{MT} \\
5 \mid & \bar{r} & 3, 4, \text{MT}
\end{array}
$$

$$
\begin{array}{lll}
\text{b.} \quad 1 \mid & (p \equiv q) \supset r & \text{P} \\
2 \mid & (p \lor q) \supset (p \equiv q) & \text{P} \\
3 \mid & \bar{r} & \text{P}
\end{array}
$$

$$
\begin{array}{lll}
4 & -(p \equiv q) & 3, 1, \text{MT} \\
5 & -(p \vee q) & 4, 2, \text{MT}
\end{array}
$$

In using these rules it is important to keep in mind that we are playing a very rigid "game" here. Unless the schemata involved conform to the exact form of the rule, the rule is not legitimately applied. It is very tempting to infer 'p' from '$\bar{p} \supset q$' and '$\bar{q}$' by saying to oneself, "if '$\bar{p} \supset q$' is true and 'q' is false, then '$\bar{p}$' must be false, that is, 'p' is true". But this inference would be absolutely incorrect if we used modus tollens alone; for in this case our W is 'q' and our S is '$\bar{p}$'; thus our $-W$ would be '$\bar{q}$' and our $-S$ should be '$\bar{\bar{p}}$'. For modus tollens requires that we infer the result by prefixing a negation sign to the antecedent of the conditional $S \supset W$. Of course, we shall eventually be able to derive 'p' from '$\bar{p} \supset q$' and '$\bar{q}$', but we shall need one more rule to do it. Exacting attention to form is needed in these matters. Do not confuse '$\bar{p} \cdot q$' with '$-(p \cdot q)$' and wrongly obtain '$\bar{p}$' from both '$p \supset p \cdot q$' and '$\bar{p} \cdot q$', using only modus tollens. The implication holds, to be sure, but other rules are needed to justify the derivation.

Modus ponens and modus tollens may be used together, and here are two examples of this:

$$
\begin{array}{llll}
\text{a.} & 1 & \bar{\bar{p}} \supset r & \text{P} \\
& 2 & \bar{p} \supset s & \text{P} \\
& 3 & q \supset \bar{s} & \text{P} \\
& 4 & q & \text{P} \\
& 5 & \bar{s} & 3, 4, \text{MP} \\
& 6 & \bar{\bar{p}} & 2, 5, \text{MT} \\
& 7 & r & 6, 1, \text{MP}
\end{array}
\qquad
\begin{array}{llll}
\text{b.} & 1 & p \cdot q \supset r & \text{P} \\
& 2 & \bar{r} & \text{P} \\
& 3 & \bar{s} \supset p \cdot q & \text{P} \\
& 4 & \bar{\bar{s}} \supset q & \text{P} \\
& 5 & -(p \cdot q) & 1, 2, \text{MT} \\
& 6 & \bar{\bar{s}} & 3, 5, \text{MT} \\
& 7 & q & 4, 6, \text{MP}
\end{array}
$$

One last note of caution: Just as we cannot derive 'p' from '$\bar{p} \supset q$' and '$\bar{q}$' using modus tollens, so also we cannot use it to derive '$\bar{p}$' from '$p \supset \bar{q}$' and 'q'. This time it is because 'q' lacks two negation signs. This incompleteness in our rules will be remedied shortly.

1.6.2.3 DOUBLE-NEGATION INTRODUCTION AND ELIMINATION

The gap we have noticed in our rules of inference can be easily closed by introducing two new rules. The first, *double-negation introduction*, allows us to write in a derivation the result of prefixing two negation signs to a previous item of a derivation. The second allows us to eliminate initial pairs of negation signs. Schematically, we have

DOUBLE-NEGATION INTRODUCTION S

.

.

.

$\therefore --S$

DOUBLE-NEGATION ELIMINATION $--S$

$\cdot$

$\cdot$

$\cdot$

$\therefore S$

The reason for $--S$ consists in a numeral referring back to S followed by 'DNI'; that for S, obtained by double-negation elimination, consists in a numeral referring back to $--S$ followed by 'DNE'. These rules, like our other rules, are to be applied to *whole* schemata. As tempting as it may be, we *cannot* use double-negation introduction to infer directly, say, '$p \lor \bar{\bar{r}}$' from '$p \lor r$'. Nor can we use double-negation elimination to go in the opposite direction. These rules apply only to whole schemata, and not to their parts.

We can use all four rules together in the same derivation. The utility of this is illustrated in the following examples.

EXAMPLES

a. 1 | p P
    2 | $\bar{\bar{p}} \supset \bar{q}$ P
    3 | $\bar{r} \supset q$ P
    4 | $\bar{\bar{p}}$ 1, DNI
    5 | $\bar{q}$ 4, 2, MP
    6 | $\bar{\bar{r}}$ 3, 5, MT
    7 | r 6, DNE

b. 1 | $(p \lor q) \supset (p \equiv r)$ P
    2 | $s \supset -(p \equiv r)$ P
    3 | $p \supset (p \lor q)$ P
    4 | $\bar{\bar{p}}$ P
    5 | p 4, DNE
    6 | $p \lor q$ 5, 3, MP
    7 | $p \equiv r$ 6, 1, MP
    8 | $--(p \equiv r)$ 7, DNI
    9 | $\bar{s}$ 8, 2, MT

c. 1 | $\bar{p} \cdot q$ P
    2 | $-(p \lor q) \supset -(\bar{p} \cdot q)$ P
    3 | $--(\bar{p} \cdot q)$ 1, DNI
    4 | $--(p \lor q)$ 2, 3, MT
    5 | $p \lor q$ 4, DNE

EXERCISES FOR SECS. 1.6.2.1 TO 1.6.2.3

For each of the following, derive the schema in the left column from those in the right.

1. s $p \supset q,$ $q \supset r,$ $r \supset s,$ p

2. s $p,$ $p \supset q,$ $p \supset (q \supset r),$ $q \supset (r \supset s)$

3. $p \vee r$ $p,$ $(q \supset r) \supset (p \vee r),$ $p \supset (q \supset r)$

4. $\bar{p}$ $\bar{q},$ $p \supset s,$ $s \supset r,$ $r \supset q$

5. $\bar{\bar{p}}$ $q,$ $q \supset (\bar{p} \supset s),$ $q \supset \bar{s}$

6. $-(p \cdot q)$ $\bar{\bar{p}},$ $p \supset \bar{r},$ $p \cdot q \supset \bar{r}$

7. $p \vee q$ $p \supset (-(p \vee q) \supset \bar{r}),$ $\bar{\bar{p}},$ $p \supset r$

8. p $r,$ $\bar{r} \supset \bar{q},$ $q \supset s,$ $s \supset p$

9. $p \equiv q$ $s \supset -(p \vee q),$ $\bar{p} \supset (p \vee q),$ $p \supset (p \equiv q),$ $\bar{\bar{s}}$

10. q $s,$ $\bar{r} \supset \bar{s},$ $r \supset (p \supset q),$ $r \supset \bar{\bar{p}}$

1.6.2.4   TWO RULES FOR CONJUNCTION

The two rules for conjunction are quite simple. One of them, *simplification*, permits us to infer either of the two components of a conjunction. The other, the *principle of conjunction*, allows us to infer the conjunction of two components from the components themselves. These rules are schematically presented as follows:

SIMPLIFICATION

$S \cdot W$ or $S \cdot W$

   .   .

   .   .

   .   .

$\therefore S$ $\therefore W$

As a reason for S (or W) write a numeral referring back to $S \cdot W$ followed by 'S'.

PRINCIPLE OF CONJUNCTION

    S or W

     .   .

     .   .

     .   .

    W S

     .   .

     .   .

     .   .

$\therefore S \cdot W$ $\therefore S \cdot W$

As a reason for $S \cdot W$ write numerals referring back to S and W followed by 'PC'. *We shall also construe the principle of conjunction as permitting the inference of $S \cdot S$ from just S alone.* We may now do some examples.

EXAMPLES

a.
1	$p \cdot (\bar{q} \supset \bar{p})$	P
2	p	1, S
3	$\bar{q} \supset \bar{p}$	1, S
4	$\bar{\bar{p}}$	2, DNI
5	$\bar{\bar{q}}$	3, 4, MT
6	q	5, DNE
7	$p \cdot q$	6, 2, PC

b.
1	$p \cdot (q \cdot r)$	P
2	p	1, S
3	$q \cdot r$	1, S
4	q	3, S
5	r	3, S
6	$p \cdot r$	2, 5, PC
7	$(p \cdot r) \cdot q$	4, 6, PC
8	$p \cdot ((p \cdot r) \cdot q)$	2, 7, PC

c.
1	$p \cdot r$	P
2	$q \cdot \bar{s}$	P
3	$(p \cdot q) \supset (r \lor s)$	P
4	p	1, S
5	q	2, S
6	$p \cdot q$	4, 5, PC
7	$r \lor s$	6, 3, MP

d.
1	$p \supset (q \supset r)$	P
2	$p \cdot q$	P
2	p	2, S
4	$q \supset r$	1, 3, MP
5	q	2, S
6	r	4, 5, MP

EXERCISES FOR SEC. 1.6.2.4
For each of the following, derive the schema in the left column from those in the right.

1.	r	$p \cdot (p \supset q),\quad q \supset r$
2.	$\bar{\bar{s}}$	$p \cdot q,\quad p \supset (r \supset s),\quad q \supset r$
3.	$p \cdot r$	$p \cdot (p \supset (q \supset \bar{\bar{r}})),\quad \bar{\bar{p}} \supset q$
4.	$p \cdot \bar{p}$	$(r \supset p) \cdot (r \supset \bar{p}),\quad (p \lor q) \cdot (\bar{r} \supset -(p \lor q))$
5.	$(p \equiv s) \cdot q$	$p \cdot (r \cdot p \supset (p \equiv s)),\quad r \cdot (p \cdot r \supset q)$
6.	$p \cdot q$	$q \cdot p$
7.	$p \cdot p$	p

8. $(p \cdot q) \cdot r$ $\qquad$ $p \cdot (q \cdot r)$

9. $q \cdot p$ $\qquad$ $p \cdot s, \quad r \supset q, \quad \bar{r} \supset \bar{s}$

10. $\bar{p}$ $\qquad$ $r \cdot ((r \cdot r) \supset (p \supset -(r \cdot r)))$

1.6.2.5 THREE RULES FOR DISJUNCTION

A disjunction is true if at least one of its components is true. Let us mirror this by means of a rule of inference: We shall permit ourselves to infer any disjunction from either of its components. This rule is called the rule of *addition*, and is pictured schematically by

$$
\begin{array}{ccc}
S & \text{or} & W \\
\cdot & & \cdot \\
\cdot & & \cdot \\
\cdot & & \cdot \\
\therefore S \vee W & & \therefore S \vee W
\end{array}
$$

As a reason for $S \vee W$ we write a numeral referring back to S (or W) followed by 'add', for "addition". In actual practice this rule lets us add *any* schema to a schema already in a derivation. The schema added need not appear previously in the derivation. We may either 'add' the schema to the left or to the right. We must be sure, however, to separate the schemata by a disjunction sign. This is illustrated in the following example.

EXAMPLE

1	p	P
2	$p \vee p$	1, add
3	$q \vee p$	1, add
4	$p \vee q$	1, add
5	$p \vee ((r \supset s) \cdot (p \equiv \bar{q}))$	1, add

Besides the rule of addition, we have rules which allow us to derive things from disjunctions. The first of these, the *disjunctive syllogism*, allows us to derive components of a disjunction from the disjunction itself and the *negation* of the other component. Schematically:

$$
\begin{array}{cccccccc}
S \vee W & & S \vee W & & -S & & -W \\
\cdot & & \cdot & & \cdot & & \cdot \\
\cdot & & \cdot & & \cdot & & \cdot \\
\cdot & & \cdot & & \cdot & & \cdot \\
-S & \text{or} & -W & \text{or} & S \vee W & \text{or} & S \vee W \\
\cdot & & \cdot & & \cdot & & \cdot \\
\cdot & & \cdot & & \cdot & & \cdot \\
\cdot & & \cdot & & \cdot & & \cdot \\
\therefore W & & \therefore S & & \therefore W & & \therefore S
\end{array}
$$

As the reason for S (or W) we write numerals referring back to $-S$ (or $-W$) and $S \lor W$, followed by 'DS'. Here are illustrations of this rule:

EXAMPLE

1	$\bar{p}$	P
2	$p \lor (q \lor \bar{r})$	P
3	r	P
4	$q \lor \bar{r}$	2, 1, DS
5	$\bar{\bar{r}}$	3, DNI
6	q	5, 4, DS

Note that the form of disjunctive syllogism does *not* permit us to go directly from steps 2 and 5 to step 6. We must first obtain '$q \lor \bar{r}$' as an item of the derivation. By the same token, we cannot pass directly from '$q \lor \bar{r}$' and 'r' to 'q' and must route ourselves through double-negation introduction.

Another rule used in connection with disjunctions is the rule of *simple dilemma*. It is so complex that it is far easier to represent it diagrammatically than to describe it in words.

Thus its form follows:

$S \lor W$

.

.

.

$S \supset E$

.

.

.

$W \supset E$

.

.

.

$\therefore E$

The order of the schema $S \lor W$, $S \supset E$, $W \supset E$ does not matter. (There are thus six different variations of the form of this rule.) Moreover, S and W may be the same schema, in which case one of the conditionals may be omitted. As a reason for E, write numerals referring back to $S \lor W$, $S \supset E$, and $W \supset E$, followed by 'SD'. The rule is illustrated in the following examples.

EXAMPLES

| a. | 1 | $p \lor q$ | P |
| | 2 | $p \supset (q \lor r)$ | P |

$$
\begin{array}{lll}
3 & q \supset (q \lor r) & \text{P} \\
4 & q \lor r & 1, 2, 3, \text{SD}
\end{array}
$$

b.
$$
\begin{array}{lll}
1 & p \supset (p \lor r) & \text{P} \\
2 & p \lor p & \text{P} \\
3 & p \lor r & 1, 2, \text{SD}
\end{array}
$$

c.
$$
\begin{array}{lll}
1 & p & \text{P} \\
2 & p \supset r & \text{P} \\
3 & q \supset r & \text{P} \\
4 & q \lor p & 1, \text{add} \\
5 & r & 4, 2, 3, \text{SD}
\end{array}
$$

Tradition has given us the title "simple dilemma" to our last rule, and a few words about this title are appropriate. Someone is faced with a *dilemma* when he is faced with a difficult choice between two alternatives. The choice may be difficult because each of the alternatives is attractive (The you-can't-have-your-cake-and-eat-it dilemma) or because each of the alternatives is unattractive (the worst-of-two-evils dilemma). A very useful way to get the advantage of an opponent in a debate is to involve him in a dilemma. One shows that the opponent has two or more alternatives open to him and that each alternative involves the opponent in some unfavorable consequence. The form of such arguments is readily apparent: A or B are the alternatives; A leads to C; B leads to D; but both C and D are unattractive. Such arguments were known by the ancients as dilemmas. The relationship to our current rule should now be clear: the disjunction represents the two alternatives, and the conditionals represent the consequences of these alternatives. Our particular dilemma is called "simple" because each alternative has the same consequence. Here are two examples of the use of simple dilemmas in ordinary language.

EXAMPLES

a. You must go via the shore route or the inland route. If you go by the shore route, you will pay tolls; likewise, if you go inland. So you will pay tolls.

b. If I desert, I shall be shot; but if I go forward I shall be shot. I must desert or go forward. So I shall be shot.

EXAMPLES

a.
$$
\begin{array}{lll}
1 & p \cdot (\bar{p} \lor (p \supset q)) & \text{P} \\
2 & p & 1, \text{S} \\
3 & \bar{p} \lor (p \supset q) & 1, \text{S} \\
4 & \bar{\bar{p}} & 2, \text{DNI} \\
5 & p \supset p & 3, 4, \text{DS} \\
6 & q & 2, 5, \text{MP}
\end{array}
$$

b.
1	p	P
2	$\bar{q} \supset -(p \lor q)$	P
3	$p \lor q$	1, add
4	$--(p \lor q)$	3, DNI
5	$\bar{\bar{q}}$	4, 2, MT
6	q	5, DNE
7	$p \cdot q$	1, 6, PC

c.
1	$(r \lor s) \supset (p \lor q)$	P
2	$[(p \supset s) \cdot (q \supset s)] \cdot r$	P
3	r	2, S
4	$(p \supset s) \cdot (q \supset s)$	2, S
5	$p \supset s$	4, S
6	$q \supset s$	4, S
7	$r \lor s$	3, add
8	$p \lor q$	7, 1, MP
9	s	8, 5, 6, SD
10	$\bar{\bar{s}}$	9, DNI
11	$r \cdot \bar{\bar{s}}$	10, 3, PC

d.
1	$(p \lor q) \lor \bar{r}$	P
2	$(p \lor q) \supset s \cdot \bar{q}$	P
3	r	P
4	$\bar{\bar{r}}$	3, DNI
5	$p \lor q$	1, 4, DS
6	$s \cdot \bar{q}$	5, 2, MP
7	$\bar{q}$	6, S
8	p	5, 7, DS
9	$p \cdot r$	8, 3, PC

EXERCISES FOR SEC. 1.6.2.5

For each of the following, derive the schemata in the left column from those in the right.

1. p $q \cdot (q \supset (r \lor p))$, $\bar{r}$

2. $r \lor p$ $\bar{\bar{r}} \cdot s$

3. p $q \cdot (q \supset r)$, $p \lor \bar{r}$

4. $p \lor p$ $p \cdot p$

5. $p \lor (q \supset p)$ $r \cdot ((r \lor p) \supset \bar{s})$, $s \lor \bar{\bar{p}}$

6. $s \cdot q$ $(p \supset q) \cdot (p \lor r)$, $(r \supset q) \cdot (\bar{q} \lor s)$

7. $q \lor p$ $p \cdot \bar{p}$

8. q $p \cdot \bar{p}$

9. $q \cdot \bar{q}$ $p \supset q,$ $r \supset q,$ $\bar{q} \cdot (-(p \lor r) \supset q)$
10. q $p \supset r,$ $p \cdot (r \supset (\bar{p} \lor \bar{r}))$

1.6.2.6 TWO RULES FOR THE BICONDITIONAL

The choice of our rules for the biconditional should be guided by our knowledge of its relationship to the conditional. We want a rule that is something like modus ponens. In this case, however, we allow ourselves to infer any component of a biconditional from the biconditional itself and the other component. Thus we can schematize this rule by

$S \equiv W$ S W $S \equiv W$
.   .   .   .
.   .   .   .
.   .   .   .
S or $S \equiv W$ or $S \equiv W$ or W
.   .   .   .
.   .   .   .
$\therefore W$ $\therefore W$ $\therefore S$ $\therefore S$

We shall call this rule *modus ponens for the biconditional*. Accordingly, as the reason for W (or S) write numerals referring back to $S \equiv W$ and S (or W) followed by 'MPB'.

The next rule for the biconditional allows us to infer a biconditional from two conditionals. Let us call it the *principle of the biconditional*. Schematically, it runs as follows:

$S \supset W$ $S \supset W$
.   .
.   .
.   .
$W \supset S$ or $W \supset S$
.   .
.   .
.   .
$\therefore S \equiv W$ $\therefore W \equiv S$

As the reason for $S \equiv W$ (or $W \equiv S$) write numerals referring back to $W \supset S$ and $S \supset W$ followed by 'PB'. Here are a few examples employing the new rules.

EXAMPLES

a. 1 | $p \equiv (r \lor s)$ P
    2 | $(r \supset q) \cdot p$ P

$$
\begin{array}{lll}
3 & s \supset q & \text{P} \\
4 & p & 2, \text{S} \\
5 & r \vee s & 4, 1, \text{MPB} \\
6 & r \supset q & 2, \text{S} \\
7 & q & 5, 6, 3, \text{SD}
\end{array}
$$

b.
$$
\begin{array}{lll}
1 & p \supset q & \text{P} \\
2 & r \cdot p & \text{P} \\
3 & q \supset (\bar{p} \vee (q \supset p)) & \text{P} \\
4 & p & 2, \text{S} \\
5 & q & 1, 4, \text{MP} \\
6 & \bar{p} \vee (q \supset p) & 5, 3, \text{MP} \\
7 & \bar{\bar{p}} & 4, \text{DNI} \\
8 & q \supset p & 6, 7, \text{DS} \\
9 & p \equiv q & 1, 8, \text{PB}
\end{array}
$$

c.
$$
\begin{array}{lll}
1 & p \cdot (p \equiv q) & \text{P} \\
2 & r \equiv q & \text{P} \\
3 & p & 1, \text{S} \\
4 & p \equiv q & 1, \text{S} \\
5 & q & 3, 4, \text{MPB} \\
6 & r & 5, 2, \text{MPB}
\end{array}
$$

EXERCISES FOR SEC. 1.6.2.6

For each of the following, derive the schemata in the left column from those in the right.

1. p $q \cdot (q \supset (q \equiv p))$

2. $q \cdot p$ $q \cdot p \equiv (q \vee p), \quad (r \equiv \bar{\bar{p}}) \cdot r$

3. $p \equiv q$ $(p \supset q), \quad (r \supset (q \supset p)), \quad (\bar{r} \supset \bar{s}) \cdot s$

4. $r \cdot q$ $(p \vee \bar{q}) \supset (q \equiv p), \quad r \cdot (r \equiv p)$

5. $(\bar{q} \equiv r) \cdot (r \equiv \bar{q})$ $\bar{p} \supset (\bar{q} \supset r), \quad (p \supset s) \cdot (\bar{s} \supset (r \supset \bar{q})), \quad \bar{s}$

6. $\bar{\bar{p}}$ $(r \vee q) \equiv (r \supset p), \quad (q \supset p) \cdot \bar{s}, \quad -(r \vee q) \supset s$

7. p $(q \equiv r) \supset \bar{\bar{p}}, \quad (s \supset (q \supset r)) \cdot (r \supset (q \supset r)),$
   $(s \vee r) \cdot (r \supset q)$

8. $p \cdot q$ $--(p \vee r) \equiv ((s \supset q) \vee \bar{r}), \quad \bar{r} \cdot q$

9. s $(p \equiv q) \cdot (q \equiv \bar{p}), \quad p \cdot (p \vee s)$

10. $p \cdot q$ $p \equiv r \cdot s, \quad (r \equiv (\bar{s} \vee s)) \cdot p$

1.6.2.7 THE RULES SUMMARIZED

The following table summarizes our rules.

CONNECTIVES INVOLVED	RULES	LABELS
	$\dfrac{S}{--S}$	DNI
	$\dfrac{--S}{S}$	DNE
$\cdot$	$\dfrac{S \quad W}{S \;\cdot\; W}$	PC
	$\dfrac{S \;\cdot\; W}{S}$ and $\dfrac{S \cdot W}{W}$	S
$\vee$	$\dfrac{S}{S \vee W}$ and $\dfrac{W}{S \vee W}$	add
$\supset$	$\dfrac{S \quad S \supset W}{W}$	MP
$\equiv$	$\dfrac{S \equiv W \quad S}{W}$ and $\dfrac{S \equiv W \quad W}{S}$	MPB
$-, \supset$	$\dfrac{S \supset W \quad -W}{-S}$	MT
$-, \vee$	$\dfrac{S \vee W \quad -S}{W}$ and $\dfrac{S \vee W \quad -W}{S}$	DS
$\supset, \vee$	$\dfrac{S \supset E \quad W \supset E \quad S \vee W}{E}$	SD
$\supset, \equiv$	$\dfrac{S \supset W \quad W \supset S}{S \equiv W}$ and $\dfrac{S \supset W \quad W \supset S}{S = W}$	PB

EXERCISES FOR SEC. 1.6.2.7

A. For each of the following, derive the schemata in the left column from those in the right.

1. q $p \equiv q,$ $((r \supset p) \cdot (s \vee r)) \cdot \bar{\bar{s}}$
2. $p \equiv q$ $-(p \supset q) \supset -(r \vee s),$ $((q \supset p) \vee \bar{r}) \cdot r$
3. $p \cdot (p \vee r)$ $(q \supset \bar{\bar{p}}) \cdot (s \supset \bar{p}),$ $--(q \vee s)$
4. $\bar{p}$ $(s \supset \bar{q}) \cdot (s \vee r),$ $\bar{r} \cdot (\bar{r} \equiv q)$
5. s $(p \equiv \bar{p}) \cdot p$
6. $\bar{p}$ $(r \vee s) \cdot (r \supset \bar{q}),$ $(s \supset \bar{q}) \cdot (p \supset \bar{\bar{q}})$

7. $p \equiv \bar{q}$ $p \supset (p \supset \bar{q})$, $s \vee \bar{\bar{p}}$, $(-(\bar{q} \supset p) \supset s) \cdot \bar{s}$

8. $p \vee (s \supset q)$ $p \cdot q \vee s$, $(\bar{\bar{s}} \supset q) \cdot \bar{q}$

9. $s \cdot q$ $(p \supset s) \cdot (p \vee \bar{q})$, $r \cdot (r \equiv q)$

10. $s \supset r$ $(p \supset q) \supset (s \supset r)$, $-(p \supset q) \supset s$, $((s \supset -(p \cdot q)) \cdot p) \cdot q$

B. Establish the validity of each of the following arguments by means of a derivation.

  1. The game is over if it is past noon, while the public square is full only if it is past noon. The public square is full unless it is raining, but it is not raining. Hence the game is over.

  2. The ship will radio us just in case it is in trouble. If the ship is not in trouble, then it is not the case that either its boiler has exploded or there is a fire on the bridge. There is a fire on the bridge; so the ship will radio us.

  3. Despite the fact that the line is long, we shall be able to see the movie. If the line is long and we are able to see the movie, we are fortunate. If we are either fortunate or knowledgeable, we can be satisfied. Hence the line is long, but we can be satisfied.

  4. If war is declared, I shall join the Army or the Navy. If I join the latter, I shall serve two years; but I shall also serve two years if I join the former. War will be declared unless the administration changes its policies, and that will not happen. So I shall serve two years.

  5. The barber shaves himself just in case he does not shave himself, and he does shave himself. Hence there really is no barber.

  6. If the market rallies, then provided that I am prudent, I can make a profit. Unless the market does not rally, I am prudent if I can make a profit; moreover, the market will rally. Thus I am prudent just in case I can make a profit.

  7. If they do not kill some cows, the Indians will starve. They will kill some cows only if their religious beliefs are modified. While we shall make efforts to modify those beliefs, they will not be modified. Consequently, the Indians will starve.

  8. If the hens are in the road, there is a break in the fence. Someone was careless in case there is a break in the fence. Unless it is not the case that someone was careless, I shall give the farmhands a lecture; but the hens are in the road. Hence I shall give the farmhands a lecture.

  9. The book is entertaining just in case it is racy. It is racy only if it is not in the school library. Provided that James or Ralph read the book, it is entertaining. Ralph did read the book. Therefore it is not in the school library.

 10. If the fire dies and no one starts another, then the house will be cold. If Jones is at home, the fire will die, while if no one else is there, no one will start another. Jones is at home when and only when no one else is there, and he is at home if it is Saturday. Moreover, it is Saturday. So the house will be cold.

1.6.3 CONDITIONAL PROOFS

1.6.3.1 INTRODUCTION

Our rules of inference are still incomplete. Demonstrating this would take us beyond the scope of this book, but experimentation with a few examples will probably convince you of its likelihood. Try, for example, to derive '$p \supset q$' from 'q', or '$p \supset r$' from '$p \supset q$' and '$q \supset r$', or '$p \supset (q \supset r)$' from '$p \cdot q \supset r$'. If you use only the rules of inference given so far, you will not be able to do it. Yet you can easily verify that 'q' implies '$p \supset q$', '$p \supset q$' and '$q \supset r$' imply '$p \supset r$', and '$p \cdot q \supset r$' implies '$p \supset (q \supset r)$'. Or try to prove a valid schema; that is, derive it from no premises at all. You cannot even begin; the rules are applicable only if one or more schemata are already given. Consequently, in order to have a complete set of rules of inference, we must add to our previous rules or expand our methods for constructing derivations.

There is a method for constructing arguments which is frequently used by mathematicians, scientists, and laymen which we can adopt and put into a form suitable for derivations. First, however, we should look at some examples of it.

EXAMPLE 1

If I go to your party, I shall regret it later. For assume that I go. Then I shall drink too much. And then I shall get sick. Then I shall regret going, later.

The conclusion of this argument is

(a)   If I go to your party, I shall regret it later

and it has the form '$p \supset q$'. Notice that there are no *explicit* premises given in this argument. The statement 'I shall go to your party' is not asserted outright, but is offered as a mere supposition. Given this supposition, the author then infers that he will drink too much and get sick and consequently later regret going to the party. Thus, to convert this argument to a formally valid one, we must supply suppressed premises which the author obviously had in mind:

(b)   If I go to your party, I shall drink too much.

(c)   If I drink too much, I shall get sick.

(d)   If I get sick, I shall later regret going to your party.

These have the forms '$p \supset r$', '$r \supset s$', and '$s \supset q$', respectively. Once (b), (c), and (d) are added as premises, the argument is valid, for '$p \supset r$', '$r \supset s$', and '$s \supset q$' imply '$p \supset q$'. Let us add these premises and formalize the resulting argument:

1	$p \supset r$	P
2	$r \supset s$	P
3	$s \supset q$	P
4	Assume p	

5	r	1, 4, MP
6	s	2, 5, MP
7	q	6, 3, MP
8	$p \supset q$	

Steps 4 and 8 are not permitted by our previous rules of inference, and so the derivation is not correct as it stands. Nonetheless, the diagram of this argument reveals the basic technique applied in Example 1: *In order to establish a conditional of the form S ⊃ W, assume S and proceed to derive W as if S had been given as an additional premiss.* As the diagram shows, the extra premiss, 'p', is indispensable for obtaining 'r', 's', and 'q'.

Let us consider one more example.

EXAMPLE 2

If I attend the lectures, then if I study hard I shall pass the course. For assume that I attend the lectures. Next assume that I study hard. Then I shall both attend the lectures and study hard. And so I shall pass the course.

The conclusion of this argument is

(e)   If I attend the lectures, then if I study hard, I shall pass the course

and it has the form '$p \supset (q \supset r)$'. This argument makes use of *two* assumptions, namely, 'I attend the lectures' and 'I study hard'; and the argument also has an implicit premiss, namely,

(f)   If I both attend the lectures and study hard, I shall pass the course.

Let us add (f) and diagram the resulting argument:

1	$p \cdot q \supset r$	P
2	Assume p	
3	Assume q	
4	$p \cdot q$	2, 3, PC
5	r	4, 1, MP
6	$q \supset r$	
7	$p \supset (q \supset r)$	

In this example our rules fail to provide for steps 2, 3, 6, and 7, but the method for constructing the "derivation" is fairly clear: we want to derive '$p \supset (q \supset r)$' from '$p \cdot q \supset r$'; so we write

1	$p \cdot q \supset r$	P
	$p \supset (q \supset r)$	

But '$p \supset (q \supset r)$' is a conditional; so we apply the technique of Example 1 and write

$$
\begin{array}{ll}
1 & p \cdot q \supset r \qquad\quad \text{P} \\
2 & \text{Assume } p \\
  & q \supset r \\
  & p \supset (q \supset r)
\end{array}
$$

If we can derive '$q \supset r$' from 'p', then the method of Example 1 will allow us to infer '$p \supset (q \supset r)$'. But wait; '$q \supset r$' is a conditional; so let us apply the technique again:

$$
\begin{array}{ll}
1 & p \cdot q \supset r \\
2 & \text{Assume } p \\
  & \text{Assume } q \\
  & \\
  & r \\
  & q \supset r \\
  & p \supset (q \supset r)
\end{array}
$$

Now it is easy to fill in the steps from 'q' to 'r'.

This technique of assuming antecedents and deriving consequents certainly seems quite useful. First of all, it provides us with more information to work with, because when we assume an antecedent we get an additional schema to use. Second, it allows us to simplify our problems; instead of deriving a conditional, we have only to derive its consequent. But perhaps this method could be *too useful*; perhaps it will make our system of rules unsound. For example, suppose we constructed a derivation as follows:

$$
\begin{array}{lll}
 & 1 & p \supset q \qquad\quad \text{P} \\
 & 2 & p \supset \bar{q} \qquad\quad \text{P} \\
(A) & 3 & \text{Assume } p \\
 & 4 & q \qquad\qquad\quad 1, 3, \text{MP} \\
 & 5 & \bar{q} \qquad\qquad\quad 2, 3, \text{MP} \\
 & 6 & q \cdot \bar{q} \qquad\qquad 4, 5, \text{PC}
\end{array}
$$

This is obviously incorrect since the two premisses of this derivation do not imply its conclusion. Indeed, if we could construct derivations in this way, then we could derive any conclusion we wanted from every set of premisses. For example, we could derive 'r' from 'p' as follows:

$$
\begin{array}{lll}
(B) & 1 & p \qquad\qquad\qquad \text{P} \\
 & 2 & \text{Assume } q \cdot \bar{q} \\
 & 3 & q \qquad\qquad\qquad 2, \text{S} \\
 & 4 & q \vee r \qquad\qquad 3, \text{add} \\
 & 5 & \bar{q} \qquad\qquad\qquad 2, \text{S} \\
 & 6 & r \qquad\qquad\qquad 4, 5, \text{DS}
\end{array}
$$

These two examples clearly show that if we incorporate the method of introducing assumptions into our derivations, then some sort of restrictions will be necessary.

1.6.3.2 LINES OF ARGUMENT

Let us study the derivations (A) and (B) above and determine where things have gone wrong. First, the assumptions used in (A) and (B) are not used to establish conditionals. Second, as Examples 1 and 2 make quite clear, an assumption really belongs to a line of argument which is subordinate to the main one originating from the premisses. For the premisses are asserted outright, while the assumptions are introduced as mere suppositions which are useful for establishing conditionals. Thus we have a choice of two restrictions to make on the introduction of assumptions:

1 An assumption may be introduced into derivation only for the purpose of establishing a conditional, and the assumption introduced must be antecedent to the conditional in question.
2 Each assumption introduced must belong to a different line of argument than the premisses of the derivation.

Because we shall later introduce assumptions into derivations for purposes other than establishing conditionals, the first restriction is *too restrictive*. This leaves the second restriction, which makes use of the imprecise notion of a line of argument. Before the second restriction can be of any use to us, we must remove this difficulty.

All the steps of derivations have a common vertical line passing by them. This line will be used to indicate the *main line of argument* of a derivation. Thus subordinate lines of argument can be indicated by additional vertical lines. To return to the derivations of Examples 1 and 2, we can add vertical lines to indicate the lines of argument as follows:

	1	$p \supset r$	P
	2	$r \supset s$	P
	3	$s \supset q$	P
(1)	4	Assume p	
	5	r	1, 4, MP
	6	s	2, 5, MP
	7	q	6, 3, MP
	8	$p \supset q$	

(2)	1	$p \cdot q \supset r$	P
	2	Assume p	
	3	Assume q	
	4	$p \cdot q$	2, 3, PC
	5	r	1, 4, MP

$$6 \quad | \quad q \supset r$$
$$7 \quad | \quad p \supset (q \supset r)$$

The new vertical lines show that steps 4 to 7 of (1) belong to a line of argument subordinate to that of the other steps of (1), and that steps 3 to 5 of (2) belong to a line of argument subordinate to that of steps 2 and 6, which in turn belong to one which is subordinate to that of steps 1 and 7. The idea here is that steps which depend on assumptions belong to lines of argument which are subordinate to that of steps which do not depend on those assumptions.

Thus we see that the line of argument to which a step belongs can be indicated by means of vertical lines. Let us adopt this method and lay down the following stipulations:

1   Two steps in a derivation belong to the *same line* of argument if and only if exactly the same vertical lines pass by both of them.
2   One step in a derivation, S, belongs to a line of argument *subordinate* to that of another step, W, if and only if (*a*) every vertical line which passes to the left of W also passes by S and (*b*) at least one additional vertical passes by S and not by W.

It will be simpler to speak of 'lines' instead of 'lines of arguments'. Observe that if S belongs to a line subordinate to that of W, and W in turn belongs to one which is subordinate to that of E, then the line to which S belongs is also subordinate to that of E. Returning to (2) above, steps 3 to 5 belong to the same line, and this line is subordinate to that of steps 2 and 6. On the other hand, steps 1 and 7 belong to the *main* line of argument, that is, *the line to which every other line is subordinate*.

It is possible to have derivations in which the lines of two steps cannot be compared, because some of the vertical lines passing alongside of one do not pass alongside the other, and conversely. For example, suppose that we used the method of assumptions to derive '$(p \supset q) \cdot (r \supset s)$' from '$p \equiv q$' and '$r \equiv s$'. Since the conclusion we seek is a conjunction, the problem reduces to the following:

$$
\begin{array}{ll}
p \equiv q & \text{P} \\
r \equiv s & \text{P} \\
? & \\
p \supset q & \\
r \supset s & \\
(p \supset q) \cdot (r \supset s) &
\end{array}
$$

But now we have two conditionals to obtain; so let us assume their antecedents in order to derive their consequents:

$$
\begin{array}{lll}
1 & p \equiv q & \text{P} \\
2 & r \equiv s & \text{P} \\
3 & \quad \text{Assume } p \\
4 & \quad q & \text{3, 1, MPB} \\
\text{(3)} \quad 5 & p \supset q \\
6 & \quad \text{Assume } r \\
7 & \quad s & \text{6, 2, MPB} \\
8 & r \supset s \\
9 & (p \supset q) \cdot (r \supset s) & \text{5, 8, PC}
\end{array}
$$

(Of course, this is not a real derivation yet, since we have not introduced rules to justify all its steps.) Since *not all* the vertical lines which pass by steps 3 and 4 also pass by steps 7 and 8 (and conversely), the line of steps 3 and 4 is not subordinate to that of steps 7 and 8, and these in turn do not belong to a line subordinate to that of steps 3 and 4. Thus the lines of these steps cannot be compared. (This is not to be viewed as an objection to lines.)

Yet how are we to introduce new vertical lines into our derivations? All our previous derivations used only one vertical line, and consequently, all their steps belonged to the main line of argument. The answer to our question is this: Every time we introduce a new assumption, we must also introduce a new vertical line. This is formulated more precisely in the following rule:

Rule of assumption: *Any schema S may be written down as a new step of a derivation provided that a new vertical line is initiated to the left of S.*

As the reason for *S* we write 'A' for 'assumption'. We must continue to pass the new vertical line (and all the previous ones) alongside of any subsequent steps. The only way that we can discontinue this vertical line is by means of an application of the rule of conditional proof or of the rule of indirect proof. (These rules will be stated later.)

A few comments on the rule of assumption are in order. First, the rule of assumption allows us to introduce *any schema whatsoever* as a new step in a derivation. But being able to assume anything we choose does not mean that we can prove whatever we choose. For every time we introduce an assumption, we must also initiate a new vertical line; and as we shall shortly see, these vertical lines give rise to restrictions which prevent the completely arbitrary use of assumptions. Thus, although we can introduce assumptions with complete freedom, it will not always serve our purpose to do so. In general, it is useful to introduce an assumption only if we expect to use it in applying the rules of conditional or indirect proof. Second, once an assumption is introduced, *it needs no further justification*, and is to be treated as an additional premiss.

The premisses of a derivation will, of course, belong to the same line, and this will be the main line of the derivation. To rule out 'derivations' such as (A) and (B) we now lay down a restriction:

The premisses and conclusion of a derivation must belong to the main line.

Now let us see how this affects (A) and (B). When we draw in the vertical lines, we obtain:

(A)	1	$p \supset q$	P		(B)	1	p	P
	2	$p \supset \bar{q}$	P			2	$q \cdot \bar{q}$	A
	3	p	A			3	q	2, S
	4	q	1, 3, MP			4	$q \vee r$	3, add
	5	$\bar{q}$	2, 3, MP			5	$\bar{q}$	2, S
	6	$q \cdot \bar{q}$	4, 5, PC			6	r	5, 4, DS

Since '$q \cdot \bar{q}$' does not belong to the same level as '$p \supset q$' and '$p \supset \bar{q}$', it cannot be the conclusion of (A); so it has not been derived from these premisses. Similarly, 'r' has not been derived from 'p'. Indeed, since (A) and (B) have no conclusions, they are not even derivations. We are not able to discontinue the vertical lines in these derivations, but we are able to discontinue them in (1), (2), and (3). This is because step 8 in (1), steps 6 and 7 in (2), and steps 5 and 8 in (3) will be justified by the rule of conditional proof; but this is another matter which we shall come to in a few paragraphs.

First we need one more restriction. Consider the following "derivation":

(C)	1	p	P
	2	r	A
	3	$r \vee s$	2, add
	4	$r \supset (r \vee s)$	(conditional proof)
	5	$p \cdot r$	1, 2, PC

It will turn out that stopping the second vertical at step 4 is justified; nonetheless, it looks as if we have been able to derive '$p \cdot r$' from 'p'. This is certainly undesirable since 'p' does not imply '$p \cdot r$'. Notice that 'r' belongs to a line which is subordinate to that of '$p \cdot r$'; thus derivations such as (C) can be excluded by means of the following restriction:

A step obtained by means of one of the 11 rules of inference must belong to a line which is the same as or subordinate to the lines to which the steps from which it is obtained belong.

Thus, if we obtain a schema S, say, 'q', from one or more schemata, say, '$p \supset q$' and 'p', by means of one of the 11 rules of inference, say, modus ponens, then every vertical line which passes by *any* of the latter schemata must also pass by s. In the case of '$p \supset q$', 'p', and 'q', we can have

p	P		p	P		$p \supset q$	P	
$p \supset q$	A	or	$p \supset q$	P	or	r	A	
q	MP		q	MP		p	A	
						q	MP	

but not

p	P		$p \supset q$	P		$p \supset q$	P	
$p \supset q$	A	or	r	A	or	r	A	
q			p	A		p	A	
			q			q	.	

This restriction also excludes the following "derivation":

(D)
1 | p | P
2 | r | A
3 | $r \lor s$ | 2, add
4 | $r \supset (r \lor s)$ | (conditional proof)
5 | q | A
6 | $q \cdot r$ | 2, 5, PC
7 | $q \supset q \cdot r$ | (conditional proof)

Since 'p' does not imply '$q \supset q \cdot r$', we clearly want to avoid "derivations" such as (D). This "derivation" is illegitimate because '$q \cdot r$' does not belong to a line which is the same or subordinate to those of both 'q' and 'r'; for while 'q' and '$q \cdot r$' belong to the same line, the lines of 'r' and '$q \cdot r$' are incomparable.

1.6.3.3   THE RULE OF CONDITIONAL PROOF

At last we are ready to state the rule of conditional proof. This rule is a formal and precise version of the rule which is used informally (together with the method of assumptions) to establish a conditional. The only reason we have introduced line-of-argument vertical lines, the rule of assumption, and the two restrictions is to allow for a precise and "safe" formulation of this rule and the rule of indirect proof. The statement of the rule now follows:

> The rule of conditional proof: *If the schema S has been introduced in a derivation as an assumption, and if the schema W is the last step which has been obtained so far in the derivation, and if it belongs to the same line as S, then the vertical line passing immediately to the left of S and W may be discontinued, and as the next step we may write S ⊃ W.*

As the reason for $S \supset W$, we write a numeral referring to S; then a hyphen followed by a numeral referring to W and 'CP'. The number of steps between S and W does not matter; nor does it matter whether other assumptions or other applications of the rule occur between S and W. The statement of this rule is rather complicated, but the idea is really quite simple, as the following diagram of the rule shows:

```
|  S        A
|  .
|  .
|  .
|  W
S ⊃ W      CP
```

This rule also allows S and W to be the same schema and even the same step. For example, we can derive '$r ⊃ r$' from 'r' as follows:

```
1 | r          P
2 |  | r       A
3 | r ⊃ r      2-2, CP
```

If you return to (1), (2), and (3), you can now verify that step 8 of (1), steps 6 and 7 of (2), and steps 5 and 8 of (3) are justified by the rule of conditional proof.

Before we illustrate this rule in further examples, it is useful to summarize it and the concomitant restrictions in the following table:

Assumption: | S A | 1 Continue all vertical lines which pass by the left of previous steps except those stopped by CP.
(New vertical line)

Conditional proof:

```
              |  S      A
              |  .
              |  .
              |  .
              |  W
        S ⊃   W
```
(Discontinue the innermost vertical line, but continue all others.)

2 The premises and conclusion of a derivation must belong to the main line of the derivation.

3 If S is to be obtained from S_1, S_2, or S_3 by one of the rules of inference, then S must belong to a line which is the same or subordinate to that of each of S_1, S_2, and S_3.

You may wonder whether it really is "safe" to use the rule of conditional proof and the rule of assumption. The answer is that it is safe, in the sense that these and our previous rules form a sound system of rules. The proof of this is rather advanced and is given in the Appendix.

Now let us turn to some examples.

EXAMPLE 1. To derive '$p \supset r$' from '$p \supset (q \lor r)$' and '$\bar{q}$'. Setting this problem up, we first obtain

$$\begin{array}{ll} p \supset (q \lor r) & \text{P} \\ \bar{q} & \text{P} \\ ? & \\ p \supset r & \end{array}$$

But '$p \supset r$' is a conditional; so let us assume 'p' and try to derive 'r':

$$\begin{array}{ll} p \supset (q \lor r) & \text{P} \\ \bar{q} & \text{P} \\ \quad p & \text{A} \\ \quad ? & \\ \quad r & \\ p \supset r & \text{CP} \end{array}$$

But completing this is easy, since we now have 'p' and merely have to get 'r':

$$\begin{array}{lll} 1 & p \supset (q \lor r) & \text{P} \\ 2 & \bar{q} & \text{P} \\ 3 & \quad p & \text{A} \\ 4 & \quad q \lor r & \text{3, 1, MP} \\ 5 & \quad r & \text{2, 4, DS} \\ 6 & p \supset r & \text{3-5, CP} \end{array}$$

EXAMPLE 2. To derive '$p \supset (q \supset r)$' from '$q \supset (p \supset r)$'. When we set this up, we have

$$\begin{array}{ll} q \supset (p \supset r) & \text{P} \\ ? & \\ p \supset (q \supset r) & \end{array}$$

Since our conclusion is a conditional, the next move is to go to

$$\begin{array}{ll} q \supset (p \supset r) & \text{P} \\ \quad p & \text{A} \\ \quad ? & \\ \quad q \supset r & \\ p \supset (q \supset r) & \text{CP} \end{array}$$

But this leads us to

$$\begin{array}{ll} q \supset (p \supset r) & \text{P} \\ \quad p & \text{A} \\ \quad \quad q & \text{A} \\ \quad \quad ? & \end{array}$$

$$\begin{array}{ll} \quad\quad r & \\ \quad q \supset r & \text{CP} \\ p \supset (q \supset r) & \text{CP} \end{array}$$

Now a complete derivation is quickly obtainable:

1	$q \supset (p \supset r)$	P
2	$\quad p$	A
3	$\quad\quad q$	A
4	$\quad\quad p \supset r$	1, 3, MP
5	$\quad\quad r$	2, 4, MP
6	$\quad q \supset r$	3-5, CP
7	$p \supset (q \supset r)$	2-6, CP

EXAMPLE 3.   To derive '$(r \supset p) \supset (r \supset q)$' from '$p \supset q$'.

a.
$$\begin{array}{ll} p \supset q & \text{P} \\ ? & \\ (r \supset p) \supset (r \supset q) & \end{array}$$

b.
$$\begin{array}{ll} p \supset q & \text{P} \\ \quad r \supset p & \text{A} \\ \quad ? & \\ \quad r \supset q & \\ (r \supset p) \supset (r \supset q) & \text{CP} \end{array}$$

c.
$$\begin{array}{ll} p \supset q & \text{P} \\ \quad r \supset p & \text{A} \\ \quad\quad r & \text{A} \\ \quad\quad ? & \\ \quad\quad q & \\ \quad r \supset q & \text{CP} \\ (r \supset p) \supset (r \supset q) & \text{CP} \end{array}$$

d.
1	$p \supset q$	P
2	$\quad r \supset p$	A
3	$\quad\quad r$	A
4	$\quad\quad p$	2, 3, MP
5	$\quad\quad q$	4, 1, MP
6	$\quad r \supset q$	3-5, CP
7	$(r \supset p) \supset (r \supset q)$	2-6, CP

EXAMPLE 4.   To derive '$r \lor s$' from '$p \lor q$', '$p \supset r$', and '$q \supset s$'.

a.
$$\begin{array}{ll} p \lor q & \text{P} \\ p \supset r & \text{P} \\ q \supset s & \text{P} \\ ? & \\ r \lor s & \end{array}$$

b.
$$\begin{array}{ll} p \lor q & \text{P} \\ p \supset r & \text{P} \\ q \supset s & \text{P} \\ ? & \\ p \supset (r \lor s) & \\ q \supset (r \lor s) & \\ r \lor s & \text{SD} \end{array}$$

c.
$$\begin{array}{ll} p \lor q & \text{P} \\ p \supset r & \text{P} \\ q \supset s & \text{P} \\ \quad p & \text{A} \\ \quad ? & \\ \quad r \lor s & \end{array}$$

d.
1	$p \lor q$	P
2	$p \supset r$	P
3	$q \supset s$	P
4	$\quad p$	A
5	$\quad r$	4, 2, MP
6	$\quad r \lor s$	5, add

$p \supset (r \lor s)$	CP
q	A
?	
$r \lor s$	
$q \supset (r \lor s)$	CP
$r \lor s$	SD

7	$p \supset (r \lor s)$	4-6, CP
8	, q	A
9	s	8, 3, MP
10	$r \lor s$	9, add
11	$q \supset (r \lor s)$	8-10, CP
12	$r \lor s$	1, 7, 11, SD

This example is interesting in two respects. First, it illustrates a rule of inference known as *complex dilemma*. This rule, which allows us to pass from $S \lor W, S \supset E, W \supset N$ to $E \lor N$ is not included among our 11 rules of inference. Nonetheless, we can get the *effect* of this rule, because whenever we want to go from three schemata of the form $S \lor W, S \supset E, W \supset N$ to one of the form $E \lor N$, we need only carry out the 12 steps applied in (d) with respect to the schemata in question. Second, the solution of this example required much more ingenuity than any of our previous examples. In passing from (a) to (b), some insight was necessary. Of course, it did not come completely out of the blue, since *simple dilemma* was one of the few ways to proceed from these premises.

EXAMPLE 5.   To derive 'p' from '$p \lor p$'.

a.
$p \lor p$
?
p

b.
$p \lor p$	
?	
$p \supset p$	
p	SD

c.
1	$p \lor p$	P
2	p	A
3	$p \supset p$	2-2, CP
4	p	1, 3, SD

EXAMPLE 6.   To derive '$p \lor q$' from '$q \lor p$'.

a.
$q \lor p$	P
?	
$p \lor q$	

b.
$q \lor p$	P
?	
$q \supset (p \lor q)$	
$p \supset (p \lor q)$	
$p \lor q$	SD

c.
1	$q \lor p$	P
2	q	A
3	$p \lor q$	2, add
4	$q \supset (p \lor q)$	2-3, CP
5	p	A
6	$p \lor q$	5, add
7	$p \supset (p \lor q)$	5-6, CP
8	$p \lor q$	1, 4, 7, SD

EXAMPLE 7.   To derive '$\bar{p}$' from '$p \supset q$' and '$p \supset \bar{q}$'.

a.
$p \supset q$	P
$p \supset \bar{q}$	P

b.
$p \supset q$	P
$p \supset \bar{q}$	P

$$\begin{array}{|l} ? \\ \bar{p} \end{array}$$

$$\begin{array}{|ll} ? \\ p \supset -(p \supset p) \\ \quad\begin{array}{|l} p \end{array} & A \\ p \supset p & CP \\ --(p \supset p) & DNI \\ \bar{p} & MT \end{array}$$

c.
$$\begin{array}{|ll} p \supset q & P \\ p \supset \bar{q} & P \\ \quad\begin{array}{|l} p \\ ? \\ -(p \supset p) \end{array} \\ p \supset -(p \supset p) & CP \\ \quad\begin{array}{|l} p \end{array} & A \\ p \supset p & CP \\ --(p \supset p) & DNI \\ \bar{p} & MT \end{array}$$

d.
1	$p \supset q$	P
2	$p \supset \bar{q}$	P
3	$\quad p$	A
4	$\quad q$	1, 3, MP
5	$\quad \bar{q}$	2, 3, MP
6	$\quad q \vee -(p \supset p)$	4, add
7	$\quad -(p \supset p)$	5, 6, DS
8	$p \supset -(p \supset p)$	3-7, CP
9	$\quad p$	A
10	$p \supset p$	9 9, CP
11	$--(p \supset p)$	10, DNI
12	$\bar{p}$	11, 8, MT

As you will be able to see later, this example shows us how to dispense with the rule of indirect proof. Nonetheless, the rule is so important and useful that we shall retain it. (A separate section will be devoted to explaining it.)

1.6.3.4 PROOFS OF THEOREMS

A *proof* is a derivation without premisses. At first sight this concept of a proof might seem absurd to you. For how can a derivation proceed if it has no premisses? Before the rules of assumption and conditional proof were introduced, derivations could not proceed unless they had premisses; in other words, before the introduction of these rules, proofs as such were impossible. But now we can proceed to construct proofs by using the rule of assumption to take our first steps. Since every derivation begins with one vertical line—the main line—the first step in a proof will have two vertical lines to its left.

EXAMPLE.   Proof of '$p \supset (p \lor q)$'.

```
1 | |  p                    A
2 | |  p ∨ q                1, add
3 |  p ⊃ (p ∨ q)            1-2, CP
```

The conclusion of a proof, that is, the last step of the main line of the proof, is the schema proved by means of the proof. Schemata which can be proved are called (truth-functional) *theorems*. (A proof, to be a proof, must be the proof of some theorem.) Since our rules are sound, *every theorem is valid;* since the rules are complete, *every valid TFS is a theorem.* Consequently, proofs and derivations provide an alternative method for establishing validity, implications, and equivalences.

EXAMPLES

1   Proof of '$(p \cdot q \supset r) \supset (p \supset (q \supset r))$' worked out:

a.
```
| |  p · q ⊃ r                       A
|    ?
|    p ⊃ (q ⊃ r)
|   (p · q ⊃ r) ⊃ (p ⊃ (q ⊃ r))      CP
```

b.
```
| |  p · q ⊃ r                       A
| |  p                               A
| |  ?
| |  q ⊃ r
| |  p ⊃ (q ⊃ r)                     CP
|   (p · q ⊃ r) ⊃ (p ⊃ (q ⊃ r))      CP
```

c.
```
1 | |  p · q ⊃ r                     A
2 | |  p                             A
3 | |  q                             A
4 | |  p · q                         2, 3, PC
5 | |  r                             1, 4, MP
6 | |  q ⊃ r                         3-5, CP
7 |  p ⊃ (q ⊃ r)                     2-6, CP
8 | (p · q ⊃ r) ⊃ (p ⊃ (q ⊃ r))      1-7, CP
```

2   Proof of '$p \equiv p \cdot p$':

```
1 | |  p                  A
2 | |  p · p              1, PC
3 |  p ⊃ p · p            1-2, CP
4 | |  p · p              A
5 | |  p                  4, S
```

| 6 | $p \cdot p \supset p$ | 4-5, CP |
| 7 | $p \equiv p \cdot p$ | 3, 6, PB |

3 Proof of '$(p \equiv q) \supset (q \equiv p)$':

1		$p \equiv q$	A
2		p	A
3		q	1, 2, MPB
4		$p \supset q$	2-3, CP
5		q	A
6		p	5, 1, MPB
7		$q \supset p$	5-6, CP
8		$q \equiv p$	4, 7, PB
9	$(p \equiv q) \supset (q \equiv p)$	1-8, CP

4 Proof of '$(p \supset q) \cdot \bar{q} \supset \bar{p}$':

1		$(p \supset q) \cdot \bar{q}$	A
2		$p \supset q$	1, S
3		$\bar{q}$	1, S
4		$\bar{p}$	2, 3, MT
5	$(p \supset q) \cdot \bar{q} \supset \bar{p}$	1-4, CP

EXERCISES FOR SEC. 1.6.3

A. Furnish reasons for these derivations.

1.
1		$p \supset q \cdot r$	P
2		p	
3			s	
4			$q \cdot r$	
5			q	
6			$q \cdot s$	
7		$s \supset q \cdot s$	
8	$p \supset (s \supset q \cdot s)$	

2.
1		$(p \supset q) \supset r$	P
2		$p \supset (p \supset q)$	P
3		p	
4		$p \supset q$	
5		r	
6		$r \lor s$	
7	$p \supset (r \lor s)$	

3.
1		$\bar{\bar{s}}$	P
2			$q \equiv s$	
3			s	
4			q	
5				r	

$\begin{array}{ll} 6 & \quad\quad r \cdot q \\ 7 & \quad\quad r \supset r \cdot q \\ 8 & \quad (q \equiv s) \supset (r \supset r \cdot q) \end{array}$

4. $\begin{array}{lll} 1 & p & \quad\quad\quad\quad P \\ 2 & \quad q \supset q \\ 3 & \quad p \cdot p \\ 4 & \quad p \\ 5 & (q \supset q) \supset p \\ 6 & \quad p \\ 7 & \quad\quad q \\ 8 & \quad q \supset q \\ 9 & p \supset (q \supset q) \\ 10 & p \equiv (q \supset q) \end{array}$

5. $\begin{array}{lll} 1 & p \lor q & \quad\quad P \\ 2 & p \supset r & \quad\quad P \\ 3 & q \supset s & \quad\quad P \\ 4 & \quad p \\ 5 & \quad r \\ 6 & \quad r \lor s \\ 7 & p \supset (r \lor s) \\ 8 & \quad q \\ 9 & \quad s \\ 10 & \quad r \lor s \\ 11 & q \supset (r \lor s) \\ 12 & r \lor s \end{array}$

6. $\begin{array}{lll} 1 & r \lor s & \quad\quad P \\ 2 & \quad \bar{r} \\ 3 & \quad s \\ 4 & \bar{r} \supset s \\ 5 & \quad \bar{s} \\ 6 & \quad r \\ 7 & \quad\quad p \\ 8 & \quad\quad p \cdot r \\ 9 & \quad p \supset p \cdot r \\ 10 & \bar{s} \supset (p \supset p \cdot r) \end{array}$

B. For each of the following, derive the schemata in the left column from those in the right.

1. $p \supset s$ $(p \supset r) \cdot (r \supset s)$

2. $(\bar{q} \supset s) \supset (\bar{q} \supset r)$ $\bar{q} \supset (s \supset r)$

3. $p \supset (q \supset r)$ $q \supset (p \supset r)$

4. $(p \supset q) \cdot (q \supset p)$ $p \equiv q$

5. $\bar{q} \supset \bar{p}$ $p \supset q$

6. $p \cdot q \supset r$ $p \supset (q \supset r)$

7. $p \supset q \cdot q$ $p \supset q$

8. p $(q \supset \bar{\bar{q}}) \supset p$

9. $p \supset (\bar{\bar{p}} \supset \bar{\bar{q}})$ $p \supset q$

10. $p \supset q$ $(p \supset r) \cdot (p \supset \bar{r})$

11. p $\qquad\qquad\qquad$ $p \equiv (p \supset q)$

12. $p \lor q$ $\qquad\qquad\quad$ $q \lor p$

13. $p \lor \bar{\bar{q}}$ $\qquad\qquad\quad$ $p \lor q$

14. $\bar{p} \supset q$ $\qquad\qquad\quad$ $p \lor q$

15. $(p \supset q) \supset q$ $\qquad\quad$ $p \lor q$

C. Prove these TFS.

1. $(p \supset (q \supset r)) \supset ((p \supset q) \supset (p \supset r))$

2. $(p \supset q) \supset ((r \supset p) \supset (r \supset q))$

3. $p \supset \bar{\bar{p}}$

4. $\bar{\bar{p}} \supset p$

5. $p \supset p \cdot p$

6. $p \cdot q \equiv q \cdot p$

7. $p \supset p$

8. $p \supset (p \lor p)$

9. $(p \lor p) \supset p$

10. $p \equiv (p \lor p \cdot q)$

11. $(p \supset \bar{q}) \equiv (q \supset \bar{p})$

12. $(p \cdot q \lor p \cdot r) \equiv p \cdot (q \lor r)$

13. $(p \cdot q) \cdot r \equiv r \cdot (q \cdot p)$

14. $(p \lor q \cdot r) \equiv (p \lor q) \cdot (p \lor r)$

15. $(p \equiv q) \supset (q \equiv p)$

16. $(p \equiv q) \cdot (q \equiv r) \supset (p \equiv r)$

17. $p \equiv p$

18. $p \supset (\bar{p} \supset q)$

19. $((q \supset p) \supset r) \supset (p \supset r)$

20. $(p \supset q) \supset (p \cdot r \supset q \cdot r)$

21. $(p \supset q) \supset ((p \lor r) \supset (q \lor r))$

22. $(p \supset q) \supset ((p \lor q) \supset q)$

23. $((p \equiv q) \equiv r) \supset (p \supset (q \equiv r))$

24. $((p \equiv p) \equiv q) \equiv q$

25. $(p \supset (q \supset r)) \equiv (q \supset (p \supset r))$

1.6.4 INDIRECT PROOFS

Indirect proofs, also known as *reductio ad absurdum* proofs, are frequently encountered in informal arguments. Their formalization via the method of assumptions will provide us with another powerful extension of our methods of derivation. But first let us consider some informal arguments in order to see the naturalness and plausibility of our formal rule of indirect proofs.

EXAMPLE FROM MATHEMATICS. To prove: There is no greatest natural number.

Proof: Assume that there is a greatest natural number. Then by adding 1 to it we get a greater one. This contradicts our assumption. So there cannot be a greatest natural number.

EXAMPLE FROM LOGIC.   To prove: A schema cannot be both valid and also consist of only one statement letter.

Proof: Suppose that this were possible. The schema, since it just consists of one statement letter, might as well be, say, 'p'. But this (or any other statement letter) comes out true when interpreted as true, and false when interpreted as false. Nonetheless, our schema is also supposed to be true for all interpretations. We have arrived at a contradiction. So what we supposed must be false.

EXAMPLE FROM ORDINARY INTERCOURSE

You grant that if Jones committed the crime, then Dillinger was there. But you also grant that if Jones committed the crime, Dillinger was not there. So you must admit that Jones did not commit the crime. For if he did, Dillinger would have been there and not there, and this is a contradiction.

All these examples have something in common: to show that something is false, we assume that it is true. Then either the negation of the assumption or a contradiction is derived from this assumption. In either case the assumption is shown to lead to absurdity. On this basis the conclusion is deemed established. The method is thus indirect: we do not directly derive a conclusion, but rather show that, granted the premises, its negation leads to absurdity.

To obtain the formal correlate of this method, we shall add two or more rules to our previous ones, namely, the rule of reiteration and the rule of indirect proof.

The rule of reiteration is a rule that allows us to repeat a schema in a line which is the same or subordinate to that of its original occurrence. It is more of a convenience than a necessity, for by using it we can simplify the statement of the rule of indirect proof. On the other hand, even in the presence of the simplified rule of indirect proof, there are ways to dispense with the rule of reiteration. But before going into this, let us state the rule.

Rule of reiteration: *Any schema which has already occurred in a derivation may be added as a new step, provided that the line of the new occurrence is the same as or subordinate to that of the earlier occurrence.*

Reason: A numeral referring to the first occurrence followed by 'R'. The diagrammatic representation of reiteration is

S	P		S	
.			.	
.		or	. .	
.			.	
S	R		. . .	.
				.
				.
				. R
			. . .	S

EXAMPLE.   To prove: $p \supset (q \supset p)$.

Proof: 1 | | | p | A
2 | | | q | A
3 | | | p | 1, R
4 | | $q \supset p$ | 2-3, CP
5 | $p \supset (q \supset p)$ | 1-4, CP

The last schema can also be proved without using reiteration:

1 | | | p | A
2 | | | q | A
3 | | | $p \cdot p$ | 1, PC
4 | | | p | 3, S
5 | | $q \supset p$ | 2-4, CP
6 | $p \supset (q \supset p)$ | 1-5, CP

Moreover, by generalizing the "trick" used here, it is possible to dispense with reiteration entirely. For to repeat a schema S at the same or lower level, we need only first infer $S \cdot S$ and then obtain S by simplification. As a short-cut, however, we shall retain the rule of reiteration.

The rule of indirect proof may now be stated.

Rule of indirect proof: *Suppose that S has been introduced by the rule of assumption and that S, W, and $-W$ all belong to the same line. Then if W or $-W$ is the last step to date, the vertical line passing by both S, W, and $-W$ may be discontinued, with $-S$ being written as the next step.*

Reason: Hyphenated numerals referring to S and W (or $-W$ if it is last) followed by 'IP'. The diagrammatic representation of this rule is thus

S		S
.		.
.		.
.		.
W	or	$-W$

(Also S and W may be the same.)

a. 1 | $p \supset q$ | P
    2 | $p \supset \bar{q}$ | P
    3 | p | A
    4 | q | 3, 1, MP
    5 | $\bar{q}$ | 3, 2, MP
    6 | $\bar{p}$ | 3-5, IP

b. 1 | $p \supset \bar{p}$ | P
    2 | p | A
    3 | $\bar{p}$ | 1, 2, MP
    4 | $\bar{p}$ | 2-3, IP

c. 1 | p | P
    2 | $\bar{p}$ | P
    3 | $\bar{q}$ | A
    4 | p | 1, R
    5 | $\bar{p}$ | 2, R
    6 | $\bar{\bar{q}}$ | 3-5, IP
    7 | q | 6, DNE

[The rule of reiteration is introduced to permit derivations such as (c); without the rule the statement of IP would have to be quite complicated.]

A TRICK. We cannot argue directly as follows:

$-S$ A
.
.
.
W
$-W$
S IP

because S is not the negation of $-S$. But we can get the effect of this type of argument as follows:

$-S$ A
.
.
.
W
$-W$

$$\begin{array}{ll} --S & \text{IP} \\ S & \text{DNE} \end{array}$$

EXAMPLES

1   To prove: '$(p \lor p) \supset p$' without using SD.

a.
$$\begin{array}{ll} p \lor p & \text{A} \\ \\ p & \\ (p \lor p) \supset p & \text{CP} \end{array}$$

b.
$$\begin{array}{ll} p \lor p & \\ \bar{p} & \\ ? & \\ \bar{\bar{p}} & \text{IP} \\ p & \text{DNE} \\ (p \lor p) \supset p & \end{array}$$

c.
$$\begin{array}{lll} 1 & p \lor p & \text{A} \\ 2 & \bar{p} & \text{A} \\ 3 & p & 1, 2, \text{DS} \\ 4 & \bar{\bar{p}} & 2\text{-}3, \text{IP} \\ 5 & p & 4, \text{DNE} \\ 6 & (p \lor p) \supset p & 1\text{-}5, \text{CP} \end{array}$$

2   To derive '$-(p \cdot \bar{q})$' from '$p \supset q$'.

a.
$$\begin{array}{ll} p \supset q & \text{P} \\ ? & \\ \\ -(p \cdot \bar{q}) & \end{array}$$

b.
$$\begin{array}{ll} p \supset q & \\ p \cdot \bar{q} & \\ ? & \\ \\ q & \\ \bar{q} & \\ -(p \cdot \bar{q}) & \text{IP} \end{array}$$

c.
$$\begin{array}{lll} 1 & p \supset q & \text{A} \\ & p \cdot q & \text{A} \\ & p & 2, \text{S} \\ & q & 3, 1, \text{MP} \\ & \bar{q} & 2, \text{S} \\ & -(p \cdot \bar{q}) & 2\text{-}5, \text{IP} \end{array}$$

3   To prove '$p \lor \bar{p}$'.

a.
$$\begin{array}{ll} ? & \\ \\ p \lor \bar{p} & \end{array}$$

b.
$$\begin{array}{ll} -(p \lor \bar{p}) & \text{A} \\ ? & \\ --(p \lor \bar{p}) & \text{IP} \\ p \lor \bar{p} & \text{DNE} \end{array}$$

c.
$$
\begin{array}{ll}
-(p \lor \bar{p}) & \text{A} \\
? & \\
p \lor \bar{p} & \\
--(p \lor \bar{p}) & \text{IP} \\
p \lor \bar{p} & \text{DNE}
\end{array}
$$

d.
$$
\begin{array}{ll}
-(p \lor \bar{p}) & \text{A} \\
? & \\
\\
\bar{p} & \\
p \lor \bar{p} & \text{add} \\
--(p \lor \bar{p}) & \text{IP} \\
p \lor \bar{p} & \text{DNE}
\end{array}
$$

e.
$$
\begin{array}{lll}
1 & -(p \lor \bar{p}) & \text{A} \\
2 & p & \text{A} \\
3 & p \lor \bar{p} & 2,\ \text{add} \\
4 & -(p \lor \bar{p}) & 1,\ \text{R} \\
5 & \bar{p} & 2\text{-}4,\ \text{IP} \\
6 & p \lor \bar{p} & 5,\ \text{add} \\
7 & --(p \lor \bar{p}) & 1\text{-}6,\ \text{IP} \\
8 & p \lor \bar{p} & 7,\ \text{DNE}
\end{array}
$$

4   To prove: $(p \cdot \bar{p}) \supset \bar{q}$.

Proof:
$$
\begin{array}{lll}
1 & p \cdot \bar{p} & \\
2 & q & \text{A} \\
3 & p & \text{A} \\
4 & \bar{p} & 3,\ \text{S} \\
5 & \bar{q} & 3,\ \text{S} \\
6 & (p \cdot \bar{p}) \supset \bar{q} & 1\text{-}6,\ \text{CP}
\end{array}
$$

5   To prove: $((p \supset q) \supset p) \supset p$.

Proof:
$$
\begin{array}{lll}
1 & (p \supset q) \supset p & \text{A} \\
2 & \bar{p} & \text{A} \\
3 & p & \text{A} \\
4 & \bar{q} & \text{A} \\
5 & p & 3,\ \text{R} \\
6 & \bar{p} & 2,\ \text{R} \\
7 & \bar{\bar{q}} & 4\text{-}6,\ \text{IP} \\
8 & q & 7,\ \text{DNE} \\
9 & p \supset q & 3\text{-}8,\ \text{CP} \\
10 & p & 9,\ 1,\ \text{MP} \\
11 & \bar{\bar{p}} & 2\text{-}11,\ \text{IP} \\
12 & p & 12,\ \text{DNE} \\
13 & ((p \supset q) \supset p) \supset p & 1\text{-}13,\ \text{CP}
\end{array}
$$

6   Two ways to derive 'q' from 'p' and '$\bar{p}$':

a. 1 | p | P
    2 | $\bar{p}$ | P
    3 | $p \lor q$ | 1, add
    4 | q | 2, 3, DS

b. 1 | p | P
    2 | $\bar{p}$ | P
    3 | $\bar{q}$ | A
    4 | p | 1, R
    5 | $\bar{p}$ | 2, R
    6 | $--q$ | 3-5, IP
    7 | q | 6, DNE

These "tricks" are good ones to remember. They are formal kin of the law that states that an inconsistent schema implies every schema. They are good to use whenever you know you are able to obtain a schema and its negation in the same line.

[*Exercise:* Shorten the proof in Example 5 by using (a) above.]

7 To prove: $-(p \lor q) \supset \bar{p} \cdot \bar{q}$.

Proof: 1 | $-(p \lor q)$ | A
          2 | p | A
          3 | $p \lor q$ | 2, add
          4 | $-(p \lor q)$ | 1, R
          5 | $\bar{p}$ | 2-4, IP
          6 | q | A
          7 | $p \lor q$ | 6, add
          8 | $-(p \lor q)$ | 1, R
          9 | $\bar{q}$ | 6-8, IP
          10 | $\bar{p} \cdot \bar{q}$ | 10, 5, PC
          11 | $-(p \lor q) \supset \bar{p} \cdot \bar{q}$ | 1-11, CP

8 To derive '$\bar{p} \lor \bar{q}$' from '$-(p \cdot q)$'.

Solution: 1 | $-(p \cdot q)$ | P
             2 | $-(\bar{p} \lor \bar{q})$ | A
             3 | $\bar{p}$ | A
             4 | $\bar{p} \lor \bar{q}$ | 3, add
             5 | $-(\bar{p} \lor \bar{q})$ | 2, R
             6 | $\bar{\bar{p}}$ | 3-5, IP
             7 | p | 6, DNE
             8 | $\bar{q}$ | A

9	$\bar{p} \vee \bar{q}$	8, add
10	$-(\bar{p} \vee \bar{q})$	2, R
11	$\bar{\bar{q}}$	8-10, IP
12	q	11, DNE
13	$p \cdot q$	12, 7, PC
14	$-(p \cdot q)$	1, R
15	$--(\bar{p} \vee \bar{q})$	2-14, IP
16	$\bar{p} \vee \bar{q}$	15, DNE

EXERCISES FOR SEC. 1.6.4

A. Prove these TFS.

1. $-(p \cdot \bar{p})$
2. $(p \supset q) \cdot (p \supset \bar{q}) \supset \bar{p}$
3. $-[(p \cdot q) \cdot (\bar{p} \vee \bar{q})]$
4. $-(\bar{p} \vee \bar{q}) \supset p$
5. $(\bar{p} \supset r) \supset ((\bar{p} \supset \bar{r}) \supset p)$
6. $p \cdot q \supset -(\bar{p} \vee \bar{q})$
7. $p \cdot \bar{q} \supset -(p \supset q)$
8. $(\bar{p} \vee \bar{q}) \supset -(p \cdot q)$
9. $p \supset -(\bar{p} \equiv p)$
10. $-(p \equiv \bar{p})$
11. $-(\bar{p} \vee \bar{q}) \supset p \cdot q$
12. $-(p \cdot \bar{q}) \supset (p \supset q)$
13. $((p \supset q) \vee r) \supset (p \cdot \bar{q} \supset r)$
14. $p \cdot (p \equiv \bar{q}) \supset -(p \equiv q)$
15. $(p \equiv \bar{q}) \equiv -(p \equiv q)$
16. $((\bar{q} \supset p) \supset \bar{q}) \supset \bar{q}$
17. $((q \supset p) \supset q) \supset q$
18. $-(p \supset q) \supset p \cdot \bar{q}$
19. $-(p \supset q) \supset -(\bar{q} \supset \bar{p})$
20. $((p \supset q) \supset q) \supset (\bar{p} \supset q)$
21. $--(p \vee \bar{p})$
22. $((p \supset q) \supset q) \supset --(p \vee q)$
23. $(p \supset q) \supset --(\bar{p} \vee q)$
24. $-(p \cdot \bar{q}) \supset (\bar{p} \vee q)$
25. $(p \supset q) \vee (p \supset \bar{q})$

B. Establish the validity of the following arguments by means of derivations.

1. The Martians will not attack unless they are provoked, but they will be provoked only if we do not pay tribute to them. Hence the Martians will attack only if we do not pay tribute to them.

2. It is not the case that if the war is over, then the stock market goes up. If the war is over, everyone is rejoicing, and the stock market does not go up, then there is good will. Everyone is rejoicing. Hence there is good will.

3. I do not have any money. So if I have money, I am very rich.

4. Unless there is a traffic jam, the bridge is up. If there is a traffic jam, the car will overheat, but it will run out of gas in case the bridge is up. Hence, if the car does not run out of gas, it will overheat.

5. The milk product will be used for cheese or for butter. The milk product will be sold provided that if it is not used for butter then it is used for cheese. Hence the milk product will be sold.

6. If you make a lot of money, you will pay taxes, but if you do not make a lot of money, you will still pay taxes. So you will pay taxes.

7. That sentence is true just in case it is false. Hence that sentence is both true and false, provided that it is false just in case it is not true.

8. Unless Johnson calls, we shall be at the beach if it does not rain. It will not rain, but we shall not be at the beach. Hence Johnson will call.

9. You will take logic or mathematics if you are an undergraduate. However, if you are not an undergraduate, you will study and also take logic. Hence, if you do not take logic, you will take mathematics.

10. The child will be tall and thin only if he is blond and blue-eyed; nonetheless, he will not be tall in case he is blond and blue-eyed. He will be thin. So he will not be tall.

C. Questions about derivations

1. Show that MT is dispensable (if the other rules are retained), that is, that we can always fill the dots of

| $S \supset W$
| $-W$
| .
| .
| .
| $-S$

without using MT. (We shall need to use IP.)

2. Show that we can always complete the dots of

| $S \supset W$
| $W \supset E$
| .
| .
| .
| $S \supset E$

3. Show that MP is dispensable (if the other rules are retained).

4. Show that DNI is dispensable (if the other rules are retained).

5. Show that we can always fill the dots of

| $S \lor W$
| .
| .
| .
| $W \lor S$

PART TWO: ONE-VARIABLE QUANTIFICATION THEORY

2.1 QUANTIFIERS AND ONE-VARIABLE QUANTIFICATIONAL SCHEMATA

Our current techniques for assessing the validity of arguments are limited to those whose validity turns upon the truth-functional structure of their premises and conclusions. However, many intuitively correct deductive arguments go beyond truth-functional logic because their correctness depends upon the *internal* structure of the *simple* statements which they contain. Here are some simple examples of such arguments:

(1) George is a good swimmer. So someone is a good swimmer.

(2) Someone goes to law school. Only A students go to law school. Hence someone is an A student.

(3) All who are bald are shy. Everyone who is shy is smart. Thus everyone who is bald is smart.

(4) Someone is the father of all the children in this room. Thus every child in this room has a father.

Although the correctness of each of these arguments is intuitively clear, none would be counted as valid if tested according to our truth-functional techniques. Argument (2), for example, has the truth-functional form 'p, q $\therefore$ r' (since its premises and conclusion are three distinct simple statements), and thus is not truth-functionally valid.

Because some correct deductive arguments, such as those above, are not truth-functionally valid, additional types of validity and techniques for determining them are necessary. These are furnished in another branch of logic known as *quantification theory*. Quantification theory includes truth-function theory, but it also deals with such logical words as 'all', 'every', 'any', 'some', 'there is', 'there are', 'no', and 'none'. These words can be used to indicate quantity in the sense that they can be used to answer a "how many" question: "How many came to class today?" "Everyone did". "Someone did". "None did". Consequently, logicians have named such words quantifiers. That is how quantification theory obtained its name.

Our study of quantification theory will parallel our study of truth-function theory. First we shall pay some attention to the logical structure of simple statements and introduce new symbols to symbolize quantifiers. Then we shall turn to quantificational schemata, discuss their interpretations, and define the concept of validity for them. Finally, we shall take up proofs and derivations in quantification theory. To make things easier, we shall begin by introducing only two quantifiers. Subsequently, we shall add other quantifiers, and develop out of them a full quantification theory.

2.1.1   SUBJECT-PREDICATE STATEMENTS

Let us first look at the sentences which express the most elementary of simple statements. These sentences are composed of proper names of definite persons, places, times, or things, called the subjects of the sentences, and verbal phrases, called the grammatical predicates of the sentences. Some examples follow:

John is a man.	The President gave a talk.
New York is a city.	Two is even.
George runs.	'$p \lor q$' is valid.
Last year was a leap year.	The rocket soared.

Let us abbreviate these sentences by replacing the subjects of each by a small letter, and the predicates by a capital letter. The small letters which abbreviate the subjects are called *individual constants*, and the capital letters abbreviating the predicates are called *predicate constants*. Our abbreviations are

jM	pT
nC	tE
gR	sV
lL	rS

It will be convenient in our later work for us to write predicate constants first and follow them by individual constants. So let us do it now. This gives us

Mj	Tp
Cn	Et
Rg	Vs
Ll	Sr

2.1.2   VARIABLES

There is nothing very radical about what we have done. The expression '*Cn*', for example, is nothing but an abbreviation of 'New York is a city'. Instead of abbreviating names of months, states, degrees, etc., only, we have abbreviated whole sentences. Yet this very simple step helps us to recognize important logical patterns. We can see, for example, that

Cn   (New York is a city)
Cc   (Chicago is a city)
Ch   (Honolulu is a city)
Cm   (Mexico is a city)

are all related. Each has the same predicate constant and a different individual constant. Thus each of these abbreviated sentences can be obtained from the expression '*Cx*' by replacing the letter '*x*' by an individual constant.

The lowercase letter '*x*' (and later '*u*', '*v*', '*w*', and '*y*') is called a *variable*. While neither an individual constant nor a schematic letter, it is somewhat akin to both; it marks the places in a sentence which may be filled by nouns. In logic and mathematics, variables also fill the role of pronouns. This can be illustrated by rewriting

(1)   For every number x, $x + x = 2x$

without variables. The result is

(2)   The sum of a number with itself equals two times itself

where the role of the variable '*x*' has been taken over by the pronoun 'itself'. Since (1) is much more compact and perspicuous than (2), the advantage of using variables instead of ordinary pronouns in mathematical formulas is obvious. The comparison of variables with pronouns is a useful one, and we shall return to it again.

2.1.3   THE UNIVERSAL QUANTIFIER

That the introduction of variables into mathematics had important consequences for the development of that subject is amply confirmed by the history of mathematics. It is interesting that the introduction of variables also had a very important role in the history of logic. Until the end of the last century our understanding of the logic of the quantifiers was quite limited. Indeed, it was hardly any better than it was in the time of ancient Greece, when Aristotle first investigated quantificational logic. Then, in 1879, the great German logician Gottlob Frege published an epoch-making work in which he formulated the first complete system of quantification theory. The key to his success was simple: he used variables to reformulate sentences of ordinary language. In this way he succeeded in symbolizing the quantifiers, and from there on it was relatively smooth sailing.

We have already applied part of Frege's insight in noting that 'Cn', 'Cc', 'Ch', 'Cm', and 'Cx' are all related. Suppose that we now want to symbolize

(4)   Everything is a city

by using variables. This may be paraphrased as

(5)   Everything is such that it is a city.

This contains a pronoun; so let us replace it by a variable, and also write a variable after 'everything', since this is the antecedent of the pronoun 'it'. In this way we get

(6)   Everything x is such that x is a city.

Now let us replace 'Everything x is such that' by '(x)', and 'is a city' by a predicate constant. This results in

(7) $(x) Cx$

which is merely an abbreviated way of saying that everything is a city. Applying this to our previous examples of abbreviated statements, we obtain

$(x)Mx$	(everything is a man)
$(x)Rx$	(everything runs)
$(x)Lx$	(everything is a leap year)
$(x)Tx$	(everything gave a talk)
$(x)Ex$	(everything is even)
$(x)Vx$	(everything is valid)
$(x)Sx$	(everything soared)

The expression '(x)', which is called a *universal quantifier*, may be read alternatively as

every x	all x
for anything x	for any x
for everything x	for every x
for all things x	for all x
everything x is such that	every x is such that
anything x is such that	any x is such that
all things x are such that	all x are such that
no matter which x	no matter which x you choose

The contexts in which '(x)' occurs determine which reading is the smoothest. Thus '$(x)(x$ is red)' probably reads better as 'Every x is red' than as 'For any x, x is red' or as 'Everything x is such that x is red'.

A statement such as '$(x)(x$ is mortal)', which begins with a universal quantifier governing the whole sentence, is called a *universal quantification*. The part governed by the quantifier is the *scope* of the quantifier. Thus the scope of the universal quantification '$(x)(x$ is mortal)' is simply 'x is mortal'. Like negation, universal quantifiers have the shortest scope that grammar and parentheses allow. For example, the scope of '(x)' in

(8) $(x)(x$ is red) $\lor (1 + 1 = 2)$

is simply 'x is red', whereas in

(9) $(x)[(x$ is red) $\lor (1 + 1 = 2)]$

its scope is the rest of the statement. You should note, by the way, that although (9) is a universal quantification, (8) is a disjunction with a universal quantification as a component.

Every universal quantification has the form

$(x)(\cdots x \cdots)$

where '$\cdots x \cdots$' represents a statement in which a subject term has been replaced by the variable 'x'. The universal quantification '$(x)(\cdots x \cdots)$' is true if and only if '$\cdots x \cdots$' becomes a true statement whenever 'x' is interpreted as naming some actual object. Thus, to take a simple example, '$(x)(x$ is identical with itself)' [or in abbreviated form, '$(x)Ix$'] is true; because since *everything* is identical with itself, 'Ix' will always yield a true statement when 'x' is interpreted as the name of some thing. On the other hand, '$(x)Cx$' is false, since 'Cx' is false when 'x' is interpreted as, say, Hawaii. If a universal quantification, say, '$(x)Ix$', is true, then whenever we drop the universal quantifier '(x)' and replace the occurrences of 'x' in its scope by the name of some actual thing, we must obtain a true statement. For example, since '$(x)Ix$' is true, 'Ia', 'Ib', 'Ic', etc., where 'a', 'b', 'c', etc., are conceived as names of objects, must also be true. On the other hand, if one of these statements were false, the universal quantification '$(x)Ix$' would have to be false too.

In logic, when we say 'all x' or '(x)', we mean everything without exception. In this respect logic differs a little from ordinary language. When a tyrannical king says "Cut off everybody's head", he hardly means that we should cut off everybody's head and make no exceptions. Surely, his head is to be left untouched! What the king means is "Cut off everybody's head except mine and yours". His use of 'everybody' is to be given a noninclusive interpretation; it does not refer to everyone, all inclusively. In logic, however, the quantifiers have an inclusive interpretation, so that if we symbolized a statement such as the king's, we should need to make his implicit exceptions explicit. Although the inclusive interpretation of universal quantification is simply a consequence of our explanation of the universal quantifier, it can be further illustrated by comparing universal quantifications with conjunctions. Suppose, for the sake of illustration, that there were only five things, a, b, c, d, and e. Then, to say that everything is red, that is,

(1) $(x)Rx$

would amount to saying that a is red, b is red, etc., that is,

(2) $Ra \cdot Rb \cdot Rc \cdot Rd \cdot Re$

On this hypothetical world (1) would be true if and only if (2) were. Now (2) is true if and only if all its conjuncts are; one exception makes it false. But the same also holds of (1), and thus we have the parallel between conjunction and universal quantification.

Nonetheless, we cannot dispense with universal quantification and use conjunction in its place. There is first of all a practical difficulty: there are so many things that our conjunctions would be unmanageably long. Next there are two theoretical difficulties. First, just what things there are, is and probably will always remain open to question. Does God exist? Is there life on the other planets? Does the cancer virus exist? Many consider these to be unsolved questions, and at any stage in human history there will be similar open questions. In the present context this is reflected by our uncertainty as to what conjuncts to include when expanding a universal quantification in terms of conjunction. Second, mathematics asserts that there are infinitely many numbers—indeed, so many that there is no way to name them all; so, if quantification theory is to be applicable to mathematics, it is impossible in principle to expand universal quantification in terms of conjunction. And of course we want to be able to use quantification theory in mathematics.

2.1.4   COMPLEX UNIVERSAL QUANTIFICATIONS

So far we have only considered simple-subject—predicate statements and the universal quantifications related to them. Now let us turn to compounds of simple-subject—predicate sentences and the universal quantifications related to these. If 'Cc' abbreviates 'Chicago is a city' and 'Pc' abbreviates 'Chicago is densely populated', then

(1) $Cc \supset Pc$

abbreviates 'If Chicago is a city, then Chicago is densely populated'. By extension, then,

(2) $Cx \supset Px$

abbreviates 'If x is a city, then x is densely populated'; so

(3) $(x)(Cx \supset Px)$

symbolizes

(4)   For everything x, if x is a city, then x is densely populated,

or in other words,

(5)   Everything which is a city is densely populated

or more simply,

(6)   All cities are densely populated.

Statements (3) to (6) are true if and only if, given anything x, if x is a city, then x is densely populated. Thus they are false if there is one city which is not densely populated. For as the parentheses indicate, the scope of '(x)' in (3) is '$Cx \supset Px$'; so for (3) to be true, '$Cx \supset Px$' must be true whenever 'x' is interpreted as naming an actual thing. But '$Cx \supset Px$' will be true if 'x' is interpreted as naming something densely populated — because it will have a true consequent — or as naming something which is not a city — because it will have a false antecedent. Thus the only case in which '$Cx \supset Px$' is false is when 'x' is taken as naming a city which is not densely populated.

This example illustrates an important point about symbolizing by means of the universal quantifier. When we symbolized 'Everything is a city' we wrote '$(x)Cx$'. And in general, we can replace 'everything' by '(x)'. But when it comes to a phrase such as 'all cities', the matter becomes more subtle. We cannot symbolize 'All cities are densely populated' by '$(x)(Cx \cdot Px)$'. This says of everything that it is *both* a city and densely populated. When we assert that all cities are densely populated, we are not asserting that everything is a city, but rather that everything is such that *if* it is a city, *then* it is densely populated. Thus we write '$(x)(Cx \supset Px)$'. Generally,

(7)   Everything is an F

is rendered by

(8) $(x)Fx$

whereas

All F are G;   Each F is a G;   Every F is a G; etc.

are all rendered by

(9) $(x)(Fx \supset Gx)$

The forms (8) and

(10) $(x)(Fx \cdot Gx)$

differ considerably from (9). Both (8) and (10) will be false if even one thing is not an F, whereas this one non-F has no effect on (9). This form is false only if there are F's which are not G. This leads to a surprising consequence. For symbolizing

(11)   All unicorns eat oats

yields

(12) $(x)(Ux \supset Ox)$

which is true if, whenever 'x' is interpreted as naming an actual object, '$Ux \supset Ox$' is true. But since there are no unicorns, 'Ux' must always be false when 'x' is interpreted as naming an *actual* object; so '$Ux \supset Ox$' must always be true, and thus (12) is true. On the other hand, by the same reasoning,

(13)   All unicorns do not eat oats

which is symbolized by

(14) $(x)(Ux \supset -Ox)$

must also be true! Although this is a surprising consequence, it is not a dangerous one; for since there are no unicorns, we cannot use (12) or (14) to show that any particular unicorn does or does not eat oats. Generally, if there are no F, then both '$(x)(Fx \supset Gx)$' and '$(x)(Fx \supset -Gx)$' are true. This traces back to the decision, made some chapters ago, to symbolize conditionals by means of the '$\supset$'. Although this gives rise to a few anomalies, most logicians agree that the simplification gained is well worth the price. Of course, if there were unicorns, (12) or (14), and possibly both, would be false. For there would be either unicorns who ate oats [falsifying (14)] or unicorns who did not eat oats [falsifying (12)].

To say that nothing is red is simply to say that everything is not red. Thus 'Nothing is red' is symbolized as

(15) $(x) - Rx$

As a general rule 'Nothing is F' can be rendered by

(16) $(x) - Fx$

Moreover, to say that nothing red is yellow, or no red things are yellow, is to say that nothing is both red and yellow, that is,

(17) $(x) - (Rx \cdot Yx)$

or equivalently,

(18) $(x)(Rx \supset -Yx)$

[Since '$-(p \cdot q)$' and '$p \supset \bar{q}$' are equivalent, (17) and (18) will also turn out to be equivalent.] Thus, in general, 'No F are G' may be rendered

$(x)-(Fx \cdot Gx)$

or as

$(x)(Fx \supset -Gx)$

Let us summarize the preceding discussion with a table. The general forms in ordinary language are on the left, and their symbolizations are on the right.

Everything is an F.
All are F. $(x)Fx$
Anything is an F.

All F are G.
Everything which is an F is a G.
Any F is a G.
Every F is a G. $(x)(Fx \supset Gx)$
Each F is a G.
All which are F are G.

Nothing is an F.
Everything is not F. $(x) - Fx$
All things are not F.

No F are G. $(x)(Fx \supset -Gx)$
Nothing which is an F is a G.   or
All F are not G. $(x) - (Fx \cdot Gx)$

EXERCISES FOR SECS. 2.1.1 TO 2.1.4

A. Supposing the universe to be limited to a, b, c, and d, expand the quantifications in the following in favor of conjunction.
  1. $(x)Rx$
  2. $(x)Rx \cdot (x)Mx$
  3. $-(x)Rx$
  4. $(x)(Rx \supset Mx)$
  5. $(x) - Rx \lor (x)Rx$
B. Which of the following are true?
  1. $(x)(x = x \lor -(x = x))$
  2. $(x)(x = x) \lor -(x)(x = x)$
  3. $(x)(x = x) \lor (x) - (x = x)$

   4. $(x)(x = x) \cdot (x) - (x = x)$
   5. $(x)(x = 0 \supset x = 1)$
   6. $(x)(x = 0 \supset x + x = x)$
   7. $(x)(x = 0) \supset (x)(x + x = x)$
   8. $(x)(x = x \supset x \supset 0)$
   9. $-(x)(-(x = x) \supset x = 0)$
   10. $(x)(x = 0) \lor (x)(x = 1 \supset -(x = 0))$

C. Symbolize the following, using quantifiers and the suggested individual and predicate constants.

   1. Everything is an apple. (A)
   2. If everything is an apple, John is an apple. (A,j)
   3. Nothing is an apple. (A)
   4. Nothing is both an apple and a pear. (A,P)
   5. If nothing lives, then Adam does not live. (L,a)
   6. All apples are fruits. (A,F)
   7. All pears are fruits and juicy. (P,F,J)
   8. No fish are pears. (F,P)
   9. No pears are fish. (F,P)
   10. No fish which has a caudal fin is an eel. (F,C,E)
   11. If no dogs are fish, then no dogs have gills. (D,F,G)
   12. Every living thing breathes. (L,B)
   13. If each man loves himself, no man kills himself. (L,K)
   14. All who love feel, but not all who feel love. (L,F)
   15. All persons who interrupted will report to the office. (P,I,R)

2.1.5   EXISTENTIAL QUANTIFIERS

The quantifiers 'all' and 'no' are symbolized using '(x)', but this still leaves unsymbolized such quantifiers as 'some' and 'at least one'. To handle these the *existential quantifier* '$(\exists x)$' is introduced. This quantifier may be read alternatively as

for some x for at least one x
some x are such that   at least one x is such that
there are x such that   there are x which
there is at least one x such that   . . . exists

As is evident from its readings, the existential quantifier is used primarily to assert existence. Thus '$(\exists x)(x$ is red$)$', '$(\exists x)(x$ is a city$)$', and '$(\exists x)(x$ is a unicorn$)$' assert the existence, respectively, of something red, cities, and unicorns. A statement which begins with an existential quantifier and which is completely governed by it is called an *existential quantification*. The scope of the quantifier is the rest of the statement it governs; and like the negation sign and the universal quantifier, an existential quantifier always has the shortest scope which parentheses and grammar permit. For example, in

(1) $(\exists x)(x$ is a unicorn$) \supset (x)(x$ is a unicorn$)$

or more briefly, '$(\exists x)Ux \supset (x)Ux$', the scope of '$(\exists x)$' is the first occurrence of 'Ux'. On the other hand, the scope of '$(\exists x)$' extends over the whole of this statement:

(2) $(\exists x)(Ux \supset (x)Ux)$

The first statement asserts that if anything is a unicorn, then everything is. It is a conditional. The second one states that there is something such that, if *it* is a unicorn, then everything is. This is an existential quantification of a conditional.

Every existential quantification has the form

(3) $(\exists x)(\cdots x \cdots)$,

where '$\cdots x \cdots$' is the scope of '$(\exists x)$'. An existential quantification, '$(\exists x)$ $(\cdots x \cdots)$', is true if and only if *there is at least one thing* such that when 'x' is interpreted as naming it, '$\cdots x \cdots$' becomes a true statement. Note that although '$(\exists x)$' can be read as 'There are some x', logic requires only one thing for the corresponding existential quantification to be true. This is a bit divergent from ordinary language, where 'some' frequently means more than one. Thus I should certainly mislead you if I said 'I'll bring some sandwiches for us' and then brought only one. But what I said would be true if I expressed it by '$(\exists x)(x$ is a sandwich and I'll bring x for us)'. On the other hand, '$(\exists x)$' does not exclude the possibility of more than one x; '$(\exists x)(x$ is red)' is true if one, two, or all things are red. [Both the pantheist and the monotheist will admit the truth of '$(\exists x)(x$ is a God)', although both would add that it does not express the whole truth. The atheist, naturally, would not accept even this statement.]

Universal quantification has its truth-functional parallel in conjunction; existential quantification in disjunction. Thus, if there were only five things, a, b, c, d, and e,

(4) $(\exists x)(x$ is red$)$

would be true if and only if

(5) $(a$ is red$) \lor (b$ is red$) \lor (c$ is red$) \lor (d$ is red$) \lor (e$ is red$)$

were true. But (5) is true if at least one of its components is true, and false only if all its components are false. But we cannot dispense with existential quantification in favor of disjunction, for the same reasons that we cannot dispense with universal quantification: practically speaking, our disjunctions would be too long; theoretically speaking, we should not know *how long* to make them, and the needs of mathematics would make any disjunction too short.

2.1.6 COMPLEX EXISTENTIAL QUANTIFICATIONS
Sentences of the form 'Something is an F', 'There are F', or 'F exist' are symbolized by

(1) $(\exists x)Fx$

but these are the simplest existential quantifications. They will not do for 'Some cows jumped over the moon', for example. To say that some cows jumped over the moon is to say that there is something which is a cow and which jumped over the moon, that is,

(2) $(\exists x)(x$ is a cow $\cdot x$ jumped over the moon)

or in abbreviated form, '$(\exists x)(Cx \cdot Jx)$'. In general,

(3)   Some F are G

and its variants — there are F which are G, at least one F is a G, something which is an F is a G, some F do G — are symbolized by

(4) $(\exists x)(Fx \cdot Gx)$

This must be carefully distinguished from

(5) $(\exists x)(Fx \supset Gx)$

The truth of (4) requires that there be at least one thing which is both F and G. Yet (5) will be true if in case there are no F or at least one thing is a G. For if there are no F, 'Fx' will be false whenever 'x' is taken as a name; so it will be false at least once, thus making '$Fx \supset Gx$' true at least once. On the other hand, if there is at least one G, 'Gx' will be true at least once, and so will '$Fx \supset Gx$'. Thus, for example,

(6) $(\exists x)(x$ is a unicorn $\cdot x$ eats oats)

is false because there are no unicorns, while, because of the same fact,

(7) $(\exists x)(x$ is a unicorn $\supset x$ eats oats)

is true.

The sentence

(8)   Something is not evil

is symbolized by

(9) $(\exists x) - Ex$

but

(10) Some kings are not evil

is *not* symbolized by '$(\exists x) - (Kx \cdot Ex)$', but rather by

(11) $(\exists x)(Kx \cdot -Ex)$

In general,

(12) Some F are not G

and its variants are rendered by

(13) $(\exists x)(Fx \cdot -Gx)$

This contrasts with

(14) $(\exists x) - (Fx \cdot Gx)$

which is true if something is either not an F or not a G; and so it is true even if everything is not an F. The truth of (13), however, requires something to be both an F and not a G; and so it requires something to be an F. The sentence 'Something is not both a unicorn and large', which has the form (14), is true because there are no unicorns. But, 'Something is a unicorn and not large', which has the form (13), is false, also because there are no unicorns.

EXERCISES FOR SECS. 2.1.5 AND 2.1.6

A. Supposing the universe to be limited to a, b, c, and d, expand the quantifications in the following in favor of conjunction and disjunction.

1 $(\exists x)Rx$
2. $(\exists x)Rx \cdot (\exists x)Gx$
3. $(\exists x)(Rx \cdot Gx)$
4. $(\exists x)Rx \supset (x)Gx$
5. $(\exists x)(Rx \supset (x)Gx)$
6. $(x)Fx \supset (\exists x)Fx$
7. $-(\exists x) Rx \vee (x) \quad Rx$
8. $(\exists x)(Rx \equiv Gx)$
9. $(\exists x)Rx \equiv (x)Rx$

B. Which of the following are true?

1. $(\exists x)(x = x)$
2. $(\exists x) - (x = x)$
3. $(\exists x)(x = 0)$
4. $(x)(x = 0) \supset (\exists x)(x = 0)$

   5. $-(\exists x)(x = 0) \equiv (x)-(x = 0)$
   6. $(\exists x)(x = 0 \lor x = 1)$
   7. $(\exists x)(x = 0 \cdot x = 1)$
   8. $(\exists x)(x = 0 \cdot x = 1) \supset (x)(x = 0 \cdot x = 1)$
   9. $(\exists x)(x = 0 \cdot (x)(x = 0))$
 10. $-(\exists x)(x = x) \supset (\exists x)(x = x)$

C. Symbolize the following, using the suggested individual and predicate constants and quantifiers.

   1. There are cats. (C)
   2. If Tabby is a cat, then something is a cat. (C,t)
   3. Black cats exist, but purple ones do not. (B,C,P)
   4. Some cats are furry, although there are no scaly cats. (C,F,S)
   5. Some people live in cities. (P,L)
   6. Some people who live in cities are rich. (P,L,R)
   7. If all people who live in cities are rich, then some people do not live in cities. (P,L,R)
   8. Some people do not drive. (P,D)
   9. Some people who do not drive take buses. (P,D,B)
 10. John and some students will be at home. (S,H,j)
 11. If no unicorns exist, then all unicorns wear saddles. (U,S)
 12. No cat is a dog, but some dogs look like pigs. (C,D,L)
 13. If everyone present contributes, then someone present will give \$100. (P,C,G)
 14. Some of those who contributed and gave \$100 were not present. (P,C,G)
 15. Either some people think very hard or no smart people exist. (P,T,S)

2.1.7 FREE AND BOUND VARIABLES

We have already remarked that variables and pronouns are quite similar Let us now pursue some of the parallels between them. Pronouns have antecedents. What acts as an antecedent for a variable? We need only compare 'Something James sent for came today' or 'There is something which James sent for and which came today' with

$(\exists x)$(James sent for $x \cdot x$ came today)

to see that quantifiers are the "antecedents" of variables. But the same pronoun can have one antecedent in one context and another antecedent in a different context. For example, in

The cow who jumped over the moon broke her leg; but the girl who jumped the fence was arrested for it

the first occurrence of 'who' and 'her' refer to the moon-jumping cow, while their second occurrences refer to the fence-jumping girl. Similarly, in

$(\exists x)(x$ came to dinner$) \vee (x)-(x$ came to dinner$)$

the first occurrence of the variable 'x' is linked to '$(\exists x)$', while its second occurrence is linked to '(x)'. These linkages become even more important when the scope of one quantifier falls within the scope of another, as in

$(\exists x)(x$ is a person $\cdot$ (x is loved $\supset (x)(x$ is a person $\supset x$ is loved$)))$

(This means that there is a person such that every person is loved if this one is.) The first two occurrences of the variable 'x' in the last statement have '$(\exists x)$' as their "antecedent", while the last two have '(x)' as theirs. Instead of saying that an occurrence of a variable has a given quantifier as its antecedent in a given context, we shall say that the occurrence of the variable is bound to the occurrence of the quantifier. Precisely, *an occurrence of a variable 'x' in a sentence is bound to an occurrence of a quantifier '(x)'* [or '$(\exists x)$'] in the sentence just in case the given occurrence of 'x' falls within the scope of the occurrence of '(x)' [or '$(\exists x)$'], and not within the scope of a later occurrence of a quantifier.†

EXAMPLES. The arrows indicate the bounds between occurrences of variables and quantifiers.

a. $(x)(Bx \cdot Mx = Cx) \cdot (\exists x)(Mx \cdot (Cx \supset (x)(Mx \supset Cx)))$

b. $(x)((\exists x)(Mx \cdot Bx) \supset (Mx \equiv (x)(Bx \equiv -Cx)))$

An occurrence of a variable which is bound to some occurrence of a quantifier is called a *bound occurrence* of the variable. An occurrence of a variable which is not a bound occurrence is called a *free occurrence* of the variable.

EXAMPLES

a. $Bx \cdot (x)(Bx \supset Mx)$
     free   bound

b. $(\exists x)(Bx \cdot Cx) \supset ((x)Bx \supset (Mx \equiv Cx))$
     bound   bound   free

A sentence which contains no free occurrences of a variable is called a *closed sentence*. A sentence can be closed because it contains no variables at all or because all the variables which it contains have only bound occurrences.

---

†For the purposes of this and the next two definitions, appearances of 'x' in '(x)' or '$(\exists x)$' do not count as occurrences of the variable 'x'.

EXAMPLES OF CLOSED SENTENCES

a.   John drowned the pussy in the well.
b.   If John drowned the pussy in the well, he will be punished.
c. $(\exists x)(x$ drowned the pussy in the well$)$
d.   John drowned the cat $\vee$ $(x)(x$ is a person $\supset -(x$ drowned the cat$))$

A sentence which is not closed is called an *open sentence*. Thus open sentences must contain one or more free occurrences of variables.

EXAMPLES OF OPEN SENTENCES

a. x drowned the cat.
b. x drowned the cat $\supset -($John drowned the cat$)$
c. x killed $x \supset -(x$ will go to heaven$)$
d. $(\exists x)(x$ killed $x) \supset -(x$ will go to heaven$)$

Open sentences can be compared with sentences which contain antecedentless pronouns, for free occurrences of variables are like antecedentless pronouns. For example, if someone asks

Did he pass the course?

and you have no idea of who *he* is, then you cannot answer the question. You would not know what the antecedent of 'he' is, and so you would not know to whom 'he' refers. Again, unless you knew the antecedent for 'he' in

He passed the course

you could not tell whether this is true or false. This is also the case with an open sentence, for example,

x passed the course.

We do not know whether this means that something passed the course, that everything did, or that some particular person, whom 'x' is supposed to name, passed the course. For this reason, *open sentences do not express statements*.

2.1.8   ONE-VARIABLE QUANTIFICATIONAL SCHEMATA

We first directed our attention toward simple-subject – predicate sentences. These have the form 'Fa', where 'F' is a predicate and 'a' is a noun. Then we introduced the simple quantifications related to the sentences. They have the forms '$(x)Fx$' and '$(\exists x)Fx$', where again 'F' is a predicate. This led us to truth-functional compounds of simple-subject – predicate sentences and the quantifications related to them. Here are some examples of these forms:

$(Fa \lor Ga) \supset Hb$

$(x)(Fx \supset Ha \cdot Gx)$

$(\exists x)(Fx \cdot Gx \equiv Ha)$

Here 'F', 'G', and 'H' represent predicates, and 'a' and 'b' represent nouns. Next we considered truth-functional compounds of these sentences and the quantifications related to them. In this way we obtained sentences having forms of the following complexity:

$[Fa \supset (x)(Gx \lor Hx)] \supset (\exists x)Fx$

$(x)[Fx \supset ((\exists x)(Gx \cdot Ha) \equiv (x)Hx)]$

$-(\exists x)Fx \lor (x)[Fx \supset (\exists x)(Gx \cdot Hx)]$

Now it is desirable to have schemata which diagram sentences having all these forms.

The first step in this direction consists in the introduction of *predicate letters*. These letters are similar to statement letters, except that they represent predicates rather than statements. We shall use 'F', 'G', 'H', and 'K' as predicate letters, and to ensure an unending supply of them, we shall also count

'F_1', 'G_1', 'H_1', 'K_1', 'F_2', 'G_2', 'H_2', 'K_2', etc.

as predicate letters. In addition to predicate letters, we also need individual constants to represent nouns; so let us use

'a', 'b', 'c', 'd', 'e', 'a_1', 'b_1', 'c_1', 'd_1', 'e_1', etc.

This also gives us an inexhaustible supply of individual constants. Now we are in a position to build the schemata, which we shall call *one-variable quantificational schemata.*

Since quantification theory is supposed to extend truth-function theory, we shall also classify truth-functional schemata as quantificational schemata. Thus the first rule is

Rule 1   Every TFS is a one-variable quantificational schemata (OVQS).

Next we have

Rule 2   If Φ is a predicate letter and α is the variable 'x' or an individual constant, then $\Phi\alpha$ is a OVQS.†

According to Rule 2, 'Fa', 'Gb', 'Hx', and 'K_2c' are all OVQS.

---

†We shall now begin to use the Greek letters 'Φ', 'Ψ', 'α', and 'β' to talk about expressions. The capital letters 'Φ' and 'Ψ' will ordinarily be used to stand for arbitrary predicate letters, while the lowercase letters 'α' and 'β' will be used to stand for arbitrary individual constants and variables.

The next rule allows us to form truth-functional compounds of OVQS.

Rule 3.   If S and W are OVQS, so are $-S$, $(S \cdot W)$, $(S \vee W)$, $(S \supset W)$, and $(S \equiv W)$.

Finally, a rule for forming quantifications:

Rule 4.   If S is an OVQS, then so are $(x)S$ and $(\exists x)S$.

EXAMPLES.   By Rule 2, 'Gx', 'Gb', and 'Hx' are OVQS. By Rule 1, so are 'p', 'q', and 'r'. Thus, by Rule 3, '$(Fx \vee p)$', '$((Gb \equiv q) \supset Hx)$', and '$(r \cdot -Fx)$' are OVQS. Hence, by Rule 4, '$(x)(Fx \vee p)$', '$(\exists x)((Gb \equiv q) \supset Hx)$', and '$(x)(r \cdot -Fx)$' are also OVQS.

The rules also count such expressions '$(x)p$', '$(x)(\exists x)Fx$', and '$(x)Fa$' as OVQS. These expressions contain occurrences of quantifiers to which no occurrence of a variable is bound. For this reason they are called *vacuous quantifications*. It is technically convenient to count them as OVQS, and they will be treated as equivalent to the OVQS which are produced from them by omitting the vacuous quantifiers. Thus '$(x)p$' and '$(\exists x)p$' will be equivalent to simply 'p'.

The definitions of *bound to*, *free*, and *bound* occurrences of variables and *open* and *closed* schemata exactly parallel the definitions given above for the case of sentences. We shall not bother to state them here.

EXAMPLES

a.   A closed schema. Arrows indicate bindings.

$$(x)((Fx \cdot Ga) \equiv (p \cdot Gx))$$

b.   An open schema. The arrow indicates the binding.

$$((\exists x)Fx \supset Gx)$$
free

The rules for omitting parentheses from TFS will be extended to cover OVQS. However, no new rules will be added.

EXAMPLE

Abbreviated OVQS	*Unabbreviated OVQS*
$(x)(Fx \vee Gx) \cdot (\exists x)Fx \supset Hx$	$(((x)(Fx \vee Gx) \cdot (\exists x)Fx) \supset Hx)$
$(x)(Fx \cdot Gx \vee Hx \vee Kx)$	$(x)(((Fx \cdot Gx) \vee Hx) \vee Kx)$

Although a test procedure for recognizing OVQS will not be stated, there is one, and it closely follows that presented for TFS. Thus *there is a decision procedure for OVQS*.

EXERCISES FOR SECS. 2.1.7 AND 2.1.8

A. Draw arrows to indicate the bonds between the various occurrences of variables and quantifiers in these OVQS.

    1. $(x)Fx \cdot Fa \supset (\exists x)Fx \cdot Gx$

    2. $(x)(Fx \cdot (\exists x)Gx) \vee ((x)Fx \supset Gx)$

    3. $(\exists x)((x)Fx \equiv Gx) \cdot Hx$

    4. $(x)(Fx \equiv Hx \cdot (\exists x)Gx) \cdot Hx$

B. Circle the free occurrences of variables in the examples of (A).

C. Which of the following OVQS are open? Closed?

    1. $(x)(Fx \vee Gx) \cdot (\exists x)Hx$

    2. $(x)(Fx \vee Gx) \cdot Hx$

    3. $(x)(Fx \vee Gx) \cdot Ha$

    4. $(x)(Fx \vee Gx) \cdot p$

D. Which of the following are genuine *unabbreviated* OVQS?

    1. $(x)(Fx \vee Gx) \supset Hx$

    2. $(x)Fa$

    3. $(((x)Hx \cdot (x)Gx) \equiv Hx)$

    4. $(\alpha)S$

    5. $((x)p \vee -p)$

2.2 OVQS AND THEIR INTERPRETATIONS

Because of the presence of quantifiers, predicate letters, and free occurrences of variables, the problem of interpreting OVQS is much more complex than the problem of interpreting TFS. Our approach to the problem will take us through several stages, and it will be some time before we actually arrive at our final definition of an interpretation of an OVQS.

Let us begin by considering the idea that an interpretation of an OVQS is a *statement* which we obtain from the OVQS by replacing

1 Its statement letters (if any) by statements
2 Its predicate letters (if any) by grammatical predicates
3 Its free occurrences of 'x' (if any) and its individual constants by proper names of actual objects

Of course, a statement letter is to be replaced throughout by the same statement, although the same statement may be used to replace two or more statement letters. Similar comments apply to predicate letters, individual constants, and free occurrences of 'x'. It is clear that interpreting an OVQS always produces a true-or-false statement. So we may speak of OVQS as *coming out true* (or false) under a given interpretation, just as we spoke of TFS as coming out true (or false).

EXAMPLES.   Schema: $(x)(Fx \supset Gx) \lor Hx \cdot (\exists x)(Gx \cdot Ha) \cdot p.$

True Interpretations:

a. $(x)(x$ is a cow $\supset x$ is a mammal$) \lor 2$ is odd $\cdot (\exists x)(x$ is a mammal $\cdot 3$ is odd$) \cdot 1 + 1 = 2$

b. $(x)(x$ is a city $\supset x$ is a state$) \lor 6$ is even $\cdot (\exists x)(x$ is a state $\cdot 8$ is even$) \cdot (1 + 3 = 4)$

False Interpretations:

c. $(x)(x$ is a city $\supset x$ is a state$) \lor 7$ is even $\cdot (\exists x)(x$ is a state $\cdot 3$ is even$) \cdot (7 + 7 = 15)$

d. $(x)(x$ is a cow $\supset x$ is a bird$) \lor$ The sun is blue $\cdot (\exists x)(x$ is a bird $\cdot$ The sun is blue$) \cdot (7 + 7 = 14)$

2.2.1   INTRODUCING OPEN SENTENCES

The first problem we must tackle concerns the replacement of predicate letters by grammatical predicates. When the 'F' of 'Fx' is replaced by a grammatical predicate, we obtain an open sentence, which may be read 'x is an F', 'x is F', or '$xF's$'. These natural readings of 'Fx' are available so long as we replace 'F' by grammatical predicates such as 'jumps', 'red', 'rose', and 'whale'. However, it is also desirable to obtain open sentences such as

(1) x gave a wallet to the brother of x's butcher

or its equivalent from 'Fx' by making a suitable replacement for 'F'. Since 'F' must be replaced by a single unbroken phrase, the closest we can get to (1) is something like

(2) x gave a wallet to the brother of the former's butcher.

But at least this seems to mean the same thing as (1), and it *does* allow us to find a phrase which can replace 'F' in 'Fx' and still permit one of the three natural readings 'x is an F', 'x is F', or '$xF's$'. However, as we turn to more complex open sentences, we shall have to go through even more subtle verbal gymnastics in order to find a single unbroken phrase for 'F' to represent. Of course, we can avoid this unpleasant prospect by shunning these sentences altogether, but this would impose unnecessarily serious limitations upon the applications of the techniques we are presently developing. The same techniques which attest to the validity of

Alexander the Great ruled Greece.
Hence $(\exists x)(x$ ruled Greece$)$

also attest to the validity of

A strong wind tore down my oak and then blew itself out.
Hence: $(\exists x)(x$ tore down my oak and then x blew x out)

Thus it would surely be a mistake to exclude applications such as the last just to avoid the unappealing job of rephrasing complex sentences.

Fortunately, we can avoid extensive verbal gymnastics and still retain all the applications of our techniques. The trick to this consists in modifying our approach to the replacement of predicate letters. Instead of replacing predicate letters themselves, we shall replace whole contexts, 'Fx', 'Fa', 'Fb', etc., in one blow. Instead of viewing 'F' as representing a grammatical predicate, we shall view 'Fx' as representing an open sentence and 'Fa' as the closed sentence arising from this open sentence by replacing 'x' by 'a'. Thus, to interpret 'F' in the context 'Fx', we merely replace 'Fx' by an open sentence, and to interpret it in the context 'Fa', we first replace the free occurrences of 'x' by 'a' in this open sentence, and then replace 'Fa' by the resulting closed sentence. (Afterward, we can replace 'x' and 'a' by proper names.)

Let us call the operation whereby 'Fx' is replaced by an open sentence '$\cdots x \cdots$', and 'Fa' by the closed sentence '$\cdots a \cdots$', the introduction of an open sentence at an occurrence of a predicate letter. More precisely, an open sentence '$\cdots x \cdots$' is *introduced at an occurrence of a predicate letter* Φ *in an* OVQS S by

1 Replacing Φx by '$\cdots x \cdots$' if the occurrence of Φ in question has 'x' attached to it; or by
2 Replacing $\Phi\alpha$ by '$\cdots \alpha \cdots$' if the occurrence of Φ has an individual constant α attached to it, where α has replaced all free occurrences of 'x' in '$\cdots x \cdots$'.

EXAMPLES

	Schemata	Open sentences	Results
a.	$(x)Fx \lor Fa$	$F : x$ loves x	$(x)(x$ loves $x) \lor (a$ loves $a)$
b.	Fa	$F : (\exists x)(x$ loves $a)$ $\lor (x$ loves $x)$	$(\exists x)(x$ loves $a) \lor a$ loves a
c.	$(\exists x)(Fb \supset Gx)$	$F : x^x = 0$ $G : x + x = 1$	$(\exists x)(b^b = 0 \supset x + x = 1)$
d.	$(\exists x)Hx \supset Ha$	$H : x \cdot a = 1$	$(\exists x)(x \cdot a = 1) \supset (a \cdot a = 1)$
e.	$(\exists x)Fx \cdot Fa$	$F : (x)(x = x) \equiv (x = x)$	$(\exists x)[(x)(x = x) \equiv (x = x)]$ $\cdot [(x)(x = x) \equiv (a = a)]$

Now we can give another characterization of the interpretation of an

OVQS. (We still have a way to go before we arrive at our final characterization.) We shall now interpret predicate letters by introducing open sentences at their occurrences. Thus, *at least at this stage of the game*, an interpretation of an OVQS is a statement [or, strictly speaking, a quasi-statement due to (1) below] which is produced from the schema by replacing

1   Its statement letters (if any) by 'T' or 'F'
2   Its individual constants and free occurrences of 'x' (if any) by proper names of actual objects
3   Its predicate letters (if any) by the results of introducing open sentences at their occurrences

[We may always think of 'T' as representing some true statement, say, '$(x)(x = x)$', and 'F' some false one, say, '$-(x)(x = x)$'. Since statement letters appear only in truth-functional contexts — even in OVQS — the true or false statement selected is immaterial to the truth-value which the OVQS received upon interpretation.]

Both open and closed schemata become true or false (quasi-) statements upon interpretation. The open ones do so because free occurrences of 'x' are replaced by proper names. These proper names and the ones which replace individual constants are names of actual objects. This requirement is imposed so that an OVQS can never be interpreted as a statement about fictional entities such as Santa Claus or Zeus — statements which some philosophers and logicians do not think have truth-values. Here are some examples of schemata and their interpretations.

EXAMPLES

	Schemata	*Assignments*	*Results*	*Truth-value*
a.	$(x)Fx \supset p$	$F : x = x$	$(x)(x = x) \supset T$	T
		$p : T$		
b.	$(x)(Fx \cdot Fa) \supset p$	$F : x = x$	$(x)(x = x \cdot 0 = 0) \supset F$	F
		$p : F$		
		$a : 0$		
c.	$(\exists x)(Fx \supset Gx)$	$F : x$ is a person	$(\exists x)(x$ is a person $\supset x$	
	$\lor p \cdot Gx$	$G : x$ is a goat	is a goat$) \lor T \cdot$ Big	
		$p : T$	Ben is a goat	T
		$x :$ Big Ben		

Comment: The right disjunct is false, but the left one is true. For at least one thing is a goat; so 'x is a person $\supset x$ is a goat' is true of it by virtue of a true consequent.

d.	$(\exists x)(Fx \lor -Fx)$	$F : x + 3 = 10$	$(\exists x)(x + 3 = 10 \lor$	T
			$-(x + 3 = 10))$	

Comment: There is at least one thing a; so no matter how 'F' is interpreted, 'Fa' or '$-Fa$' will be true; so this schema will be true for all interpretations of 'F'.

e. $(\exists x)(Fx \cdot -Fx)$ $F : x = x$ $(\exists x)(x = x \cdot -(x = x))$
    $\cdot Ga \supset (p \lor \bar{p})$ $G : x = 0$ $\cdot 1 = 0 \supset (T \lor - T)$ T
    $a : 1$
    $p : T$

Comment: This schema will always come out true, since its consequent is a valid TFS. Notice also that its antecedent will always be false: nothing is both F and not F.

EXERCISES FOR SEC. 2.2.1

A. 1. Introduce the open sentence 'x loves x' at the occurrences of 'F' in these OVQS.
    a. Fa
    b. $Fa \cdot Fb$
    c. $Fx \cdot Fa$
    d. $Fa \cdot (x)Fx$
    e. $(x)(Fx \supset Fx \cdot Fa)$

    2. Introduce the open sentence '$(x)(x$ loves $x) \supset x$ loves x' at the same occurrences of 'F'.

B. 1. Find an open sentence which, when introduced, at the occurrence of 'F' in
    $(x)Fx \supset (\exists x)Fx$
    will yield
    $(x)(x$ loves Adam $\cdot (\exists x)(x$ loves Adam)$) \supset (\exists x)(x$ loves Adam $\cdot (\exists x)(x$ loves Adam)$)$

    2. Find an open sentence which, when introduced at the occurrences of 'F' in
    $(\exists x)(Fx \supset (x)Fx) \lor Fx$
    will yield
    $(\exists x)((x$ harms x's neighbor) $\supset (x)(x$ harms x's neighbor)$) \lor (x$ harms x's neighbor)

2.2.2 UNIVERSES OF DISCOURSES

Our journey has only begun. The next examples will show that a radical change must be made to our approach to the interpretations of OVQS. Consider the schema

(1) $(\exists x)Fx \cdot (\exists x) - Fx$

In order for this schema to have *at least one* true interpretation, at least two things must exist. For if nothing existed, '$(\exists x)Fx$' would be false no matter how interpreted; while if only one thing existed, for all interpretations of

'F', either '$(\exists x)Fx$' or '$(\exists x) - Fx$' would have to be false, since this one thing could not be both F and not F. So if less than two things existed, (1) would be false for all interpretations. Thus its negation

(2) $-((\exists x)Fx \cdot (\exists x) - Fx)$

would be true for all interpretations.

  Next consider the schema

(3) $(\exists x)(Fx \cdot Gx) \cdot (\exists x)(-Fx \cdot Gx) \cdot (\exists x)(Fx \cdot -Gx)$

For this to have at least one true interpretation, there must be at least three things: one to be both an F and a G, another to be a G but not an F, and another to be an F but not a G. If nothing existed, all (3)'s conjuncts would come out false no matter how 'F' were interpreted. If only one thing existed, one conjunct might come out true for a given interpretation, but the others would have to come out false for the same interpretation. Finally, if only two things existed, at most two of the conjuncts could come out true for a given interpretation. Since (2) would be false for all interpretations if less than three things existed, its negation

(4) $-[(\exists x)(Fx \cdot Gx) \cdot (\exists x)(Fx - Gx) \cdot (\exists x)(Fx \cdot -Gx)]$

would come out true for all interpretations under the same condition.

  Let us take a bolder step and consider three predicate letters, 'F', 'G', and 'H'. By means of these we can build the following 2^3, that is, 8 conjunctions:

$Fx \cdot Gx \cdot Hx$, $Fx \cdot Gx \cdot -Hx$, $Fx \cdot -Gx \cdot Hx$, $Fx \cdot -Gx \cdot -Hx$,
$-Fx \cdot Gx \cdot Hx$, $-Fx \cdot Gx \cdot -Hx$, $-Fx \cdot -Gx \cdot Hx$, $-Fx \cdot -Gx \cdot -Hx$

Notice that, for a given assignment to 'x', 'F', 'G', and 'H', one and only one of these conjuncts can come out true. Next suppose that there are only 7 things. Then if we fix the interpretations of 'F', 'G', and 'H' and assign a different one of these things to each occurrence of 'x' in the conjunctions (repeating once), at least one of the conjunctions will come out false. Thus, if there were only 7 things, then for every interpretation of 'F', 'G', and 'H', at least one of the 8 existential quantifications of these 8 conjunctions would come out false. Thus, under the same condition,

(5) $-[(\exists x)(Fx \cdot Gx \cdot Hx) \cdot (\exists x)(Fx \cdot Gx \cdot -Hx) \cdot (\exists x)(Fx \cdot -Gx \cdot Hx) \cdot$
    $(\exists x)(Fx \cdot -Gx \cdot -Hx) \cdot (\exists x)(-Fx \cdot Gx \cdot Hx) \cdot (\exists x)(-Fx \cdot Gx \cdot -Hx) \cdot$
    $(\exists x)(-Fx \cdot -Gx \cdot Hx) \cdot (\exists x)(-Fx \cdot -Gx \cdot -Hx)]$

would come out true for all interpretations. To find a schema which would be true for all interpretations if there existed, say, only 5 things, we need only take the negation of the conjunction of the first 6 of the conjoined existential quantifications.

These considerations can be made quite general. Given n predicate letters, we can build 2^n conjunctions such as those formed above. Then we can form the existential quantifications of all these conjunctions, conjoin these, and negate the result. This yields a schema similar in form to (5), which would be true for all interpretations if there were less than 2^n things. By existentially quantifying, conjoining, and negating only the first m of the 2^n conjunctions, we can also find a schema which would be true for all interpretations provided that there were less than m things. Thus there is a mechanical procedure for constructing schemata which will be true for all interpretations if less than n things exist, for any finite number n.

The point of all this is: Suppose that there are only a finite number of things, say, $10^{1,000,000}$; then there are certain schemata, determined by the above procedure, which are true for all interpretations. Now suppose that some new things are created tomorrow — a new galaxy comes into existence or a baby is born — then the very same schemata would cease to be true for all interpretations and be false for one or more interpretations. Hence, if we define 'valid' as 'true for all interpretations', then, *according to our present notion of interpretation*, the number of things which exist might be an important factor in determining which schemata are valid and which are not. This would be a serious impediment to logic. First, there might be no objective way to settle disputes as to how many things exist, and so the objectivity of logic itself would be threatened. Second, logic is one of the chief tools we have for investigating reality, and it would be a grave mistake to fashion it in such a way that minor changes in the very object of our investigation — reality — could significantly alter our methods for investigating it. Since logic is one of our tools for determining what exists, it must be made independently of any assumptions concerning what exists or the number of existing things.

This defect in our notion of interpretation can be corrected by introducing the notion of a *universe of discourse* and then redefining the notion of interpretation so that a schema is not interpreted without qualification but is *interpreted in a universe of discourse*. Naturally, we must discuss universes of discourse first.

The term 'universe of discourse' is used by logicians to refer to the class of things which happen to be the present subject of discussion. Thus, if the subject under discussion is people, the universe of discourse is the class of people. If the topic of discussion is planets, the universe of discourse is the class of planets, and if the topic is numbers and cows, the universe of discourse is the class of numbers and cows. Since any class of things can be a subject for discussion, any class of things can be a universe of discourse. Because things which ordinarily would be taken to be rather unrelated can be discussed at one and the same time, universes of discourse can even be classes of very unrelated things. For example, we can have universes of discourse consisting of cows and crows, people and numbers, electrons and neuroses, or U.S. Presidents, university students, and Hawaiian beaches. Since there are universes of discourses containing numbers, there are universes of discourses which contain infinitely many members. This will prevent the problem which arose in connection with our previous notion of interpretation from arising in connection with the notion of an interpretation in a universe of discourse.

For our technical convenience we shall introduce two restrictions on universes of discourses:

1   They must have at least one member.
2   Their members must be actual things.

There are ways to treat the notion of interpretation in connection with universes of discourses which are empty or which contain fictitious entities — such as Santa Claus or Pegasus — but they are too complicated for an elementary text. In order to retain infinite universes of discourses, we shall count numbers as actual things, and so some actual things do not have spatial or temporal locations.

One further advantage of using universes of discourses has to do with showing invalidity. It is often much easier to show that a schema has a false interpretation in some well-defined universe of discourse than it would be to show that it has a false interpretation in the actual universe. For the limits of the latter are still unknown and will probably always remain so.

2.2.3 TRUTH IN A UNIVERSE OF DISCOURSE

As laymen, we frequently restrict ourselves to a particular universe of discourse for the purpose of more conveniently expressing quantifications and determining their truth-values. We are much more likely to say, for example,

(1)   Someone ate my porridge

than

(2)   Something is a person and ate my porridge.

Moreover, we usually assent to the truth of (1) as soon as we verify that somebody, say, Goldilocks, did eat our porridge. That Goldilocks is a person goes without saying; for our implicit assumption is that (for the present moment) we are talking about people only; so the names we use refer exclusively to persons. On the other hand, to establish (2) we should be more explicit: we should verify that some particular entity, say, Goldilocks, is a person and also ate our porridge.

The same idea can be applied to '(x)' and '$(\exists x)$'. If our universe of discourse is the class of persons, than we can simply construe '(x)' as 'for every person x' and '$(\exists x)$' as 'There is a person x'. *Under this condition*

(3) $(x)(x$ is a mammal)

(4) $-(\exists x)(x$ is 1,000 years old)

both express truths. It is important to realize that (3) and (4) express truths only because the universe of discourse is restricted to persons; for (3) and (4) would both be false if we extended the universe of discourse to also include, say, giant redwoods. Then '(x)' and '$(\exists x)$' would be construed as 'for all persons and redwoods x' and 'There is at least one person or redwood x', respectively. The same technique can be extended to other universes of discourse, say, the class of nonnegative integers. When the universe of discourse is taken as this class,

(5) $(x)(x + x \geq x)$

(6) $-(\exists x)(1 + x = 0)$

(7) $(\exists x)(x + x = x \supset x = 0)$

are all true. But if we extend this universe to include the negative integers, (6) becomes false because $1 + (-1) = 0$.

Instead of saying that a statement becomes true when the universe of discourse is taken as a given class, let us say that *the statement is true in the given universe of discourse*. Also let us use the shorter term 'universe' in place of 'universe of discourse'. When our attention is restricted to a particular universe U, '(x)' comes to mean 'for all x in U' and '$(\exists x)$' comes to mean 'for some x in U'. Thus a universal quantification

$(x)(\cdots x \cdots)$

is true in a universe U if and only if for every choice of x in U, $(\cdots x \cdots)$ is true. Likewise

$(\exists x)(\cdots x \cdots)$

is true in U if and only if there is an x in U such that $(\cdots x \cdots)$. A statement which does not contain quantifiers will count as true in a universe if and only if it is true without qualification. Since all the statements we shall treat are composed of quantifications and nonquantifications by means of truth-functions and quantifiers, we now have a basis for determining whether they are true in a given universe.

EXAMPLE.   Let U be the class consisting of the numbers 1 and 2, that is $U = \{1,2\}$.† Then

$(x)(x = 1 \lor x = 2)$
$(\exists x)(x + x = x) \supset (x)(x + x = x)$
$(1.1 = 1 \cdot 1.2 = 2) \supset (x)(1.x = x)$

are all true in U, while

$(\exists x)(x = 3)$
$(x)(x = 1 \lor x = 2) \supset (x)(x + 1 = 2)$
$(\exists x)(x + 1 = 2 \cdot x + 2 = 1)$

are all false in U.

EXERCISES FOR SECS. 2.2.2 AND 2.2.3

A.   Which of the following are true in the universe of humans? Of positive whole numbers?

1. $(\exists x)(x$ has arms$)$
2. $(x)(x > 0)$
3. $(x)(x$ eats $\supset x$ has a digestive system$)$
4. $(x)(x + x < 3 \supset x = 1)$
5. $(\exists x)(x$ is a man$) \cdot ((x)(x$ is a number$) \supset (\exists x)(x$ is a number$))$

B.   For each of the following specify a universe in which it is true. Also specify one in which it is false.

1. $(x)(x + 0 = x)$
2. $(\exists x)(x$ is a general$)$
3. $(x)(x = 0)$
4. $(\exists x)(x > 0) \supset (x)(x > 0)$
5. $(x)(x$ is a man $\supset x$ is bald$)$

C.   Suppose that U_1 and U_2 are two universes and that A is a statement which is true in both. Further, suppose that there is a universe U_3 which contains everything that belongs to both U_1 and U_2. Need A be true in U_3?

Hint: Consider the statement
$((\exists x)(x$ is a king$) \lor (\exists x)(x$ is a president$)) \cdot (\exists x)(x$ is a human$)$

---

†Mathematicians use the expression '$\{a,b,c, \cdots,f\}$' to denote a class consisting of a finite number of objects $a,b,c, \cdots,f$, and we shall adopt this notation too.

2.2.4 INTERPRETATIONS IN UNIVERSES OF DISCOURSES

We can now repair our concept of interpretation by introducing the concept of an interpretation in a universe of discourse. The main difference between this and our previous conception of interpretation is that we now replace individual constants and free occurrences of 'x' by proper names of objects which belong to the universe in which the schema is interpreted. Since replacing an individual constant or a free occurrence of 'x' by the proper name of an object amounts to assigning that object to the individual constant or the free occurrences of 'x', we may characterize our concept of interpretation as follows:

An interpretation of a schema S in a universe U is an assignment of

1 Truth-values to the statement letters (if any) of S
2 Open sentences to the predicate letter (if any) of S
3 Objects in U to the individual constants (if any) of S
4 An object in U to the free occurrences of 'x' (if any) in S

EXAMPLES

a. *Schema:* $(x)Fx \equiv Ga \cdot Fx$
    Universe: positive integers
    Assignments: $x : 0,$ $F : x + x = x$
                     $a : 1,$ $G : x - x - 0$
    Result of interpretation: $(x)(x + x = x) \equiv 1 - 1 = 0 \cdot 0 + 0 = 0$

b. *Schema:* $(x)(Fx \supset p) \equiv (\exists x) Fx \supset p$
    Universe: mankind
    Assignments: $p : T$ $F : x$ is a woman
    Result of interpretation: $(x)(x$ is a woman $\supset T) \equiv (\exists x)(x$ is a woman $\supset T)$

Interpreting a schema in a universe U produces a true or false statement. However, it is important to observe that the truth-value of this statement may not agree with its truth-value *in U*; that is, the statement might be true but not true in U, or false but not false in U. For example, suppose that '$(x)Fx$' and '$(\exists x)Gx$' are interpreted in the universe of positive integers by assigning 'x is greater than 0' to 'F' and 'x is less than 0' to 'G'. Then the statements produced are

(1) $(x)(x$ is greater than 0)

(2) $(\exists x)(x$ is less than 0)

The first is true in U, but not true without qualification; for every positive integer is greater than 0, but -6 is not. On the other hand, the second statement is false in U, but not false without qualification. (Why?)

Previously, we called a schema true for a given interpretation if and only if it came out true (without qualification) for the interpretation. Now, however, we shall introduce the concept *true for an interpretation in a universe U*. A schema S is true for an interpretation I in a universe U if and only if (a) I is an *interpretation of S in U* and (b) I interprets S as *true in U*. According to this definition, (1) above is true in the universe of positive integers when 'F' is assigned 'x is greater than 0', while (2) is false in the same universe when 'G' is assigned 'x is less than 0'.

TFS are interpreted in a given universe by assigning truth-values to their statement letters. For every universe there is at least one statement which is true in it, namely, '$(x)(x = x)$', and so there is also at least one statement which is false in it, namely, '$-(x)(x = x)$'. We know that it makes no difference which statement is assigned to a statement letter; only the truth-value of this statement has any effect on the truth-value of the whole schema under the given interpretation. Indeed, whenever we assign T to a statement letter, we can think of ourselves as replacing the letter by '$(x)(x = x)$'; for this is true in every universe. Likewise, whenever we assign F to a statement letter, we can imagine that we are replacing it by '$-(x)(x = x)$'. Thus a TFS which is true for a given interpretation in a given universe will be true for the same interpretation in any other universe. Consequently, a TFS is true for an interpretation in a universe U if and only if it comes out true without qualification for the interpretation.

This invariance under changes of universe carries over to certain other schemata which contain statement letters. For example,

(3) $(x)Fx \supset p$

will become true in any universe when 'p' is assigned T, because whether '$(x)Fx$' becomes true or false in the universe, (3) will become true by virtue of a true consequent. Similarly,

(4) $p \supset (\exists x)Fx$

will become true in any universe when 'p' is interpreted as F. Moreover,

(5) $(x)Fx \supset (p \lor \bar{p})$

(6) $p \cdot p \supset (\exists x)Fx$

come out true for all interpretations in every universe. Nonetheless, even if a schema contains statement letters, the assignments to its other letters may be an important factor in determining whether it comes out true in one universe and false in another. The schema

(7) $(\exists x)Fx \supset p$

for example, is true in the universe of infants when 'p' is assigned F and 'F' is assigned 'x can run a mile'; but for the same assignments to 'F' and 'p', it is false in the universe of antelopes.

EXAMPLES

Schemata:
a. $(Ha \lor p) \supset (x)Hx$
b. $(\exists x)Hx \supset (x)Hx$

Interpretations:
A. $U = \{1,2,3\}$ $p : T,$ $H : x$ is even, $a : 2$
B. $U - \{1/4\}$ $p : F,$ $H : 2x = 1/2,$ $a : 1/4$
C. $U =$ The class of U.S. Presidents
     $H : x$ was elected for more than one term
     $a :$ Roosevelt

Truth-value in U:
a for A: False. 1 and 3 are not even; so '$(x)(x$ is even)' is false in $\{1,2,3\}$, but '2 is even $\lor T$' is true in $\{1,2,3\}$.

a for B: True. If $x = 1/4$, then $2x = 1/2$; so '$(x)(2x = 1/2)$' is true in this U; moreover, '2.1/4 = 1/2 $\lor$ F' is also true in U.

a for C: False. Not every U.S. President was elected for more than one term; so '$(x)(x$ was elected for more than one term)' is false in U, but the other component is true in U.

b for A: False. '$(\exists x)(x$ is even)' is T in U, but '$(x)(x$ is even)' is false in U.

b for B: True. Both antecedent and consequent are true in U since $2.1/4 = 1/2$.

b for C: False. Some U.S. Presidents were elected for more than one term, but not all of them were.

EXERCISES FOR SEC. 2.2.4
A.   Do the following come out true or false for the interpretations in the indicated universes?

   1. *Schema:* $(x)Fx \lor p$ *Universe:* mankind
       Assignments: $p : T,$ $F : x$ is a woman

   2. *Schema:* $(\exists x)(Fx \cdot ((x)Gx \lor Ga))$ *Universe:* class of positive whole numbers
       Assignments: $a : 25,$ $F : x = 5 + 5,$ $G : x = 20 + 6$

   3. *Schema:* $p \supset (x)(Fx \equiv Ga)$ *Universe:* class of positive whole numbers
       Assignments: $p : T,$ $F : x > 0,$ $G : x > 2,$ $a : 3$

4. *Schema:* $p \lor (x)(Fx \lor Gx)$ *Universe:* mankind
   Assignments: $p : F$, $F : x$ is a student, $G : x$ is a teacher
5. *Schema:* $-(x)Fx \supset -(\exists x)Fx$ *Universe:* $\{1\}$
   Assignment: $F : x = 1$
6. *Schema:* $(x)(Fx \lor Gx)$ *Universe:* $\{1,2\}$
   Assignments: $F : x = 1$, $G : x = 2$
7. *Schema:* $(x)(p \supset Fx) \cdot Ga$ *Universe:* $\{1,2,3\}$
   Assignments: $p : T$, $a : 2$, $F : x = x$, $G : 1 + 1 = x$
8. *Schema:* $p \cdot (\exists x)(Fx \supset Fx)$ *Universe:* $\{1\}$
   Assignments: $p : T$, $F : x = 2$

B. For each of the following OVQS, specify a universe and a true interpretation of it in that universe. Also specify a universe and a false interpretation.

1. $(x)Fx$
2. $(\exists x)Fx \cdot p \supset (x)Fx \cdot p$
3. $(Fa \lor Ga) \cdot (x)Hx$
4. $(x)Fx \equiv (x)Gx$
5. $((\exists x)Fx \lor (\exists x)(Fx \cdot Gx)) \equiv Ga$
6. $(x)(Fx \supset Gx) \cdot Ga$
7. $-(\exists x)Fx \lor (x)Fx$
8. $-[(\exists x)Fx \cdot (\exists x) - Fx]$

2.2.5 VALIDITY

When a schema is true for all interpretations in a universe U, we shall say that it is *valid in U*. If a schema has at least one true interpretation, a universe U, then we shall say that it is *consistent in U*. It follows that every schema which is valid in a universe U is also consistent in it. But the converse does not hold: '$(\exists x)Fx$' is consistent in the universe of positive integers (assign 'x is even' to 'F'), but not valid in it (assign 'x is negative' to 'F').

Of course, a schema which is valid in one universe need not be valid in another one. For example, the schema

$$(\exists x)Fx \supset (x)Fx$$

is valid in every universe which has exactly one member but not valid in any larger universe. To see that the first half of this claim is true, notice that, in any universe with exactly one member, this member is an F only if every member is an F (since there are no other members). To see that the other half is true, let U be any universe with two or more members. Then let a and b represent two distinct members of U and assign 'x is a' to 'F'. Then '$(\exists x)(x$ is $a)$' is true in U, but '$(x)(x$ is $a)$' is not.

In the last section we observed that a TFS which comes out true in a given universe for a given assignment to its statement letters comes out true in every other universe for the same assignment. Thus a TFS which is valid in one universe is valid in every universe. Consequently, a TFS which is truth-functionally valid is valid in every universe. There are also other schemata besides truth-functionally valid TFS which are valid in every universe. These are the schemata which we shall call *quantificationally valid*. Or, stated in other words:

A schema is quantificationally valid if and only if it is valid in every universe, that is, true for every interpretation in every universe.

We shall also say that a schema is *quantificationally consistent* just in case it is consistent in some universe. Since a TFS which is consistent in one universe is consistent in every universe, a TFS which is truth-functionally consistent is also quantificationally consistent. Thus, as far as TFS are concerned, there is no difference between truth-functional validity and consistency and quantificational validity and consistency. For this reason we shall henceforth use the terms 'valid' and 'consistent' to mean 'quantificationally valid' and 'quantificationally consistent', respectively.

The relationships between validity and consistency which we observed earlier in truth-function theory continue to obtain. These will be stated again now:

1 S is valid if and only if $-S$ is inconsistent.
2 S is consistent if and only if $-S$ is invalid.
3 If S is valid, then S is consistent.
4 If S is inconsistent, then S is invalid.

The first of these relationships will be established here; the others are left as exercises. [Note that (3) and (4) are equivalent by taking 'inconsistent' and 'invalid' as 'not consistent' and 'not valid', for '$p \supset q$' is equivalent to '$\bar{q} \supset \bar{p}$'.] Suppose, first, that S is a valid schema. Then it is true for all interpretations in all universes. So $-S$ must be false for all interpretations in all universes; hence S is inconsistent. Conversely, if $-S$ is inconsistent, it is false for all interpretations in all universes; so S is true for the same interpretations and is therefore valid.

EXAMPLE 1.   Valid schemata and informal proofs of their validity

a. $(x)Fx \cdot (x)Gx \supset (x)(Fx \cdot Gx)$

Proof: Suppose U is a universe. If 'F' and 'G' are interpreted so that either '$(x)Fx$' or '$(x)Gx$' is false in U, then (a) is true in U. Thus suppose (the only other case) that 'F' and 'G' are interpreted so that '$(x)Fx \cdot (x)Gx$' is true in U. Then everything in U is both F and G. Thus '$(x)(Fx \cdot Gx)$' is true in U. Thus (a) is true for all interpretations in U. Since U is an arbitrary universe, (a) is valid.

b. $(x)(Fx \supset p) \equiv ((\exists x)Fx \supset p)$

Proof: Let U be a universe. Suppose 'p' is assigned T. Then '$Fx \supset p$' is true of all x in U; so '$(x)(Fx \supset p)$' is true in U. Likewise, '$(\exists x)Fx \supset p$' is true in U. Note both components become true regardless of the interpretation give to 'F'. Next suppose that 'p' is assigned 'F'. Then '$(\exists x)Fx \supset p$' is false in U if and only if 'F' is interpreted so that something in U is an F. By the same token '$(x)(Fx \supset p)$' is false in U if and only if something in U is an F (for taking 'x' as a name of it would make '$Fx \supset p$' false). Thus, if 'F' is interpreted so that something is an F, both sides of the biconditional (b) are false in U; so it is true in U. On the other hand, if 'F' is interpreted otherwise, both sides are true in U and (b) is again true in U. Hence (b) is true in U for every interpretation of 'p' and 'F'. Since U is arbitrary, (b) is valid.

Comment on this proof: In this and in the last proof, the method of proof by cases has been used. Thus the arguments essentially follow the structure of *simple dilemma*. In this proof the second case had two subcases. The argument ran as follows. Case I: 'p' is true. Then (b) is true in U no matter how 'F' is interpreted. Case II: 'p' is false. Subcase 1: 'F' is interpreted so that something in U is an F. Then (b) is true in U. Subcase 2: 'F' is otherwise; then (b) is true in U. For a proof by cases to be *sound* the cases and subcases considered must *exhaust* all the cases and subcases. Where there are two exhaustive cases, for example, the argument has the form '$p \vee \bar{p}$, $p \supset q, p \supset q \therefore q$', which is valid and sound (if our arguments for '$p \supset q$' and '$\bar{p} \supset q$' are sound). If there are really three cases but we recognize only two, then the argument takes the form '$p \vee q, p \supset r, q \supset r \therefore r$'. To be sure, this argument is valid, but even if '$p \supset r$' and '$q \supset r$' are true, the argument fails to be sound: '$p \vee q$' is false since it does not exhaust the possibilities. To obtain a sound argument in this example, we need one of the form '$p \vee q \vee s$, $p \supset r, s \supset r \therefore r$'.

c. $(\exists x)[(x)Fx \supset Fx]$

Proof: Suppose that U is any universe. If 'F' is interpreted so that '$(x)Fx$' is false in U, then '$(x)Fx \supset Fx$' is true in U for every x in U. Since there is an x in U, (c) is true in U. If 'F' is interpreted otherwise, '$(x)Fx$' is true in U. Thus everything in U is an F. But since there is something which belongs to U, '$(x)Fx \supset Fx$' is true of it. So (c) is true in U. Thus (c) is true in U for all interpretations, and is valid.

EXAMPLE 2.   Consistent but invalid schemata

d. $(\exists x)(Fx \cdot Ga)$

Let $U = \{1,2\}$, and interpret 'F' as '$x = 2$', 'G' as '$x + 1 = 2$', and 'a' as 1. Then, since $1 + 1 = 2$ and $2 = 2$, there is an x in U such that $x = 2.1 + 1 = 2$; so (d) is true in U. Thus there is a universe U and interpretation of (d) such that (d) is true in U. Hence (d) is consistent.

e. $(\exists x)(Fx \cdot Gx) \cdot (\exists x)(Fx \cdot -Gx) \cdot (\exists x)(-Fx \cdot Gx)$

Let $U = \{1,2,3\}$. Assign '$x = 1 \vee x = 2$' to 'F' and '$x = 2 \vee x = 3$' to 'G'. Then, since

$(1 = 1 \vee 1 = 2) \cdot (1 = 1 \vee 1 = 3),\qquad (2 = 1 \vee 2 = 2) \cdot -(2 = 1 \vee 2 = 3),$
$-(3 = 1 \vee 3 = 2) \cdot (3 = 1 \vee 3 = 3)$

are true, (e) becomes true in U. So (e) is consistent.
[*Exercise:* Furnish false interpretations in some U of (d) and (e).]

EXAMPLE 3.   Inconsistent schemata. The negations of (a), (b), and (c) furnish examples. (Why?)

EXERCISES FOR SEC. 2.2.5

A. Which of the following schemata are invalid? Provide a false interpretation for those that are.
1. $(x)Fx \supset Fa$
2. $p \cdot (x)Fx$
3. $(x)(Fx \vee -Fx)$
4. $Fa \supset (\exists x)Fx$
5. $(\exists x)Fx \cdot (\exists x)Gx \supset (\exists x)(Fx \cdot Gx)$
6. $(\exists x)(Fx \cdot -Fx)$
7. $p \vee \bar{p} \vee (x)Fx$
8. $(x)(Fx \supset Fx)$
9. $(x)Fx \cdot (x)Gx \supset (x)Fx$

B. For each of the following schemata specify a universe in which it is valid and also one in which it is not valid.
1. $(\exists x)Fx \supset (x)Fx$
2. $(\exists x)(Fx \supset Gx) \equiv (\exists x)(-Fx \vee Gx)$
3. $-[(\exists x)Fx \cdot (\exists x) - Fx]$
4. $-[(\exists x)(Fx \cdot Gx) \cdot (\exists x)(Fx \cdot -Gx) \cdot (\exists x)(-Fx \cdot Gx)]$
5. $(\exists x)(Fx \cdot Gx) \cdot (\exists x)(Fx \cdot -Gx) \supset ((\exists x)(-Fx \cdot Gx) \supset (x)-(-Fx \cdot -Gx))$

C. True or false?
1. An OVQS that is obtained from a valid TFS by replacing one or more of its statement letters by OVQS (with the same OVQS replacing a statement letter throughout the TFS) is also valid.
2. The existential quantification of a valid open OVQS is also valid.
3. An OVQS may be consistent in one universe but not in another.
4. A TFS may be consistent in one universe but not in another.
5. The universal quantification of any valid OVQS is also valid.

2.2.6 IMPLICATION AND EQUIVALENCE

Our approach to quantificational implication and equivalence will model that taken earlier in truth-function theory. Thus we shall begin by introducing the concept of a simultaneous interpretation in a universe U of two or more schemata. This is simply an assignment of truth-values, open sentences, and objects *in* U to the statement letters, predicate letters, and individual constants or free occurrences of 'x', respectively, of all the schemata to be simultaneously interpreted in U. This ensures that each schema is interpreted in U and that the same truth-value, open sentence, or object in U is assigned to a statement letter, predicate letter, individual constant, or free occurrence of 'x', respectively, throughout the interpretation.

EXAMPLE

Schemata to be interpreted
$(x)Fx \cdot p$, $Fa \cdot Gx \cdot p$, $(\exists x)Fx \lor Ga \cdot Gx$
Assignments
$U : \{1,2\}$, $F : x = 1$ $G : x = 2$
$a : 2$ $x : 1$ $p : T$
Results
$(x)(x = 1) \cdot T$, $2 = 1 \cdot 1 = 2 \cdot T$, $(\exists x)(x = 1) \lor 2 = 2 \cdot 1 = 2$

We can now define implication and equivalence as follows:

> *An* OVQS S quantificationally-implies *an* OVQS W *just in case every simultaneous interpretation in every universe U of S and W which makes S true in U also makes W true in U.*

> *An* OVQS S *is* quantificationally equivalent *to an* OVQS W *just in case S and W have the same truth-value in U for every simultaneous interpretation in every universe U.*

EXAMPLES

a.   '$(x)Fx$' implies '$(\exists x)Fx$'.

Proof: Let U be any universe, and consider any simultaneous interpretation in U of the two schemata in U. If '$(x)Fx$' is made true in U, then 'Fx' is made true in U for all assignments of objects in U to 'x'. Hence 'Fx' is made true in U for some assignment to 'x' in U. Thus '$(\exists x)Fx$' is made true in U. So '$(x)Fx$' implies '$(\exists x)Fx$'.

b.   '$(x)(Fx \cdot Gx)$' is equivalent to '$(x)Fx \cdot (x)Gx$'.

Proof: Let U be any universe, and consider any simultaneous interpretation in U of the two schemata. If '$(x)(Fx \cdot Gx)$' is made true in U, then '$Fx \cdot Gx$' is made true for all assignments from U to 'x'. Thus, so are 'Fx' and 'Gx'.

Hence '$(x)Fx$' and '$(x)Gx$' are both made true in U, and consequently, so is their conjunction. If '$(x)(Fx \cdot Gx)$' is made false in U, then for some assignment from U to 'x', 'Fx' or 'Gx' is made false in U. Hence either '$(x)Fx$' or '$(x)Gx$' is made false in U, and so their conjunction is made false in U. This means that the two schemata have the same truth-value in U for every simultaneous interpretation in every universe U; that is, they are quantificationally equivalent.

If S and W are TFS, then S quantificationally-implies W if and only if S truth-functionally implies W. For a simultaneous interpretation of S and W and a simultaneous interpretation in a universe U are one and the same thing if S and W are TFS. By the same token, if S and W are TFS, then they are quantificationally equivalent just in case they are truth-functionally equivalent. For this reason we can drop the adverb "quantificationally" and simply speak of implication and equivalence, whether or not the schemata in question are TFS or other OVQS.

Suppose that S implies W, and consider any interpretation in any universe U of $S \supset W$. This furnishes a simultaneous interpretation in U of S and W, and as S implies W, S cannot be true in U while W is false in U. Hence $S \supset W$ is true in U also. But since U and the interpretation of $S \supset W$ in U are arbitrary, $S \supset W$ is valid. Conversely, if $S \supset W$ is valid, it is true in U for every interpretation in every universe U. Thus there is no simultaneous interpretation in any universe U which makes S true in U and W false in U. This means that S implies W. Therefore S *implies W just in case $S \supset W$ is valid*. Similar reasoning establishes that S *is equivalent to W just in case $S \equiv W$ is valid*.

The laws of implication and equivalence which were stated in truthfunction theory have exact analogs in one-variable quantification theory. For reference they will be restated again:

1   *Every schema implies itself.*
2   *If S implies W and W implies E, then S implies E.*
3   *Valid schemata are implied by all schemata, but imply valid schemata only.*
4   *Inconsistent schemata imply all schemata, but are implied by inconsistent ones only.*
5   *Every schema is equivalent to itself.*
6   *If S is equivalent to W, then W is equivalent to S.*
7   *If S is equivalent to W and W is equivalent to E, then S is equivalent to E.*
8   *All valid schemata are equivalent and to each other only.*
9   *All inconsistent schemata are equivalent and to each other only.*

Since the proofs of these laws closely mimic those given for their correspondents in truth-function theory, they will be left as exercises. For the sake of illustration, law 2 will be proved here. Thus let us suppose that S implies W and W implies E. We want to show that S implies E. To this end consider any interpretation of $S \supset E$ in any universe U. If this makes S false in U, then it makes $S \supset E$ true in U. But suppose that it makes S true in U. Then let us extend this interpretation so that W is interpreted in U. (W may not be interpreted in U because it contains additional statement or predicate letters, individual constants, or free occurrences of 'x' which do not occur in either S or E.) It does not matter how we extend this interpretation; so let us assign some object in U to any individual constants or free occurrences of 'x' which have not been interpreted yet, and let us assign '$x = x$' to all uninterpreted predicate letters and T to all the uninterpreted statement letters. We now have a simultaneous interpretation in U of $S, W, E, S \supset W$, $W \supset E$, and $S \supset E$. Moreover, so far as $S \supset E$ is concerned, this is the same as our original interpretation of it. By assumption, then, S is made true in U. But then, since $S \supset W$ and $W \supset E$ are valid, both W and E must be made true in U. Thus $S \supset E$ is true in U. Hence, whether S is true or false in $U, S \supset E$ is true in U. Thus $S \supset W$ is valid, and S implies E.

The two laws of interchange hold in one-variable quantification theory. However, we shall postpone our treatment of them until we treat equivalence in the context of full quantification theory.

2.2.7 STATEMENTS AND ARGUMENTS

A truth of one-variable quantification theory (or an OV-truth) is a statement which can be obtained from a *closed* valid OVQS by replacing its statement letters by statements, its predicate letters by open sentences, and its individual constants by proper names. Each occurrence of a statement letter, individual constant, or predicate letter must be replaced by the same statement, proper name, or open sentence. (Strictly speaking, the open sentences are introduced at the occurrences of the predicate letters.) Roughly speaking, then, an OV-truth is a statement which can be diagrammed by a valid closed OVQS.

Every OV-truth is true, for an OV-truth is the result of interpreting a valid OVQS in the universe of all things, and the schema must come out true for this interpretation.

EXAMPLES

a. If everything is red, the moon is red.
    Diagram: $(x)Fx \supset Fa$

b. If no person came to class, then it is false that some person came to class.
    Diagram: $(x)(Fx \supset -Gx) \supset -(\exists x)(Fx \cdot Gx)$

c. Everything obeys the law of gravitation just in case there is nothing which does not obey it.

Diagram: $(x)Fx \equiv -(\exists x) - Fx$

One may also define the concept of a falsehood of one-variable quantification theory, and in terms of this and the concept of an OV-truth, define the concept of a contingency of one-variable quantification theory. The details of these definitions are left to the reader. Notice that every tautology is an OV-truth, every contradiction is an OV-falsehood, but not every truth-functional contingency is an OV-contingency. The statement 'John is a student only if something is a student' is a truth-functional contingency since its truth-functional form is '$p \supset q$', but the same statement is an OV-truth.

One statement *A OV-implies* a statement *B* just in case there are OVQS *S* and *W* such that *S* implies *W*, and *A* can be obtained from *S*, and *B* from *W*, by replacing statement letters by statements, individual constants by proper names, and predicate letters by open sentences. Naturally, any statement letter, individual constant, or predicate letter which appears in both *S* and *W* must have the same replacement made for it in both instances. Roughly speaking, then, *A* OV-implies *B* just in case there is a simultaneous diagramming of *A* and *B* such that the schema diagramming *A* implies the one diagramming *B*.

EXAMPLES

a. 'Nothing is in the box' OV-implies 'The pencil is not in the box'. For '$(x)-Fx$' implies '$-Fa$'.

b. 'Every man is mortal' implies 'No man is not mortal'. For '$(x)(Fx \supset Gx)$' implies '$(x)-(Fx \cdot -Gx)$'.

Two statements are OV-equivalent just in case they OV-imply each other. The two statements given in the last example are OV-equivalent since '$(x)(Fx \supset Gx)$' and '$(x)-(Fx \cdot -Gx)$' imply each other. Clearly, two statements are OV-equivalent just in case equivalent OVQS diagram them.

If *A* truth-functionally implies *B*, then a TFS diagramming *A* implies one diagramming *B*. But every TFS is an OVQS. So if *A* truth-functionally implies *B*, then *A* OV-implies *B*. The converse does not hold, however, for examples (a) and (b) above are cases of OV-implication which are not truth-functional implications. Similarly, *A* is truth-functionally equivalent to *B* only if *A* and *B* are OV-equivalent, but not conversely. Since truth-functional implication and equivalence are species of OV-implication and equivalence, we shall no longer use the prefix 'OV' when speaking of implication and equivalence.

An argument is OV-valid just in case its premises imply its conclusion.

Every truth-functionally valid argument is OV-valid, but not every OV-valid argument is truth-functionally valid. Henceforth we shall speak of valid arguments and leave the 'OV' understood.

EXAMPLES

a. All children grow old. Peter Pan is a child. Hence he will grow old.
   Diagram: $(x)(Fx \supset Gx)$, Fa ∴ Ga

b. Everybody on the team is a poor loser, and no one worth nominating is a poor loser. So nobody on the team is worth nominating.
   Diagram: $(x)(Fx \supset Gx) \cdot (x)(Hx \supset -Gx)$ ∴ $(x)(Fx \supset -Hx)$

c. Something disturbed this trap. So something disturbed this trap or failed to see it.
   Diagram: $(\exists x)Fx$ ∴ $(\exists x)(Fx \lor Gx)$

d. Kind men exist, and no kind man abandons his mother. So some men do not abandon their mothers.
   Diagram: $(\exists x)(Fx \cdot Gx) \cdot (x)(Fx \cdot Gx \supset -Hx)$ ∴ $(\exists x)(Gx \cdot -Hx)$

EXERCISES FOR SECS. 2.2.6 AND 2.2.7

A. By means of simultaneous interpretations, establish the following.
   1. '$(\exists x)Fx$' does not imply '$(x)Fx$'.
   2. '$p \lor \bar{p}$' is not equivalent to '$(x)(Fx \cdot Ga)$'.
   3. '$(x)(Fx \lor Gx)$' does not imply '$(x)Fx \lor (x)Gx$'.
   4. '$(\exists x)(Fx \supset p)$' is not equivalent to '$(\exists x)Fx \supset p$'.
   5. '$(x)(Fx \supset p)$' is not equivalent to '$(x)Fx \supset p$'.
B. Establish the following.
   1. An OV-truth is implied by every statement.
   2. An argument with an OV-falsehood as a conclusion must have at least one false premiss.
   3. Every contradiction is an OV-falsehood.
   4. If an argument is truth-functionally valid, then it is OV-valid.

2.3 DERIVATIONS

2.3.1 INTRODUCTION

You will recall that there are mechanical decision procedures for determining *truth-function* validity, implication, etc. All these methods are based upon the possibility of carrying out a complete truth-value analysis of a TFS. There is nothing like a complete truth-value analysis of an OVQS, however, because each OVQS has an infinite number of interpretations. It is tempting to conclude, therefore, that there are no mechanical decision procedures for one-variable validity, implication, etc. Actually, this conclusion is false, for there are mechanical decision procedures available for these cases too. But they are far too complicated to be introduced in a text of this sort, and in any case they are not as efficient as the means we shall use, that is, derivations.

The rules of derivation which we shall use are both complete and sound; that is, they permit us to prove all and only valid OVQS. Yet the construction of a proof of a schema is not a purely mechanical affair and usually requires some insight and ingenuity on our part. (This is something which should already have been apparent in truth-function theory.) Thus we might try very hard to prove a particular schema and still fail to do so. But this cannot be taken as evidence for the invalidity of the schema, since there may be a proof which we have not discovered. If we attempt to prove a TFS and meet with no success, then of course we can always check the TFS for validity. But we cannot do this for those OVQS which are not TFS. Thus our rules of derivation do not furnish a decision procedure for the validity of OVQS. What they *do* furnish is called a *proof procedure*, that is, a method which will produce a proof of a schema *if* it is valid, but which will not tell us that the schema is invalid if it happens to be. Since a schema is inconsistent just in case its negation is valid, our proof procedure can also be used to establish that a schema is inconsistent *if* it happens to be. But there are also schemata which are neither valid not inconsistent, and our proof procedure will not establish the consistency or invalidity of these schemata; nor of their negations.

There are even ways to mechanize our proof procedure. Here is a description of a rather clumsy and inefficient method: We design a machine which generates all sequences of schemata by starting with shortest sequences. As it generates a sequence it checks it to see if it is a proof — this can always be checked mechanically. If it is a proof, it lists the schema proved. Since every valid schema has a proof, every valid schema will eventually be listed. Now suppose that we wanted to use this machine to determine whether a particular schema S was valid. Then we should start the machine and see whether it listed S. It is quite possible that S would be listed after a short time. But suppose that the machine had been running for a long time and S had not been listed. This still does not mean that S will not be listed at some time. And unless we already knew that S was invalid (and so would never be listed), we could not predict that S would never be listed. So the mere fact that the machine has not listed S *yet* is not evidence of its invalidity. (Just as the mere fact that we have not been able to discover a proof of S is not evidence of its invalidity.) Thus, even this *mechanical proof procedure* for valid OVQS does not yield a decision procedure. The moral is that one-variable quantification theory is going to place much greater demands upon our ingenuity than truth-function theory did.

2.3.2 EXTENDING THE TRUTH-FUNCTIONAL RULES

Since we shall forgo test procedures for validity in one-variable quantification theory, we had better get on with the job of setting up rules of inference for this branch of logic. We shall make extensive use of the foundations which have been already laid in truth-function theory. Our derivations will continue to follow the same general style; that is, vertical lines, numbered steps, and reasons will be employed. Moreover, we shall extend our truth-functional rules to cover quantificational schemata. In other words, *we may continue to apply MP, DNI, SD, CP, IP, etc., even when the steps involved in these applications are* OVQS. Two examples should make clear what this extension permits.

EXAMPLES

a. To prove: $Fx \cdot (x)Gx \supset (Fx \lor Gx)$.

1	$Fx \cdot (x)Gx$	A
2	Fx	1, S
3	$Fx \lor Gx$	2, add
4	$Fx \cdot (x)Gx \supset (Fx \lor Gx)$	1-3, CP

b. To prove: $-[(\exists x)Fx \cdot Ga] \supset ((\exists x)Fx \supset -Ga)$.

Proof:

1	$-[(\exists x)Fx \cdot Ga]$	A
2	$(\exists x)Fx$	A
3	Ga	A
4	$(\exists x)Fx \cdot Ga$	2, 3, PC
5	$-[(\exists x)Fx \cdot Ga]$	1, R
6	$-Ga$	3-5, IP
7	$(\exists x)Fx \supset -Ga$	2-6, CP
8	$-[(\exists x)Fx \cdot Ga] \supset ((\exists x)Fx \supset -Ga)$	1-7, CP

The extension of our truth-functional rules enables us to prove every *truth-functionally valid* OVQS, that is, every OVQS which can be obtained from a valid TFS by replacing some or all the statement letters of the TFS by OVQS. (Here a statement letter must be replaced throughout by the same OVQS.)

EXAMPLES OF TRUTH-FUNCTIONALLY VALID OVQS

a. TFS: $p \cdot q \supset p$
OVQS: $Fx \cdot (x)Gx \supset Fx$

b. TFS: $(p \equiv q) \supset (q \equiv p)$
OVQS: $(Fa \equiv (\exists x)(Fx \vee Gx)) \supset ((\exists x)(Fx \vee Gx) \equiv Fa)$

It is easy to see why every truth-functionally valid OVQS must be provable by means of the extended truth-functional rules. For let S be such an OVQS. Then it must be obtainable from a valid TFS W by replacing the statement letters of W by schemata. Since W is a valid TFS, it has a proof which uses only the truth-functional rules. But if we replace all the statement letters of W in both W and its proof by the same schemata which were used to produce S, then we shall obtain a proof of S which uses the same rules.

EXAMPLE.   A proof of '$Fx \cdot (x)Gx \supset Fx$' produced from a proof of '$p \cdot q \supset p$'.

1		$p \cdot q$	A	1		$Fx \cdot (x)Gx$	A
2		p	1, S	2		Fx	1, S
3	$p \cdot q$ p		1-2, CP	3	$Fx \cdot (x)Gx$ Fx		1-2, CP

We shall also say that one OVQS S truth-functionally implies another OVQS W just in case $S \supset W$ is truth-functionally valid. It follows from what we have just shown that if S truth-functionally implies W, then we can derive W from S by using only the extensions of our truth-functional rules.

EXAMPLE.   '$((x)Fx \supset Gx) \cdot -Gx$' truth-functionally implies '$(x)Fx \supset Hx$'.

1	$((x)Fx \supset Gx) \cdot -Gx$	P
2	$(x)Fx \supset Gx$	1, S
3	$-Gx$	1, S
4	$(x)Fx$	A
5	$-(x)Fx$	2. 3, MT
6	$(x)Fx \vee Hx$	4, add
7	Hx	5, 6, DS
8	$(x)Fx \supset Hx$	4-7, CP

EXERCISES FOR SECS. 2.3.1 AND 2.3.2

A.   For each of the following, derive the schemata in the left column from those in the right.

1. $Fa \supset Ga$	$\bar{F}a \vee Ha,$	$Ha \supset Ga$
2. $(x)Fx \cdot Ga$	$(x)Fx \equiv Ga,$	$-Ga \supset Ga$
3. $(x)Fx \supset (\exists x)Hx$	$(x)Fx \supset p,$	$-(\bar{p} \cdot q) \supset (\exists x)Hx$

4. $(x)Gx \lor (x)Hx$	$(x)Hx \lor (x)Gx$
5. $-(p \cdot (x)Fx)$	$p \supset -(x)Fx$

B. Establish the following implications by means of derivations.

1. 'Adam is a father' implies 'If Adam is not a father, then all men are bald'.
2. 'Unless everything has disappeared, nothing has' implies 'If not everything has disappeared, then nothing has'.
3. 'John is my friend, but Bill is not' implies 'It is not the case that if John is my friend then Bill is too'.
4. 'Some people are late or the clock is wrong' implies 'It is false that both it is not so that some people are late and the clock is not wrong'.

C. True or false?

1. There is a proof procedure for truth-functional implication.
2. There is a decision procedure for truth-functional consistency.
3. The rules of derivation in this book furnish decision procedures for OV-validity.
4. The rules of derivation in this book furnish proof procedures for OV-inconsistency.
5. There is a proof procedure for OV-equivalence.
6. A proof procedure for both validity and invalidity amounts to a decision procedure for validity.
7. If the negation of a schema is provable, then the schema is inconsistent.
8. If a schema is derivable from every schema, then it is valid.
9. Some invalid schemata are provable.
10. The conjunction of every two valid schemata is provable.

2.3.3   UNIVERSAL INSTANTIATION

We can hardly expect to make much progress in demonstrating validity without introducing rules of inference dealing with quantifiers themselves. Thus far we can only establish the validity of truth-functionally-valid OVQS. Similarly, any implications that we can establish at this point are basically truth-functional implications. We are presently unable to prove the validity of even

$(x)Fx \supset Fx$
$(x)Fx \supset (\exists x)Fx$

These defects will be remedied by adding four rules for handling quantifiers. Two rules allow us to drop initial quantifiers from quantifications. Since, figuratively speaking, these lead from general statements to statements about particular instances, they are known as rules of *instantiation*. The other two rules permit us to prefix quantifiers, and thus to form quantifications. They lead from the particular to the general, and are consequently known as rules of *generalization*.

The first rule to be introduced concerns the removal of universal quantifiers, and so it is known as *universal instantiation* (called UI, for short). From the intuitive standpoint, UI is the rule which permits us to infer anything about some particular object which we already know to hold for every object in general. From the formal standpoint it permits us to drop a universal quantifier or do this and replace all occurrences of 'x' which were bound to the quantifier by an individual constant. Thus, schematically, UI runs as follows:

$$(x)(\cdots x \cdots) \qquad \text{or} \qquad (x)(\cdots x \cdots)$$
$$(\cdots x \cdots) \quad \text{UI} \qquad\qquad (\cdots \alpha \cdots) \quad \text{UI}$$

where α is any individual constant.

To obtain a more exact statement of UI it will be wise for us first to introduce some notation for talking about schemata. Let S_x be any OVQS ('x' may or may not occur in S_x). Then let S_α be the OVQS which results from S_x by replacing all free occurrences of 'x' (if any) in S_x by α; where α is 'x', then S_x and S_α are the same. This is also true when 'x' has no free occurrences in S_x.

EXAMPLES

	S_x	S_b
a.	$Fx \cdot (x)(Gx \supset Hx)$	$Fb \cdot (x)(Gx \supset Hx)$
b.	$(x)Fx$	$(x)Fx$
c.	$Fx \lor ((\exists x)Gx \supset Hx)$	$Fb \lor ((\exists x)Gx \supset Hb)$

UI may now be stated precisely as follows:

Universal instantiation: *From (x)S_x we may infer S_α, where α is 'x' or any individual constant.*

Reason for S_α: a numeral referring to S_x followed by 'UI'.

UI may also be applied to vacuous universal quantifications, for S_x need not contain free occurrences of 'x'. [A vacuous universal quantification, recall, is one of the form $(x)S$, where 'x' does not occur free in S.] Thus 'p', for instance, may be inferred from '$(x)p$' by UI. Further examples of correct and incorrect applications of UI now follow.

EXAMPLES

Correct Applications of UI:

a.	1	$(x)Fx$	P	b.	1	$(x)(Fx \supset Gx \cdot (\exists x)Fx)$	P
	2	Fx	1, UI		2	$Fx \supset Gx \cdot (\exists x)Fx$	1, UI

c.	1	$(x)(Fx \equiv Ga \cdot (x)Gx)$	P	d.	1	$(x)Fx$	P
	2	$Fx \equiv Ga \cdot (x)Gx$	1, UI		2	Fa	1, UI
					3	Fb	1, UI
					4	Fx	1, UI

e. 1 | $(x)(Fx \lor Gx \cdot Hb)$ P
    2 | $Fx \lor Gx \cdot Hb$ 1, UI
    3 | $Fa \lor Ga \cdot Hb$ 1, UI
    4 | $Fb \lor Gb \cdot Hb$ 1, UI
    5 | $Fc \lor Gc \cdot Hb$ 1, UI

Incorrect Applications of UI:

f. 1 | $(x)Fx \supset Gx$ P   (Incorrect: Step 1 is not a universal
    2 | $Fx \supset Gx$ 1, UI   quantification.)

g. 1 | $(x)(Fx \supset Gx)$ P   (Incorrect: All free occurrences of 'x'
    2 | $Fa \supset Gx$ 1, UI   have not been replaced by 'a'.)

h. 1 | $(x)(Fx \lor Gx)$ P   (Incorrect: All free occurrences of
    2 | $Fa \lor Gb$ 1, UI   'x' have not been replaced by the
       | same constant.)

i. 1 | $(x)(Fx \lor (\exists x)(Gx \cdot Hx))$ P   (Incorrect: A bound occurrence of
    2 | $Fa \lor (\exists x)(Gx \cdot Ha)$ 1, UI 'x' in S_x has been replaced by 'a'.)

As noted, none of these steps follow the form of UI. Moreover, in each case, the first steps fail to imply the second steps. This is demonstrated by interpreting all the first steps as true and simultaneously interpreting the second steps as false. If the universe is taken as the class of persons, the following assignments will give all the schemata the required truth-values (in this universe): x : George Washington; a : Mrs. Washington; b : James Madison; F : x is a male; G : x is a female; H : x ran a beauty parlor. We shall verify that these assignments work for example i; the others are left as exercises. Under the given interpretation, steps 1 and 2 of example i will become, respectively:

(1) $(x)(x$ is a male $\lor (\exists x)(x$ is a female $\cdot x$ ran a beauty parlor))

(2) Mrs. Washington is a male $\lor (\exists x)(x$ is a female $\cdot$ Mrs. Washington ran a beauty parlor)

Statement (1) is true in the universe of persons. Some female persons have run beauty parlors; so '$(\exists x)(Gx \cdot Hx)$' becomes true. Hence '$Fx \lor (\exists x)(Gx \cdot Hx)$' becomes true for all persons x, making (1) true. However, (2) is false in this universe. Since Mrs. Washington is neither a male nor ran a beauty parlor, the left disjunct is false. Moreover, 'x is a female $\cdot$ Mrs. Washington ran a beauty parlor' is a false conjunction for all persons x.

We shall now turn to some more serious examples involving the use of UI. Note that UI is treated on a par with the other rules of inferences insofar as the restrictions concerning lines of argument, reiteration, and the use of conditional and indirect proofs are concerned.

EXAMPLES. To derive 'Fa' from '$(x)(-Fx \supset Gx)$' and '$(x) - Gx$'.

Derivation:

1	$(x)(-Fx \supset Gx)$	P
2	$(x) - Gx$	P
3	$-Fa \supset Ga$	1, UI
4	$-Ga$	2, UI
5	$--Fa$	3, 4, MT
6	Fa	5, DNI

Comment: Choosing 'a' when applying UI was the key to success here.

b. To prove: $(x)Fx \supset Fx \cdot Fa$.

Proof:

1	$(x)Fx$	A
2	Fx	1, UI
3	Fa	1, UI
4	$Fx \cdot Fa$	2, 3, PC
5	$(x)Fx \supset Fx \cdot Fa$	1-4, CP

c. To prove: $(x)(Fx \supset Gx) \cdot (x)(Gx \supset Hx) \supset (Fx \supset Hx)$.

Proof:

1	$(x)(Fx \supset Gx) \cdot (x)(Gx \supset Hx)$	A
2	Fx	A
3	$(x)(Fx \supset Gx)$	1, S
4	$Fx \supset Gx$	3, UI
5	Gx	2, 4, MP
6	$(x)(Gx \supset Hx)$	1, S
7	$Gx \supset Hx$	6, UI
8	Hx	5, 7, MP
9	$Fx \supset Hx$	2-8, CP
10	$(x)(Fx \supset Gx) \cdot (x)(Fx \supset Hx) \supset (Fx \supset Hx)$	1-9, CP

EXERCISES FOR SEC. 2.3.3

A. Prove these OVQS.

1. $(x)Fx \supset (Fa \lor Gb)$
2. $(x)(Fx \cdot Gx) \supset Fa \cdot Ga$
3. $(x)Fx \cdot (x)Gx \supset Fx \cdot Gb$
4. $(x)(Fx \cdot Gx) \supset Fx \cdot Gb$
5. $(x)(Fx \supset (x)Gx) \supset (Fa \supset Ga)$
6. $(x)Fx \supset -(x) - Fx$
7. $(x)(Fx \lor Gx) \supset (-Fa \supset Ga)$
8. $(x)(Fx \cdot (x)(Gx \equiv Fx)) \supset (Fa \cdot Gb) \cdot Gc$
9. $Fa \cdot -Ga \supset -(x)(Fx \supset Gx)$
10. $-Fa \cdot -Ga \supset -(x)(Fx \lor Gx)$

B. Establish the *invalidity* of these OVQS by providing false interpretations of them.
1. $(x)(Fx \lor Gx) \supset (Fa \lor Gb)$
2. $(x)(Fx \lor Gx) \supset ((x)Fx \lor (x)Gx)$
3. $(x)(Fx \supset Gx) \supset Fa \cdot Ga$
4. $-(x)Fx \supset (x) - Fx$
5. $((x)Fx \supset (x)Gx) \supset (Fa \supset Ga)$

2.3.4 EXISTENTIAL GENERALIZATION

The next rule, *existential generalization* (EG, for short), is used to generate existential quantifications from previous steps in a derivation. The rule draws its intuitive basis from the fact that if some particular thing, say, the moon, has a property, then something or other has that property. The formal rule has two options: (1) from any schema we may infer the existential quantification of it or (2) from a *closed* schema which contains an individual constant we may first obtain an open schema by replacing one or more occurrences of this individual constant by 'x' and then infer the existential quantification of this open schema. There is an important restriction on (2): no occurrences of the individual constant within the scope of quantifiers may be replaced by 'x'. Thus the rule will let us infer '$(\exists x)Fx$' from 'Fx' and also from 'Fa'. From the informal point of view we may thus infer 'Something is an F' from either 'x is an F' or 'a is an F'.

There is a brief and precise statement of the rule which encompasses both options. This now follows.

Existential generalization: *From S_α we may infer $(\exists x)S_x$, where α is 'x' or an individual constant.*

The reason for $(\exists x)S_x$ is a numeral referring to S_α. S_x and S_α are related again as they are in the case of UI, which not only allows for both options of the rule, but also permits the inference of vacuous existential quantifications. The schematic form of the rule is, simply,

$$(\cdots x \cdots) \qquad \text{or} \qquad (\cdots \alpha \cdots)$$
$$\therefore (\exists x)(\cdots x \cdots) \quad \text{EG} \qquad (\exists x)(\cdots x \cdots)$$

The examples of correct and incorrect applications of EG will indicate why we must be so particular in passing from $(\cdots \alpha \cdots)$ to $(\exists x)(\cdots x \cdots)$.

EXAMPLES

Correct Applications of EG:

a.	1	Fx	P		b.	1	Fa	P
	2	$(\exists x)Fx$	1, EG			2	$(\exists x)Fx$	1, EG
						3	$(\exists x)Fa$	1, EG

c. $\begin{array}{ll} 1 & Fx \lor Gx \qquad\qquad \text{P} \\ 2 & (\exists x)(Fx \lor Gx) \qquad \text{1, EG} \end{array}$ d. $\begin{array}{ll} 1 & Fa \lor Ga \qquad\qquad \text{P} \\ 2 & (\exists x)(Fx \lor Gx) \quad \text{1, EG} \end{array}$

e. $\begin{array}{lll} 1 & Fa \equiv Ga \cdot Hb & \text{P} \\ 2 & (\exists x)(Fx \equiv Gx \cdot Hb) & \text{1, EG} \\ 3 & (\exists x)(Fa \equiv Ga \cdot Hx) & \text{1, EG} \\ 4 & (\exists x)(Fx \equiv Ga \cdot Hb) & \text{1, EG} \\ 5 & (\exists x)(Fa \equiv Gx \cdot Hb) & \text{1, EG} \end{array}$

Incorrect Applications of EI:

f. $\begin{array}{lll} 1 & Fx \supset Gx & \text{P} \\ 2 & (\exists x)Fx \supset Gx & \text{1, EG} \end{array}$ (Incorrect: This is not an existential quantification.)

g. $\begin{array}{lll} 1 & Fa \equiv Gb & \text{P} \\ 2 & (\exists x)(Fx \supset Gx) & \text{1, EG} \end{array}$ (Incorrect: Two different constants have been replaced by 'x'.)

h. $\begin{array}{lll} 1 & Fa \cdot (\exists x)(Fa \cdot Gx) & \text{P} \\ 2 & (\exists x)(Fx \cdot (\exists x)(Fx \cdot Gx)) & \text{1, EG} \end{array}$ (Incorrect: An occurrence of 'a' within the scope of '$(\exists x)$' has been replaced.)

The incorrect examples fail to conform to the form of EG. In addition, in each example, step 1 also fails to imply step 2. The interpretations necessary to show this are as follows: Let U be the class of positive integers. In example f, assign '1' to 'x', 'x is even' to 'F', and '$x + 2 = 4$' to 'G'. In example g, assign 'x is even' to 'F', 'x is odd' to 'G', '2' to 'a', and '3' to 'b'. Repeat the assignments given for example g in example h. It is easily verified that these interpretations make each step 1 true in U and each step 2 false in U. Hence none of the first steps imply the second ones.

EXAMPLES EMPLOYING EG

a. To derive '$(\exists x)Fx \lor (\exists x)Gx$' from '$Fa \lor Gb$'.

Derivation: $\begin{array}{lll} 1 & Fa \lor Gb & \text{P} \\ 2 & \quad Fa & \text{A} \\ 3 & \quad (\exists x)Fx & \text{2, EG} \\ 4 & \quad (\exists x)(Fx \lor (\exists x)Gx) & \text{3, add} \\ 5 & Fa \supset ((\exists x)Fx \lor (\exists x)Gx) & \text{2-4, CP} \\ 6 & \quad Gb & \text{A} \\ 7 & \quad (\exists x)Gx & \text{6, EG} \\ 8 & \quad (\exists x)Fx \lor (\exists x)Gx & \text{7, add} \\ 9 & Gb \supset ((\exists x)Fx \lor (\exists x)Gx) & \text{6-8, CP} \\ 10 & (\exists x)Fx \lor (\exists x)Gx & \text{1, 5, 9, SD} \end{array}$

b. Prove: $Fa \cdot (-Fa \lor Ga) \supset (\exists x)(Fa \cdot Gx) \cdot (\exists x)(Fx \cdot Gx)$

Proof:

1		$Fa \cdot (-Fa \lor Ga)$	A
2		Fa	1, S
3		$-Fa \lor Ga$	2, S
4		$--Fa$	2, DNI
5		Ga	3, 4, DS
6		$Fa \cdot Ga$	2, 5, PC
7		$(\exists x)(Fa \cdot Gx)$	6, EG
8		$(\exists x)(Fx \cdot Gx)$	6, EG
9		$(\exists x)(Fa \cdot Gx) \cdot (\exists x)(Fx \cdot Gx)$	7, 8, PC
10		$Fa \cdot (-Fa \lor Ga) \supset (\exists x)(Fa \cdot Gx) \cdot (\exists x)(Fx \cdot Gx)$	1-9, CP

c.   Prove: $(\exists x)(Fx \supset Fa) \cdot (\exists x)(Fa \supset Fx)$.

1	Fa	A
2	$Fa \supset Fa$	1-1, CP
3	$(\exists x)(Fx \supset Fa)$	2, EG
4	$(\exists x)(Fa \supset Fx)$	2, EG
5	$(\exists x)(Fx \supset Fa) \cdot (\exists x)(Fa \supset Fx)$	3, 4, PC

EXAMPLES INVOLVING BOTH UI AND EG

d.   Prove: $(x)Fx \supset (\exists x)(Fx \cdot Fa)$.

Proof:

1		$(x)Fx$	A
2		Fx	1, UI
3		Fa	1, UI
4		$Fx \cdot Fa$	2, 3, PC
5		$(\exists x)(Fx \cdot Fa)$	4, EG
6		$(x)Fx \supset (\exists x)(Fx \cdot Fa)$	1-5, CP

(*Exercise.* Give an alternative proof which uses UI only once. *Hint:* Obtain '$Fa \cdot Fa$'.)

e.   Prove: $(p \supset (x)Fx) \supset (p \supset (\exists x)Fx)$.

Proof: (Worked out)

(1)

$$
\begin{array}{|l}
\;\; \begin{array}{|l} p \supset (x)Fx \\ ? \\ p \supset (\exists x)Fx \end{array} \\
(p \supset (x)Fx) \supset (p \supset (\exists x)Fx) \qquad\qquad \text{CP}
\end{array}
$$

(2)

$$
\begin{array}{|l}
\;\; \begin{array}{|l} p \supset (x)Fx \\ \;\; \begin{array}{|l} p \\ ? \\ (\exists x)Fx \end{array} \\ p \supset (\exists x)Fx \end{array} \\
(p \supset (x)Fx) \supset (p \supset (\exists x)Fx) \qquad\qquad \text{CP}
\end{array}
$$

(3) 1 | $p \supset (x)Fx$ A
     2 | | | p A
     3 | | | $(x)Fx$ 1, 2, MP
     4 | | | Fx 3, UI
     5 | | | $(\exists x)Fx$ 4, EG
     6 | $p \supset (\exists x)Fx$ 2-5, CP
     7 | $(p \supset (x)Fx) \supset (p \supset (\exists x)Fx)$ 1-6, CP

f. Prove: $(x)Fx \supset -(x) - Fx$.

Proof: (Worked out)

(1) | | | $(x)Fx$
    | | | ?
    | | $-(x) - Fx$
    | | $(x)Fx \supset -(x) - Fx$ CP

(2) | | | $(x)Fx$
    | | | | $(x) - Fx$
    | | | | ?
    | | | $-(x) - Fx$ IP
    | | $(x)Fx \supset -(x) - Fx$ CP

(3) 1 | | | $(x)Fx$ A
     2 | | | | $(x) - Fx$ A
     3 | | | | Fx 1, UI
     4 | | | | $-Fx$ 2, UI
     5 | | | $-(x) - Fx$ 2-4, IP
     6 | | $(x)Fx \supset -(x) - Fx$ 1-5, CP

g. Prove: $-(\exists x)Fx \supset -(x)Fx$.

Proof: (Worked out)

(1) | | | $-(\exists x)Fx$
    | | | ?
    | | $-(x)Fx$
    | $-(\exists x)Fx \supset -(x)Fx$

(2) | | | $-(\exists x)Fx$
    | | | $(x)Fx$
    | | | ?
    | | $-(x)Fx$
    | $-(\exists x)Fx \supset -(x)Fx$

(3) 1 | | | $-(\exists x)Fx$ A
     2 | | | | $(x)Fx$ A
     3 | | | | Fx 2, UI
     4 | | | | $(\exists x)Fx$ 3, EG
     5 | | | | $-(\exists x)Fx$ 1, R
     6 | | | $-(x)Fx$ 2-5, IP
     7 | | $-(\exists x)Fx \supset -(x)Fx$ 1-6, CP

EXERCISES FOR SEC. 2.3.4
A. Prove these OVQS.

    1. $Fa \supset (\exists x)Fx \cdot Fa$

2. $Fa \supset (\exists x)(Fx \cdot Fa)$
3. $Fa \cdot Ga \supset (\exists x)(Fx \cdot Gx)$
4. $Fa \cdot Ga \supset (\exists x)(Fx \cdot Ga)$
5. $(\exists x)(Fx \supset --Fx)$
6. $(\exists x)(Fx \supset Fa)$
7. $(\exists x)(Fx \cdot Gx \supset Fx)$
8. $(\exists x)(Fx \cdot Ga \supset Fa)$
9. $(x)Fx \cdot (x) - Fx \supset (\exists x)(Gx \cdot -Gx)$
10. $(x)Fx \supset (\exists x)(Fx \vee Hx)$
11. $(\bar{p} \vee (x)Fx) \supset (p \supset (\exists x)Fx)$
12. $(\exists x)((x)Fx \supset Fx)$
13. $-(x)(Fx \equiv -Fa)$
14. $(x)(Fx \cdot (x)Gx) \supset (\exists x)(Fx \cdot (\exists x)Gx)$
15. $(x)(Fx \vee Gx) \cdot (x) - Fx \supset (\exists x)Gx$
16. $(p \vee (x)Fx) \supset (p \vee (\exists x)Fx)$
17. $(x)(Fx \supset p) \supset ((x)Fx \supset p)$
18. $(\exists x)(Fx \supset (\exists x)Fx)$
19. $-((x)Fx \cdot (x) - Fx)$
20. $(\exists x)((Fx \supset Ga) \vee (Fb \supset -Ga))$

B. Establish the *invalidity* of these OVQS by providing false interpretations of them.
1. $Fa \cdot Gb \supset (\exists x)(Fx \cdot Gx)$
2. $Fa \cdot (x)(Gx \cdot Ha) \supset (\exists x)(Fx \cdot (x)(Gx \cdot Hx))$
3. $(x)(Fx \supset Gx) \supset (\exists x)(Fx \cdot Gx)$
4. $(\exists x)Fx \supset (\exists x) - Fx$
5. $(x)(Fx \vee Gx) \supset ((x)Fx \vee (x)Gx)$

2.3.5 UNIVERSAL GENERALIZATION

Although we are now armed with rules for dropping universal and adding existential quantifiers, it is apparent that we must also have rules for adding universal quantifiers and for dropping existential ones. For example, if we hope to prove

(1) $(x)(-Fx \vee Gx) \supset (x)(Fx \supset Gx)$

(2) $(\exists x)(Fx \cdot Gx) \supset (\exists x) - (-Fx \vee -Gx)$

then we ought to have rules for adding and dropping both kinds of quantifiers. The obvious way to attack (1), for example, is to assume '$(x)(-Fx \vee Gx)$', use UI to obtain '$-Fx \vee Gx$', take familiar truth-functional steps to obtain '$(Fx \supset Gx)$', and then add '(x)' and apply the rule of conditional proof. However, we do not have a rule for adding '(x)' yet. This rule will be called *universal generalization*, but right now we must seek a satisfactory formulation of it.

A look at informal proofs was helpful in formulating the rules of conditional and indirect proofs, and it does not seem to be a bad idea now. Thus consider the following examples.

EXAMPLE 1.   To prove that $a + (b + 1) = (a + b) + 1$, for all numbers a and b, given that $m + (n + i) = (m + n) + i$, for all numbers m, n, and i.

Informal Proof: Let a and b be arbitrary numbers. Since $m + (n + i)$ $= (m + n) + i$ is true for all numbers m, n, and i, it is true for a, b, and 1. Hence, $a + (b + 1) = (a + b) + 1$. Thus, *since a and b are arbitrary, $a + (b + 1)$ $= (a + b) + 1$, for all numbers a and b.*

EXAMPLE 2.   To prove that replacing all the statement letters in any valid TFS by the statement letter 'p' always yields valid results.

Informal Proof: Let S be any TFS. Suppose that S is valid. Then suppose W is the schema obtained from S by making the indicated replacements. Then for every interpretation of W there is some interpretation of S in which all the statement letters are interpreted alike, so that S and W both come out true or both come out false. But S is true under every interpretation. Thus so is W. *Since S is arbitrary, we have: All TFS which are valid yield valid results when 'p' replaces all their statement letters.*

By inspecting these examples and paying particular attention to the italicized sentences, you will observe that the informal versions of universal generalization conform to the following patterns:

(A)   Let x be any object

.
.
.

$$(\cdot \cdot x \cdot \cdot)$$
$$\therefore (x)(\cdot \cdot \cdot x \cdot \cdot \cdot)$$

(B)   Let x be an arbitrary F (number, schema, person)

.
.
.

$$(\cdot \cdot \cdot x \cdot \cdot \cdot)$$
$\therefore$ For any x which is an F, $(\cdot \cdot \cdot x \cdot \cdot \cdot)$

In (B) a particular universe of discourse is tacitly assumed, while in (A) the universe of discourse is completely unrestricted. Nonetheless, (B) can be reduced to (A); for whenever we desire to use (B), we can substitute the following complex form of (A):

Let x be any object

$$
\begin{array}{|l}
Fx \\
\cdot \\
\cdot \\
\cdot \\
(\cdots x \cdots) \\
\end{array}
$$
$Fx \supset (\cdots x \cdots)$ CP
$\therefore (x)(Fx \supset (\cdots x \cdots))$

Consequently, we can disregard (B) and focus upon (A). Furthermore, we can rewrite this as

$(\cdots x \cdots)$
$\therefore (x)(\cdots x \cdots)$ (where x is arbitrary)

Now (A) looks like UI and EG. Yet there is a big difference: (A) has a requirement that x be arbitrary. But what can this possibly mean from a formal point of view? Informally, the meaning is fairly clear. The object x is supposedly selected at random; it serves as a mere representative of all objects, and none of its peculiarities may intrude into the argument at hand. With this understanding (A) seems to be a correct way to argue: If we can show that for any x chosen at random $(\cdots x \cdots)$, then, clearly, $(x)(\cdots x \cdots)$ holds. Of course, we must be sure not to use any of the properties of the x we select as a representative. For example, it is wrong to argue:

Let 36 be any object.
$36 = 18 + 18$.
Hence $(x)(x = 18 + 18)$.

This argument appealed to one of the properties of 36, and so it does not treat 36 as *just any object*. If a given object is to play the role of *an arbitrarily selected object in the course of an argument, then the argument must not use any previous knowledge that we have about this object in particular.* (Of course, we can apply knowledge that we might have of objects in general.)

 In formalizing *universal generalization*, it is useful to let variables play the roles of names of arbitrary objects. Moreover, the arguments in which arbitrary objects figure are really subsidiary arguments such as those used in conditional and indirect proofs. Consequently, they will be set off as subordinate lines of argument by rewriting (A) as

$$
x \begin{array}{|l}
\cdot \\
\cdot \\
\cdot \\
(\cdots x \cdots) \\
\end{array}
$$
$(x)(\cdots x \cdots)$

The 'x' written to the left of the vertical line is used to indicate that 'x' serves as the name of an arbitrarily selected object during the course of the subordinate line of argument. We shall call such subordinate lines of argument *restricted subproofs*. These subproofs are restricted because, when applying one of the rules of inference, we shall not be able to refer back to steps which occur outside a restricted subproof *if* these steps contain free occurrences of 'x'. Thus, for instance, inferences with the following patterns of subordinate lines of arguments will be incorrect:

$$
\begin{array}{lll}
1 \mid Fx & & \\
\quad x \mid \ \cdot & & \\
\qquad \cdot & & \\
\qquad \cdot & & \\
\quad \ \mid Fx & 1,\ \mathrm{R} &
\end{array}
\qquad
\begin{array}{lll}
1 \mid Fx & & \\
\quad x \mid \ \cdot & & \\
\qquad \cdot & & \\
\qquad \cdot & & \\
\quad \ \mid Fx \lor Gx & 1,\ \mathrm{add} &
\end{array}
$$

However,

$$
\begin{array}{lll}
\quad x \mid \ \cdot & & \\
\qquad \cdot & & \\
\qquad \cdot & & \\
\quad \ \mid Fx & & \\
\quad \ \mid \ p & & \\
\quad \ \mid Fx & \mathrm{R} &
\end{array}
\qquad
\begin{array}{lll}
\quad x \mid \ \cdot & & \\
\qquad \cdot & & \\
\qquad \cdot & & \\
\quad \ \mid Fx & & \\
\quad \ \mid Fx \lor Gx & \mathrm{add} &
\end{array}
$$

will be correct, because the schemata containing free occurrences of 'x' have (let us assume) already been legitimately obtained *within* the restricted subproof. Intuitively, these restrictions are justified as follows: Schemata with free occurrences of 'x' which occur before a restricted subproof has been initiated represent "previous information" about the object x. Consequently, using these schemata in the restricted subproof is tantamount to using previous information about x. Since 'x' is supposed to denote an arbitrary object for the purposes of the restricted subproof, it is illegitimate to use the previous information about it. Of course, there are more formal reasons for imposing the restrictions; namely, without them we could prove invalid schemata and justify invalid inferences. We shall illustrate this as soon as the rule of universal generalization has been stated.

In universal generalization, all we are supposed to know about the object x is that it is an object; consequently, we really are supposed to start from scratch. We could reflect this formally by having restricted subproofs begin without assumptions. However, in extending the rule of assumption, it is technically convenient to introduce the symbol '$\triangle$' to serve as a blank assumption and let the subproofs begin with blank assumptions. Then we initiate restricted subproofs by applying the following new clause of the rule of assumption.

New clause to the rule of assumption: *At any stage in a derivation we may write down '$\triangle$' provided that we simultaneously initiate a new vertical and write 'x' to the left of the vertical line.*

This rule lets us initiate the restricted subproofs which are applied in the rule of universal generalization. Consequently, such subproofs will be called UG *subproofs*.

Now let us state the rule of universal generalization (or UG, for short).

Rule of universal generalization: *Let S_x be the last step to date in a UG subproof. Then we may terminate this restricted subproof and write $(x)S_x$ as the next step.*

Reason: Hyphenated numerals referring to '$\triangle$' and S_x followed by 'UG'.

Schematically:

$$x \; \Big| \; \triangle \qquad A$$

$$\cdot$$
$$\cdot$$
$$\cdot$$

$$S_x$$
$$(x)S_x \qquad \text{UG}$$

Let us illustrate UG first with three examples and then return to the discussion of restricted subproofs and the restrictions based upon them.

EXAMPLES

a. To derive '$(x)(Fx \cdot Gx)$' from '$(x)Fx \cdot (x)Gx$'.

Derivation: (Worked out)

(1)
$$
\begin{array}{ll}
(x)Fx \cdot (x)Gx & \text{P} \\
? & \\
(x)(Fx \cdot Gx) &
\end{array}
$$

(2)
$$
\begin{array}{lll}
& (x)Fx \cdot (x)Gx & \text{P} \\
x \,| & \triangle & \text{A} \\
& ? & \\
& Fx \cdot Gx & \\
& (x)(Fx \cdot Gx) & \text{UG}
\end{array}
$$

(3)
$$
\begin{array}{llll}
1 & (x)Fx \cdot (x)Gx & \text{P} \\
2 \; x| & \triangle & \text{A} \\
3 & (x)Fx & 1, \text{S} \\
4 & (x)Gx & 1, \text{S} \\
5 & Fx & 3, \text{UI} \\
6 & Gx & 4, \text{UI} \\
7 & Fx \cdot Gx & 5, 6, \text{PC} \\
8 & (x)(Fx \cdot Gx) & 2\text{-}7, \text{UG}
\end{array}
$$

Comment: Steps (3) and (4) are correct because 'x' does not occur free in step (1)

b. To derive '$(x)(Fx \supset Hx)$' from '$(x)(Fx \supset Gx)$' and '$(x)(Gx \supset Hx)$'.

Derivation: (Worked out)

(1) | $(x)(Fx \supset Gx)$ P
| $(x)(Gx \supset Hx)$ P
| ?
| $(x)(Fx \supset Hx)$

(2) | $(x)(Fx \supset Gx)$ P
| $(x)(Gx \supset Hx)$ P
x | $\triangle$ A
| ?
| $Fx \supset Hx$
| $(x)(Fx \supset Hx)$ UG

(3) | $(x)(Fx \supset Gx)$ P
| $(x)(Gx \supset Hx)$ P
x | $\triangle$ A
| | Fx A
| | ?
| | Hx
| $Fx \supset Hx$ CP
| $(x)(Fx \supset Hx)$ UG

(4) 1| $(x)(Fx \supset Gx)$ P
2| $(x)(Gx \supset Hx)$ P
3| x | $\triangle$ A
4| | | Fx A
5| | | $Fx \supset Gx$ 1, UI
6| | | $Gx \supset Hx$ 2, UI
7| | | Gx 4, 5, MP
8| | | Hx 7, 6, MP
9| | $Fx \supset Hx$ 4-8, CP
10| $(x)(Fx \supset Hx)$ 3-9, UG

c. To prove: $(x)(Fx \supset (Fx \lor Gx))$.

Proof: (Worked out)

(1)   ?
    $(x)(Fx \supset (Fx \lor Gx))$

(2) x | $\triangle$
| | ?   A
| | $Fx \supset (Fx \lor Gx)$
| $(x)(Fx \supset (Fx \lor Gx))$ UG

(3) 1 | x | $\triangle$ A
2 | | | Fx A
3 | | | $Fx \lor Gx$ 2, add
4 | | $Fx \supset (Fx \lor Gx)$ 2-3, CP
5 | $(x)(Fx \supset (Fx \lor Gx))$ 1-4, UG

Comment: Notice how using CP or IP within a restricted subproof helps remove the handicap of starting from scratch.

Now for the restrictions on UG: First, suppose that we could use "information" about 'x' in the sense that we allowed schemata to be the assumptions in UG subproofs. Then we could *prove every universal quantification* as follows:

1 | x | $(\cdots x \cdots)$ A
2 | | $(x)(\cdots x \cdots)$ 1-1, UG   (incorrect)

Since many universal quantifications, for instance, '$(x)Fx$', are invalid, this would destroy the soundness of our rules.

Next, suppose that we could use previous information about 'x' by reiterating or applying rules of inference to steps containing free occurrences of 'x' which occur outside of restricted subproofs. Then we could construct proofs of invalid schemata such as the following:

1 | | | Fx A
2 | | x | $\triangle$ A
3 | | | | Fx 1, R   (incorrect)
4 | | | $(x)Fx$ 2-3, UG
5 | | $Fx \supset (x)Fx$ 1-4, CP

1 | | | Fx A
2 | | x | $\triangle$ A
3 | | | | $--Fx$ 1, DNI (incorrect)
4 | | | $(x)--Fx$ 2-3, UG
5 | | $Fx \supset (x)--Fx$ 1-4, CP

So, once again, violating the restrictions would destroy the soundness of UG. Therefore all the restrictions are necessary.†

On the other hand, it is permissible to use previous steps which contain bound occurrences of 'x' in restricted subproofs as long as these steps do not also contain free occurrences of 'x'. This is because in such steps 'x' is bound to quantifiers; so the "previous information" we have about x represents "information" about objects in general.

Now let us summarize UG and the concomitant restrictions.

UG x | $\triangle$ A
            | .
            | .
            | .
            | $(\cdots x \cdots)$
       $(x)(\cdots x \cdots)$ UG

---

†In the Appendix the soundness of this and all the other rules will be demonstrated. This will show that the restrictions are also sufficient.

Restrictions:

1   No steps containing free 'x' may be reiterated into a restricted subproof.
2   No previous step containing a free occurrence of 'x' may be used in an application of a rule of inference to produce a new step which is to appear in a restricted subproof *unless* the previous step already occurs in the subproof. (It must also meet the other restrictions on lines of argument, etc.)

Now for some more examples using UG.

EXAMPLES

a.   To derive '$(x)Fx$' from '$(x)(Fx \cdot Gx) \cdot Hx$'.

Derivation: (Worked out)

(1) | $(x)(Fx \cdot Gx) \cdot Hx$ P   (2) | $(x)(Fx \cdot Gx) \cdot Hx$ P
      | ? | $(x)(Fx \cdot Gx)$ S
      | $(x)Fx$ x| △   A
                                                       | ?
                                                       | Fx
                                                       | $(x)Fx$ UG

(3)   1| $(x)(Fx \cdot Gx) \cdot Hx$ P
      2| $(x)(Fx \cdot Gx)$ 1, S
      3| x| △   A
      4| | $Fx \cdot Gx$ 2, UI
      5| | Fx 4, S
      6| $(x)Fx$ 3-5, UG

Comment: Simplification must be applied to step 1 *first* because it contains a free occurrence of 'x'. Otherwise '$Fx \cdot Gx$' could not be obtained in the restricted subproof.

b.   To derive '$(x)Fx$' from '$-(\exists x) - Fx$'.

Derivation: (Worked out)

(1) | $-(\exists x) - Fx$ P   (2) | $-(\exists x) - Fx$ P
      | ? x| △
      | $(x)Fx$ | ?
                                                  | Fx
                                                  | $(x)Fx$

(3) | $-(\exists x) - Fx$ P
   x| △   A
      | | $-Fx$ A

```
  | | | ?
  | | | − −Fx            IP
  | | Fx                 DNE
  | (x)Fx                UG
```

(4) 1 | −(∃x) − Fx   P
    2 | x | △   A
    3 | | | −Fx   A
    4 | | | (∃x) − Fx   3, EG
    5 | | | −(∃x) − Fx   1, R
    6 | | − − Fx   3-5, IP
    7 | | Fx   6, DNE
    8 | (x)Fx   2-7, UG

c.   To derive '(x)(p ⊃ Fx)' from 'p ⊃ (x)Fx'.

Derivation: (Partially worked out)

(1) | p ⊃ (x)Fx   P   (2) | p ⊃ (x)Fx   P
    | ? | x | △   A
    | (x)(p ⊃ Fx) | | ?
                                  | | p ⊃ Fx
                                    | (x)(p ⊃ Fx)   UG

(3) | p ⊃ (x)(Fx)   P
    | x | △   A
    | | | p   A
    | | | ?
    | | | Fx
    | | p ⊃ Fx   CP
    | (x)(p ⊃ Fx)   UG

(*Exercise:*   Complete the derivation.)

d.   To derive '(∃x)Fx' from '−(x) − Fx'.

Derivation: (Partially worked out)

(1) | −(x) − Fx   P   (2) | −(x) − Fx   P
    | ? | | −(∃x)Fx   A
    | (∃x)Fx | | ?
                                      | − −(∃x)Fx   IP
                                      | (∃x)Fx   DNE

(3) | −(x) − Fx   P
    | | −(∃x)(Fx)   A
    | | x | △   A

$$
\begin{array}{ll}
\quad\quad\quad ? & \\
\quad\quad\quad -Fx & \\
\quad\quad (x)-Fx & \text{UG} \\
\quad\quad -(x)-Fx & \text{R} \\
\quad --(\exists x)Fx & \text{IP} \\
\quad (\exists x)Fx & \text{DNE}
\end{array}
$$

(*Exercise:* Complete this derivation. *Hint:* Use IP.)

Comment: Experimentation should convince you that replacing (2) above by

(2′) $-(x)-Fx$

.

.

.

Fx

$(\exists x)Fx$ EG

would prove to be futile.

e.   To derive '$(x)(Fx \lor p)$' from '$(x)Fx \lor p$'.

Derivation: (Partially worked out)

(1) $\begin{array}{ll} (x)Fx \lor p & \text{P} \\ ? & \\ (x)(Fx \lor p) & \end{array}$ (2) $\begin{array}{ll} (x)Fx \lor p & \text{P} \\ x\ \triangle & \text{A} \\ \quad (x)Fx \lor p & \text{R} \\ \quad ? & \\ \quad Fx \lor p & \\ (x)(Fx \lor p) & \text{UG} \end{array}$

(*Exercise:* Complete this derivation. *Hint:* Obtain '$Fx \lor p$' by SD and use CP to obtain the two required conditionals.)

f.   To derive '$(x)Fx \lor p$' from '$(x)(Fx \lor p)$'.

Derivation: (Partially worked out)

(1) $\begin{array}{ll} (x)(Fx \lor p) & \\ ? & \\ (x)Fx \lor p & \end{array}$ (2) $\begin{array}{ll} (x)(Fx \lor p) & \\ \quad -[(x)Fx \lor p] & \text{A} \\ \quad ? & \\ --[(x)Fx \lor p] & \text{IP} \\ (x)Fx \lor p & \text{DNE} \end{array}$

(3) $\begin{array}{ll} (x)(Fx \lor p) & \text{P} \\ \quad -[(x)Fx \lor p] & \text{A} \\ \quad . & \\ \quad . & \end{array}$ (4) $\begin{array}{ll} (x)(Fx \lor p) & \text{P} \\ \quad -[(x)Fx \lor p] & \text{A} \\ \quad . & \\ \quad . & \end{array}$

$$\begin{array}{ll}
\vdots & \\
-(x)Fx & \\
\vdots & \\
\vdots & \\
-p & \\
x\ \triangle & \text{A} \\
\ ? & \\
\ Fx & \\
(x)Fx & \text{UG} \\
--[(x)Fx \lor p] & \text{IP} \\
(x)Fx \lor p & \text{DNE}
\end{array}$$

$$\begin{array}{ll}
\vdots & \\
-(x)Fx & \\
\vdots & \\
\vdots & \\
-p & \\
x\ \triangle & \text{A} \\
\quad -Fx & \text{A} \\
\quad Fx \lor p & \text{UI} \\
\quad Fx & \text{DS} \\
\quad --Fx & \text{IP} \\
\quad Fx & \text{DNE} \\
(x)Fx & \text{UG} \\
--[(x)Fx \lor p] & \text{IP} \\
(x)Fx \lor p & \text{DNE}
\end{array}$$

(*Exercise:* Complete this derivation. *Hint:* Two uses of IP and truth-functional rules will do the job easily.)

Comment: This example is unusually difficult because the restrictions on UG block the most obvious moves to make in constructing a derivation in this case. Yet if one can take simple truth-function steps "in the head" — this corresponds to the parts left for completion — a solution can be found fairly quickly. This comment also applies to the next example, which is also fairly difficult.

g.   To derive '$(\exists x)(Fx \supset p)$' from '$(x)Fx \supset p$'.

Derivation: (Partially worked out)

(1)
$$\begin{array}{ll}
(x)Fx \supset p & \text{P} \\
? & \\
(\exists x)(Fx \supset p) &
\end{array}$$

(2)
$$\begin{array}{ll}
(x)Fx \supset p & \text{P} \\
\quad -(\exists x)(Fx \supset p) & \text{A} \\
\quad ? & \\
\quad \vdots & \\
\quad \vdots & \\
\quad \vdots & \\
\quad (\exists x)(Fx \supset p) &
\end{array}$$

(3)
$$\begin{array}{ll}
(x)Fx \supset p & \text{P} \\
\quad -(\exists x)(Fx \supset p) & \text{A} \\
\quad x\ \triangle & \text{A} \\
\quad\quad ? & \\
\quad\quad Fx & \\
\quad (x)Fx & \text{UG} \\
\quad \vdots &
\end{array}$$

(4)
$$\begin{array}{ll}
(x)Fx \supset p & \text{P} \\
\quad -(\exists x)(Fx \supset p) & \text{A} \\
\quad x\ \triangle & \text{A} \\
\quad\quad -Fx & \text{A} \\
\quad\quad \vdots & \\
\quad\quad \vdots & \\
\quad\quad \vdots &
\end{array}$$

$$
\begin{array}{l}
\quad\quad \cdot \\
\quad\quad \cdot \\
(\exists x)(Fx \supset p) \\
\quad\quad \cdot \\
\quad\quad \cdot \\
\quad\quad \cdot \\
(\exists x)(Fx \supset p)
\end{array}
$$

$$
\begin{array}{ll}
Fx \supset p & \\
(\exists x)(Fx \supset p) & \text{EG} \\
-(\exists x)(Fx \supset p) & \text{R} \\
--Fx & \text{IP} \\
Fx & \text{DNE} \\
(x)Fx & \text{UG} \\
\quad\quad \cdot & \\
\quad\quad \cdot & \\
\quad\quad \cdot & \\
(\exists x)(Fx \supset p) & \text{EG} \\
\quad\quad \cdot & \\
\quad\quad \cdot & \\
\quad\quad \cdot & \\
(\exists x)(Fx \supset p) &
\end{array}
$$

(*Exercise:* Complete this derivation. *Hint:* '$Fx \supset p$' can be derived from 'p' and also from '$-Fx$'.)

EXERCISES FOR SEC. 2.3.5

A. Supply the reasons for these derivations.

1.
$$
\begin{array}{lll}
1 & (x)Fx & \text{P} \\
2 & x \quad \triangle & \\
3 & \quad Fx & \\
4 & \quad --Fx & \\
5 & \quad Fx \cdot --Fx & \\
6 & (x)(Fx \cdot --Fx) &
\end{array}
$$

2.
$$
\begin{array}{lll}
1 & p & \text{P} \\
2 & x \quad \triangle & \\
3 & \quad\quad Fx & \\
4 & \quad\quad p \cdot Fx & \\
5 & \quad Fx \supset p \cdot Fx & \\
6 & (x)(Fx \supset p \cdot Fx) &
\end{array}
$$

3.
$$
\begin{array}{lll}
1 & (x)Fx \supset (x)Gx & \text{P} \\
2 & (x)(Fx \cdot Gx) & \text{P} \\
3 & x \quad \triangle & \\
4 & \quad Fx \cdot Gx & \\
5 & \quad Fx & \\
6 & (x)Fx & \\
7 & (x)Gx &
\end{array}
$$

4.
$$
\begin{array}{lll}
1 & x \quad \triangle & \\
2 & \quad\quad Fx & \\
3 & \quad Fx \supset Fx & \\
4 & (x)(Fx \supset Fx) & \\
5 & x \quad \triangle &
\end{array}
$$

$$
\begin{array}{ll}
6 & \quad\ \ \ Fx \\
7 & \quad\ \ \ Fx \lor Gx \\
8 & \quad\ \ Fx \supset (Fx \lor Gx) \\
9 & (x)(Fx \supset (Fx \lor Gx)) \\
10 & (x)(Fx \supset (Fx \lor Gx)) \cdot (x)(Fx \supset Fx)
\end{array}
$$

B. Prove these OVQS.

1. $(x)(Fx \cdot Gx) \supset (x)(Fx \lor Hx)$
2. $(x)(Fx \lor Gx) \cdot (x) - Fx \supset (x)Gx$
3. $((\exists x)Fx \supset p) \supset (x)(Fx \supset p)$
4. $((x)Fx \lor p) \supset (x)(Fx \lor p)$
5. $(x)(Fx \supset Gx) \supset (x)(-Gx \supset -Fx)$
6. $(x)(Fx \lor Gx) \supset (x) - (-Fx \cdot -Gx)$
7. $(x) - (Fx \cdot -Fx)$
8. $-(x)(Fx \cdot Gx) \cdot (x)Fx \supset -(x)Gx$
9. $(x)((Fx \supset Fx) \cdot p) \equiv p$
10. $(x)(p \lor Fx) \supset -(\bar{p} \cdot -(x)Fx)$

2.3.6 EXISTENTIAL INSTANTIATION

Our final rule will permit us to drop existential quantifiers, and for this reason it is called *existential instantiation* (EI, for short). This rule, which also makes use of restricted subproofs, has an informal counterpart. Consequently, it may be easier to understand the rule if we study some informal examples first.

EXAMPLE FROM MATHEMATICS. To prove that if $a < b$, then $a < b + 1$, given that $a < b \equiv (\exists x)(a + (x + 1) = b)$.

Informal Proof: Suppose that $a < b$. Then $(\exists x)(a + (x + 1) = b)$. Now let x be any object such that $a + (x + 1) = b$. Then $a + (x + 1) + 1 = b + 1$. Taking c as $x + 1$, we have $a + (c + 1) = b + 1$. Hence $(\exists x)(a + (x + 1) = b + 1)$. So $a < b + 1$.

EXAMPLE FROM LOGIC. To prove if $S \cdot W$ is consistent, so is S.

Informal Proof: Suppose that $S \cdot W$ is consistent. Then there is a true interpretation of $S \cdot W$ in some universe. Let U be such a universe and I a true interpretation of $S \cdot W$ in U. Then I also interprets S as true in U. So there is a true interpretation of S in some universe, and S is consistent.

These arguments proceed as follows: We start with an existential quantification '$(\exists x)(\cdots x \cdots)$'. Given the truth of this, there must be at least one object which satisfies the condition '$(\cdots x \cdots)$'. Consequently, we are justified in picking an object to represent any and all the objects which satisfy the condition. However, except for satisfying this condition, the object must be treated as entirely arbitrary. Then we continue our argument until we establish a statement which is not about our representative object. Now we are safe; having dispensed with the arbitrary object, we can return to the original line of argument from which we started.

Schematically:

$(\exists x)(\cdots x \cdots)$

Let x be any object such that $(\cdots x \cdots)$

.

.

.

        A (A does not mention x)

Once we reach 'A', the restrictions on x may be dropped.

Drawing upon the lessons we learned from UG, we can begin to formulate our new rule by using restricted subproofs. Thus we should start with

$(\exists x)(\cdots x \cdots)$

$\quad x|(\cdots x \cdots)\quad$ A

.

.

.

Unlike a UG subproof, this restricted subproof is permitted to have a schema as an assumption. The object x does not have to be completely arbitrary, because it is supposed to be one of the x's which makes '$(\exists x)(\cdots x \cdots)$' true. Consequently, we can assume that x is arbitrary except for satisfying '$(\cdots x \cdots)$'. This object is to count as arbitrary until we no longer need it, that is, until we can deduce a statement which is not about it in particular. Formally, this corresponds to deriving a schema which does not contain free occurrences of 'x'. Letting W stand for such a schema, our formal schema must be continued to

$(\exists x)(\cdots x \cdots)$

$\quad x|\quad(\cdots x \cdots)\quad$ A

.

.

.

$\quad W\quad$ (W does not contain free occurrences of 'x'.)

Since we no longer need to treat 'x' as standing for an arbitrary object, we can terminate the restricted subproof and write W at a less subordinate line of argument.

Schematically:

$(\exists x)(\cdots x \cdots)$

$\quad x|\quad(\cdots x \cdots)\quad$ A

.

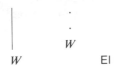

W   EI

Naturally, we must still give a precise formulation to EI. The first step toward doing this is to extend the rule of assumption once again by means of a new clause. This will justify initiating EI subproofs.

New clause to the rule of assumption: *If the schema $(\exists x)S_x$ is the last step to date in a derivation, then we may write S_x as the next step provided that we simultaneously initiate a new vertical line and write 'x' to the left of it.*

The restricted subproofs initiated by means of this clause of the rule of assumption will be called *EI subproofs*. The two restrictions concerning reiteration and the premisses for rules of inference in UG subproofs continue to hold for EI subproofs.

The rule of existential instantiation may now be stated.

Rule of existential instantiation: *Suppose that W is the last step to date in an EI subproof whose assumption is S_x. Then, if W does not contain free occurrences of 'x', the EI subproof may be discontinued and W may be written again as the next line (and outside the EI subproof).*

Reason: A numeral referring to $(\exists x)S_x$, hyphenated numerals referring to S_x and W, followed by 'EI'.

Before demonstrating the necessity for the restrictions on EI subproofs, let us illustrate EI with several examples.

EXAMPLES

a.   To derive '$(\exists x)(Fx \lor Gx)$' from '$(\exists x)Fx$'.

Derivation:

(1)   1 | $(\exists x)Fx$ P
      2 | x | Fx A
      3 | | $Fx \lor Gx$ 2, add
      4 | | $(\exists x)(Fx \lor Gx)$ 3, EG
      5 | $(\exists x)(Fx \lor Gx)$ 1, 2-4, EI

Comment: Before a restricted EI subproof can be terminated, we must obtain a schema which does not have free occurrences of 'x'. Since '$(\exists x)(Fx \lor Gx)$' does not, and since this was the conclusion we were aiming for, it also made an appropriate conclusion for the restricted EI subproof.

b. To derive '$(\exists x)Fx$' from '$(x)(Gx \supset Fx)$' and '$(\exists x)Gx$'.

Derivation: (Worked out)

(1) | $(x)(Gx \supset Fx)$ P   (2) | $(x)(Gx \supset Fx)$ P
     | $(\exists x)Gx$ P | $(\exists x)Gx$ P
     | ? x| Gx A
     | $(\exists x)Fx$ | ?
                                                 | $(\exists x)Fx$
                                             | $(\exists x)Fx$ EI

(3) 1| $(x)(Gx \supset Fx)$ P
     2| $(\exists x)Gx$ P
     3|x| Gx A
     4| | $Gx \supset Fx$ 1, UI
     5| | Fx 3, 4, MP
     6| | $(\exists x)Fx$ 5, EG
     7| $(\exists x)Fx$ 2, 3-6, EI

Comment: Frequently, in dropping quantifiers while constructing a derivation, one has a choice between dropping universal or existential quantifiers
first. Since dropping existential quantifiers entails initiating restricted subproofs, it is usually wiser to drop these first. Then one is always free to drop
the universal quantifiers later, because the universal quantifications do not
contain free occurrences of 'x'.

c. To derive '$-(x)Fx$' from '$(\exists x) - Fx$'.

Derivation: (Worked out)

(1) | $(\exists x) - Fx$ P   (2) | $(\exists x) - Fx$ P
     | ? | $(x)Fx$ A
     | $-(x)Fx$ | ?
                                              | $-(x)Fx$ IP

(3) | $(\exists x) - Fx$ P
     | | $(x)Fx$ A
     | | $(\exists x) - Fx$ R
     | |x| $-Fx$ A
     | | | ?
     | | ?   EI
     | $-(x)Fx$ IP

(4) 1| $(\exists x) - Fx$ P
     2| | $(x)Fx$ A
     3| | $(\exists x) - Fx$ 1, R
     4| |x| $-Fx$ A
     5| | | Fx 2, UI

6		$Fx \lor -(\exists x) - Fx$	5, add
7		$-(\exists x) - Fx$	5, 4, DS
8		$-(\exists x) - Fx$	3, 4-7, EI
9	$-(x)Fx$		2-8, IP

Comment: We need to derive a contradiction from '$(x)Fx$' in order to use IP, and we already have one in 'Fx' and '$-Fx$'. However, these appear inside a restricted EI subproof; so neither they nor their conjunction can be brought out of it. Yet, from a schema and its negation, we can derive any schema. So all we have to do is derive any schema which does not contain free occurrences of 'x' and which negates something already obtained in the derivation. This was done by deriving '$-(\exists x) - Fx$' from 'Fx' and '$-Fx$'.

Now we are in a better position to appreciate the restrictions that govern EI. Their necessity will be demonstrated by showing that relaxing anyone of them permits the derivation of invalid schemata.

First, let us relax the restriction on the assumptions in EI subproofs. Then, for example, we can prove the invalid schema '$(\exists x)Fx \supset (\exists x)Gx$':

1		$(\exists x)Fx$	A
2	x	Gx	A (incorrect)
3		$(\exists x)Gx$	2, EG
4		$(\exists x)Gx$	1, 2-3, EI
5	$(\exists x)Fx \supset (\exists x)Gx$		1-4, CP

Next let us relax the restrictions on reiteration into restricted subproofs. Then we can prove the invalid schema '$(\exists x)Fx \cdot (\exists x)Gx \supset (\exists x)(Fx \cdot Gx)$'.

1	$(\exists x)Fx \cdot (\exists x)Gx$	A
2	$(\exists x)Fx$	1, S
3	x Fx	A
4	$(\exists x)Gx$	1, S
5	x Gx	A
6	Fx	3, R (incorrect)
7	$Fx \cdot Gx$	5, 6 PC
8	$(\exists x)(Fx \cdot Gx)$	7, EG
9	$(\exists x)(Fx \cdot Gx)$	4, 5-8, EI
10	$(\exists x)(Fx \cdot Gx)$	2, 3-9, EI
11	$(\exists x)Fx \cdot (\exists x)Gx \supset (\exists x)(Fx \cdot Gx)$	1-10, CP

If we relax the restriction on the rules of inference, then we need only make a simple modification of this derivation to obtain one of the invalid schema, '$(\exists x)Fx \cdot (\exists x)Gx \supset (\exists x)(--Fx \cdot Gx)$'. Step 6 is replaced by '$--Fx$', and 'Fx' in all subsequent steps (except for its first occurrence in step 11) is replaced by '$--Fx$'. The reasons remain the same except for step 6. This has as its reason: 3, DNI. Consequently, this step is also incorrect.

The upshot of these examples is that, without the restrictions, EI would not be a sound rule of inference.

EXAMPLES

a.   To derive '$(\exists x)Fx \lor (\exists x)Gx$' from '$(\exists x)(Fx \lor Gx)$'.

Derivation: (Partially worked out)

(1) | $(\exists x)(Fx \lor Gx)$ P   (2) | $(\exists x)(Fx \lor Gx)$ P
? | x | $Fx \lor Gx$ A
$(\exists x)Fx \lor (\exists x)Gx$ | ?
| $(\exists x)Fx \lor (\exists x)Gx$
| $(\exists x)Fx \lor (\exists x)Gx$ EI

(3) | $(\exists x)(Fx \lor Gx)$ P
x | $Fx \lor Gx$ A
| Fx A
| $(\exists x)Fx$ EG
| $(\exists x)Fx \lor (\exists x)Gx$ add
| $Fx \supset [(\exists x)Fx \lor (\exists x)Gx]$ CP
| ?
| $(\exists x)Fx \lor (\exists x)Gx$ SD
$(\exists x)Fx \lor (\exists x)Gx$ EI

(*Exercise:*   Complete this derivation.)

b.   To derive '$(\exists x)(Fx \lor Gx)$' from '$(\exists x)Fx \lor (\exists x)Gx$'.

Derivation: (Partially worked out)

(1) | $(\exists x)Fx \lor (\exists x)Gx$ P
? |
$(\exists x)(Fx \lor (Gx)$ |

(2) | $(\exists x)Fx \lor (\exists x)Gx$ A
| $(\exists x)Fx$ A
x | Fx A
| $Fx \lor Gx$ add
| $(\exists x)(Fx \lor Gx)$ EG
| $(\exists x)(Fx \lor Gx)$ EI
| $(\exists x)Fx \supset (\exists x)(Fx \lor Gx)$ CP
| ?
| $(\exists x)(Fx \lor Gx)$ SD

(*Exercise:* Complete this derivation.)

c. To derive '$p \supset (\exists x)Fx$' from '$(\exists x)(p \supset Fx)$'.

Derivation: (Partially worked out)

(1) | $(\exists x)(p \supset Fx$ P   (2) | $(\exists x)(p \supset Fx)$ P
     | ? | x| $p \supset Fx$ A
     | $p \supset (\exists x)Fx$ | | ?
                                                    | | $p \supset (\exists x)Fx$
                                                    | $p \supset (\exists x)Fx$ EI

(3) | $(\exists x)(p \supset Fx)$ P
     | x| $p \supset Fx$ A
     | | | p A
     | | | ?
     | | $(\exists x)Fx$
     | | $p \supset (\exists x)Fx$ CP
     | $p \supset (\exists x)Fx$ EI

(*Exercise:* Complete this derivation.)

d. To derive '$(\exists x)(p \supset Fx)$' from '$p \supset (\exists x)Fx$'.

Derivation: (Partially worked out)

(1) | $p \supset (\exists x)Fx$ P   (2) | $p \supset (\exists x)Fx$ P
     | ? | | $-(\exists x)(p \supset Fx)$ A
     | $(\exists x)(p \supset Fx)$ | | ?
                                                    | ?
                                                    | $(\exists x)(p \supset Fx)$

(3) | $p \supset (\exists x)Fx$ P   (4) | $p \supset (\exists x)Fx$ P
     | | $-(\exists x)(p \supset Fx)$ A | | $-(\exists x)(p \supset Fx)$ A
     | | ? | | | $-p$ A
     | | p | | | ?
     | | $(\exists x)Fx$ MP | | | $p \supset Fx$
     | | x| Fx A | | | $(\exists x)(p \supset Fx)$ EG
     | | | ? | | | $-(\exists x)(p \supset Fx)$ R
     | | | $p \supset Fx$ | | $--p$ IP
     | | | $(\exists x)(p \supset Fx)$ EG | | p DNE
     | | $(\exists x)(p \supset Fx)$ EI | | $(\exists x)Fx$ MP
     | | ? | | x| Fx A
     | $(\exists x)(p \supset Fx)$ | | | ?
                                                        | | | $p \supset Fx$
                                                        | | | $(\exists x)(p \supset Fx)$ EG

$$\left|\; \begin{array}{l} | \quad (\exists x)(p \supset Fx) \qquad \text{EI} \\ ? \\ (\exists x)(p \supset Fx) \end{array}\right.$$

(*Exercise:* Complete this derivation.)

Comment: This example is difficult since the restrictions block the obvious move, namely, to set up the derivation as follows:

$$\left|\; \begin{array}{l} p \supset (\exists x)Fx \\ \quad \left|\; \begin{array}{l} p \\ (\exists x)Fx \\ \quad x\left|\; \begin{array}{l} Fx \\ ? \end{array}\right. \\ Fx \end{array}\right. \\ p \supset Fx \\ (\exists x)(p \supset Fx) \end{array}\right.$$

The next example is much easier.

e.   To derive '$(\exists x)Fx \supset p$' from '$(x)(Fx \supset p)$'.

Derivation: (Partially worked out)

(1) $\left|\; \begin{array}{ll} (x)(Fx \supset p) & \text{P} \\ ? \\ (\exists x)Fx \supset p \end{array}\right.$ (2) $\left|\; \begin{array}{ll} (x)(Fx \supset p) & \text{P} \\ \quad \left|\; \begin{array}{l} (\exists x)Fx \qquad \text{A} \\ ? \\ p \end{array}\right. \\ (\exists x)Fx \supset p & \text{CP} \end{array}\right.$

(3) $\left|\; \begin{array}{ll} (x)(Fx \supset p) & \text{P} \\ \quad \left|\; \begin{array}{l} (\exists x)Fx \qquad\qquad \text{A} \\ \quad x\left|\; \begin{array}{l} Fx \qquad\qquad \text{A} \\ ? \\ p \end{array}\right. \\ p \qquad\qquad\qquad \text{EI} \end{array}\right. \\ (\exists x)Fx \supset p & \text{CP} \end{array}\right.$

(*Exercise:* Complete this derivation.)

EXERCISES FOR SEC. 2.3.6

A.   Supply reasons for these derivations.

1. $\begin{array}{ll} 1 & | \quad (\exists x)(Fx \cdot Gx) \qquad\qquad \text{P} \\ 2 & x| \quad Fx \cdot Gx \end{array}$

$$
\begin{array}{ll}
3 & \quad\quad Fx \\
4 & \quad\quad --Fx \\
5 & \quad\quad (\exists x)--Fx \\
6 & \quad (\exists x)--Fx
\end{array}
$$

2.
$$
\begin{array}{lll}
1 & \quad (\exists x)((x)Fx \cdot Gx) & \quad\quad P \\
2 & \quad x\;\; (x)Fx \cdot Gx & \\
3 & \quad\quad Gx & \\
4 & \quad\quad (\exists x)Gx & \\
5 & \quad\quad (x)Fx & \\
6 & \quad\quad x\;\; \triangle & \\
7 & \quad\quad\quad Fx & \\
8 & \quad\quad\quad Fx \cdot (\exists x)Gx & \\
9 & \quad\quad (x)(Fx \cdot (\exists x)Gx) & \\
10 & \quad (x)(Fx \cdot (\exists x)Gx) &
\end{array}
$$

3.
$$
\begin{array}{lll}
1 & \quad (x)Fx & \quad\quad P \\
2 & \quad (\exists x)-Fx & \quad\quad P \\
3 & \quad x\;\; -Fx & \\
4 & \quad\quad Fx & \\
5 & \quad\quad Fx \vee p & \\
6 & \quad\quad p & \\
7 & \quad p &
\end{array}
$$

4.
$$
\begin{array}{lll}
1 & \quad (x)Fx & \quad\quad P \\
2 & \quad x\;\; \triangle & \\
3 & \quad\quad\quad (\exists x)Gx & \\
4 & \quad\quad\quad x\;\; Gx & \\
5 & \quad\quad\quad Fx & \\
6 & \quad\quad\quad Gx \cdot Fx & \\
7 & \quad\quad\quad (\exists x)(Gx \cdot Fx) & \\
8 & \quad\quad\quad (\exists x)(Gx \cdot Fx) & \\
9 & \quad\quad\quad (\exists x)(Gx \cdot Fx) \vee Hx & \\
10 & \quad\quad (\exists x)Gx \supset ((\exists x)(Gx \cdot Fx) \vee Hx) & \\
11 & \quad (x)((\exists x)Gx) \supset ((\exists x)(Gx \cdot Fx) \vee Hx)) &
\end{array}
$$

B. Prove these OVQS.

1. $(x)(Fx \supset Gx) \supset -(\exists x)(Fx \cdot -Gx)$

2. $(\exists x)(Fx \cdot Gx) \supset (\exists x)Fx \cdot (\exists x)Gx$

3. $(\exists x)Fx \supset (\exists x)(Gx \supset Fx)$

4. $(x)(Fx \supset Gx) \supset ((\exists x)-Gx \supset (\exists x)-Fx)$

5. $(\exists x)Fx \cdot p \equiv (\exists x)(Fx \cdot p)$

6 $-(\exists x)Fx \supset (x)(Fx \supset Gx)$

7. $((\exists x)Fx \supset (x)Fx) \supset -((\exists x)Fx \cdot (\exists x)-Fx)$

8. $((\exists x)Fx \supset (x)Fx) \supset ((x)Fx \vee (x)-Fx)$

9. $(\exists x)(Fx \supset (x)Fx)$

10. $(\exists x)((\exists x)Fx \supset Fx)$

2.4 PARAPHRASING AND DIAGRAMMING STATEMENTS

We have already touched briefly upon the problem of paraphrasing statements involving quantification. This brief discussion, occurring as it did

when the quantifiers were first introduced, helped to familiarize us with quantification. However, now we must approach the more difficult task of paraphrasing. For statement paraphrasing followed by statement dia-gramming is essential to the application of formal logic to arguments in ordinary language. This should be a familiar story by now. Unfortunately, it is also by now familiar that paraphrasing can be taught only by example and learned only by osmosis and imitation. With this in mind, let us turn to some of the new problems that confront us now that not only truth-functional connectives but also quantifiers are present.

2.4.1   VARIANTS ON THE FORM: ALL F ARE G

Statements of the form 'All F are G' such as

All whales are mammals
All my friends are hoboes
All mynahs are birds
All Mary's brothers are lawyers

assert that all things which are F—whales, my friends, mynahs, Mary's brothers—are G—respectively, mammals, hoboes, birds, lawyers. Conse-quently, they may be paraphrased by statements of the form '$(x)(Fx \supset Gx)$'. There are many obvious variants to the form "All F are G", and they can be easily spotted. Here are some examples of variants of the four examples given above:

Each whale is a mammal.
Any friend of mine is a hobo.
Every mynah is a bird.
All Mary's brothers have become lawyers.

Generally, any statement which asserts that each thing which is an F is also a G may be paraphrased similarly. The problem is one of determining which statements make such assertions.

The problem can be made easier by learning a few of the common forms which such claims may take. The following is a list of some, but not all, of these forms, each being accompanied by an example:

F are G: Lions are carnivorous.
F G: Cats care for their young.
The F is a G: The elephant is a large animal.
An F is a G: A shark is a dangerous fish.
F are always G: Triangles are always three-sided.
F are universally G: Murderers are universally dangerous.
What F's G's: What goes up comes down.
If it is an F, it is a G: If it is a jet, it is a plane.

Paraphrases of these examples are thus

$(x)(x$ is a lion $\supset x$ is carnivorous)
$(x)(x$ is a cat $\supset x$ cares for its young)
$(x)(x$ is an elephant $\supset x$ is a large animal)
$(x)(x$ is a shark $\supset x$ is a dangerous fish)
$(x)(x$ is a triangle $\supset x$ is three-sided)
$(x)(x$ is a murderer $\supset x$ is dangerous)
$(x)(x$ goes up $\supset x$ comes down)
$(x)(x$ is a jet $\supset x$ is a plane)

However, even these forms are not always tantamount to '$(x)(Fx \supset Gx)$', and one must be on the lookout for exceptions. For example,

Congressmen are visiting Leavenworth

does not usually mean that all congressmen are visiting Leavenworth, but rather that some congressmen are visiting it. Again,

The captain is a good man

is usually about one man and has the form 'Fa' as opposed to

The captain is an army officer who outranks lieutenants

which is generally intended to refer to all army captains.
   Another exception is

An elegant woman is a hostess at Charlie's

which is paraphrased by

$(\exists x)(x$ is an elegant woman $\cdot x$ is a hostess at Charlie's)

and so contrasts with

An elegant woman is beautiful to behold

or in other terms,

$(x)(x$ is an elegant woman $\supset x$ is beautiful to behold)

Similarly, contrast the pair

What I want is what I get.
What I want is a strong drink.

The first may be rendered

$(x)($ I want $x \supset$ I get $x)$

while the second is merely a reformulation of the simple-subject–predicate statement

I want a strong drink.

There is a more amusing type of exception that is well known to logicians. Examples of this type are the following statements:

Highwaymen are numerous.
Geniuses are few.
Applicants are lacking.
The wicked are plentiful.
The eagle is becoming extinct.

These statements are best viewed as asserting something about a whole class rather than about the individual members of this class. Thus, when we say that geniuses are few, we mean that there are not many of them, we do not mean that Einstein, say, is few. Thus such statements should *not* be paraphrased by statements of the form '$(x)(Fx \supset Gx)$'. Failure to recognize this can lead to silly arguments, which have served as logician's jokes, such as the following:

Hawaiians are dying out: $(x)(x$ is a Hawaiian $\supset x$ is dying out)
Kimo is a Hawaiian: Kimo is a Hawaiian.
∴ Kimo is dying out: Kimo is dying out. (UI, MP)

One should not regard these or any other exceptions with mere idle curiosity. They have been offered to emphasize how fallible our "rules" for paraphrasing can be. This is an area in which each statement must be viewed as unique, and paraphrased by means of sympathetic attention to context and the author's probable intention. The sooner one appreciates this, the fewer mistakes in paraphrasing one will make.

Another family of statements fall into the 'All F are G' category, but beginners often find them difficult to recognize because F and G appear in reverse order. Three, but not all, of the forms that such statements take follow, with examples:

Only G are F: Only the rich are members of Old Oak.
None but G are F: None but A students are honors graduates.
All is G that is F: All is well that ends well.

The first statement does not assert that all rich people are members of Old Oak; it asserts that all members of Old Oak are rich. Likewise, the second statement affirms that all honors graduates are A students, and not that all A students are honors graduates. The last statement similarly says that all that ends well is well, and not that all that is well also ends well. Here are more examples in this general family:

None but the brave deserve the fair.

They also serve who only stand and wait.
God helps them that help themselves.
Base is the slave that pays.
Only the godless are damned.

And their paraphrases:

$(x)(x$ deserves the fair $\supset x$ is brave)
$(x)(x$ is a person who stands and waits $\supset x$ also serves)
$(x)(x$ is a person who helps himself $\supset$ God helps $x)$
$(x)(x$ is a slave that pays $\supset x$ is base)
$(x)(x$ is damned $\supset x$ is godless)

Finally, let us collect a few odds and ends that deserve mention. First, there is the use of pronouns as substitute universal quantifiers. Some examples of this have already appeared, but here is another:

He who hesitates is lost.

This paraphrases as

$(x)(x$ is a person who hesitates $\supset x$ is lost)

A related construction is found in 'all who', 'each one who', etc., as in

All who attended voted

which is paraphrased by

$(x)(x$ is a person who attended $\supset x$ voted)

Of course, this use of pronouns must not be confused with their use to refer to definite things. The contrast is brought out by means of the following pair of statements:

He who does evil will be punished.
He does evil and will be punished.

Another method for saying that 'All F are G' is supplied by infinitives. A couple of examples follow:

To know her is to love her.
To live is to suffer.

Their respective paraphrases are thus

$(x)(x$ knows her $\supset x$ loves her)
$(x)(x$ lives $\supset x$ suffers)

As a final device, let us consider disclaimer phrases such as 'no matter who', 'even the oldest', and 'no matter how'. This use is illustrated in the following examples:

No matter how stupid she may be, a beautiful woman merits attention.
No matter who requests admission, he will be denied.
Even the largest man can get through this hole.
The smallest worm will squirm when stepped upon.

These phrases serve as substitute universal quantifiers, since, by denying the existence of the most likely type of exception to a given regularity, they implicitly assert that there are no exceptions. So they may be put as follows:

$(x)(x$ is a beautiful woman $\supset x$ merits attention)
$(x)(x$ requests admission $\supset x$ will be denied)
$(x)(x$ is a man $\supset x$ gets through this hole)
$(x)(x$ is a worm $\supset x$ will squirm if stepped upon)

EXERCISES FOR SEC. 2.4.1

Paraphrase these statements, using logical notation. Reveal as much logical structure as possible, and insert necessary parentheses.

1. Bats are mammals.
2. Sparrows are not mammals.
3. The horse is a hooved animal.
4. All students who took the test passed.
5. Each person will be granted a hearing.
6. Any student who applies will be admitted.
7. Squares are rectangles, but not all rectangles are squares.
8. The mayor is a good man, but the senator is not.
9. Dogs have paws.
10. Dogs stole the meat.
11. A cool drink is always refreshing.
12. Although the pretenders were many, the genuine kings were few.
13. Only those who study will pass.
14. Those who study hard will pass.
15. Every finger was painted.
16. All and only those who apply will be given permission.
17. He who seeks will find.
18. None but those who seek deserve to find.
19. Sad is the man who frowns.
20. The team members will bring dates.
21. To try is to succeed, but to despair is to fail.
22. Gentlemen are always well-born and educated.

23. Only licensed physicians can charge for medical treatment.
24. Shark bites are always fatal.
25. Only citizens of the United States can vote in U.S. elections.
26. Citizens of the United States can vote only in U.S. elections.
27. None but the insecure are jealous.
28. All vegetables are both delicious and nutritious.
29. Every student is either a graduate or an undergraduate.
30. Dogs are expensive if and only if they are pedigreed.

2.4.2 VARIANTS OF THE FORM: NO F ARE G

Much of what we have learned about the form 'All F are G' can be transferred to the form 'No F are G'. This is not to say that the forms have the same variants or the same exceptions to their variants; it is only to say that many of the devices used to express variants of the first form have analogs in the variants of the second form. One must guard against treating the two as exactly alike, however, for this can easily lead one astray. The form 'No F are G' may be rendered by '$(x)(Fx \supset -Gx)$' or by '$(x) - (Fx \cdot Gx)$'. The first is the more customary rendition and will be used here, but the second is perfectly acceptable and should be used when it simplifies a problem at hand.

Some of the simple variants on 'No F are G' are illustrated by the following examples:

None of the crew survived.
An elephant is not a fish.
Good students are not playboys.
Nothing valuable is sold cheaply.
A right triangle never contains an obtuse angle.
If it is a bird, then it is not a mammal.
The horse is not carnivorous.

Their paraphrases are

$(x)(x$ belonged to the crew $\supset -(x$ survived$))$
$(x)(x$ is an elephant $\supset -(x$ is a fish$))$
$(x)(x$ is a good student $\supset -(x$ is a playboy$))$
$(x)(x$ is valuable $\supset -(x$ is sold cheaply$))$
$(x)(x$ is a right triangle $\supset -(x$ contains an obtuse angle$))$
$(x)(x$ is a bird $\supset -(x$ is a mammal$))$
$(x)(x$ is a horse $\supset -(x$ is carnivorous$))$

These examples must not be taken as illustrating hard-and-fast rules. Thus, as exceptions, we have

The captain is not a brave fellow.
Good students are not easy to find.

The last will give rise to an amusing argument if *misinterpreted:*

Good students are not easy to find.
Johnson is a good student.
∴ Johnson is not easy to find.

The forms

Only G are not F
None but G are not F

are paraphrased as '$(x)(-Fx \supset Gx)$'. Thus

Only the inattentive do not pass
None but the lazy do not succeed

are rendered

$(x)(x$ does not pass $\supset x$ is inattentive)
$(x)(x$ does not succeed $\supset x$ is lazy)

The statement

One is wise who does not question his spouse

is similar, being paraphrased as

$(x)(-(x$ questions his spouse) $\supset x$ is wise)

One's expectation is that the constructions 'None but G are F', 'Only G are F', and 'G are those who F', which are variants of 'All F are G', would give rise to analogous variants of 'No F are G', but there are no direct analogs and the nearest things to them are such forms as 'Only non-G are F' or 'None but non-G are F'. Examples of this are

Only noncombatants are spared.
None but the nonconformists wear beards.

They may be paraphrased as

$(x)(x$ is spared $\supset -(x$ is a combatant))
$(x)(x$ wears a beard $\supset -(x$ is a conformist))

Infinitives may be used to express variants of 'No F are G', as in

To know her is to not love her

which paraphrases as

$(x)(x$ knows her $\supset -(x$ loves her$))$

However, one must be careful in paraphrasing such statements and pay particular attention to the position of the negative particles. Thus

To know her is not to love her

can probably be paraphrased as

$-(x)(x$ knows her $\supset x$ loves her$)$

but it certainly does not mean that all who know her do not love her.

2.4.3   MISCELLANEOUS VARIANTS

After such a lengthy discussion of 'All F are G' and 'No F are G', we shall not have to say much about 'Some F are G' or 'Some F are not G'. It is worthwhile to give a few examples of variants of these forms, however, so that they can more easily be spotted later. To this end let us look at the following examples:

Horses are sometimes black.
A lady came to the dance.
Something red flashed through the sky.
Black crows exist.
Russians are in attendance.
Kings are sometimes not tyrants.

Their paraphrases are

$(\exists x)(x$ is a horse $\cdot x$ is black$)$
$(\exists x)(x$ is a lady $\cdot x$ came to the dance$)$
$(\exists x)(x$ is red $\cdot x$ flashed through the sky$)$
$(\exists x)(x$ is black $\cdot x$ is a crow$)$
$(\exists x)(x$ is a Russian $\cdot x$ is in attendance$)$
$(\exists x)(x$ is a king $\cdot -(x$ is a tyrant$))$

Contrast these, however, with the following *nonvariants:*

Horses are not sold as meat
A lady did not invite me
Russians are not present

which paraphrase as

$(x)(x$ is a horse $\supset -(x$ is sold as meat$))$
$(x)(x$ is a lady $\supset -(x$ did not invite me$))$
$(x)(x$ is a Russian $\supset -(x$ is in attendance$))$

Furthermore, do not be misled by the construction 'There are no', which is used to *deny* rather than to assert existence. Thus

There are no just wars
There is no such thing as a round square

are paraphrased as

$-(\exists x)(x$ is just $\cdot$ x is a war)
$-(\exists x)(x$ is round $\cdot$ x is square)

The following statements all belong to a family which has not made an appearance yet:

All and only my classmates are invited.
One is wise if and only if he knows his sons.
Something is feared just in case it is unknown.

These statements are related by being paraphrasable into the form '(x) $(Fx \equiv Gx)$'; thus we have

$(x)(x$ is my classmate $\equiv x$ is invited)
$(x)(x$ is wise $\equiv x$ knows his sons)
$(x)(x$ is feared $\equiv x$ is unknown)

Sometimes people will use a variant of 'All F are G' when they intend to say that 'All and only F are G'. This is because the former is shorter and easier to say. So it is necessary to pay attention to context and other cues to avoid being misled in this case. Frequently, this shortcut is used in giving definitions. We have, for example,

A bachelor is an unmarried man

meaning

$(x)(x$ is a bachelor $\equiv x$ is an unmarried man)

and

To be is to be perceived

meaning

$(x)(x$ is a being $\equiv x$ is perceived)

2.4.4 COMPOUND TERMS
Many of the previous forms reappear with compound F or G. Thus, for example,

All black horses are wild

is paraphrased by

$(x)(x$ is black $\cdot$ x is a horse $\supset$ x is wild)

Similarly,

No fat men live past 90
Some women who are ambitious drive their husbands crazy
Some wild mushrooms are not poisonous

may be paraphrased as

$(x)(x$ is fat $\cdot$ x is a man $\supset$ $-(x$ will live past 90))
$(\exists x)(x$ is a woman $\cdot$ x is ambitious $\cdot$ x drives her husband crazy)
$(\exists x)(x$ is wild $\cdot$ x is a mushroom $\cdot$ $-(x$ is poisonous))

Often a compound will be couched within a compound, as in the following examples:

All cats are safe if they are not rabid.
A shark is dangerous only when it is hungry.
No lion should be petted unless it is muzzled.

Here the best strategy is to paraphrase inward; thus

$(x)(x$ is a cat $\supset$ x is safe if not rabid)
$(x)(x$ is cat $\supset$ $(-(x$ is rabid) $\supset$ x is safe))

$(x)(x$ is a shark $\supset$ x is dangerous only when it is hungry)
$(x)(x$ is a shark $\supset$ $(x$ is dangerous $\supset$ x is hungry))

$(x)(x$ is a lion $\supset$ x should not be petted unless it is muzzled)
$(x)(x$ is a lion $\supset$ $(-(x$ should be petted) $\vee$ x is muzzled))

When dealing with these examples, however, one must beware of subtleties. For example,

Apples and pears are fruits

does not mean that everything which is both an apple and a pear is a fruit; it means that things which are apples or pears are fruits, and so it is paraphrased as

$(x)((x$ is an apple $\vee$ x is a pear) $\supset$ x is a fruit)

Another type of nuance is illustrated by

Large ants inflict bad bites.

Given our present apparatus, the phrase 'large ant' must be treated as a single unit. It does not mean 'both large and an ant', for then

Large ants are large

would be a logical truth. What it means is 'ant larger than most ants', and this phrase cannot be further analyzed using just our current techniques.

2.4.5 TIMES AND PLACES

Quantifiers are also used to refer to times and places. The reference may be made explicit by means of phrases such as 'everywhere', 'wherever', 'nowhere', and 'someplace', or it may be left implicit. Let us consider the explicit cases first. A bevy of them are provided by the following statements:

Everywhere that Mary went the lamb was sure to go.
Nowhere does the road fork.
Where there is smoke there is fire.
John never asked her out.
Whenever it rains, it pours.

These statements are paraphrased as follows:

(x)(Mary went to x ⊃ The lamb was sure to go to x)
$(x) - $(The road forks at x)
(x)(Smoke is at x ⊃ Fire is at x)
$(x)-$(John asked her out a time x)
(x)(It rains at time x ⊃ It pours at time x)

For the implicit references we must turn to statements such as the following:

John hangs up his hat when he comes home.
I loved him when he was single.
John may be found with Mary.
The colonel inspected the entire perimeter.

By paraphrasing these as follows, the references to times and places become explicit:

(x)(John comes home at time x ⊃ John hangs up his hat at time x)
$(\exists x)$(I loved him at time x · He was single at time x)
$(\exists x)$(John is at place x · Mary may be found at place x)
(x)(x is a place on the perimeter ⊃ The colonel inspected place x)

Some constructions used to refer to times have also been used in other connections, and we must take care not to confuse these roles. Thus consider the function of 'always' in

Sadie always gets what she's after.
I always leave my son with a baby-sitter.
This sign always is found at an intersection.

In the first statement 'always' is used to refer to all things; in the second, to all times; and in the third, to all places. Thus, as paraphrases, we have

(x)(Sadie is after x $\supset$ Sadie gets x)
(x)(I leave my son at time x $\supset$ My son is with a baby-sitter at time x)
(x)(This sign is at place x $\supset$ An intersection is at place x)

Again compare the following uses of 'if':

A man is good father if he loves his children
It is cold if it is snowing
Everyone will be good if the world is saved

which are paraphrased by

(x)(x is a man $\supset$ (x loves his children $\supset$ x is a good father))
(x)(It is snowing at time x $\supset$ It is cold at time x)
The world is saved $\supset$ (x)(x is a human $\supset$ x will be good)

EXERCISES FOR SECS. 2.4.2 TO 2.4.5

Paraphrase these statements, using logical notation. Reveal as much structure as possible, and insert necessary parentheses.

1. No elephants are pink.
2. No careful drivers have accidents.
3. All those in the room are not required to attend.
4. Nobody who asked was refused.
5. Great artists are not skillful.
6. Great artists are not always pretty.
7. Great artists are never pretty.
8. Never are the rich taxed.
9. The goat is not a bovine.
10. None of the students submitted homework.
11. None but the students submitted homework.
12. To refuse aid is to not help.
13. To attend class is not to learn.
14. Some of the wisest men are foolish about women.
15. His visits are sometimes disastrous.
16. No pink elephants exist.
17. A large coach stopped in front of the house.

18. Diamonds are sometimes cheap.
19. Something is expensive when and only when it is in demand.
20. There are no ladies present.
21. An isosceles triangle is one with two equal sides.
22. All and only the imprudent are unrewarded.
23. A spendthrift is never rich.
24. To be great is to be immortal.
25. A black horse is never white.
26. No old ladies will be invited.
27. No old ladies are in the room.
28. Not all old ladies are in the room.
29. A horse should not be ridden if it is not over two years old.
30. Cows and goats can be milked.
31. Each student will be tested unless he is excused.
32. A crowd will become a mob only if it is enraged.
33. There are wild animals that cannot be tamed.
34. Heavy feathers are feathers, but they are not heavy.
35. Beets and potatoes are root crops.
36. Every man or woman over twenty-one can vote.
37. No person who is under twenty-one or a felon can vote.
38. My dog is always hungry.
39. My dogs are always beagles.
40. Although black dogs are never barkers, they are sometimes biters.
41. If it snows in the mountains, the roads freeze.
42. If all the snowflakes melt, then there will be no snowballs on the window.
43. Wherever there is a city, there is a smog problem.
44. Whenever he visits, he stays for dinner.
45. A teacher is effective if and only if his students learn.

2.4.6 'ANY' AND 'EVERY'

Paraphrasing statements in which the words 'any' and 'every' occur can be quite tricky, since in some contexts these words are interchangeable, while in other contexts their meanings differ markedly. Consider, for example,

Any man is mortal.
Every man is mortal.
All men are mortal.

They all say the same thing; so it appears as if 'any', 'every', and 'all' are interchangeable. However, compare the following:

If any man is immortal, medical science is incorrect.
If every man is immortal, medical science is incorrect.

Here 'any' means 'some'; so this pair are paraphrased as

$(\exists x)(x$ is a man $\cdot$ x is immortal$)$ $\supset$ Medical science is incorrect
$(x)(x$ is a man $\supset$ x is immortal$)$ $\supset$ Medical science is incorrect

A similar case is provided by the next couple:

John cannot beat any player
John cannot beat every player

which may be paraphrased as

$-(\exists x)(x$ is a player $\cdot$ John can beat $x)$
$-(x)(x$ is a player $\supset$ John can beat $x)$

The last pair differed in meaning, yet the next do not.

John can beat any player.
John can beat every player.

Problems of scope further complicate things when we turn to examples such as

If anything happens, the newspaper is informed.
If anything happens, the newspaper reports it.

In the last example, 'it' refers to 'anything'; so in paraphrasing the example, the quantifier corresponding to 'anything' must bind the variable corresponding to 'it'. This excludes

$(x)(x$ happens$)$ $\supset$ The newspaper reports x
$(\exists x)(x$ happens$)$ $\supset$ The newspaper reports x

and narrows the choice to

$(x)(x$ happens $\supset$ The newspaper reports $x)$
$(\exists x)(x$ happens $\supset$ The newspaper reports $x)$

Obviously, the last of these is wrong, since it says there is a *thing* such that, if it happens, the newspaper reports it, when what we want to say is that the newspaper reports *everything* that happens. Thus the final pair of paraphrases is

$(\exists x)(x$ happens$)$ $\supset$ The newspaper is informed
$(x)(x$ happens $\supset$ The newspaper reports $x)$

The same phenomenon may be observed with respect to occurrences of 'someone', 'something', etc. Thus, compare these examples pairwise:

If something is wrong, the mayor will let us know.
If something is wrong, the mayor will rectify it.

If someone calls, I shall be told.
If someone calls, his message will be taken.

A fire is some place unless it has rained.
A fire is some place unless the chief goes there.

The last pair may be paraphrased as

$(\exists x)$(A fire is at place x) $\vee$ It has rained
(x)(A fire is at x $\vee$ The chief goes to x)

2.4.7   DEPTH OF ANALYSIS

When paraphrasing statements it is often important to decide on the amount of their structure to reveal. The more probing analyses of a statement naturally end up exposing more of its form, but often a fairly superficial exposé will suffice for the purpose at hand. If, for example, an argument can be validated by purely truth-functional techniques, then it is unnecessary to bring quantification theory into the problem at all. This is true even when the argument contains statements involving quantifiers. To be more concrete, consider the following argument:

It is raining everywhere in Connecticut.
Assuming that today is Saturday, the game is off if it is raining everywhere in Connecticut.
Hence today is Saturday only if the game is off.

This argument has the truth-functional form

$p, q \supset (p \supset r) \therefore q \supset r$

and so it is valid. The statement 'It is raining everywhere in Connecticut' has been diagrammed as simply 'p', but it admits of the more complex diagram '$(x)(Fx \supset Gx)$'. It should be clear that there is no need to use this diagram or to give a deeper analysis of the argument. Purely truth-functional techniques suffice.

On the other hand, one may find that, although a quantificational analysis is needed for certain parts of an argument, a purely truth-functional analysis will serve for the rest of it. As an example consider this argument:

No man kissed his wife at the station, but some men who boarded the train saluted the conductor.
Thus some men boarded the train.

In order to demonstrate the validity of this argument it is necessary to lay bare the quantificational structure of all of the conclusion and of the last clause of the premiss. The first clause of the premiss may be treated as a single unit, however, though it does contain quantificational structure. This simple analysis of the argument gives it the form

$p \cdot (\exists x)(Fx \cdot Gx \cdot Hx) \therefore (\exists x)(Fx \cdot Gx)$

whereas a more thorough analysis would give it the form

$(x)(Jx \supset -Kx) \cdot (\exists x)(Fx \cdot Gx \cdot Hx) \therefore (\exists x)(Fx \cdot Gx)$

Clearly, in this case, the deeper analysis is inefficient and superfluous.

There are, as one might expect, no hard-and-fast rules for determining how much structure to lay bare. But it is useful to look for recurring phrases and terms. If a phrase occurs as a unit in both premisses and conclusion, then it probably may be left unanalyzed. But if it occurs whole in one place and parts of it appear elsewhere, then the whole should probably be analyzed into its parts. Of course, if someone's aim is to give as deep an analysis of a statement as possible, then let him analyze away. But significantly simpler schemata and demonstrations of validity will be gotten by revealing no more structure than is required. Notice, however, that these remarks are concerned chiefly with demonstrations of *validity*, and do not constitute a blanket authorization to use purely truth-functional techniques. For many a valid argument will appear to be invalid if only truth-functionally analyzed. If validity is established by one of the simpler analyses, then this is all that is needed. As long as one fails to establish validity, however, a further analysis is required, until the deepest analysis is reached. Then, if the argument still turns out to be invalid, the verdict must be accepted.

Another area of simplification concerns universes of discourses. Suppose that all the statements involved in a particular problem are about a limited category of objects such as humans or numbers. Then many of the references to humans (or numbers) in these statements can be absorbed by the quantifiers of their paraphrases. Thus, if the universe of discourse is limited to humans, 'All humans', 'all persons', or 'everyone' can be paraphrased simply as '(x)'. The expressions 'some person', 'someone', 'somebody', etc., may be treated similarly. Thus, under such circumstances,

Everyone is for himself
Nobody lives forever
Some people drive me crazy
No one can remain under water without air for ten minutes

may be paraphrased as, simply,

$(x)(x$ is for himself$)$
$(x)-(x$ lives forever$)$

($\exists x$)(x drives me crazy)
(x) $-$ (x can remain under water without air for ten minutes)

Of course, when the universe of discourse is not limited to humans, such paraphrases may not be satisfactory. Other things besides humans can or cannot be for themselves, live forever, drive me crazy, or remain under water without air for ten minutes. Thus it is possible for a true statement about humans to be paraphrased as a false one about everything. The statement about remaining under water is a case in point. To avoid such possibilities, when the universe of discourse is unlimited, one should make references to humans explicit in paraphrasing. The four statements given above would then be paraphrased as

(x)(x is a human $\supset$ x is for himself)
(x)(x is a human $\supset$ $-$(x lives forever))
($\exists x$)(x is a human $\cdot$ x drives me crazy)
(x)(x is a human $\supset$ $-$(x can remain under water without air for ten minutes))

Sometimes the references to humans can be tacked on to the predicates. For example, instead of using the last paraphrase of 'Some people drive me crazy', it might be possible to use

($\exists x$)(x is a person who drives me crazy)

The acceptability of such paraphrases will depend upon other considerations than one's universe of discourse. In the given example, it will depend upon the depth of the analysis required of 'person who drives me crazy'. Here are some other examples of "tacking on":

All wise people live long : (x)(x is a wise person $\supset$ x lives long)
No fat men run fast: (x)(x is a fat man $\supset$ (x runs fast))

When the universe of discourse is limited to a particular category, simpler paraphrases, and consequently simpler schemata, become possible. Another bonus is the superfluity of certain implicit premises. Thus, when the universe of discourse is limited to humans, arguments will often have implicit premises to the effect that everything which did such and such is human or that some particular person mentioned in the argument is a human. For example, consider the arguments

John kissed Mary.
Hence somebody kissed Mary.

All who voted stood on line.
None but those who had coffee stood on line.
Thus all who voted are people who had coffee.

If the universe of discourse were taken as unlimited, these would be paraphrased as

John kissed Mary
∴ (∃x)(x is a person · x kissed Mary)

(x)(x voted ⊃ x stood on line)
(x)(x stood on line ⊃ x had coffee)
∴ (x)(x voted ⊃ x is a person · x had coffee)

and consequently, they are valid only if we supply the implicit premisses

John is a person
(x)(x voted ⊃ x is a person)

On the other hand, by taking the universe of discourse as limited to humans, we not only obtain the following simpler paraphrases,

John kissed Mary
∴ (∃x)(x kissed Mary)

(x)(x voted ⊃ x stood on line)
(x)(x stood on line ⊃ x had coffee)
∴ (x)(x voted ⊃ x had coffee)

but the extra premisses also become unnecessary.

EXERCISES FOR SECS. 2.4.6 AND 2.4.7

A. Paraphrase these statements, using logical notation. Reveal as much logical structure as possible, and insert necessary parentheses.
   1. Anyone can buy a Cadillac if he has the money.
   2. Not everybody can buy a gun if he wishes to buy one.
   3. Not every student wants a car; moreover, it is false that any student has the money to buy a car.
   4. If anyone listens, he will hear us, and if anyone hears us, we shall be in trouble.
   5. If somebody calls me, I shall call him back, but somebody will call me only if the lines are open.
   6. Anyone is welcome unless we are closed.
   7. Anyone is welcome so long as he behaves.
   8. The mayor cannot meet everybody, but anybody he meets will remember him.
   9. If some student asks for the money, it will be given to him.
   10. If some student asks about his grade, we shall have to check our records.
B. Paraphrase these statements, first using only logical statement connectives. Then paraphrase them using quantifiers and statement connectives.

1. If all cows give milk, then either some of our animals are not cows or some of them are sick.
2. If a man is great only if he is known, then no men in this town are great.
3. Some people smoke, some drink, while some neither smoke nor drink.
4. If large amounts of money are hard to earn, then the man who earns a large amount of money is either very smart or very lucky.
5. Unless neither nuts nor berries are fruits, some birds and some squirrels eat fruits.
6. If some man knocks at the door now, then all the girls will hide in the closets.
7. If someone knocks at the door, then he will be sent away, although everything necessary for our protection is available.
8. A large toad sat on the log, but no snakes or rats were in the field.
9. If students will work only if they are coerced, then if some students are working, some students are coerced.
10. If no sailors swim but all airmen sail, then sailors are neither swimmers nor fliers.

C. Paraphrase the following statements twice. For the first time assume that the universe of discourse is restricted to persons. For the second time assume that it is unrestricted.

1. Everybody in the room will stand up.
2. Nobody answered the door.
3. If someone looks in the window, he will see quite a sight.
4. Anyone who has a horse needs oats.
5. I did not see anyone, but if anyone was there, he was hiding.
6. The ones who bought candy paid for it.
7. No one who entered the room left.
8. Someone received a prize just in case he bought a ticket.

2.4.8   FROM PARAPHRASES TO SCHEMATA

Once a statement is completely paraphrased, it is relatively easy to obtain a schema which diagrams it. We start by replacing all component statements which are to be left unanalyzed by statement letters. Of course, we use different statement letters for different statements, and the same statement letter for all repetitions of a statement. For example, if the paraphrase we end with is

$(x)(x$ loves cats $\supset x$ hates dogs$) \cdot$ Tabby loves cats $\supset (7 + 3 = 10 \equiv ($Rover hates dogs $\vee (6 - 3 + 3 \supset 7 + 3 = 10)))$

and '$7 + 3 = 10$', '$6 - 3 + 3$', and 'Rover hates dogs' are not subject to further analysis, then they can be replaced, respectively, by statement letters to yield, say,

$(x)(x$ loves cats $\supset x$ hates dogs$) \cdot$ Tabby loves cats $\supset (p \equiv (q \vee (r \supset p)))$

Next we turn to the components which are to be analyzed as simple-subject – predicate sentences. Their subjects are replaced by individual constants, and their predicates by predicate letters. Different subjects and predicates are replaced by different constants and predicate letters and recurrences of the same subject or predicate by the same constant or predicate letter. Thus, if all the simple components of

John is a Boy Scout · Jane is a Girl Scout ≡ (John is in school ∨ Jane runs · −(George is a Boy Scout))

are analyzed in terms of subjects and predicates, a schema diagramming the statement would be

$Fa \cdot Gb \equiv (Ka \lor Hb \cdot -Fc)$

Returning to our first example and treating 'Tabby' as a subject yields

$(x)(x$ loves cats $\supset x$ hates dogs$) \cdot Fa \supset (p \equiv (q \lor (r \supset p)))$

An expression is replaced by a constant or predicate letter only when it is explicitly analyzed as a subject or predicate. In the first example, the simple sentence 'Rover hates dogs' occurred, but because it was treated as an unanalyzed unit, neither 'Rover' nor 'hates dogs' was replaced by a constant or predicate letter. We can even conceive of an example where one occurrence of 'John', say, would be taken as a subject, as in 'John killed a cat', but where another occurrence would be treated as part of the predicate, as in 'Frank struck John's car'. Then 'John' would be replaced in the first occurrence by a constant, but not in the second.

Once the simple-subject – predicate sentences and unanalyzed statements have been disposed of, only open sentences, truth-functional connectives, and quantifiers remain. Thus, to obtain a schema, we need only replace the open sentences by predicate letters with 'x' appended to them. In so doing, different open sentences are replaced by different predicate letters, while the same open sentence is replaced by the same predicate letter in all its occurrences. Moreover, if a given predicate letter has been used to replace a predicate part of a simple-subject – predicate sentence, then the predicate letter must also be used when this predicate part makes up one of the open sentences. For example, if a component statement, 'John killed John's brother', has been diagrammed as 'Ka', where 'K' represents 'x killed x's brother', then the component '$(\exists x)(x$ killed x's brother$)$' must be diagrammed as '$(\exists x)Kx$'. Thus, to return to our first example, we may finally diagram it by

$(x)(Fx \supset Gx) \cdot Fa \supset (p \equiv (q \lor (r \supset p)))$

Here 'F' has to be chosen to represent 'x loves cats', since it has already fulfilled this role in diagramming 'Tabby loves cats'.

Finally, although each statement to be diagrammed may ordinarily be treated as a separate entity, such need not be the case when a problem involves two or more statements. This happens when one attempts to determine equivalences or implications. Then a "simultaneous diagramming" is necessary, that is, the same individual constants, statement, or predicate letters are reused when representing elements common to the several statements. For example, to establish that 'Any friend of John's is a friend of mine' and 'George is a friend of John's' imply 'George is a friend of mine', we should use the same constant to represent all occurrences of 'George' and the same predicate letter to represent all occurrences of 'a friend of John's' and 'a friend of mine'. Thus the three statements could be diagrammed by '$(x)(Fx \supset Gx)$', 'Fa', and 'Ga'.

EXERCISES FOR SEC. 2.4.8

A. Obtain schemata which diagram the statements given in the previous exercises of Sec. 2.4. Reveal as much structure as possible.
B. By means of derivations, establish equivalences between these paired statements.
   1. All cats are black: If something is not black, then it's not a cat.
   2. There are no round squares: No round thing is square.
   3. Apples and pears are fruits: Apples are fruits, and pears are fruits.
   4. No fish are mammals: No mammals are fish.
   5. Some people are not fat: Not all people are fat.
   6. If someone is a student, then if he is a graduate, he is not an undergraduate: A student who is a graduate is not an undergraduate.
   7. If anyone called the police, the club was raided: If the club was not raided, then no one called the police.
   8. Everyone danced and sang: Everyone danced and everyone sang.
   9. The cat is a carnivorous animal: No noncarnivorous animal is a cat.
   10. Any place there is smoke there is fire: There are no places with smoke and without fire.
C. By means of derivations establish the validity of the following arguments.
   1. All students take mathematics or logic. Joe is a student who is not taking mathematics. Hence Joe is taking logic.
   2. Anybody who buys a car needs gas, and everyone who needs gas buys it. So if someone does not buy gas, then he does not buy a car.
   3. If someone took the test, then Jack will work tonight. Anyone who works tonight will sleep late tomorrow. Alice took the test. So someone will work tonight and sleep late tomorrow.
   4. Birds have wings, but bald eagles are birds. It follows that bald eagles have wings or beaks.
   5. All integers are rational numbers. Some integers are prime numbers. Hence some rational numbers are prime numbers.

6. Babies are illogical. Nobody is despised who can manage a crocodile. Illogical people are despised. So babies cannot manage crocodiles so long as they are people.

7. Every living thing is a plant or an animal. John's goldfish is alive, but it is not a plant. Something has a heart provided that it is an animal. So John's goldfish has a heart.

8. Lions are dangerous animals. Some lions are tame. Therefore dangerous animals exist.

9. Whenever John buys a Coke, he buys a cake. John bought a Coke yesterday. If John bought both a Coke and a cake yesterday, then all his friends visited him. Hence everyone is either not a friend of John's or visited him.

10. An atom is indivisible, but molecules are not. So nothing is both an atom and a molecule.

11. Any lady who drives a car wears a hat, while anyone who wears a hat has a bald spot. Although not all ladies drive cars, ladies do drive cars. So there are ladies who have bald spots.

12. No one wants to go to jail. So there is someone who would like to eat cake if he wanted to go to jail.

13. Whoever stole the car sold it. Someone sold the car only if he signed the registration. So anyone who did not sign the registration did not steal the car.

14. Anyone who attends college takes courses or drops out. Anyone who takes courses works hard. Anyone who drops out is drafted. So provided that a person attends college, he works hard or is drafted.

15. If no bats are vampires, then no ghost stories are true. All stories about houses are true. There are ghost stories about houses. Consequently, vampire bats exist.

16. Only lawyers can practice law. If everybody practices law only if everyone is a lawyer, then there are law schools which grant many degrees. For these reasons there are law schools that grant many degrees.

17. There are fast horses which are brown. Unless nothing is a fast brown horse, no little horses are fast horses. So something is a fast horse only if it is either brown or not a little horse.

18. Acrobats are bold, and so are airmen. Everyone here is an acrobat or an airman. So no one here is not bold.

19. Each and every war is unjust, but some wars are understandable. Thus unjust but understandable things do exist.

20. Everyone has a heart. So someone has hair and a heart just in case he has hair, and anyone who does not have a heart has x-ray vision.

2.5 ONE-VARIABLE QUANTIFICATION THEORY AND BASIC CLASS THEORY

Classes are among the most important objects of mathematics. There are even good grounds for arguing that classes are the fundamental objects of mathematics, for it has been shown that numbers, functions, series, limits, and all other mathematical objects can be construed as classes. Logicians have played an important role in the reduction of mathematics to class theory, and the investigation of class theory is one of the more important applications of logic. We cannot hope to develop class theory thoroughly in this book, but we can use one-variable quantification theory to study some elementary portions of class theory. This will be our project in this section.

2.5.1 CLASSES AND MEMBERSHIP

A class is a collection of things which share a property in common. The collection is not a heap, however; classes are not spatiotemporal objects. Thus we can speak of the class of blue ribbons or the class of positive integers or even the class of classes. The common properties which the things in a class share need not be some simple, or "neat", property. Thus there is the class of U.S. Presidents who lived in the nineteenth century and the class of things which are either bald people or milkless cows. Indeed, given any open sentence (_____ x _____), one can speak of the class of x's such that (_____ x _____).

A class contains all and only those things which have the property determining the class. Thus the class of men contains all and only men, the class of crows contains all and only crows, etc. To symbolize the membership of an object x in a class A, we use the symbol 'ϵ' and write

$x \in A$

Thus, 'John ϵ the class of men' means 'John is a member of the class of men'. If A is a class with a finite number of members $a,b,c,d, \ldots ,h$, then we can write

$A = \{a,b,c,d, \ldots ,h\}$

but of course, if A has infinitely many members, this is not possible. Suppose that

$A = \{1,2,3,4,5\}$

then the following are true:

$1 \in A, \quad 2 \in A, \quad 3 \in A$

while the following are false:

$6 \in A, \quad 0 \in A, \quad 2^5 \in A, \quad$ The Sun ϵA

Classes which have the same members count as identical classes. To express that A and B are identical classes, we write

$A = B$

Thus the following holds:

(1) $A = B \equiv (x)(x \in A \equiv x \in B)$

which simply states that A and B are identical classes if and only if they have the same members. Since every U.S. President must be over twenty-one, the class of U.S. Presidents over twenty-one is the same as the class of U.S. Presidents.

There are also classes which have no members. For example, the class of unicorns, the class of round squares, and the class of U.S. Presidents under twenty-one are memberless classes. Let A and B be two memberless classes, and let x be any object. Then both '$x \in A$' and '$x \in B$' are false; so '$x \in A \equiv x \in B$' is true. Since x is arbitrary, '$(x)(x \in A \equiv x \in B)$' is true; and then by (1), $A = B$. Thus all memberless classes are identical, and there is only one empty (memberless, null) class. This is denoted by '$\emptyset$'. Thus we have

(2) $(x)-(x \in \emptyset)$

There are also classes which contain everything, such as the class of all things, the class of things which are blue or not blue, and the class of things which are identical with themselves. Again, it follows from (1) that all these classes are identical; thus there is only one universal class. The universal class is denoted by 'V'; so we have

(3) $(x)(x \in V)$

We have naively assumed that every property determines a class, which contains all and only those things which have the property. In 1901, Bertrand Russell showed that this assumption can lead to contradictions. His argument ran roughly as follows: Classes have properties and can belong to classes. Some classes belong to themselves; for example, the class of classes is a class; so it belongs to itself. Other classes do not belong to themselves; for example, the class of men is not a man; so it does not belong to itself. To say that a class x belongs to itself is to say that $x \in x$, so to say that x does not belong to itself is to say $-(x \in x)$. Now consider the class of classes which do not belong to themselves. Call it R. Then

$(x)(x \in R \equiv -(x \in x))$

So, by UI,

$R \in R \equiv -(R \in R)$

and this is a contradiction!

Much of class theory since Russell's discovery has been devoted to determining which classes may be assumed to exist without engendering contradictions. The goal is to develop a class theory which will be both consistent and sufficiently rich to provide a foundation for the rest of mathematics. We cannot explore these interesting problems in this book. Instead, we shall assume that we are already given a universe of objects and limit the classes we deal with to classes of things in this universe. We shall also construct our notation for class theory so that we shall be unable to express the membership of one class in another. In particular, we shall not be able to write '$R \in R$' or '$-(R \in R)$', and so will avoid Russell's contradiction by being unable to *formulate* it.

For objects x in the universe and any class A of objects in the universe, we can express '$x \in A$', but not '$A \in x$', or '$A \in B$', where B is a class of objects in the universe.

We can think of the universe as a square.

The universe V

Then our classes can be represented as regions in the universe:

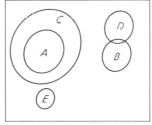

The universe V and classes A, B, C, D, E

2.5.2 COMPLEMENTS AND SUBCLASSES

The *complement* of a class A, written '$\bar{A}$', is the class of things which are not members of A. Thus we have

(4) $(x)(x \in \bar{A} \equiv -(x \in A))$

Pictorially, if A represents one region in the square, $\bar{A}$ represents the rest of the square.

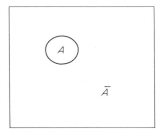

Since the universe V is the whole square, the empty class is represented by no region in the square. We do have, however,

(5) $\bar{V} = \emptyset$

(6) $\bar{\emptyset} = V$

When every member of the class A is also a member of the class B, then A is a *subclass* of B. This is written '$A \subseteq B$'; so we have

(7) $A \subseteq B \equiv (x)(x \in A \supset x \in B)$

Since '$x \in \emptyset$' is false for any choice of x, while '$x \in V$' is true for any choice of x, both '$(x)(x \in \emptyset \supset x \in A)$' and '$(x)(x \in A \supset x \in V)$' are true of any class A. Hence, by (7), we also have

(8) $A \subseteq V$

(9) $\emptyset \subseteq A$

We can represent the subclass relation pictorially by drawing one region within another. (Of course, this does not work with the empty class unless we think of it as within every region.) The diagrams are often useful for understanding why a statement about classes is true. Thus consider

(10) $A \subseteq B \cdot B \subseteq C \subset A \subseteq C$

If we first represent '$A \subseteq B \cdot B \subseteq C$', we shall see that we have already represented '$A \subseteq C$'.

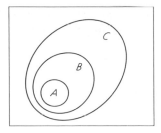

Similarly, the truth of

(11) $A \subseteq B \equiv \overline{B} \subseteq \overline{A}$

can be seen from the next diagram.

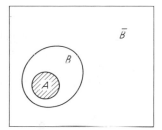

The unshaded region is $\overline{A}$

2.5.3   INTERSECTIONS AND UNIONS

The class of things which two classes have in common is called their *intersection*. The intersection of A and B is written '$A \cap B$'. Consequently,

(12) $(x)(x \in A \cap B \equiv x \in A \cdot x \in B)$

holds. If two classes share members in common, then their intersection is represented by the overlapping portions of the regions which represent them.

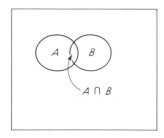

If two classes have no common members, then their intersection is simply the empty class. It is easy to see that the following must hold:

(13) $A \cap B = B \cap A$

(14) $A \cap (B \cap C) = (A \cap B) \cap C$

(15) $A \cap A = A$

(16) $A \cap \emptyset = \emptyset$

(17) $A \cap V = A$

(18) $A \cap B \subseteq A$

The class of things which belong to either one (or both) of two classes is called their *union*. The union of A and B is written '$A \cup B$'; so we have

(19) $(x)(x \in A \cup B \equiv (x \in A \lor x \in B))$

In terms of regions, the union of two classes consists of the portion of the square occupied by both regions. If A and B do not have any members in common, then the region representing $A \cup B$ will be broken into two disjointed portions. One can easily see that the following hold:

(20) $A \cup B = B \cup A$

(21) $A \cup (B \cup C) = (A \cup B) \cup C$

(22) $A \cup A = A$

(23) $A \cup \emptyset = A$

(24) $A \cup V = V$

(25) $A \subseteq A \cup B$

(26) $A \cap (B \cup C) = (A \cap B) \cup (A \cap C)$

(27) $A \cup (B \cap C) = (A \cup B) \cap (A \cup C)$

(28) $A \cap B \subseteq A \cup B$

(29) $A \cap \overline{A} = \emptyset$

(30) $A \cup \overline{A} = V$

EXERCISES FOR SECS. 2.5.1 TO 2.5.3
A.   True or false?
    1.   2 ϵ the class of even numbers

2. $(x)(x \in V \lor x \in \emptyset)$
3. $3 \in \{2,4,6\}$
4. $3 \in \{2,4,6\} \cup \{3,5,7\}$
5. $3 \in \{2,4,6\} \cap \{3,5,7\}$
6. $\{2\} = \{1,2\} \cap \{2,3\}$
7. The class of even numbers $\cap$ the class of odd numbers $= \emptyset$
8. The class of odd numbers $\cup$ the class of all numbers $=$ the class of odd numbers
9. $\emptyset \cup \{1\} = V$
10. $\{1,2\} \subseteq \{1\} \cup \{2\} \cup \{3\}$
11. $\{1\} \cap \{2\} \subseteq \emptyset$
12. $\{1,2,3\} \cap \{\overline{1}\} = \{1,2,3,4\}$
13. $\{3,2\} \subseteq \{2,3,4\} \cap \{3,5\}$
14. $V \subseteq A \supset A = V$
15. $(A \cap \emptyset) \cup A = A$

B. Derive contradictions from each of the following:

1. $(x)(x \in R \equiv -(x \in x \cdot x \in x))$ [*Hint:* use UI and replace 'x' by 'R'.]
2. $(x)(x \in R \equiv -(x \in x) \cdot (x \in x \supset x \in x))$
3. $(x)(x \in R \equiv -(x \in x \lor x \in x \cdot -(x \in x)))$
4. $(x)(x \in V) \cdot (x)(x \in R \equiv x \in V \cdot -(x \in x))$

2.5.4   PROOFS IN CLASS THEORY

Although it is fairly easy to convince oneself of the truths of class theory which have been cited, it is interesting to know that it is possible to construe all these truths as merely *translations* of valid OVQS. For then basic class theory can be viewed as one-variable quantification theory in a new guise. The rest of this chapter will be devoted to carrying out this project. But first it will be necessary to specify the apparatus of basic class theory more precisely.

The capital letters 'A', 'B', 'C', and 'D' will be used as class terms. They are supposed to represent arbitrary classes. We shall also use '$\emptyset$' and 'V' as class terms which represent the empty and universal class. From class terms, further class terms can be formed, using '$-$', '$\cup$', '$\cap$', and parentheses in the obvious way. Thus '$A \cup B$', '$(A \cap \emptyset)$', '$A \cap (B \cup C)$', and '$(\emptyset \cap V) \cup A$' are class terms. The task of specifying precise rules for forming class terms is left to the reader. (Note that in the examples given, outermost parentheses have been discarded and that, of course, 'x' is not a class term.)

The simple sentences of class theory are of three forms,

$$x \in \alpha, \qquad \alpha = \beta, \qquad \alpha \subseteq \beta$$

where α and β are class terms. Thus the following are among the simple sentences of class theory:

$$A = B \cup C, \qquad x \in B \cup C, \qquad \emptyset = \overline{(A \cap B)}$$

The other sentences are composed from simple sentences in the usual way by using truth-functions and quantifiers. The precise specification of the rules for forming these sentences is also left as an exercise.

It must be emphasized that class terms are not to be treated as individual constants; that is, they cannot be replaced by, or replace, the variable 'x'. Consequently, neither UI nor EG can be applied to class terms. Notice that if class terms were replaceable by a variable, and conversely, then we should obtain expressions such as

$$x \in x, \qquad A \in x, \qquad x = A, \qquad x \subseteq A$$

which have not been admitted among the sentences of class theory.

Next we shall give the *translation rules* for translating sentences of class theory into OVQS. The double arrow '↔' will be used to indicate that the expressions on either side of it are translations of each other. The first rule is simply

R1. $x \in \alpha \leftrightarrow \alpha x$

where α is one of 'A', 'B', 'C', or 'D'. R1 states that '$x \in A$' translates as 'Ax', '$x \in B$' translates as 'Bx', etc. Notice that this rule applies only to the class terms 'A', 'B', 'C', and 'D'. The other rules apply to all class terms, and the Greek letters 'α' and 'β' will be used in stating them to represent arbitrary class terms. The rules now follow:

R2. $x \in \bar{\alpha} \leftrightarrow -(x \in \alpha)$

R3. $x \in \alpha \cap \beta \leftrightarrow x \in \alpha \cdot x \in \beta$

R4. $x \in \alpha \cup \beta \leftrightarrow x \in \alpha \vee x \in \beta$

R5. $\alpha \subseteq \beta \leftrightarrow (x)(x \in \alpha \equiv x \in \beta)$

R6. $\alpha = \beta \leftrightarrow (x)(x \in \alpha \equiv x \in \beta)$

R7. $x \in \emptyset \leftrightarrow Ax \cdot -Ax$

R8. $x \in V \leftrightarrow Ax \vee -Ax$

The motivation behind most of these rules should be clear from the introductory discussion of classes. Rules 7 and 8 merit additional comment, however. They are formulated so that '$(x)(x \in V)$' and '$(x) - (x \in \emptyset)$' will become theorems of class theory. There are several ways to do this; for example, '$(x)(x \in V)$' and '$(x) - (x \in V)$' could be added as premises of every proof in class theory; but it is simpler to guarantee that they will be translated as valid OVQS, and this is what R7 and R8 accomplish.

By applying these rules it is clearly possible to translate every sentence of class theory into an OVQS. (Purists may object that, since 'Ax', 'Bx', etc., are not OVQS, we do not end with genuine OVQS. This problem is easily overcome by replacing 'A' by 'F', 'B' by 'G', etc., but we shall not bother to do so.) We start by applying R5 and R6. This will produce sentences built from sentences of the form

$x \in \alpha$

where α is a class term, via truth-functions and quantifiers. Then successive applications of the other rules (the order is immaterial when several are applicable) will finally eliminate 'ϵ' and class terms in favor of 'Ax', 'Bx', etc., so that the result will be an OVQS.

Notice that these rules will also convert every OVQS into a sentence of class theory. For simply applying R1 throughout an OVQS will do that. The rules were not designed with this in mind, however.

EXAMPLE.   The translation of '$B = V \cup C \supset B \cap C = \bar{B}$'.

Translation Step-by-step:

1   $B = V \cup C \supset B \cap C = \bar{B}$
2   $(x)(x \in B \equiv x \in V \cup C) \supset B \cap C = \bar{B}$ R6
3   $(x)(x \in B \equiv x \in V \cup C) \supset (x)(x \in B \cap C \equiv x \in \bar{B})$ R6
4   $(x)(x \in B \equiv (x \in V \lor x \in C)) \supset (x)(x \in B \cap C \equiv x \in \bar{B})$ R4
5   $(x)(x \in B \equiv (x \in V \lor x \in C)) \supset (x)(x \in B \cdot x \in C \equiv x \in \bar{B})$ R3
6   $(x)(x \in B \equiv (x \in V \lor x \in C)) \supset (x)(x \in B \cdot x \in C \equiv -(x \in B))$ R2
7   $(x)(x \in B = (Ax \lor -Ax \lor x \in C)) \supset (x)(x \in B \cdot x \in C \equiv -(x \in B))$ R8
8   $(x)(Bx \equiv (Ax \lor -Ax \lor x \in C)) \supset (x)(x \in B \cdot x \in C \equiv -(x \in B))$ R1
9   $(x)(Bx \equiv (Ax \lor -Ax \lor Cx)) \supset (x)(x \in B \cdot x \in C \equiv -(x \in B))$ R1
10 $(x)(Bx \equiv (Ax \lor -Ax \lor Cx)) \supset (x)(Bx \cdot x \in C \equiv -(x \in B))$ R1
11 $(x)(Bx \equiv (Ax \lor -Ax \lor Cx)) \supset (x)(Bx \cdot Cx \equiv -(x \in B))$ R1
12 $(x)(Bx \equiv (Ax \lor -Ax \lor Cx)) \supset (x)(Bx \cdot Cx \equiv -Bx))$ R1

We can shorten this translation process noticeably by condensing successive applications of the same rule into one application. By doing this, the last example can be condensed to seven steps. This condensation will be applied to the next example.

EXAMPLE.   The translation of '$\emptyset \subseteq (A \land \bar{B}) \cap C$'.

Translation Step-by-step:

1   $\emptyset \subseteq (A \cap \bar{B}) \cap C$
2   $(x)(x \in \emptyset \supset x \in (A \cap \bar{B}) \cap C)$ R5
3   $(x)(Ax \cdot -Ax \supset x \in (A \cap B) \cap C)$ R7
4   $(x)(Ax \cdot -Ax \supset x \in A \cdot x \in \bar{B} \cdot x \in C)$ R3

5   $(x)(Ax \cdot -Ax \supset x \in A \cdot -(x \in B) \cdot x \in C)$ R2
6   $(x)(Ax \cdot -Ax \supset Ax \cdot -Bx \cdot Cx)$ R1

A *theorem* of class theory will be defined as a sentence of class theory whose translation is a valid OVQS. A *proof* of a theorem of class theory can then be defined as a proof of a valid OVQS, followed by its translation into the notation of class theory.

EXAMPLE.   Proof of '$\emptyset \subseteq B$'.

Proof:

1	x $\triangle$	A
2	$Ax \cdot -Ax$	A
3	Ax	2, S
4	$Ax \lor Bx$	3, add
5	$-Ax$	2, S
6	Bx	4, 5, DS
7	$Ax \cdot -Ax \supset Bx$	2-6, CP
8	$(x)(Ax \cdot -Ax \supset Bx)$	1-8, UG
9	$(x)(Ax \cdot -Ax \supset x \in B)$	8, R1
10	$(x)(x \in \emptyset \supset x \in B)$	9, R7
11	$\emptyset \subseteq B$	10, R5

The strategy behind proof construction in our class theory is quite simple, as may be seen from the example. Working backward, the theorem to be proved is translated step-by-step into quantificational notation. Each step of translation will be justified by one of the translation rules, of course. Our backward trip will come to an OVQS, which we then attempt to prove by the usual techniques. Once a proof of the OVQS has been found, we need only append our translation steps to it in order to obtain a proof of the class-theory theorem. This will be illustrated in the several examples that conclude this section.

EXAMPLES

a.   To prove: $(x)(x \in A) \supset A = V$.

Proof:

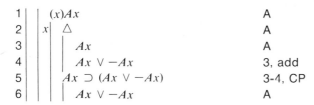

1	$(x)Ax$	A
2	x $\triangle$	A
3	Ax	A
4	$Ax \lor -Ax$	3, add
5	$Ax \supset (Ax \lor -Ax)$	3-4, CP
6	$Ax \lor -Ax$	A

7	Ax	1, UI
8	$(Ax \lor -Ax) \supset Ax$	6-7, CP
9	$Ax \equiv (Ax \lor -Ax)$	5, 8, PB
10	$(x)(Ax \equiv (Ax \lor -Ax))$	2-9, UG
11	$(x)Ax \supset (x)(Ax \equiv (Ax \lor -Ax))$	1-10, CP
12	$(x)(x \in A) \supset (x)(x \in A \equiv (Ax \lor -Ax))$	11, R1
13	$(x)(x \in A) \supset (x)(x \in A \equiv x \in V)$	12, R8
14	$(x)(x \in A) \supset A = V$	13, R6

b.   To prove: $A \subseteq A \cup B$.

Proof:

1	x	$\triangle$	A
2		Ax	A
3		$Ax \lor Bx$	2, add
4		$Ax \supset (Ax \lor Bx)$	2-3, CP
5		$(x)(Ax \supset (Ax \lor Bx))$	2-4, UG
6		$(x)(x \in A \supset (x \in A \lor x \in B))$	5, R1
7		$(x)(x \in A \supset x \in A \cup B)$	6, R4
8		$A \subseteq A \cup B$	7, R5

c.   To prove: $(\exists x)(x \in B) \supset -(B = \Lambda)$.

Proof:

1		$(\exists x)Bx$	A
2		$(x)(Bx \equiv Ax \cdot -Ax)$	A
3		$(\exists x)Bx$	1, R
4	x	Bx	A
5		$Bx \equiv Ax \cdot -Ax$	2, UI
6		$Ax \cdot -Ax$	4, 5, MP
7		Ax	6, S
8		$Ax \lor -(\exists x)Bx$	7, add
9		$-Ax$	6, S
10		$-(\exists x)Bx$	8, 9, DS
11		$-(\exists x)Bx$	3, 4-10, EI
12		$-(x)(Bx \equiv Ax \cdot -Ax)$	2-11, IP
13		$(\exists x)Bx \supset -(x)(Bx \equiv Ax \cdot -Ax)$	1-12, CP
14		$(\exists x)(x \in B) \supset -(x)(x \in B \equiv Ax \cdot -Ax)$	13, R1
15		$(\exists x)(x \in B) \supset -(x)(x \in B \equiv x \in \Lambda)$	14, R7
16		$(\exists x)(x \in B) \supset -(B = \Lambda)$	15, R6

EXERCISES FOR SEC. 2.5.4

Prove these theorems of class theory.

1. $A = B \supset A \subseteq B \cdot B \subseteq A$
2. $(x)(x \in V)$
3. $(x) - (x \in \phi)$
4. $\overline{V} = \emptyset$
5. $\overline{\emptyset} = V$
6. $A \subseteq V$
7. $\emptyset \subseteq A$
8. $A \subseteq B \cdot B \subseteq C \supset A \subseteq C$
9. $(x)(x \in A \cap B \equiv x \in B \cdot x \in A)$
10. $A \cap B = B \cap A$
11. $A \cap (B \cap C) = (A \cap B) \cap C$
12. $A \cap A = A$
13. $A \cap \emptyset = \emptyset$
14. $A \cap V = A$
15. $A \cap B \subseteq A$
16. $A \cup B = B \cup A$
17. $A \cup (B \cup C) = (A \cup B) \cup C$
18. $A \cup A = A$
19. $A \cup \emptyset = A$
20. $A \cup V = V$
21. $A \cup \overline{A} = V$
22. $A \cap \overline{A} = \emptyset$
23. $A \subseteq A \cup B$
24. $A = A \cup B \supset B \subseteq A$
25. $A \cap (B \cup C) = (A \cap B) \cup (A \cap C)$
26. $A \cup (B \cap C) = (A \cup B) \cap (A \cup C)$
27. $A \cap B \subseteq A \cup B$
28. $-(A \cap B = \emptyset) \supset (\exists x)(x \in A) \cdot (\exists x)(x \in B)$
29. $(A \cap \overline{B}) \cup B = A \cup B$
30. $(\exists x)(x \in \overline{A}) \equiv -(A = V)$

PART THREE: FULL QUANTIFICATION THEORY

3.1 QUANTIFIERS AND QUANTIFICATIONAL SCHEMATA

The greatest drawback of one-variable quantification theory is its inability to reveal the complete logical structure of statements which are concerned with relationships. This comes to the surface as soon as one raises logical questions about statements such as

(1) Every event is caused by something.

(2) There is something by which every event is caused.

It turns out that (2) implies (1) (although not conversely), but one-variable quantification theory is incapable of establishing this implication between (2) and (1). By means of its devices they are symbolized as, respectively,

(3) $(x)(x$ is an event $\supset x$ is caused by something$)$

(4) $(\exists x)($Every event is caused by $x)$

These in turn are diagrammed by

$(x)(Fx \supset Gx)$
$(\exists x)Hx$

neither one of which implies the other. Of course, part of the problem is obvious: the informal quantifiers 'something' and 'every' in (3) and (4) have remained unsymbolized. But with only one variable it is impossible to obtain a correct symbolization of these quantifiers. At best we get

(5) $(x)(x$ is an event $\supset (\exists x)(x$ is caused by $x))$

(6) $(\exists x)(x)(x$ is an event $\supset x$ is caused by $x))$

The latter is not even grammatical, while the former is equivalent to

(7) $(\exists x)(x$ is an event$) \supset (\exists x)(x$ is caused by $x)$

which hardly has the same sense as (1). (Note that in one-variable quantification theory '$(x)(Fx \supset (\exists x)Gx)$' is equivalent to '$(\exists x)Fx \supset (\exists x)Gx$').

Truth-function theory is unable to handle inferences involving quantifiers, and so we extended it to one-variable quantification theory. By the same token the present inability of one-variable quantification theory to handle arguments involving relations prompts its extension to full quantification theory. This is accomplished by two major additions. First, more variables and quantifiers will be added. This will allow (1) and (2) to be symbolized, respectively, as

(8) $(x)(x$ is an event $\supset (\exists y)(x$ is caused by $y))$

(9) $(\exists y)(x)(x$ is an event $\supset x$ is caused by $y)$

Second, the domain of quantificational schemata will be extended by admitting the new variables and quantifiers as new symbols and by allowing more than one variable or constant to be attached to a predicate letter. Two of the resulting schemata will be

$(x)(Fx \supset (\exists y)Gxy)$
$(\exists y)(x)(Fx \supset Gxy)$

which diagram (8) and (9). Nonetheless, except for these two additions, much of full quantification theory will be familiar from the one-variable branch. The same rules of inference can be used (with some additional technical restrictions), and no new rules will be necessary. Moreover, except for minor changes needed to extend them to the new schemata, the concepts of interpretation and validity used previously can be carried over to the full theory. Nonetheless, it is advisable to start once again at the beginning by returning to the analysis of simple sentences.

3.1.1 SIMPLE RELATIONAL STATEMENTS
A simple-subject – predicate statement attributes a property to the object its subject names. For example, the sentences

The New Haven Railroad is bankrupt
The Pennsylvania Railroad is solvent

attribute bankruptcy and solvency, respectively, to the New Haven and Pennsylvania Railroads. On the other hand, the statements

(1)   The New York Central merged with the Pennsylvania Railroad

(2)   The New York Central and Pennsylvania Railroads took over the New Haven Railroad

are best viewed, not as ascribing properties to any one railroad taken alone, but rather as asserting that the railroads in question stand in certain relationships to each other. Thus (1) asserts that the New York and Pennsylvania are related by means of a merger, while (2) states that these two railroads are further related to the New Haven by the takeover. Of course, it is possible to regard (1) and (2) as subject-predicate statements by selecting one of the railroads as a subject. Thus (1) can be conceived of as attributing the property of merging with the Pennsylvania to the New York Central or, with equal right, as attributing the property of merging with the New York Central to the Pennsylvania. However, it will be much more useful *not* to single out a subject in (1) and (2). Instead, we shall call (1) and (2) *relational statements* and in symbolizing them assign a separate individual constant to each of their "subjects". Thus, letting '*M*' abbreviate 'merged with' and '*T*' abbreviate 'took over', (1) and (2) can be rewritten

Mnp
Tnph

where '*h*' stands for the New Haven.

The relation of merging holds between two things; so it is called a *dyadic* relation. Similarly, any relation which relates two things is known as dyadic. Relations between three things are called *triadic*. The joint-takeover relation of (2) is thus a triadic relation. Other examples of dyadic and triadic relations are given in the following statements (the "subjects" are underlined)·

Dyadic: <u>John</u> loves <u>Mary</u>.
          <u>Jones</u> is <u>Robinson's</u> boss.
          <u>Washington</u> is south of <u>New York</u>.
          <u>Hawaii</u> is located in the <u>Pacific Ocean</u>.

Triadic: <u>John</u> sent <u>Mary</u> to <u>New York</u>.
          <u>Jones</u> gave the <u>book</u> to <u>Robinson</u>.
          <u>Washington</u> is between <u>New York</u> and <u>Richmond</u>.
          The <u>President</u> spoke in <u>Hawaii</u> on <u>Christmas Day</u>.

Moreover, relations between any number of things are possible. Those between four things are called *tetradic* relations; those between five things, *pentadic*. An example of a tetradic relation is

<u>Jones</u> paid <u>twenty dollars</u> to <u>Gomez</u> for <u>the car</u>.

In symbolizing relational statements, each thing standing in the relation asserted is represented by an individual constant. The relation itself is repre-

sented by a predicate constant. Thus the general form of statements asserting dyadic relations is given by

Fab

while triadic, tetradic, and pentadic relational statements have the respective
forms

$Fabc, Fabcd, Fabcde$

The active and passive forms of a relational statement are symbolized
alike. Thus 'John loves Mary' and 'Mary is loved by John' may both be abbreviated by 'Ljm'. Reversing order while simultaneously switching voice
affects no change in the significance of a relational statement. However,
reversing order without changing voice or changing voice without reordering
can lead to changes of meaning. Thus it is possible for 'John loves Mary' to
be true, while both 'Mary loves John' and 'John is loved by Mary' are false.
In general, 'Fab' must not be equated with 'Fba', nor '$Fabc$' with '$Fbac$',
'$Fcab$', etc.

Many relations can and do hold between a thing and itself. Thus someone
may love himself, kill himself, pat himself on the back, talk to himself about
himself. If by 'Lab', 'Kab', 'Pab', '$Tabc$' we mean 'a loves b', 'a kills b', 'a pats
b on the back', and 'a talks to b about c', respectively, then the relations to
oneself in question are formulated as 'Laa', 'Kaa', 'Paa', and '$Taaa$'. Some
relations hold only between a thing and itself. Identity is an example of such
a relation since everything is identical with itself and with nothing else. This
might prompt one to think that identity is a property, and not a relation, so
that we really ought to symbolize it as 'Ia' rather than as '$a = b$'. But notice
that this would deprive us of the means for denying identities. We could not
express, for example, the statements

$-(\text{Grant} = \text{Lincoln})$
$-(\text{Chicago} = \text{the capital of Illinois})$

Moreover, since the same person or thing is often known by different names,
we should no longer have the means for expressing highly informative true
identities such as

Hemingway $=$ the author of *The Killers*
Mark Twain $=$ Samuel Clemens
William Quinn $=$ the first governor of the state of Hawaii

Indeed, as these examples show, whether or not something is a property,
dyadic, triadic, or tetradic relation is really not a question of how many
things it can truly relate, but rather a question of grammar. Now let us think

of a predicate or relation word as containing one or more blanks which are to be filled with "subject" terms to produce simple-subject–predicate or relational statements. For instance, let us think of 'is red' and 'loves' as condensations '—is red' and '—loves—'. Then, whether or not a relation is dyadic, triadic, etc., will be simply determined by the number of blanks the symbol for it contains. On this score '=' stands for a dyadic relation.

3.1.2 VARIABLES AND QUANTIFIERS

Let us consider the relation of being *larger than*. We can affirm that one thing is larger than another without using quantifiers, namely, 'Boston is larger than New Haven'. Using one quantifier, we can even state that everything, something, or nothing is larger than a given thing; for example, '$(x)(x$ is larger than Boston)', '$(\exists x)(x$ is larger than Boston)', '$(x) - (x$ is larger than Boston)'. However, to state that everything is larger than something or that there is no larger thing, two quantifiers with different variables must be used. Thus, to start with 'Everything is larger than something', we can first write '$(x)(x$ is larger than something)'. But if we continue this symbolization, using only 'x' we can obtain only '$(x)(x$ is larger than $x)$' and '$(\exists x)(x$ is larger than $x)$'. The very simple remedy to this problem is to introduce an additional variable and write '$(x)(\exists y)(x$ is larger than $y)$'. The statement 'There is no largest thing' is a little more complicated. One might just write '$-(\exists x)(x$ is the largest thing)', but this would fail to reveal the full structure of the statement. But if we reexpress the statement as 'There is nothing which is larger than everything', then it can be symbolized via '$-(\exists x)(y)(x$ is larger than $y)$'.

The sentence '$-(\exists x)(y)(x$ is larger than $y)$' happens to be true. This is seen as follows: If there were a thing x larger than everything y, then x would be larger than itself (because it is larger than everything). But nothing is larger than itself; so there is no largest thing. The acceptability of this argument illustrates an important point about the relationship between 'x' and 'y' and the corresponding quantifiers: distinct variables need not carry references to distinct things. In other words, the something or everything of '$(\exists x)$' or '(x)' and the something or everything of '$(\exists y)$' or '(y)' can be the same thing. The sentence '$(x)(\exists y)(x$ is the same size as $y)$' will also be true if everything is the same size as only *itself*. To express a statement which is true if and only if everything is the same size as something different from itself, we should have to write '$(x)(\exists y)(-(x = y) \cdot x$ is the same size as $y)$'.

This point can be illustrated further by expanding universal and existential quantifiers in finite universes by means of conjunction and disjunction. Suppose we consider the universe U of three *distinct* things a, b, and c. Then in U,

(1) $(x)(\exists y)(x = y)$

amounts to

(2) $(\exists y)(a = y) \cdot (\exists y)(b = y) \cdot (\exists y)(c = y)$

which in turn amounts to

(3) $(a = a \lor a = b \lor a = c) \cdot (b = a \lor b = b \lor b = c) \cdot (c = a \lor c = b \lor c = c)$

Notice how 'a', 'b', and 'c' have been substituted for both 'x' and 'y'. Without such a substitution, (3) would come out false in U. For '$a = a$' is needed to make its first component true, '$b = b$' the second, and '$c = c$' the third.

To ascertain the truth-value of a statement containing more than one quantified variable we simply apply the familiar rules: '$(x)(\cdots x \cdots)$' is true if and only if '$(\cdots x \cdots)$' becomes a true statement whenever 'x' is taken as naming an actual object; '$(\exists x)(\cdots x \cdots)$' is true just in case there is some actual object such that '$(\cdots x \cdots)$' becomes a true statement when 'x' is taken as naming this object; except now 'x' may be replaced by other variables 'y', 'x', 'w', etc. Thus, '$(x)(\exists y)(x = y)$' again is true just in case '$(\exists y)(x = y)$' becomes a true statement whenever 'x' is taken as naming something. But this happens just in case there is something such that '$x = y$' in turn becomes a true statement when 'y' is taken as naming this thing. But there is such a thing, namely, the thing 'x' is taken to name. So '$(\exists y)(x = y)$' becomes true whenever 'x' is taken as naming something, and consequently '$(x)(\exists y)(x = y)$' is true also.

Since different variables need not carry distinct references, there is no difference between, say, '$(x)(x$ is red$)$' and '$(y)(y$ is red$)$'. Indeed, both are true if and only if everything is red. Similarly, '$(\exists x)(x$ is red$)$' and '$(\exists y)(y$ is red$)$' are seen to be equivalent. This sort of equivalence extends a long way, but important exceptions arise when quantifiers fall within the scope of other quantifiers. For example,

(4) $(x)(x$ is human $\supset (\exists y)(y$ is the mother of $x))$

is a simple biological truth, but if '(x)' is replaced by '(y)', we obtain the falsehood

(5) $(y)(y$ is human $\supset (\exists y)(y$ is the mother of $y))$

Excluding such exceptions, which will be characterized precisely later, '$(x)Fx$', '$(y)Fy$', '$(z)Fz$', etc., are all equivalent. They are merely variant ways of saying that everything is an F. Similarly, '$(\exists x)Fx$', '$(\exists y)Fy$', '$(\exists z)Fz$', etc., are variant and equivalent expressions for 'something is an F'. Since 'something' and 'everything' may ordinarily be rendered by '$(\exists x)$' or '$(\exists y)$', etc., and '(x)', '(y)', etc., with equal justice, '$(x)(y)Fxy$' is equivalent to '$(y)(x)Fyx$', and

'$(\exists x)(\exists y)Fxy$' to '$(\exists y)(\exists x)Fyx$'. In the first case the equivalence holds because we are dealing with mere variants of 'Everything bears F to everything'; in the second case we have variants of 'Something bears F to something'. The next pair of equivalences is even more surprising. In the last pair 'x' and 'y' are changed throughout; in the next pair 'x' and 'y' are changed only in the quantifiers. Thus we have the equivalence between '$(x)(y)Fxy$' and '$(y)(x)Fxy$' and between '$(\exists x)(\exists y)Fxy$' and '$(\exists y)(\exists x)Fxy$', and here '$Fxy$' remains unaltered throughout. The latter of these equivalences is seen to be true as follows: '$(\exists x)(\exists y)Fxy$' is true if and only if there is an x and there is a y such that Fxy, that is, if and only if something bears F to something. But this is precisely the condition under which '$(\exists y)(\exists x)Fxy$' is true. So '$(\exists x)(\exists y)Fxy$' and '$(\exists y)(\exists x) Fxy$' must both be true or both be false, and thus equivalent. The equivalence between '$(x)(y)Fxy$' and '$(y)(x)Fxy$' is demonstrated similarly. (Of course, our subsequent techniques will permit the rigorous derivation of these equivalences.)

The last pair of equivalences allows the permutation of adjacent and like quantifiers. We cannot permute adjacent and unlike quantifiers, however. Thus '$(x)(\exists y)Fxy$' is not equivalent to '$(\exists y)(x)Fxy$'. The second form is stronger and implies the first, but not conversely. For example, if it were true that something is the same size as everything, then everything would be the same size as something. Or if something created everything (including itself), then everything would be created by something, or if something caused everything, everything would have a cause. But the converses need not hold: everything is the same size as something, namely, itself, yet there is nothing such that everything is the same size as it. Every person has a father, but no person is everyone's father. Everything may have a cause, but there need not be something that caused everything. [It can be argued that confusing '$(x)(\exists y)Fxy$' with '$(\exists y)(x)Fxy$' lies behind the "first cause" argument for the existence of God.] The form '$(\exists y)(x)Fxy$' requires us to pick a y first, and then everything must bear F to it, whereas '$(x)(\exists y)Fxy$' allows the possibility of finding a different y for each x. For example, '$(x)(\exists y)(x = y)$' is true because, for each x, a y can be found (that is, x) such that $x = y$. But (as long as more than one thing exist) '$(\exists y)(x)(x = y)$' is false; for nothing y is such that everything is identical with it. The contrast between '$(\exists y)(x)(x = y)$' and '$(x)(\exists y) (x = y)$' is further emphasized by expanding the former in the universe $\{a,b,c\}$. (The latter has already been expanded above.) In $\{a,b,c\}$, '$(\exists y)(x) (x = y)$' amounts to

$$(x)(x = a) \lor (x)(x = b) \lor (x)(x = c)$$

which in turn amounts to

$$(a = a \cdot b = a \cdot c = a) \lor (a = b \cdot b = b \cdot c = b) \lor (a = c \cdot b = c \cdot c = c)$$

This is false since each conjunction has two false components. On the other hand, it implies

$$(a = a \lor a = b \lor a = c) \cdot (b = a \lor b = b \lor b = c) \cdot (c = a \lor c = b \lor c = c)$$

that is, the expansion of '$(x)(\exists y)(x = y)$' in $\{a,b,c\}$. A simple truth-functional test will prove this. Since many people tend to confuse '$(\exists y)(x)Fxy$' and '$(x)(\exists y)Fxy$', it is useful to illustrate the difference again with a diagram. Let us suppose that we have a universe of three cities, a and b and c. Let us further suppose that roads from one city to another are represented by arrows and that it is possible for roads to lead out of and back into cities (loops through suburbia). Then if 'Rxy' abbreviates 'A road leads from x to y', the following diagram verifies '$(x)(\exists y)Rxy$',

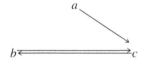

but falsifies '$(\exists y)(x)Rxy$'. In other words, in this diagram there is no Rome, no city to which all roads lead. But both '$(x)(\exists y)Rxy$' and '$(\exists y)(x)Rxy$' are verified by

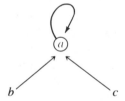

Exercise: Is it possible to construct a diagram which verifies '$(\exists y)(x)Rxy$' but not '$(x)(\exists y)Rxy$'?

With such a variety of variables before us, it is often difficult for the beginner to decide which ones to use when symbolizing a sentence. Accordingly, it will be useful for us to run through a few examples which illustrate the problem of choosing variables. To start with, consider the truth

(6)   Every man is a son of some man.

We start out by paraphrasing this as

(7) $(x)(x$ is a man $\supset x$ is a son of some man)

The variable 'x' has been used here, but any other variable will do. It is a matter of historical accident that logicians tend to use 'x' first. Next we must symbolize 'x is a son of some man'. Now a new variable must be selected. If we choose 'y', then the symbolization is '$(\exists y)(y$ is a man $\cdot x$ is the son of y)'. Any *new* variable will do, but choosing 'y' is customary. It is important to realize, however, that 'x' cannot be reused in this case. For this would yield

$(x)(x$ is a man $\supset (\exists x)(x$ is a man $\cdot x$ is the son of $x))$

which could not possibly convey the meaning of (6) because it is false. So here we have an example where the preservation of meaning requires a new variable. In the next example an old variable must be reused to preserve meaning. Thus consider

(8)   Every man loves himself.

This is rendered by

(9) $(x)(x$ is a man $\supset x$ loves $x)$

Not only must 'x' reappear in 'x loves x', but also each occurrence of 'x' must be bound to the initial '(x)'. All the following, for example, fail to match (8) in point of meaning:

$(x)(x$ is a man $\supset (\exists y)(x$ loves $y))$
$(x)(x$ is a man $\supset (\exists y)(y$ loves $y))$
$(x)(x$ is a man $\supset x$ loves $y)$

In the next example, however, it makes no difference whether new or old variables are used:

(10) If everything is red, then nothing is black.

This may be symbolized equally well by any of the following:

$(x)(x$ is red$) \supset (x) - (x$ is black$)$
$(x)(x$ is red$) \supset (y) - (y$ is black$)$
$(z)(z$ is red$) \supset (z) - (z$ is black$)$

Finally, let us symbolize a sentence where the constraints on the selection of variables vary from one part of the sentence to another:

(11)   If some philosopher contradicts every philosopher, then some philosopher contradicts himself.

The antecedent of (11), 'Some philosopher contradicts every philosopher', says that there is a philosopher who contradicts every philosopher; it does not say that for every philosopher there is some philosopher or other who contradicts him. That would be 'Every philosopher is contradicted by some philosopher'. [This is the difference between '$(\exists y)(x)Fyx$' and '$(x)(\exists y)Fyx$'.] Thus the antecedent of (11) is paraphrased as

$(\exists x)(x$ is a philosopher $\cdot$ $(y)(y$ is a philosopher $\supset x$ contradicts $y))$

Once 'x' is chosen here, we must choose 'y' or some other new variable. Clearly, the philosopher x is related to every philosopher. But if we reuse 'x', we obtain

$(\exists x)(x$ is a philosopher $\cdot$ $(x)(x$ is a philosopher $\supset x$ contradicts $x))$

This fails on two counts: it fails to bring out the connection between every philosopher and the first philosopher x, and it makes every philosopher contradict himself. That is why a new variable is necessary. The consequent of (11) is a new statement, and so the variables used in the antecedent may be repeated or disregarded. The consequent of (11) may be symbolized by '$(\exists x)(x$ is a philosopher $\cdot x$ contradicts $x)$' or '$(\exists y)(y$ is a philosopher $\cdot y$ contradicts $y)$', or etc. Naturally, we must use the same variable throughout the consequent, for this philosopher contradicts *himself.* Thus a complete symbolization of (11) is

$(\exists x)(x$ is a philosopher $\cdot$ $(y)(y$ is a philosopher $\supset x$ contradicts $y)) \supset (\exists z)(z$ is a philosopher $\cdot$ contradicts $z)$

In sum, considerations of meaning determine whether new or old variables are to be chosen and whether a given variable is to fall within the scope of a given quantifier. Where such considerations have no bearing, the choice of variables is a matter of personal preference. However, whenever a new quantifier *must* be used, a new variable *may* be used, and it is probably best to do so.

At this point it is necessary to specify our technical apparatus more precisely. In addition to 'x', the letters 'y', 'z', 'w', and 'u' will be used as *variables*, and in order to ensure an unending supply of variables, subscripted 'x', 'y', 'z', 'w', and 'u' will also count as variables. Thus 'x_1', 'y_3', 'w_5', and 'z_7' are all variables. Where α is any variable, (α) is a *universal quantifier* and $(\exists \alpha)$ is an *existential quantifier.* Thus '(x)', '(y)', '(z)', '(w)', '(z_1)', etc., are universal quantifiers, while '$(\exists x)$', '$(\exists y)$', '$(\exists z)$', '$(\exists w_2)$', etc., are existential quantifiers. Existential and universal quantifiers are read as we read '(x)' and '$(\exists x)$'. We may read '$(\exists y)$', for example, as 'There is a y', 'for some y', etc. The scope of a quantifier is as before: the shortest expression following the quantifier that grammar and parentheses permit. Thus the scope of '(x)' in '$(x)(x = x \supset (\exists y)(x = y)) \supset (\exists x)(x = x)$' is '$(x = x \supset (\exists y)(x = y))$', that of '$(\exists y)$' is '$(x = y)$', and that of '$(\exists x)$' is '$(x = x)$'.

We must also specify the distinction between free and bound occurrences of variables with some care. We shall say that *an occurrence of a variable α is bound to an occurrence of a quantifier (α)* [or $(\exists \alpha)$] in a sentence just in case the occurrence of α is within the scope of the occurrence of (α) [or $(\exists \alpha)$], but

not within the scope of a later occurrence of (α) or $(\exists\alpha)$.† Notice that an occurrence of 'x' is thus only bound to occurrences of '(x)' or '$(\exists x)$' and never
bound to '(y)' or '$(\exists z)$', for example. This convention follows a similar grammatical requirement on pronouns. Feminine pronouns, for example, never
have masculine antecedents.

EXAMPLES.   Arrows indicate bondage.

a. $(x)(x = y \supset (\exists y)(y = x \cdot (x)(x = y)))$

b. $(\exists x)(y)(x = y) \supset (x)(x = y)$

An occurrence of a variable in a sentence is *bound* just in case there is an
occurrence of a quantifier in the sentence to which it is bound. An occurrence of a variable is *free* just in case it is not bound. In example (a) the first
occurrence of 'y' is free, while in example (b) its last occurrence is free. All
other occurrences of variables in these examples are bound.

An *open sentence* is one which contains free occurrences of variables.
A *closed sentence* is one which is not open.

EXAMPLES.   a. Open sentences

$x = y$, $(\exists x)(x = y)$, $(y)(x = y)$

b. Closed sentences

$1 = 2$, $(x)(y)(x = y)$, $(\exists x)(\exists z)(x = z)$, $(1 + 1 = 3)$,

$(\exists x)(x = x)$

3.1.3 QUANTIFICATIONAL SCHEMATA

In addition to the difference due to new variables and quantifiers, one-
variable and full quantificational schemata differ by containing different
types of predicate letters. The natural diagram of a sentence such as

$(x)(x \text{ is worldly} \supset (\exists y)(y \text{ admires } x))$

would be an expression such as

$(x)(Fx \supset (\exists y)Hyx)$

and this requires the predicate letter 'H' to occur with two variables attached
to it. A sentence such as

$(\exists x)(\exists y)(\exists z)(x \text{ gave } y \text{ to } z)$

would be diagrammed by

$(\exists x)(\exists y)(\exists z)Gxyz$

†For the purposes of these definitions, appearances of α in (α) or $(\exists\alpha)$ do not count as occurrences
of the variable α.

and this requires the predicate letter 'G' to have three variables attached to it. Obviously, the number of variables attached to a predicate letter can be increased indefinitely.

Let us call an occurrence of a predicate letter with *one* variable or constant attached to it *monadic*. Thus 'Fx', 'Fa', 'Fy', and '$(x)Fx$', all contain monadic occurrences of 'F'. All occurrences of predicates in OVQS are, of course, monadic. Let us call an occurrence of a predicate letter with two (not necessarily different) variables or constants attached to it a *dyadic* occurrence of the predicate letter. Thus 'Gxy', 'Gay', 'Gyy', 'Gaa', '$(x)Gxa$', '$(\exists y)Gyy$', and '$(x)(y)Gyx$' contain dyadic occurrences of 'G'. In general, an occurrence of a predicate letter with n (not necessarily different) variables or constants attached to it is called an *n-adic* occurrence of the predicate letter. Thus '$(x)(y)(z)Hxyz$' contains a triadic occurrence of 'H', and '$(x)(\exists y)Kxaby$' a tetradic occurrence of 'K'.

The class of quantificational schemata is an extension of the class of truth-functional schemata and the class of one-variable quantificational schemata. Thus every TFS and every OVQS is a quantificational schemata (QS). The class of QS is determined precisely by the following rules:

R1   Every TFS is a QS.

R2   Every OVQS is a QS.

R3   A predicate letter with any number of variables or constants attached to it is a QS.

R4   If S and W are QS, so are $-S$, $(S \cdot W)$, $(S \vee W)$, $(S \supset W)$, $(S \equiv W)$.

R5   If S is a QS and α is a variable, then $(\alpha)S$ and $(\exists \alpha)S$ are QS.

R6   *Special restriction:*   No expression is a QS if it contains m-adic and n-adic occurrences of the same predicate letter, with $m \neq n$.

An expression is a QS if and only if its being so follows from these six rules.

The special restriction excludes expressions such as '$(x)Fx \vee Fxy$'. This not only facilitates the interpretation of QS, but also prevents us from confusing the use of 'F' as a representation of, say, a property word, with its use as a representation of a dyadic relation word. Thus if, for example, 'forest' and 'father of' occur in the same sentence, both cannot be diagrammed by 'F'. More importantly, confusing monadic and dyadic uses of 'F' might lead one to count the statement

If b is a father, then b is the father of c

as a logical truth. The special restriction guards against this sort of confusion. (Of course, 'F' may occur dyadically in one QS and monadically in another.)

Rule 5 permits vacuous quantification. This was already encountered in the case of OVQS and will be treated similarly now: a vacuous quantification is treated as equivalent to the QS which results from deleting the vacuous quantifier.

The previous definitions of free and bound occurrences of variables may be easily adapted to the case of QS, and this will not be done explicitly here. An *open* QS is one which has free occurrences of variables. A *closed* QS is one which is not open.

EXAMPLES, WITH DIAGRAMS OF CONSTRUCTION

a.

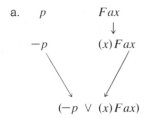

$$(-p \lor (x)Fax)$$

b. $Fx \quad \quad Gxy \quad \quad\quad Haxx$

$(Fx \supset Gxy) \quad\quad (\exists x)Haxx$

$(y)(Fx \supset Gxy)$

$((y)(Fx \supset Gxy) = (\exists x)Haxx)$

The same rules for omitting parentheses which were used for TFS and OVQS will be used for QS. Thus the schema

$$((x)Fx \supset ((((\exists x)(y)Gxy \cdot (z)Fz) \lor p) \lor Gax))$$

may be abbreviated as

$$(x)Fx \supset ((\exists x)(y)Gxy \cdot (z)Fz \lor p \lor Gzx)$$

EXERCISES FOR SECS. 3.1.1 TO 3.1.3

A. Supposing the universe to be $\{a,b,c,d\}$, expand the quantifications in these in favor of conjunction and disjunction.

1. $(x)Fx \lor (y)Gy$ 6. $(x)(Fx \supset (\exists y)Gxy)$
2. $(x)(\exists y)Gxy$ 7. $(\exists x)(Fx \supset (y)Gxy)$

   3. $(\exists y)(x)Gxy$ 8. $(x)Fxa \supset (\exists y)Fya$

   4. $(x)(y)Fxy$ 9. $(\exists x)(\exists y)(Fx \cdot -Fy)$

   5. $(y)(x)Fxy$ 10. $(x)Fx \equiv (y)Fy$

B. Paraphrase these statements, using logical symbols. Reveal as much structure as possible.

   1. Everything is like something.

   2. Something is like everything.

   3. If nothing is like itself, then nothing is like everything.

   4. Nothing is like something.

   5. There is some house in which all people live.

   6. Each person lives in some house.

   7. Some people like every painting.

   8. No painting is liked by all people.

   9. Every person who does not like his brother likes himself.

  10. Every cow is an animal, and every head of a cow is a head of an animal.

C. Determine the truth-values of the following statements (given that '$a = b$' is true just in case a and b are the same thing).

   1. $(x)(x = x)$ 6. $(x)(y) - (x = y)$

   2. $(x)(\exists y)(x = y)$ 7. $(x) - (y)(x = y)$

   3. $(x) - (\exists y)(x = y)$ 8. $(\exists y)(\exists x)(x = y)$

   4. $(x)(\exists y) - (x = y)$ 9. $(\exists y) - (\exists x)(x = y)$

   5. $(x)(y)(x = y)$ 10. $(\exists y)(x) - (x = y)$

D. Draw arrows to indicate the bonds between the occurrences of variables and quantifiers in the following:

   1. $(x)(x = y \supset (\exists y)(x = y))$

   2. $(\exists y)(y = y) \supset (x)(x = y \vee (\exists z)(x = z))$

   3. $(\exists y)(y = z) \supset (x)(x = z) \cdot (\exists y)(y = z)$

   4. $a = b \supset ((\exists x)(x = a) \vee (\exists y)(y = b))$

E. Identify the monadic, dyadic, triadic, and tetradic occurrences of predicate letters in the following lists.

   1. Fxa 5. $Haaxa$ 9. $(x)(\exists y)(z)Hzzyx$

   2. Fxx 6. Gx 10. $(x)Hxa$

   3. Ga 7. $Gzxa$ 11. $(\exists y)Hyx$

   4. $Hxyx$ 8. $(x)Gxa$ 12. $(\exists y)Gyyyy$

F. Which of the following is a genuine *unabbreviated* QS?

   1. $((p \vee q) \supset Fxa)$

   2. $(x)Fxa$

   3. $(((x)Fxy \vee Gy) \supset Fx)$

   4. $((x)Fy \supset (x)p)$

   5. $-(x)(\exists y)Fxya$

   6. $(x)Gx \supset (y)(Gy \equiv Hxy)$

3.2 QUANTIFICATIONAL SCHEMATA AND THEIR INTERPRETATIONS
3.2.1 LOGICAL PREDICATES

Logical predicates play an important role in the interpretation of QS. OVQS were interpreted by assigning open sentences to their predicate letters, but with the advent of several variables and dyadic and triadic occurrences of predicate letters, this is no longer feasible. *Logical predicates* will be introduced to fill this gap.

Before introducing logical predicates let us take a closer look at the problem which they are designed to handle. Suppose we start with the schema

(1) $(x)(Fx \supset (\exists y)(Fy \cdot Gxy))$

and wish to interpret it as the sentence

$(x)(x$ is a number $\supset (\exists y)(y$ is a number $\cdot x$ is smaller than $y))$

It is simple and natural to view 'F' as meaning 'number' and 'G' as 'smaller than'. However, as we learned from one-variable quantification theory, simple unbroken terms for 'F' and 'G' to represent are not always readily available. This problem was solved earlier by *introducing open sentences* at occurrences of predicate letters. The same approach could be applied in the present case. Thus we could think of the open sentence 'z is a number' as having been introduced at the occurrence of 'F' and the open sentence 'z is smaller than w' as having been introduced at the occurrence of 'G'. We should require thereby that 'x' replace 'z' and 'y' replace 'w'. Yet if introducing 'z is smaller than w' at 'Gxy' would yield 'x is smaller than y', then what would introducing the same open sentence at 'Gyx' yield? If the distinction between 'Gxy' and 'Gyx' is to be preserved, it would have to yield 'y is smaller than x'. Now, by just sticking with open sentences and 'x', 'y', etc., it is perfectly possible to lay down rules for the introduction of open sentences which will meet even this demand. Nonetheless, by introducing logical predicates and speaking of the introduction of logical predicates instead of open sentences, much simpler rules for interpreting schemata will be obtained.

A logical predicate looks just like an open sentence except that its free variables are replaced by circled numerals such as '①', '②', '③', etc. Thus the following are logical predicates:

① loves ②,   ① loves ①, $(x)(x = ①)$, $(x)(x = ① \cdot ② = x)$,
$(\exists y)(③ = y)$

Logical predicates are merely symbolic aids which will be used to handle the special problem of interpreting schemata. *They are constructed from open sentences by simply replacing all the free occurrences of variables by circled numerals*. The sentences from which logical predicates are obtained must not contain individual constants, and there is a restriction on the choices of circled numerals: every logical predicate must contain at least one occurrence of '①', and if it contains any other circled numbers besides '①', then it must also contain the circled numerals that precede it in the sequence of circled numerals '①', '②', '③'. '④', etc. For example, a logical predicate cannot contain '③' without also containing '①' and '②'. A logical predicate which contains only '①' is called a *one-place predicate*. One that contains only '①' and '②' is called a *two-place* predicate. More generally, a logical predicate whose greatest circled numeral is ⓝ is an *n-place* predicate.

EXAMPLES

a. One-place predicates
    ① is green,   (∃x)(① loves x),   ① + 36 = ①,   ① loves ①,
    (x)(① loves x ⊃ x loves ①)

b. Two-place predicates
    ① likes ②,   (∃x)(② gave x to ①),   ② likes ①,   (x)(① loves
    x ⊃ x loves ②)

c. Three-place predicates
    ① borrowed ② from ③,   ③ gave ② to ①,   (∃x)(① loves x · x is the
    brother of ② · ② is the father of ③)

Comment: Notice that '①' need not be the first circled numeral to appear in a logical predicate. Also, '① likes ②' is a different two-place predicate from '② likes ①'.

Now that logical predicates are on hand, the basic method for introducing them is easy enough to state: The variables or constants attached to the predicate letter at which the introduction is to take place replace the circled numerals in the logical predicate. This yields a sentence. Then this sentence is substituted for the occurrence of the predicate letter and the attached variables or constants. In this process the variable or constant which is the first one (leftmost one) attached to the predicate letter is used to replace all occurrences of '①'; the second one is used to replace all occurrences of '②'; etc. For example, if the occurrence of the predicate letter is '*Fxax*', then '*x*' replaces '①', '*a*' replaces '②', and '*x*' replaces '③'. And of course, an *n*-place predicate may be introduced only at an *n*-adic occurrence of a predicate letter. The complete process of introducing a logical predicate at the occurrence of a predicate letter is illustrated by means of the following diagram:

Schema: $\Phi\alpha_1\alpha_2 \cdots \alpha_n$
Logical predicate: $(\cdots ① \cdots ② \cdots ⓝ \cdots)$
Result: $(\cdots \alpha_1 \cdots \alpha_2 \cdots \alpha_n \cdots)$

Φ is a predicate letter, α_1, α_2, $\cdots$, α_n are variables or constants, and $\Phi\alpha_1\alpha_2 \cdots \alpha_n$ is the occurrence of Φ in the schema at which the introduction takes place.

EXAMPLES

a. *Schema:* $(x)(\exists y)Hxy \equiv Fx$
    Logical predicates: ①$+$①$=$②   (for 'H')
                              $(\exists y)($①$+$①$= y)$ (for 'F')
    Result: $(x)(\exists y)(x + x = y) \equiv (\exists x)(x + x = y)$

b. *Schema:* $(x)(Fxx \supset ((\exists y)Fya \equiv (Fyz \lor Fxy \cdot Fxx)))$
    Logical predicate: (① shouted at ②)
    Result: $(x)((x$ shouted at $x) \supset ((\exists y)(y$ shouted at $a) \equiv ((y$ shouted at $z)$
                  $\lor (x$ shouted at $y) \cdot (x$ shouted at $x)))$

c. *Schema:* Fxy
    Logical predicate: ① $<$ ②
    Result: $x < y$

d. *Schema:* Fyx
    Logical predicate: ① $<$ ②
    Result: $y < x$

Note how, in examples c and d, the important difference between 'Fxy' and 'Fyx' is preserved.

Let us consider the schema

(1) Fx

This schema represents the paradigm of an open sentence expressing that x has a given property. If that property is, for example, the property of being an uncle of someone, then 'Fx' would diagram 'x is an uncle of someone'. Likewise, 'Fx' could also diagram '$(\exists y)(x$ is an uncle of $y)$'. The last sentence is merely a paraphrase of 'x is an uncle of someone', which in turn is a paraphrase of 'x is an uncle'. No matter how we express 'uncle', whether by simply 'uncle' or by '$(\exists y)($① is an uncle of $y)$', we should expect that interpreting 'F' as 'uncle' should turn 'Fx' into an open sentence which is a paraphrase of 'x is an uncle'. Introducing '$(\exists y)($① is an uncle of $y)$', '$(\exists z)$ (① is an uncle of $z)$', or '$(\exists w)($① is an uncle of $w)$' at the occurrence of 'F' in 'Fx', all yield such sentences, namely,

$(\exists y)(x$ is an uncle of $y)$
$(\exists z)(x$ is an uncle of $z)$
$(\exists w)(x$ is an uncle of $w)$

However, if we introduce '$(\exists x)($① is an uncle of $x)$', we get

($\exists x$)(x is an uncle of x)

which says that someone is his own uncle, and is not a paraphrase of 'x is an uncle'. The logical predicates '($\exists y$)(① is an uncle of y)', '($\exists z$)(① is an uncle of z)', etc., may be introduced at 'Fx' with impunity. But when '($\exists x$)(① is an uncle of x)' is introduced, the 'x' of 'Fx' is put for '①' and becomes bound to '($\exists x$)', thereby destroying the intended meaning of 'Fx'. An occurrence of a variable which was free before the introduction did not remain so afterward.

Next consider the schema

(3) $(x)(Fx \supset (\exists y)Gyx)$

where the arrows indicate the bonds between variables. Let us interpret 'F' as 'human', that is, '① is human', and 'G' as 'sacrifices something for', that is, '($\exists z$)(① sacrifices z for ②)'. Then (3) comes to mean

(4)   Every human sacrifices something for something

or in logical notation,

(5) $(x)(x$ is a human $\supset (\exists y)(\exists z)(x$ sacrifices z for $y))$

[Remember that '($\exists y$)($\exists z$)(x sacrifices z for y)', '($\exists z$)($\exists y$)(x sacrifices z for y)', and '($\exists z$)($\exists y$)(x sacrifices y for z)' are all equivalent variants of 'x sacrifices something for something'.] So long as 'G' is interpreted as '($\exists w$)(① sacrifices w for ②)', '($\exists w$)(① sacrifices u for ②)', or any other variant logical predicate which does not contain 'x' or 'y', (3) will be interpreted as a paraphrase of (4) and (5). However, if 'G' is interpreted as '($\exists y$)(① sacrifices y for ②)', we get the ungrammatical expression

$(x)(x$ is human $\supset (\exists y)(\exists y)(x$ sacrifices y for $y))$

and if it is interpreted as '($\exists x$)(① sacrifices x for ②)', we get

(6) $(x)(x$ is human $\supset (\exists y)(\exists x)(x$ sacrifices x for $y))$

which is not an acceptable paraphrase of (4) or (5). It is not a paraphrase of (4) because it means 'If something is human, then something sacrifices itself for something'. [Recall that '$(x)(Fx \supset p)$' and '($\exists x$)$Fx \supset p$' are equivalent.] The change in meaning here is due to a realignment of bound variables. Because of the presence of '($\exists x$)' in '($\exists x$)(① sacrifices x for ②)', the second 'x' in (3) is no longer bound to '(x)'. *A bound occurrence of a variable put for a circled numeral has become bound to a new occurrence of a quantifier.*

When an occurrence of variable changes its alignment during the course of an operation by starting out free and becoming bound or by starting out bound to one occurrence of a quantifier and ending up bound to another occurrence of a quantifier, we say that the occurrence of the variable has been *captured* during the course of the operation.

EXAMPLES. Occurrences of variables in schemata captured upon introduction of a logical predicate.

a. *Logical predicate:* $(x)(① < x \supset ①^2 + x = ①)$
   Schema: $Fx \equiv ((\exists y)Fy \lor Fa)$
   captured occurrences
   Result: $(x)(x < x \supset x^2 + x = x) \equiv ((\exists y)(x)(y < x \supset y^2 + x = y)$
   $\lor (x)(a < x \supset a^2 + x = a))$

b. *Logical predicates:* $(y)(y \text{ loves } ①), (\exists x)(① \text{ sends } x \text{ to } ②)$
   Schema: $Fy \lor -(x)(Fx \equiv Gxa)$
   captured occurrences
   Result: $(y)(y \text{ loves } y) \lor -(x)((y)(y \text{ loves } x) \equiv (\exists x)(x \text{ sends } x \text{ to } a))$

Since we shall interpret predicate letters by introducing logical predicates at their occurrences, we must not allow occurrences of variables to be captured upon the introduction of logical predicates. For when capturing takes place the schema in question fails to take on its intended interpretation. When this happens, the schema may also take on a truth-value opposite to the one it should have had, and this can even affect the classification of the schema as valid or invalid. For example, we already know from one-variable quantification theory that

(7) $(x)Fx \supset Fx$

is valid, and almost the same derivation may be used to show that

(8) $(x)Fx \supset Fy$

is valid. Since (8) is valid, it should be true for every interpretation. But see what happens if we allow capturing! Interpreting 'F' as '$(\exists y)(y$ is the father of $①)$' and taking the universe as mankind, (8) becomes

(9) $(x)(\exists y)(y \text{ is the father of } x) \supset (\exists y)(y \text{ is the father of } y)$

This is, of course, false in the universe of humans: every human has a father, but none is his own father. Since such capturing must be avoided, the following restriction is imposed on the introduction of logical predicates:

Occurrences of variables from the schema put for the circled numerals must not be captured by quantifiers in the logical predicate introduced.

Several comments are pertinent to this restriction. First, we can always mechanically check for violations. We need only look at the alignments of the variables contributed by the schema before and after introduction and see if they have changed. Second, we need never worry about this restriction if the logical predicate contains no quantifiers or if its quantifiers do not contain variables which occur in the schema. For either there will be no quantifiers at all to bind the schema's variables, or else they will be the wrong kind of quantifiers. Finally, if one predicate is excluded by the restriction, one can always find an equivalent one which will not be excluded. This is done by changing the appropriate bound variables in the logical predicate. For example, the restriction prohibits the introduction of '$(\exists x)(① = x)$' at 'Fx', but does not prohibit the introduction of '$(\exists y)(① = y)$'. On the other hand, both predicates are variants of 'identical with something'. Thus, whenever possible, one should introduce only predicates which share no variables with the schemata into which introduction is to take place.

EXAMPLES

a.   The two-place predicate

$(\exists y)$(Ed spent ① for the purchase of y from ②)

may be introduced at the occurrences of 'F' in

Fab [*Result:* $(\exists y)$(Ed spent a for the purchase of y from b)]
Fxx [*Result:* $(\exists y)$(Ed spent x for the purchase of y from x)]
$(\exists z)Faz$ [*Result:* $(\exists z)(\exists y)$(Ed spent a for the purchase of y from z)]

but not at the occurrences of 'F' in 'Fxy' or '$(\exists x)Fyx$'.

b.   Find logical predicates whose introduction converts the schema

$(x)(y)(z)(Fxy \supset Fyx \cdot Fzz)$

into the following sentences:

(i) $(x)(y)(z)(x = y + x \supset y = x + y \cdot z = z + z)$
(ii) $(x)(y)(z)(x$ pledged x to $y \supset y$ pledged y to $x \cdot z$ pledged z to $z)$

Solutions:

(i) $① = ② + ①$
(ii) $①$ pledged $①$ to $②$

EXERCISES FOR SEC. 3.2.1

A.   Where possible, introduce the predicate
$(\exists y)(①$ gave y to $②)$
at the occurrences of 'F' in the following QS. When it is not possible to introduce

this predicate, find one which also means '① gave something to ②', which can be introduced.

1. $Fxa \lor Fax$ 4. $(x)(\exists z)Fxz$

2. $Fxx \supset (x)Fxa$ 5. $(\exists y)(x)Fxy$

3. Fxy 6. $Fab \equiv (x)(w)Fxw$

B. Find logical predicates whose introduction converts the schema

$(x)(\exists y)(z)Fxyz \lor (\exists y)(x)Fyxy$

into the following:

1. $(x)(\exists y)(z)(z$ gave y to x for $x) \lor (\exists y)(x)(y$ gave x to y for $y)$

2. $(x)(\exists y)(z)(y + y = x - z) \lor (\exists y)(x)(x + x = y - y)$

3. $(x)(\exists y)(z)(x$ sent z to $y \equiv z$ went to x for z's friend)

    $\lor (\exists y)(x)(y$ sent y to $x \equiv y$ went to y for y's friend)

3.2.2 INTERPRETING QUANTIFICATIONAL SCHEMATA

Because quantificational schemata include OVQS, the same considerations which arose concerning the interpretations of the latter continue to be relevant. The most important of these dealt with universes of discourse. Quantificational schemata must also be interpreted in universes of discourse; otherwise it will be possible to find schemata which are valid, given the existence of one number of objects, and invalid, given the existence of a greater number. The same OVQS which were discussed before continue to be good examples of such schemata. Practically all the things we learned about interpreting OVQS continue to apply to quantificational schemata, and hardly anything new has to be learned. The only important difference between the interpretations of the two kinds of schemata concerns predicate letters: they are no longer interpreted by means of open sentences, but are now interpreted by means of logical predicates.

Let us begin with universes of discourse. We are now able to diagram statements about the objects in universes which we could not previously diagram. Consequently, the notion of truth in a universe has a wider application than it previously had. For example, the sentences '$(x)(\exists y)(x < y)$' and '$(\exists y)(x)(y$ is a child of $x)$' were previously outside the scope of our notation. The first is true in the universe of numbers; the second is false in the universe of humans. Our notation lets us say new things about a given universe, but this is the only new thing. We need not alter the notion of a universe or the concept of truth in a universe. Therefore, since one-variable quantification theory serves as our model, we may define an interpretation of a QS as follows.

An *interpretation of a schema in a universe U* is an assignment of

1 Truth-values to the schema's statement letters (if any)
2 Objects in U to the individual constants of the schema (if any)
3 Objects in U to the variables which have free occurrences in the schema (if any)
4 n-place predicates to the predicate letters which have n-adic occurrences in the schema (if any)

[A predicate assigned under clause (4) must be introducible at all occurrences of the predicate letter to which it is assigned.]

EXAMPLES

a. *Schema:* $((x)Fx \vee p) \equiv (\exists y)(Gxy \cdot Fy)$
    Universe and assignments: U : mankind
    x: Karl Marx, $p : T$, $F :$ ① hates communism
    $G:$ ① is an enemy of ②
    Result: $((x)(x$ hates communism$) \vee T) \equiv (\exists y)($Karl Marx is an enemy of $y \cdot y$ hates communism$)$

b. *Schema:* $(\exists x)(Gxa \supset (z)(Hzza \cdot p))$
    Universe and assignments: U : the class of positive numbers $a : 0$,
    $G :$ ① $<$ ②, $H :$ ① $+$ ② $=$ ③, $p : F$
    Result: $(\exists x)(x < 0) \supset (x)(z + z = 0 \cdot F)$

c. *Schema:* $(x)(Fx \supset ((\exists z)(Fz \cdot Gzb) \vee (\exists z)(Fz \cdot Gxb)))$
    Universe and assignments: U : the class of planets
    b : the Earth, $F :$ ① belongs to the Solar System
    $G :$ ① is a satellite of ②
    Result: $(x)(x$ belongs to the Solar System $\supset ((\exists z)(z$ belongs to the Solar System $\cdot z$ is a satellite of the Earth$) \vee (\exists z)(z$ belongs to the Solar System $\cdot x$ is a satellite of the Earth$)))$

By letting 'T' represent '$(x)(x = x)$' and 'F' represent '$-(x)(x = x)$', every interpretation of a schema converts it into a statement. If an interpretation in a universe U converts a schema S into a statement which is true in U, then the schema is said to come out true (in U) for the interpretation; otherwise the schema is said to come out false for the interpretation. All the schemata in the three examples given above come out true for their respective interpretations.

A schema which is true for every interpretation in a universe U is called *valid in U*. One which is true for at least one interpretation in a universe U is said to be *consistent in U*.

EXAMPLES

a. These schemata are valid in the universe $\{1\}$: $p \vee \bar{p}$, $(\exists x)Fx \supset (x)Fx$, $(x)Fxx \supset (x)(y)Fxy$, $Fa \supset (x)Fx$.

Comment: Of these schemata, only the first is valid in a universe which contains more than one object.

b.   This schema is consistent but not valid in the universe of positive numbers: $(x)(\exists y)Gxy$. (Assign 'G' the two-place predicate '①$\leq$②' for a true interpretation; assign it ' 2 $<$ 1 ' for a false one.)

EXERCISES FOR SEC. 3.2.2

A.   What truth-values in the indicated universes do these QS have for the indicated interpretations?

    1. $(x)(\exists y)Fxy \equiv p$
       Universe: mankind
       Assignments: $p : T$, $F :$ ② is the father of ①

    2. $(x)Fxa$
       Universe: integers
       Assignments: $a : 0$, $F :$ ①$+$②$=$②

    3. $(x)(\exists y)Gxxy \vee Fz$
       Universe: $\{1,2,3\}$
       Assignments: $z : 1$, $F :$ ①$+$①$=$① $G :$ ①$\cdot$③$=$②

    4. $(x)p = Fa$
       Universe: $\{1\}$
       Assignments: $p : T$, $a : 1$, $F :$ ①$=$①

    5. $(\exists y)(Fyy \cdot Fyb)$
       Universe: $\{0,1,2\}$
       Assignments: $b : 2$, $F :$ ①$+$①$=$②

B.   Give a true interpretation in some universe and a false interpretation in another universe for each of these QS.

    1. $p \cdot (x)Fxx$ 3. $Fxy \supset (x)(y)Fxy$
    2. $(x)(\exists y)Gxy$ 4. $(\exists y)Gxay \vee (y)Gyya_{.}$

C.   Which are valid in the universe $\{1\}$? Which are consistent in that universe?

    1. $p \vee \bar{p}$ **5.** $p \cdot \bar{p}$
    2. $(x)(y)Fxy \supset p$ 6. $(\exists y)Fyy \cdot (\exists y) - Fyy$
    3. $(\exists y)(x)Fxy \supset (x)(\exists y)Fxy$ 7. $p \vee (x)(\exists y)Fxy$
    4. $(x)(\exists y)Gxy \supset (\exists y)(x)Gxy$ 8. $(x)(\exists y)Fxy \cdot (x) - Fxx$

3.2.3 VALIDITY

Validity can once again be defined in terms of validity in a universe: *a quantificational schema is valid if and only if it is valid in every universe.* This definition supersedes our previous definitions of validity and includes both truth-functional validity and one-variable validity. For every truth-functionally valid TFS is valid in the new sense, and so also is every one-variable valid OVQS. The following considerations will show this: A TFS is true for a given interpretation in a given universe if and only if it comes out true (in the original truth-functional sense) for the assignment of truth-values to its statement letters. Hence a TFS is valid (in the new sense) if and only if it is true for every assignment of truth-values to its statement letters. In other words, a TFS is quantificationally valid if and only if it is truth-functionally valid. Now for OVQS. The only difference between the previous interpretations of these schemata and the present ones is that predicate letters are now assigned one-place predicates. But this difference surely does not change a schema's truth-value under a given interpretation. Consequently, a OVQS which previously counted as valid still counts as valid, while no new valid OVQS will be added by the new definition.

The definitions of invalidity, consistency, and inconsistency follow the previous models:

A schema is *invalid* if and only if it is not valid.
A schema is *consistent* if and only if it is consistent in some universe.
A schema is *inconsistent* if and only if it is not consistent.

The relations which we noticed earlier between valid, invalid, consistent, and inconsistent TFS and OVQS also hold for quantificational schemata. The proofs of these are left as exercises, since they are familiar by now. However, as a reminder, the relationships are listed once again:

Every valid schema is *consistent* (but not conversely).
Every inconsistent schema is *invalid* (but not conversely).
A schema is *valid* if and only if its negation is inconsistent.
A schema is *consistent* if and only if its negation is invalid.

EXAMPLES OF VALID QS

a. $(x)(y)Fxy \supset (x)Fxx$

Informal Proof: Let U be any universe and I any interpretation of (a) in U. Two cases must be considered. Case I: 'F' is interpreted so that everything in U bears F to everything in U. Then everything in U must bear F to itself. That is, 'F' is interpreted so that both '$(x)(y)Fxy$' and '$(x)Fxx$' are true in U. So (a) is true in U. Case II: 'F' is interpreted otherwise. Then '$(x)(y)Fxy$' is false in U; so (a) is true in U by virtue of a false antecedent.

b. $(\exists y)(x)Fyx \supset (x)(\exists y)Fyx$

Informal Proof: Let U be any universe and I an interpretation of 'F' in U. Again two cases arise. Case I: 'F' is interpreted so that something in U bears F to everything in U. Then, given anything in U, there is something in U which bears F to it, since there is something in U which bears F to everything in U. Thus, given this interpretation of 'F', both '$(\exists y)(x)Fyx$' and '$(x)(\exists y)Fyx$' are true in U. So (b) is true in U. Case II: 'F' is interpreted otherwise. Then (b) is true in U by virtue of a false antecedent.

EXAMPLE OF AN INVALID QS

c. $(x)(\exists y)Fyx \supset (\exists y)(x)Fyx$

To show that (c) is invalid, we must specify (1) a universe U, and (2) a false interpretation of (c) in U. To do this let us take U as $\{1,2\}$ and interpret 'F' as '$①=②$'. Then (c) is interpreted as

$(x)(\exists y)(y = x) \supset (\exists y)(x)(y = x)$

which is false in $\{1,2\}$. [The choice of U is essential: (c) is true in $\{1\}$ for the same assignment to 'F'.]

EXERCISES FOR SEC. 3.2.3
A. Present *informal* proofs of the validity of these QS.
    1. $(x)(y)Fxy \supset (x)(\exists y)Fxy$
    2. $(x)(y)(Fxy \lor -Fxy)$
    3. $(\exists y)((x)Fx \supset Fy)$
    4. $(\exists y)(Fy \supset (x)Fx)$
    5. $(x)Fx \equiv (y)Fy$
B. Establish the invalidity of these QS.
    1. $(x)(\exists y)Fxy \supset (\exists y)(x)Fxy$
    2. $(x)(Fx \supset (\exists y)Gxy) \supset (\exists y)(x)(Fx \supset Gxy)$
    3. $(\exists x)(\exists y)Hxy \supset (\exists x)Hxx$
    4. $(x)(\exists y)Hxy \supset (x)Hxx$
    5. $((x)Fx \supset Fy) \cdot (x)p$

3.2.4 IMPLICATION AND EQUIVALENCE
The notion of a simultaneous interpretation in a universe U of several schemata can be defined in the manner of one-variable quantification theory. Let us assume that this has been done. Then S *implies* W means that, for every simultaneous interpretation in every universe U of S and W, if S comes out true, then so does W. S is *equivalent* to W means that S and W imply each other. It can then be shown that S implies W just in case $S \supset W$ is valid and that S is equivalent to W just in case $S \equiv W$ is valid. The laws of implication and equivalence which were stated previously can also be proved for

the case of quantification theory, but there is no need to do this here, since the new proofs mimic the earlier ones.

The discussion of one-variable equivalence postponed the two laws of interchange until they could be treated in the context of full quantification theory. Now is the time to fulfill that promise. However, it will be convenient to introduce three other laws of equivalence first.

The first of these laws is stated as follows:

LAW 1   If S implies W, then $(\alpha)S$ implies $(\alpha)W$.

Proof: Assume that S implies W, and let U be any universe and I any simultaneous interpretation of $(\alpha)S$ and $(\alpha)W$ in U. Suppose that $(\alpha)S$ is true for I. Then for all choices of α in U, S is true for I. If α does not occur free in W, then $(\alpha)W$ is a vacuous quantification. Hence the interpretation of $(\alpha)W$ already interprets W. But in this case W is true in U for I since S implies W. Hence $(\alpha)W$ is also true for I. Next consider the case in which α does occur free in W. Then the interpretation I of $(\alpha)W$ does not interpret W. However, every extension I' of I which assigns an object in U to α will be an interpretation of W. Thus consider any such I'. Since S implies W, and S is true for all choices of α in U, W will be true for I'. But then W is true for I and all choices of α in U; that is, $(\alpha)W$ is true for I. Thus, in either case, $(\alpha)S$ implies $(\alpha)W$.

The next law deals with existential quantifiers:

LAW 2   If S implies W, $(\exists\alpha)S$ implies $(\exists\alpha)W$.

Proof: If S implies W, then clearly $-W$ implies $-S$. But by Law 1, if $-W$ implies $-S$, $(\alpha)-W$ implies $(\alpha)-S$. However, $(\alpha)-W$ implies $(\alpha)-S$ only if $-(\alpha)-S$ implies $-(\alpha)-W$. The law then follows from the transitivity of implication and the equivalence of $-(\alpha)-S$ and $-(\alpha)-W$ to $(\exists\alpha)S$ and $(\exists\alpha)W$, respectively. [*Exercise:* Show that S implies W only if $-W$ implies $-S$ and that $-(\alpha)-S$ is equivalent to $(\exists\alpha)S$.]

From Laws 1 and 2 we can easily establish this law of equivalence:

LAW 3   If S and W are equivalent, then both $(\alpha)S$ and $(\alpha)W$ are equivalent and $(\exists\alpha)S$ and $(\exists\alpha)W$ are equivalent.

(*Exercise:* Establish Law 3.)

The operation of interchange works exactly as it did in truth-function theory: W' comes from S' by interchanging W with S in S' if and only if S' and W' are exactly alike, except that W occurs in one or more places in W' where S occurs in S'.

EXAMPLES

S'		W'	
$(x)Fxy \lor Gx,$	$S : Gx,$	$(x)Fxy \lor Hx \cdot p,$	$W : Hx \cdot p$
$(x)(Fx \lor p \cdot Fx),$	$S : Fx,$	$(x)((x)Fx \lor p \cdot (x)Fx),$	$W : (x)Fx$
$(x)(Fx \lor Gy),$	$S : Gy,$	$(x)(Fx \lor Fxy),$	$W : Fxy$

The second example shows that interchanging may produce vacuous quantifications, but there is no harm in this. The third example is more serious, however, for W' is not a QS, since the special restriction in the definition of QS is not met. Consequently, we will tacitly assume throughout the statements and proofs of the laws of interchange that W' is indeed a schema.

Let us turn now to the first law of interchange:

> *If S and W are equivalent and if W' comes from S' by interchanging W with S in S', then S' and W' are also equivalent.*

Proof: To prove this law we shall show that (a) the law is true for the simplest S' and (b) if the law is true for all schemata which are simpler than a given S', then it is also true for this S'. (Here one schema is simpler than another if it contains fewer occurrences of statement connectives and quantifiers.) Given (a) and (b), the law must be true for all S'. For suppose that the law did not hold for a particular S'. We may assume that this is the simplest S' for which the law does not hold. By (a) this could not be among the very simplest QS. So there are QS simpler than S' for which the law holds, and it holds for all these. But then by (b) it would have to hold for S' too, which is a contradiction.

Proof of (a):   Here neither S' nor W' can contain statement connectives or quantifiers. So S' must be S itself, and W' must be W. Hence, if S and W are equivalent, so are S' and W'.

Proof of (b):   If S' and S are the same, that is, if the interchange is carried out by replacing *all* of S' by W, then W' and W are the same; so if S and W are equivalent, so must be S' and W'. Thus we may assume that the occurrence of S in S' is a genuine part of S'. Then seven cases arise according to the form of S'. In each case it is assumed that the law holds for QS which are simpler than S'.

Case I. S' is a negation, that is, S' is $-E$. Then S is E or occurs within E. Thus W' is $-N$ where N comes from E by interchanging W with S in E. Since E is simpler than S', the law holds for it. Thus N and E are equivalent. But then so are $-E$ and $-N$. (Why?) Thus S' and W' are equivalent.

Case II. S' is $E_1 \cdot E_2$. Then W' is $N_1 \cdot N_2$, where N_1 is E_1 or comes from it by the interchange, and N_2 is E_2 or comes from it by the interchange. Since E_1 and E_2 are simpler than S', E_1 and N_1 are equivalent, and E_2 and N_2 are equivalent. Thus $E_1 \cdot E_2$ is equivalent to $N_1 \cdot N_2$.

Case III. S' is $E_1 \vee E_2$. (Proof similar to case II.)

Case IV. S' is $E_1 \supset E_2$. (Proof similar to case II.)

Case V. S' is $E_1 \equiv E_2$. (Proof similar to case II.)

Case VI. S' is $(\alpha)E$. Then W' is $(\alpha)N$ where N comes from E by the interchange. Thus N and E are equivalent. But then $(\alpha)E$ and $(\alpha)N$ are equivalent by Law 3.

Case VII. S' is $(\exists\alpha)E$. (Proof similar to case VI.)

The second law of interchange states in effect that interchange of equivalence preserves validity, consistency, implication, etc. Its precise statement and proof are so much like those given for the corresponding law in truth-function theory that we shall not present them here.

Earlier, we took notice of the equivalences between '$(x)Fx$', and '$(y)Fy$' and between '$(\exists x)Fx$' and '$(\exists y)Fy$'. More generally we have the following law of equivalence:

LAW 4   If S_α and S_β, where α and β are variables, are exactly alike except that S_α contains free occurrences of α in all and only those places where S_β contains free occurrences of β, then $(\alpha)S_\alpha$ is equivalent to $(\beta)S_\beta$ and $(\exists\alpha)S_\alpha$ is equivalent to $(\exists\alpha)S_\alpha$.

Proof for $(\alpha)S_\alpha$ and $(\beta)S_\beta$:   Let U be any universe and let I be any interpretation of $(\alpha)S_\alpha \equiv (\beta)S_\beta$ in U. We shall show that this schema must come out true for I. Since S_α and S_β differ only by containing free occurrences of α or β, $(\alpha)S_\alpha$ and $(\beta)S_\beta$ share the same free occurrences of variables, individual constants, and statement and predicate letters. These are given the same assignments by I. Now suppose I makes $(\alpha)S_\alpha$ true in U. Then for all assignments from U to α, S_α is true in U. But because S_α and S_β are indistinguishable except for the free occurrences of α and β, and because these occurrences match each other exactly, all assignments from U to β will also make S_β true. Thus if $(\alpha)S_\alpha$ is true for I, so is $(\beta)S_\beta$. By similar reasoning, if $(\alpha)S_\alpha$ is false for I, then so is $(\beta)S_\beta$. Thus $(\alpha)S_\alpha \equiv (\beta)S_\beta$ must come out true for I. Since U and I are arbitrary, the equivalence must hold.

[*Exercise:*   Carry out the proof for $(\exists\alpha)S_\alpha$ and $(\exists\beta)S_\beta$.]

EXAMPLES.   According to Law 4, the following are pairs of equivalent schemata:

$(\exists x)((z)Fxz \equiv Gx);$ $(\exists y)((z)Fyz \equiv Gy)$
$(y)(\exists z)(w)(Gxy \vee Hyzw);$ $(u)(\exists z)(w)(Gxu \vee Huzw)$

However, the following pairs of schemata do not satisfy the antecedent of Law 4, and they are not equivalent.

$(\exists x)((z)Fxz \equiv Gx);$ $(\exists z)((z)Fzz \equiv Gz)$
$(y)(\exists z)(w)(Gxy \vee Hyzw);$ $(x)(\exists z)(w)(Gxx \vee Hxzw)$

Suppose that we have a schema S which contains an occurrence of a quantifier (α) or $(\exists\alpha)$. Then suppose that we replace the occurrence of (α) or $(\exists\alpha)$ by (β), respectively, by $(\exists\beta)$, and also replace all occurrences of α bound to (α) or $(\exists\alpha)$ by β. This produces another schema, which is said to come from S by means of *a change of a bound variable*.

EXAMPLES

Old Schemata	New Schemata	Variable Changed
$(x)(Fx \supset (\exists y)(Fy \vee Gxa))$	$(z)(Fz \supset (\exists y)(Fy \vee Gza))$	x
$(y)(Fxy \equiv Gy)$	$(w)(Fxw \equiv Gw)$	y
$p \supset (w)Gw$	$p \supset (x)Gx$	w
$(z)Fxz$	$(x)Fxx$	z
$(x)(Gx \equiv (\exists y)Hxya)$	$(y)(Gy \equiv (\exists y)Hyya)$	x

As the last two examples indicate, when bound variables are changed, capturing is possible. As long as capturing is avoided, however, changes-of-bound variables can be counted upon to yield equivalent results. This is formulated by the following law:

The law governing changes of bound variables: *If W comes from S by one or more changes of bound variables, and if no capturing results from these changes, then S and W are equivalent.*

Proof: Let us first prove the law for the case in which W comes from S by means of a single change of a bound variable. Then the change affects a single occurrence of a universal or existential quantifier. We may assume that this is a universal quantifier since the argument is identical for an existential quantifier. The change affects the quantifier and its scope; that is, it affects a part $(\alpha)S'_\alpha$ of S. This part is converted to a part $(\beta)S'_\beta$ of W. Since no capturing takes place, S'_α and S'_β are related as in the antecedent of Law 4; thus $(\alpha)S'_\alpha$ and $(\beta)S'_\beta$ are equivalent. Moreover, the change of a bound variable in question has the same effect as interchanging $(\beta)S'_\beta$ with the occurrence of $(\alpha)S'_\alpha$ in S in question. Thus, by the law of interchange, S and W are equivalent.

Several changes of bound variables carried out simultaneously can be reduced to single changes carried out one at a time. Thus the simultaneous changes which transform '$(x)(y)Fxy$' to '$(z)(w)Fzw$' reduce to the single transformations of '$(x)(y)Fxy$' to '$(x)(w)Fxw$' and thence to '$(z)(w)Fzw$'. Re-routing becomes necessary to handle transformations such as that of '$(x)(y)Fxy$' to '$(y)(x)Fxy$'. If we change 'x' to 'y' or 'y' to 'x' directly, we obtain '$(y)(y)Fyy$' or '$(x)(x)Fxx$', and these will never yield '$(y)(x)Fyx$'. This problem is handled by first changing 'x' to 'z' to obtain '$(z)(y)Fzy$'. Next 'y' may be changed to 'x', yielding '$(z)(x)Fzx$', and finally 'z' may be changed to 'y'. This sort of trick will permit the reduction of all simultaneous changes of bound variables to successive changes. Thus, if W comes from S by several changes of bound variables, we may assume that all these changes are made successively instead of simultaneously. Then W is obtained from S by changing S to S_1, S_1 to S_2, S_2 to S_3, . . . , S_{n-1} to S_n, and S_n to W. Moreover, it follows from what we have already proved that S is equivalent to S_1, S_1 to S_2, S_2 to S_3, . . . , S_{n-1} to S_n, and S_n to W. Hence, by the transitivity of equivalence, S is equivalent to W.

The law governing changes of bound variables is useful to bear in mind when applying quantification theory to arguments in ordinary language. A derivation dealing with schemata containing one set of bound variables may be much more simple than one dealing with equivalent schemata containing different bound variables. By choosing the right bound variables when paraphrasing and diagramming statements, it may be possible to simplify greatly the proof of the validity of an argument. The law governing changes of bound variables tells us that bound variables can be chosen fairly freely.

EXERCISES FOR SEC. 3.2.4

A. Using the laws of this section, previous laws of implication and equivalence, and possibly some obvious truth-functional implications, establish the following:
   1. '$(x)(Fx \cdot Gx)$' implies '$(x)Gx$'.
   2. '$(\exists x) - Fx$' implies '$(\exists x)(Fx \supset Gx)$'.
   3. '$(x)--Fx$' is equivalent to '$(x)Fx$'.
   4. '$(x)(Fx \lor Gx)$' is equivalent to '$(y)(-Fy \supset Gy)$'.
   5. '$(x)Fx \lor p$' is equivalent to '$(y)Fy \lor p$'.
   6. '$(x)Fx \cdot (\exists y)Gy$' is equivalent to '$-(-(z)Fz \lor -(\exists y)Gw)$'.
   7. '$(x)(y)Fxy$' is equivalent to '$(y)(x)Fyx$'.
   8. '$(x)Fx$' implies '$(y)(Fy \lor Gy)$'.
B. 1. Establish Law 3.
   2. Supply the proofs for cases III, IV, V, and VII of the law of interchange.
   3. Carry out the remainder of the proof of Law 4.

3.3 DERIVATIONS

There is no decision procedure for quantificational validity, but there are quantificational rules of inferences which are both sound and complete. Thus, although we cannot test for validity, implication, equivalence, etc., we can use these rules to establish the presence of these properties and relations (so long as they are actually present). To be sure, even then we will depend somewhat on luck and ingenuity. But this is a familiar problem, so let us turn to the rules themselves.

The rules of inference used in quantification theory are, basically, the same as those used in one-variable quantification theory. The truth-functional rules may be reused without any change. Some slight extensions and restrictions must now accompany the rules of UI, EG, UG, and EI, but the intuitive basis of these rules remains the same. Since no further rules will be necessary, let us now reconsider the quantificational rules one at a time.

3.3.1 UNIVERSAL INSTANTIATION

This rule allowed and shall allow us to drop quantifiers from universal quantifications. In one-variable quantification theory the rule had two options: (1) a universal quantifier could be simply dropped, or (2) the universal quantifier could be dropped and the occurrences of 'x' bound to it replaced by an individual constant. In full quantification theory option (2) is extended by allowing the bound variable to be replaced by another variable. Thus we may not only pass from '$(x)Fx$' to 'Fx' or 'Fa', but also to 'Fy' or 'Fz'. However, capturing is now possible. For example, we can pass from '$(x)(\exists y)Gxy$' to '$(\exists y)Gyy$' by dropping '(x)' and replacing 'x' by 'y'. If UI is to remain sound, then such capturing must be prohibited. The last example shows that this is necessary, for '$(x)(\exists y)Gxy$' does not imply '$(\exists y)Gyy$'. [Take U as mankind and 'G' as '② is a father of ①'; then '$(x)(\exists y)Gxy$' is true in U but '$(\exists y)Gyy$' is not.]

Let S_α be any schema, and let α be any variable (which may or may not have a free occurrence in S_α). Then let S_β be the result of replacing all the free occurrences (if any) of α in S_α by β. Here β is a variable or an individual constant.

EXAMPLES

	S_α	α	S_β	β
a.	$Gx \vee (x)Fx$	x	$Gy \vee (x)Fx$	y
b.	p		p	
c.	$(x)Gxy$	y	$(x)Gxx$	x

We may now extend UI by stating it as follows:

Universal instantiation: *From $(\alpha)S_\alpha$ we may infer S_β, where β is an in-*

dividual constant or variable, provided that no free occurrence of α in S_α is within the scope of an occurrence of (β) or $(\exists_\beta)$.

The reason for S_β is a numeral referring to $(\alpha)S_\alpha$ followed by 'UI'.

Notice that β is captured in S_β just in case some free occurrence of α in S_α falls within the scope of an occurrence of (β) or $(\exists_\beta)$. For in this case the occurrence of β replacing α will end up bound to this occurrence of (β) or $(\exists_\beta)$.

EXAMPLES

Correct Applications of UI:

a.

1	$(x)(Fx \lor Gyx)$	P
2	$Fx \lor Gyx$	1, UI
3	$Fa \lor Gya$	1, UI
4	$Fy \lor Gyy$	1, UI
5	$Fz \lor Gyz$	1, UI

b.

1	$(x)(y)Fxy$	P
2	$(y)Fxy$	1, UI
3	Fxy	2, UI
4	Fxx	2, UI
5	$(y)Fay$	1, UI
6	Fab	5, UI
7	Faa	5, UI
8	$(y)Fzy$	1, UI
9	Fzz	8, UI

Incorrect Applications of UI with Capturing:

c.

1	$(x)(y)Fxy$	P
2	$(y)Fyy$	1, UI (incorrect)

d.

1	$(y)(Fxz \lor (\exists z)(Hz \cdot Fyy)$	P
2	$Fzz \lor (\exists z)(Hz \cdot Fzz)$	1, UI (incorrect)

Naturally, the examples given in one-variable quantification theory of *incorrect* applications of UI are *still* classified as incorrect. With the presence of additional variables, a new type of incorrect application has arisen. Notice that although 'Fxx' or 'Fzz' can be obtained from '$(x)(y)Fxy$' by UI, 'Fyy' cannot be obtained. [Of course, 'Fyy' can be *derived* from '$(x)(y)Fxy$', but only by deriving, say, $(x)(z)Fxz$ en route.]

EXAMPLES

a. To derive 'Faa' from 'Ga' and '$(x)(y)(Gx \cdot Gy \supset Fxy)$'.

Derivation:

1	Ga	P
2	$(x)(y)(Gx \cdot Gy \supset Fxy)$	P
3	$(y)(Ga \cdot Gy \supset Fay)$	2, UI
4	$Ga \cdot Ga \supset Faa$	3, UI
5	$Ga \cdot Ga$	1, PC
6	Faa	4, 5, MP

b. Prove: $(y)[Hxy \equiv (z)Hxz] \cdot (w)(x)Hxw \supset Hxx$.

1	$(y)[Hxy \equiv (z)Hxz] \cdot (w)(x)Hxw$	A
2	$(y)[Hxy \equiv (z)Hxz]$	1, S
3	$Hxw \equiv (z)Hxz$	2, UI
4	$(w)(x)Hxw$	1, S
5	$(x)Hxw$	4, UI
6	Hxw	5, UI
7	$(z)Hxz$	6, 3, MPB
8	Hxx	7, UI
9	$(y)[Hxy \equiv (z)Hxz] \cdot (w)(x)Hxw \supset Hxx$	1-8, CP

3.3.2   EXISTENTIAL GENERALIZATION

The new extensions and restrictions governing this rule are similar to those governing UI. Previously, there were two options to EG. (1) '$(\exists x)$' could be prefixed to an open schema containing a free occurrence of 'x' or (2) an individual constant could be replaced by 'x' in one or more of its occurrences, and then an existential quantifier binding these occurrences of 'x' prefixed to the resulting schema. Even in one-variable quantification theory, capturing can take place under option 2. This was excluded in the previous formulation of EG, although capturing was not mentioned explicitly by name. Given our additional variables, option 2 should be extended. In applying option 2, we shall replace one or more occurrences of a *free variable* or individual constant in a schema by another variable, and then bind this variable by an existential quantifier. Option 1 does not lead to unwanted capturing, for the only free variable which is bound is the one free in the schema. Option 2, however, may lead to unwanted capturing. The replacing variable may become captured by one of the quantifiers in the original schema, as when 'x' replaces 'y' or 'a' in '$(x)Fxya$' to yield '$(x)Fxxa$' or '$(x)Fxyx$'. On the other hand, when the existential quantifier is prefixed, several places may become "linked" which were not previously "linked", as when 'z' replaces 'x' in 'Fzx' to yield 'Fzz' and then '$(\exists z)$' is prefixed to produce '$(\exists z)Fzz$'. Both types of capturing must be avoided if EG is to remain sound. An example of each type of capturing should be sufficient to show this. First, note that '$(\exists x)Fxy \vee Gy$'

does not imply '$(\exists x)((\exists x)Fxx \lor Gx)$'. [Let U be the universe of numbers, assign 1 to 'y', '$\textcircled{1} < \textcircled{2}$' to '$F$', and '$-(\textcircled{1} = \textcircled{1})$' to '$G$'.] Yet, if the first type of capturing is permitted, then this step would be countenanced by EG. Second, note that 'Fxy' does not imply '$(\exists y)Fyy$'. (Let U and 'F' be the same. Assign 0 to 'x' and 1 to 'y'.) However, if the second type of capturing is permitted, EG would allow this step.

In order to extend EG while avoiding unwanted capturing, it must be restated. The following statement of the rule will suit our needs.

> Existential generalization: $(\exists_\alpha)S_\alpha$ *may be inferred from* S_β, *where β is an individual constant or free variable, provided that no free occurrence of α in S_α is within the scope of an occurrence of (β) or $(\exists_\beta)$.*

The reason for $(\exists\alpha)S_\alpha$ is a numeral referring to S_β followed by 'EG'. Here S_α and S_β are the same as the S_α and S_β of UI. Although now S_α is part of the inferred step, α still represents the quantified variable, and β the individual constant, or unquantified variable.

EXAMPLES

Correct Applications of EG:

a.
1	$Fxyy$	P
2	$(\exists x)Fxyy$	1, EG
3	$(\exists y)(\exists x)Fxyy$	2, EG
4	$(\exists z)Fxzy$	1, EG
5	$(\exists z)Fxzz$	1, EG
6	$(\exists z)Fxyz$	1, EG
7	$(\exists w)(\exists z)Fwyz$	6, EG
8	$(\exists y)(\exists w)(\exists z)Fwyz$	7, EG

b.
1	p	P
2	$(\exists x)p$	1, EG

c.
1	$Fx \lor (y)Gxay$	P
2	$(\exists x)(Fx \lor (y)Gxay)$	1, EG
3	$(\exists y)(Fy \lor (y)Gxay)$	1, EG
4	$(\exists z)(Fz \lor (y)Gzay)$	1, EG
5	$(\exists x)(\exists z)(Fz \lor (y)Gzxy)$	4, EG

The correctness of these examples may be verified by finding S_α, S_β, α, and β for each instance. In example (c) step 5, for instance, S_α is '$(\exists z)(Fz \lor (y)Gzxy)$', S_β is '$(\exists z)(Fz \lor (y)Gzay)$', α is 'x', β is 'a', and S_β comes from S_α by replacing 'x' by 'a'.

Incorrect Applications of EG:

d. $\begin{array}{ll} 1 & Fx \lor (y)Gxay \\ 2 & (\exists y)(Fy \lor (y)Gyzy) \\ 3 & (\exists x)(Fx \lor (y)Gxxy) \end{array}$ $\begin{array}{l} \text{P} \\ \text{1, EG (incorrect)} \\ \text{1, EG (incorrect)} \end{array}$

e. $\begin{array}{ll} 1 & Fxy \lor (x)Gxy \\ 2 & (\exists x)(Fxx \lor (x)Gxx) \\ 3 & (\exists x)(Fxy \lor (x)Gxx) \end{array}$ $\begin{array}{l} \text{P} \\ \text{1, EG (incorrect)} \\ \text{1, EG (incorrect)} \end{array}$

Notice the differences between the correct application of EG in example (c) and the similar but incorrect applications in example (d). Of course, the sorts of incorrect application of EG noticed in one-variable quantification theory continue to be counted as incorrect. Both types of incorrect applications can lead to invalid inferences.

EXAMPLES INVOLVING UI OR EG

a. To derive '$(\exists x)Fxx$' from '$(x)(y)Fxy$'.

Derivation: $\begin{array}{ll} 1 & (x)(y)Fxy \\ 2 & (y)Fxy \\ 3 & Fxx \\ 4 & (\exists x)Fxx \end{array}$ $\begin{array}{l} \text{P} \\ \text{1, UI} \\ \text{2, UI} \\ \text{3, EG} \end{array}$

b. To derive '$(\exists x)Fxx$' from '$(y)(x)Fxy$'.

Derivation: $\begin{array}{ll} 1 & (y)(x)Fxy \\ 2 & (x)Fxy \\ 3 & Fyy \\ 4 & (\exists x)Fxx \end{array}$ $\begin{array}{l} \text{P} \\ \text{1, UI} \\ \text{2, UI} \\ \text{3, EG} \end{array}$

Comment: UI prevents 'Fxx' from being step 3 in this example.

c. To derive '$(\exists x)Fxy$' from '$(x)Fxx$'.

Derivation: $\begin{array}{ll} 1 & (x)Fxx \\ 2 & Fyy \\ 3 & (\exists x)Fxy \end{array}$ $\begin{array}{l} \text{P} \\ \text{1, UI} \\ \text{2, EG} \end{array}$

Comment: UI prevents 'Fxy' from being taken as step 2; and if 'Fxx' is taken as step 2, '$(\exists x)Fxy$' is not permitted by EG as step 3.

d. To derive '$(\exists x)(\exists y)(Hxy \cdot Fx \cdot Fy)$' from '$Fa$' and '$(x)(Fa \supset Hax)$'.

Derivation: $\begin{array}{ll} 1 & Fa \\ 2 & (x)(Fa \supset Hax) \\ 3 & Fa \supset Haa \end{array}$ $\begin{array}{l} \text{P} \\ \text{P} \\ \text{2, UI} \end{array}$

4	Haa	1, 3, MP
5	$Haa \cdot Fa$	4, 1, PC
6	$Haa \cdot Fa \cdot Fa$	5, 1, PC
7	$(\exists y)(Hay \cdot Fa \cdot Fy)$	6, EG
8	$(\exists x)(\exists y)(Hxy \cdot Fx \cdot Fy)$	7, EG

These derivations contain illustrations of the main difference between derivations in one-variable quantification theory and full quantification theory. Since we are now dealing with several variables, our success or failure to construct a given derivation may depend upon making the right choices of variables to instantiate or generalize upon. Sometimes we may want to "identify" occurrences of variables, as in passing from '$(x)(y)Fxy$' to 'Fxx'. Sometimes we may want to "distinguish" occurrences of variables, as in passing from 'Fxx' to '$(\exists x)(\exists y)Fxy$'. UI permits the identifications, EG the distinctions. However, a general watchword is this: try the simplest way first, and if this does not work, then try fancier methods.

EXERCISES FOR SECS. 3.3.1 AND 3.3.2
Prove these QS.

1. $(x)(y)Fxy \supset Fxx$
2. $(z)(w)Fzw \supset (\exists z)Fza$
3. $(z)(w)Fzw \supset (\exists z)Fzz$
4. $(x)Fxx \supset (\exists x)(\exists y)Fxy$
5. $(x)(Fxa \supset Gxa) \cdot Fba \supset (\exists z)Gbz$
6. $(x)(y)Gxy \supset -(x)(y)-Gxy$
7. $(x)(y)(z)Hxyz \supset -(z)-Hzzz$
8. $-(x)[Hxa \cdot -Hxx]$
9. $-(x)[Hxa \equiv -Hxx]$
10. $(\exists x)(\exists y)(Fx \supset Fy)$
11. $(\exists x)(\exists y)(\exists z)(Fx \cdot Gy \supset Fz)$
12. $(x)Fx \supset -(y)-Fy$
13. $(x)(Fy \supset Gx) \supset (Fy \supset (x)Gx)$
14. $(x)(y)(Gxy \equiv (z)(Hzx \equiv Hzy)) \cdot Gab \supset (Hcb \supset Hca)$
15. $(x)(y)(z)(Fxy \cdot Fyz \supset Fxz) \cdot (x)(y)(Fxy \supset Fyx) \cdot Fab \supset Faa$

3.3.3 UNIVERSAL GENERALIZATION
The old rule of universal generalization (UG) and its companion rule for initiating restricted UG subproofs must also be extended. Naturally, UG must per-

mit us to prefix other universal quantifiers besides '(x)', and other variables besides 'x' must be permissible as restricted variables. It will also be convenient for us to be able to replace the restricted variables in a schema to be quantified by another variable, and then prefix a universal quantifier binding this new variable. In other words, if the last line of a UG subproof restricted to 'x' is, say, 'Fx', it will be convenient to be able to infer by UG not only '$(x)Fx$' but also '$(y)Fy$' or '$(z)Fz$', etc. Naturally, this extension of UG can give rise to unwanted capturing, and we shall have to take pains to restate the rule so that this is avoided. The intuitive basis of UG remains the same, however; that is, if F can be shown to hold for an arbitrarily selected object, then we may infer that F holds for all objects. Restricted subproofs and restricted variables are again used to formalize the notion of an arbitrary object.

The clause in the rule of assumption which is responsible for initiating restricted UG subproofs must be restated. The new statement is as follows:

New clause to the rule of assumption: '$\triangle$' *may be written as a new step in any derivation provided that a new vertical line is initiated at the same time and a variable β is written to the left of the vertical line.*

As the reason for '$\triangle$' we write 'A'. The portion of the proof bounded by the vertical line initiated by this rule is called a *restricted UG subproof*, and the variable β is called the *restricted variable* of the subproof, and the subproof is said to be *restricted to β*.

The same restrictions on inferences within restricted subproofs continue to hold, but instead of applying only to schemata containing free 'x', they apply to schemata containing free occurrences of the restricted variable of the subproof. Thus it is permissible to reiterate 'Fx', for example, into a subproof restricted to 'y', but not into one restricted 'x'.

The main extension of UG consists in permitting the restricted variable to be replaced before prefixing a universal quantifier. Capturing must be avoided if soundness is to be guaranteed, and it turns out that the same two types of capturing encountered when exercising option 2 of EG must be avoided now. To illustrate the first type of unwanted capturing, consider '$(x)(Fx \lor (\exists y)Gxy)$'. This does not imply '$(y)(Fy \lor (\exists y)Gyy)$', but the latter will be derivable from it if we do not exclude the first type of capturing. Here is the derivation to be exorcised:

$$
\begin{array}{lll}
1 & (x)(Fx \lor (\exists y)Gxy) & \text{P} \\
2 \;\; x & \triangle & \text{A} \\
3 & Fx \lor (\exists y)Gxy & \text{1, UI} \\
4 & (y)(Fy \lor (\exists y)Gyy) & \text{2-3, UG (incorrect)}
\end{array}
$$

Similarly, the second type of capturing must be avoided. An example illustrating this is given by '$(x)Fxy$'. This does not imply '$(y)Fyy$', but a derivation of the latter from the former is possible if the second type of capturing is permitted, namely,

$$
\begin{array}{lll}
1 & (x)Fxy & \text{P} \\
2 & x \quad \triangle & \text{A} \\
3 & \quad Fxy & \text{1, UI} \\
4 & (y)Fyy & \text{2-3, UG} \quad \text{(incorrect)}
\end{array}
$$

Finally—and *here UG is unlike EG*—if we replace any occurrence of the restricted variable in the schema to be quantified, then we must replace *all* of them. If we do not do this, other unsound derivations will be possible. For example, '$(x)Fxx$' does not imply '$(x)(y)Fxy$', but a derivation of the latter from the former would be possible if piecemeal replacements of the EG type were permitted, namely,

$$
\begin{array}{lll}
1 & (x)Fxx & \text{A} \\
2 & z \quad \triangle & \text{A} \\
3 & \quad z \quad \triangle & \text{A} \\
4 & \quad \quad Fzz & \text{1, UI} \\
5 & \quad (y)Fzy & \text{3-4, UG} \quad \text{(incorrect)} \\
6 & (x)(y)Fxy & \text{2-5, UG}
\end{array}
$$

The previous discussion leads to the following restatement of UG.

Universal generalization: *Let S_β be the last step to date in a* UG *subproof restricted to β. Then we may terminate this restricted subproof and write $(\alpha)S_\alpha$ as the next step. Here α and β are variables, and S_α and S_β are related as in* UI *and* EG, *with the additional condition that there is no free occurrence of β in $(\alpha)S_\alpha$.*

The reason for $(\alpha)S_\alpha$ consists of hyphenated numerals referring to '$\triangle$' and S_α followed by 'UG'.

The rule with its two options may be represented schematically as follows:

$$
\begin{array}{lll}
\alpha & \triangle & \\
& \cdot & \\
& \cdot & \quad\quad \text{or} \\
& \cdot & \\
& (\cdots\alpha\cdots) & \\
(\alpha)(\cdots\alpha\cdots) & \text{UG} &
\end{array}
\qquad
\begin{array}{ll}
\beta & \triangle \\
& \cdot \\
& \cdot \\
& \cdot \\
& (\cdots\beta\cdots) \\
(\alpha)(\cdots\alpha\cdots) & \text{UG}
\end{array}
$$

[α replaces all free occurrences of β in $(\cdots\beta\cdots)$; α must not be captured during the replacement and must not occur free in $(\cdots\beta\cdots)$.]

EXAMPLES

Correct Applications of UG:

a.
1	$(x)(y)Fxy$	P
2	z	$\triangle$	A
3		$(y)Fzy$	1, UI
4		Fzz	3, UI
5	$(z)Fzz$	2-4, UG

b.
1	$(x)(y)Fxy$	P
2	x	$\triangle$	A
3		$(y)Fxy$	1, UI
4		Fyy	3, UI
5	$(z)Fzz$	2-4, UG

c.
1	$(x)(y)Fxy$	P
2	x	$\triangle$	A
3		$(y)Fxy$	1, UI
4		Fxx	3, UI
5	$(y)Fyy$	2-4, UG

d.
1	$(x)(y)Fxy$	P
2	w	$\triangle$	A1
3		$(y)Fwy$	1, UI
4		Fwa	3, UI
5	$(w)Fwa$	2-4, UG

e.
1	$(x)Fx$	P
2	y	$\triangle$	A
3		Fy	1, UI
4	$(y)Fy$	2-3, UG

f.
1	$(x)(y)Fxy$	P
2	z	$\triangle$	A
3		w	$\triangle$	A
4			$(y)Fwy$	1, UI
5			Fwz	4, UI
6			$(x)Fxz$	3-5, UG
7	$(y)(x)Fxy$	2-6, UG

Comments: Note that (a) and (b) offer two different ways to derive the same schema from another. On the other hand, there is no way to make (c) correspond to (a), for the restrictions on UI make it impossible to derive 'Fyy' from '$(x)(y)Fxy$' by two steps of UI. [Of course, there are other ways to derive it: derive '$(y)Fyy$' first via (c) and then 'Fyy' by UI.]

Incorrect Applications of UG:

g.
1	$(x)Fxy$	P
2	x	$\triangle$	A
3		Fxy	1, UI
4	$(y)Fyy$	2-3, UG (incorrect: 'y' occurs free in 'Fxy'.)

h.
1	$(x)(Fx \equiv (y)Gxy)$	P
2	x	$\triangle$	A
3		$Fx \equiv (y)Gxy$	1, UI
4	$(y)(Fy \equiv (y)Gyy)$	2-3, UG (incorrect: 'y' captured.)

EXAMPLES INVOLVING THE USE OF UG

a.   To derive: '$(x)Fx \cdot (y)Fy$' from '$(z)Fz$'.

Derivation:

$$
\begin{array}{lll}
1 & (z)Fz & \text{P} \\
2 & x\; \triangle & \text{A} \\
3 & \quad Fx & \text{1, UI} \\
4 & (x)Fx & \text{2-3, UG} \\
5 & y\; \triangle & \text{A} \\
6 & \quad Fy & \text{1, UI} \\
7 & (y)Fy & \text{5-6, UG} \\
8 & (x)Fx \cdot (y)Fy & \text{4, 7, PC}
\end{array}
$$

Comment: As UG is stated, it is incorrect to proceed as follows:

$$
\begin{array}{lll}
1 & (z)Fz & \text{P} \\
2 & \quad \triangle & \text{A} \\
3 & \quad Fx & \text{1, UI} \\
4 & (x)Fx & \text{2-3, UG} \\
5 & (y)Fy & \text{2-3, UG \quad (incorrect)}
\end{array}
$$

There is nothing really wrong with step 5, however, because, if UG were modified to allow such steps, it would remain sound. Pedagogically, the present statement of UG appears to be less confusing, but the extension allowing steps such as step 5 would provide a useful shortcut. We shall not use this shortcut, however.

b.   To prove: $(x)(y)(Fxy \supset -Fyx) \supset (x)-Fxx$.

Proof: (Worked out)

(a)
$$
\begin{array}{ll}
(x)(y)(Fxy \supset -Fyx) & \text{A} \\
? & \\
(x)-Fxx & \\
(x)(y)(Fxy \supset -Fyx) \supset (x)-Fxx & \text{CP}
\end{array}
$$

(b)
$$
\begin{array}{ll}
(x)(y)(Fxy \supset -Fyx) & \text{A} \\
x\; \triangle & \text{A} \\
\quad ? & \\
\quad -Fxx & \\
(x)-Fxx & \text{UG} \\
(x)(y)(Fxy \supset -Fyx) \supset (x)-Fxx & \text{CP}
\end{array}
$$

(c)
$$
\begin{array}{ll}
(x)(y)(Fxy \supset -Fyx) & \text{A} \\
x\; \triangle & \text{A} \\
\quad Fxx & \text{A} \\
\quad ? & \\
\quad -Fxx & \text{IP} \\
(x)-Fxx & \text{UG} \\
(x)(y)(Fxy \supset -Fyx) \supset (x)-Fxx & \text{CP}
\end{array}
$$

(d)

1	$(x)(y)(Fxy \supset -Fyx)$	A
2	$x \quad \triangle$	A
3	Fxx	A
4	$(y)(Fxy \supset -Fyx)$	1, UI
5	$Fxx \supset -Fxx$	4, UI
6	$-Fxx$	3, 5, MP
7	$-Fxx$	3-6, IP
8	$(x) - Fxx$	2-7, UG
9	$(x)(y)(Fxy \supset -Fyx) \supset (x) - Fxx$	1-8, CP

Comment: This proof depends upon the "identification" of 'x' and 'y' in step 5. Suppose that we were to prove '$(x)(y)(Fxy \supset -Fyx) \supset (y) - Fyy$'. It would be natural to try to use the same proof except for replacing 'Fxx' by 'Fyy'. This will not work, however, because the restrictions on UI prevent '$Fyy \supset -Fyy$' from taking the place of step 4. On the other hand, a very simple proof can be obtained by using (d) up to and including step 7, and then changing 'x' to 'y' to obtain '$(y) - Fyy$' as step 8. [*Exercise:* Prove $(x)(y)(Fxy \supset -Fyx) \supset (y) - Fyy$.]

It is very useful to try to carry out "derivations" on an informal basis before attempting to construct a purely formal derivation. This often helps to overcome the problems involved in choosing variables. For example, an informal "derivation" of the last example might run:

1 Everything that bears F to anything does not have F borne to it in return by that thing. (Premisse)
2 Thus, if anything bore F to itself, it would have to have F borne to it in return by that thing, that is, by itself.
3 But this contradicts (1).
4 So nothing bears F to itself.

Step 2 of this "derivation" is a clue for the use of IP and for identifying 'x' and 'y'.

3.3.4 EXISTENTIAL INSTANTIATION

The extension of existential instantiation will be similar to the extension of universal generalization. New restricted variables will be permitted, and when an existential quantifier is dropped, there will be an option of replacing the variable bound to it by a new variable. The intuitive basis of EI remains the same, however. On intuitive grounds, it is quite correct to select an arbitrary F once it has been shown that some F exist. Existential instantiation and restricted EI subproofs constitute the formalization of this intuitive procedure.

First we must restate the clause of the rule of assumption which is responsible for generating EI subproofs. This is done as follows:

New clause to the rule of assumption: *If the schema, $(\exists\alpha)$, S_α is the last step to date in a derivation, then we may write S_β as the next step, provided that we simultaneously initiate a new vertical line and write a variable β to the left of it. Here S_α and S_β are related as in the statement of* UG.

The reason for S_β is simply 'A'. The subproof initiated is called a *restricted* EI *subproof, its restricted variable is β, and it is restricted to β.*

Unwanted capturing and similar problems could arise when this rule is applied. The reader may verify, however, that as stated, the rule requires that (1) β replace *all* free occurrences of α in S_α (if it replaces any), (2) β not be captured in the process, and (3) β not be free in S_α. This guarantees the soundness of the rule. Shortly, examples of incorrect applications of this rule will be given. The unsound "derivations" which they produce demonstrate the need for satisfying (1) to (3).

Existential instantiation itself must be restated because we now have other restricted variables besides 'x'. The following restatement suffices:

Existential instantiation: *Suppose that W is the last step to date in an* EI *subproof whose assumption is S_β. Then if W does not contain β free, the* EI *subproof may be discontinued, W being written again as the next step (and outside the* EI *subproof).*

As the reason for W, we write a numeral referring to $(\exists\alpha)S_\alpha$, followed by hyphenated numerals referring to S_β and W, followed by 'EI'.

EXAMPLES

Correct Applications of EI:

a.
1	$(\exists x)Fxy$	P
2	x Fxy	A
3	$(\exists z)Fzy$	2, EG
4	$(\exists z)Fzy$	1, 2-3, EI

b.
1	$(\exists x)Fxy$	P
2	w Fwy	A
3	$(\exists w)Fwy$	2, EG
4	$(\exists w)Fwy$	1, 2-3, EI

c.
1	$(\exists x)(y)Fxy$	P
2	x $(y)Fxy$	A
3	Fxx	2, UI

$$
\begin{array}{llll}
& 4 & \quad\;\; (\exists x)Fxx & 3,\text{ EG} \\
& 5 & (\exists x)Fxx & 1,\ 2\text{-}4,\text{ EI}
\end{array}
$$

d.
$$
\begin{array}{llll}
1 & (\exists x)(y)Fxy & \text{P} \\
2 & z\;| \;\; (y)Fzy & \text{A} \\
3 & \quad\;\; Fzz & 2,\text{ UI} \\
4 & \quad\;\; (\exists z)Fzz & 3,\text{ EG} \\
5 & (\exists z)Fzz & 1,\ 2\text{-}4,\text{ EI}
\end{array}
$$

e.
$$
\begin{array}{llll}
1 & (\exists x)Fx & \text{P} \\
2 & x\;| \;\; Fx & \text{A} \\
3 & \quad\;\; Fx \lor p & 2,\text{ add} \\
4 & \quad\;\; (\exists x)(Fx \lor p) & 3,\text{ EG} \\
5 & (\exists x)(Fx \lor p) & 1,\ 2\text{-}4,\text{ EI} \\
6 & (\exists x)Fx & 1,\text{ R} \\
7 & y\;| \;\; Fy & \text{A} \\
8 & \quad\;\; (\exists y)Fy & 7,\text{ EG} \\
9 & (\exists y)Fy & 6,\ 7\text{-}8,\text{ EI}
\end{array}
$$

Comment: The clause of the rule of assumption for generating EI subproofs requires that the assumption follow immediately the existential quantification concerned. For pedagogic reasons it appears best to state the rule in this way, and thus it is necessary to repeat step 1 of (e) as step 6. However, as a shortcut it would be possible to do away with these repetitions and preserve the soundness of our rules. We shall not use this shortcut, however.

Incorrect Applications of the Rule of Assumption:

f.
$$
\begin{array}{llll}
1 & (\exists x)Fxy & \text{P} \\
2 & y\;| \;\; Fyy & \text{A (incorrect: } \text{'}y\text{' is free in '}Fxy\text{'.)} \\
3 & \quad\;\; (\exists y)Fyy & 2,\text{ EG} \\
4 & (\exists y)Fyy & 1,\ 2\text{-}3,\text{ EI}
\end{array}
$$

g.
$$
\begin{array}{llll}
1 & (\exists x)((\exists y)Fxy \cdot Hx) & \text{P} \\
2 & y\;| \;\; (\exists y)Fyy \cdot Hy & \text{A (incorrect: } \text{'}y\text{' is captured.)} \\
3 & \quad\;\; (\exists y)Fyy & 2,\text{ S} \\
4 & (\exists y)Fyy & 1,\ 2\text{-}3,\text{ EI}
\end{array}
$$

h.
$$
\begin{array}{llll}
1 & (\exists x)Fxx & \text{P} \\
2 & y\;| \;\; Fxy & \text{A (incorrect: not all occurrences of '}x\text{' have} \\
& & \qquad\qquad\text{been replaced.)} \\
3 & \quad\;\; (\exists y)Fxy & 2,\text{ EG} \\
4 & (\exists y)Fxy & 1,\ 2\text{-}3,\text{ EI}
\end{array}
$$

EXAMPLES INVOLVING EI

a. To derive '$(x)(\exists y)Fxy$' from '$(\exists y)(x)Fxy$'.

Derivation: (Worked out)

(a) | $(\exists y)(x)Fxy$ | P | (b) | $(\exists y)(x)Fxy$ | P |

Layout for (a):

$(\exists y)(x)Fxy$　　P
?
$(x)(\exists y)Fxy$

Layout for (b):

$(\exists y)(x)Fxy$　　P
$y|$　$(x)Fxy$　　A
?
$(x)(\exists y)Fxy$
$(x)(\exists y)Fxy$　　EI

(c)　$(\exists y)(x)Fxy$　　　　P
$y|$　$(x)Fxy$　　　　A
　　$x|$　$\triangle$　　　A
　　　?
　　　$(\exists y)Fxy$
　　$(x)(\exists y)Fxy$　　UG
$(x)(\exists y)Fxy$　　　EI

(d)　1　$(\exists y)(x)Fxy$　　　　P
　　2　$y|$　$(x)Fxy$　　　　A
　　3　　$x|$　$\triangle$　　　A
　　4　　　Fxy　　　2, UI
　　5　　　$(\exists y)Fxy$　　4, EG
　　6　　$(x)(\exists y)Fxy$　　3-5, UG
　　7　$(x)(\exists y)Fxy$　　1, 2-6, EI

b. To derive '$(\exists x)(Fx \cdot Gxx)$' from '$(\exists x)(Fx \cdot (y)(Fy \supset Gxy))$'.

Derivation:　1　$(\exists x)(Fx \cdot (y)(Fy \supset Gxy))$　　P
　　　　　　2　$x|$　$Fx \cdot (y)(Fy \supset Gxy)$　　A
　　　　　　3　　Fx　　　2, S
　　　　　　4　　$(y)(Fy \supset Gxy)$　　2, S
　　　　　　5　　$Fx \supset Gxx$　　4, UI
　　　　　　6　　Gxx　　　3, 5, MP
　　　　　　7　　$Fx \cdot Gxx$　　3, 6, PC
　　　　　　8　　$(\exists x)(Fx \cdot Gxx)$　　7, EG
　　　　　　9　$(\exists x)(Fx \cdot Gxx)$　　1, 2-8, EI

c. To derive '$(x)((\exists y)(Hy \cdot Fxy) \supset (\exists y)(Gy \cdot Fxy))$' from '$(x)(Hx \supset Gx)$'.

Derivation: (Partially worked out)

(1)　$(x)(Hx \supset Gx)$
?
$(x)((\exists y)(Hy \cdot Fxy) \supset (\exists y)(Gy \cdot Fxy))$

(2) $\quad$ $(x)(Hx \supset Gx)$ $\qquad\qquad\qquad$ P

$\quad x$ $\triangle$ $\qquad\qquad\qquad\qquad\qquad$ A

$\qquad$?

$\qquad$ $(\exists y)(Hy \cdot Fxy) \supset (\exists y)(Gy \cdot Fxy)$

$\qquad$ $(x)((\exists y)(Hy \cdot Fxy) \supset (\exists y)(Gy \cdot Fxy))$ $\qquad$ UG

(3) $\quad$ $(x)(Hx \supset Gx)$ $\qquad\qquad\qquad$ P

$\quad x$ $\triangle$ $\qquad\qquad\qquad\qquad\qquad$ A

$\qquad$ $(\exists y)(Hy \cdot Fxy)$ $\qquad\qquad$ A

$\qquad y$ $\quad Hy \cdot Fxy$ $\qquad\qquad\qquad$ A

$\qquad\quad$?

$\qquad$ $(\exists y)(Gy \cdot Fxy)$

$\qquad$ $(\exists y)(Gy \cdot Fxy)$ $\qquad\qquad$ EI

$\qquad$ $(\exists y)(Hy \cdot Fxy) \supset (\exists y)(Gy \cdot Fxy)$ $\qquad$ CP

$\qquad$ $(x)((\exists y)(Hy \cdot Fxy) \supset (\exists y)(Gy \cdot Fxy))$ $\qquad$ UG

(*Exercise:* Complete this derivation.)

d. To derive '$(x)Fxx$' from '$(x)(y)(z)(Fxy \cdot Fyz \supset Fxz)$', '$(x)(\exists y)Fxy$', and '$(x)(y)(Fxy \supset Fyx)$'.

Derivation: (Partially worked out)

(1) $\quad$ $(x)(y)(z)(Fxy \cdot Fyz \supset Fxz)$ $\qquad\qquad$ P

$\qquad$ $(x)(\exists y)Fxy$ $\qquad\qquad\qquad\qquad$ P

$\qquad$ $(x)(y)(Fxy \supset Fyx)$ $\qquad\qquad\qquad$ P

$\qquad$?

$\qquad$ $(x)Fxx$

(2) $\quad$ $(x)(y)(z)(Fxy \cdot Fyz \supset Fxz)$ $\qquad\qquad$ P

$\qquad$ $(x)(\exists y)Fxy$ $\qquad\qquad\qquad\qquad$ P

$\qquad$ $(x)(y)(Fxy \supset Fyx)$ $\qquad\qquad\qquad$ P

$\qquad x$ $\triangle$ $\qquad\qquad\qquad\qquad\qquad$ A

$\qquad$?

$\qquad$ Fxx

$\qquad$ $(x)Fxx$ $\qquad\qquad\qquad\qquad\qquad$ UG

(3) $\quad$ $(x)(y)(z)(Fxy \cdot Fyz \supset Fxz)$ $\qquad\qquad$ P

$\qquad$ $(x)(\exists y)Fxy$ $\qquad\qquad\qquad\qquad$ P

$\qquad$ $(x)(y)(Fxy \supset Fyx)$ $\qquad\qquad\qquad$ P

$\qquad x$ $\triangle$ $\qquad\qquad\qquad\qquad\qquad$ A

$\qquad$ $(\exists y)Fxy$ $\qquad\qquad\qquad\qquad$ UI

$\qquad y$ $\quad Fxy$ $\qquad\qquad\qquad\qquad\qquad$ A

$\qquad\quad$?

$\qquad$ Fxx

$\quad\mid\;\; Fxx$	EI
$\quad (x)Fxx$	UG

(4) $\quad (x)(y)(z)(Fxy \cdot Fyz \supset Fxz)$ — P

$\quad\quad (x)(\exists y)Fxy$ — P

$\quad\quad (x)(y)(Fxy \supset Fyx)$ — P

$\quad\quad x\mid\;\triangle$ — A

$\quad\quad\quad\quad (\exists y)Fxy$ — UI

$\quad\quad\quad y\mid\; Fxy$ — A

$\quad\quad\quad\quad\quad (y)(z)(Fxy \cdot Fyx \supset Fxz)$ — UI

$\quad\quad\quad\quad\quad (z)(Fxy \cdot Fyz \supset Fxz)$ — UI

$\quad\quad\quad\quad\quad Fxy \cdot Fyx \supset Fxx$ — UI

$\quad\quad\quad\quad\quad ?$

$\quad\quad\quad\quad\quad Fxx$

$\quad\quad\quad\quad Fxx$ — EI

$\quad\quad (x)Fxx$ — UG

(*Exercise:* Complete this derivation.)

e.   Prove: $-(\exists y)(x)(Fxy \equiv -Fxx)$.

Proof: (Partially worked out)

(1) $\quad\mid\;\mid\;\; (\exists y)(x)(Fxy \equiv -Fxx)$ — A

$\quad\quad\mid\;\mid\;\; ?$

$\quad\quad\mid\; -(\exists y)(x)(Fxy \equiv -Fxx)$ — IP

(2) $\quad\mid\;\mid\;\; (\exists y)(x)(Fxy \equiv -Fxx)$ — A

$\quad\quad\mid\; y\mid\; (x)(Fxy \equiv -Fxx)$ — A

$\quad\quad\quad\quad\;\; Fyy \equiv -Fyy$ — UI

$\quad\quad\quad\quad\;\; ?$

$\quad\quad\quad\quad\; -Fyy$

$\quad\quad\quad\quad\;\; Fyy$ — MPB

$\quad\quad\quad\quad\;\; ?$

$\quad\quad\mid\;\mid\; ?$ — EI

$\quad\quad\mid\; -(\exists y)(x)(Fxy \equiv -Fxx)$ — IP

(*Exercise:* Complete this proof. *Hint:* Use IP to obtain '$-Fyy$' and then obtain '$p \cdot \bar{p}$' from 'Fyy' and '$-Fyy$'.)

f.   To derive '$(x)(-(\exists y)Fxy \supset -(\exists y)Hxy)$' from '$(x)(-Fxx \supset -(\exists y)Fyx)$' and '$(x)(y)(-Fxy \supset -Hyx)$'.

Derivation: (Partially worked out)

(1) $\quad\mid\;\; (x)(-Fxx \supset -(\exists y)Fyx)$ — P

$\quad\quad (x)(y)(-Fxy \supset -Hyx)$ — P

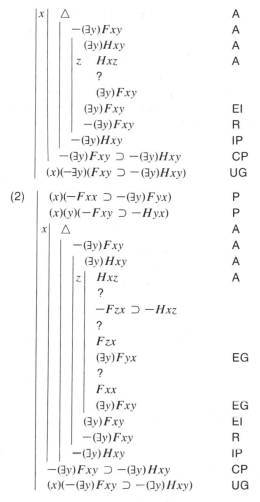

x $\triangle$	A
$-(\exists y)Fxy$	A
$(\exists y)Hxy$	A
z Hxz	A
?	
$(\exists y)Fxy$	
$(\exists y)Fxy$	EI
$-(\exists y)Fxy$	R
$-(\exists y)Hxy$	IP
$-(\exists y)Fxy \supset -(\exists y)Hxy$	CP
$(x)(-\exists y)(Fxy \supset -(\exists y)Hxy)$	UG

(2)

$(x)(-Fxx \supset -(\exists y)Fyx)$	P
$(x)(y)(-Fxy \supset -Hyx)$	P
x $\triangle$	A
$-(\exists y)Fxy$	A
$(\exists y)Hxy$	A
z Hxz	A
?	
$-Fzx \supset -Hxz$	
?	
Fzx	
$(\exists y)Fyx$	EG
?	
Fxx	
$(\exists y)Fxy$	EG
$(\exists y)Fxy$	EI
$-(\exists y)Fxy$	R
$-(\exists y)Hxy$	IP
$-(\exists y)Fxy \supset -(\exists y)Hxy$	CP
$(x)(-(\exists y)Fxy \supset -(\exists y)Hxy)$	UG

(*Exercise:* Complete this derivation.)

3.3.5 PROOFS OF INCONSISTENCY

Quantificational schemata are inconsistent if and only if they have no true interpretations in any nonempty universe. Several schemata are *jointly inconsistent* if and only if their conjunction is inconsistent. Since there are infinitely many universes, it is impossible to inspect them all to ascertain whether a given schema does or does not have a true interpretation in one of them. Consequently, one cannot demonstrate the inconsistency of a schema or the joint inconsistency of several schemata by means of an ex-

haustive examination of their interpretations. Nonetheless, proofs of inconsistency may be obtained by means of our procedures for proving validity.
For a schema S is inconsistent if and only if $-S$ is valid. Thus, to prove the
inconsistency of S it suffices to prove the validity of $-S$. Indeed, to prove that
S is inconsistent, it suffices merely to *derive a contradiction*, that is, a schema
and its negation, from S. For once we can *derive* a contradiction from S, we
can easily obtain a *proof* of the validity of $-S$ by using the rule of indirect
proof. A derivation of a contradiction from S takes the form

$$
\begin{array}{ll}
S & \text{P} \\
\cdot \\
\cdot \\
\cdot \\
W \\
-W
\end{array}
$$

and once we can carry out such a derivation, we can also obtain a proof of
the validity of $-S$ of the following form:

$$
\begin{array}{ll}
S & \text{A} \\
\cdot \\
\cdot \\
\cdot \\
W \\
-W \\
-S & \text{IP}
\end{array}
$$

Therefore, to establish the inconsistency of a schema, we derive a contradiction from it, and to establish the joint inconsistency of several schemata,
we derive a contradiction from their conjunction. The latter case can be
simplified by taking the several schemata as separate premisses of the
derivation, since in any case they could be quickly derived from their conjunction by a number of applications of simplification. Thus proofs of the
inconsistency of single schemata take the form

$$
\begin{array}{lll}
S & & \text{P} \\
\cdot \\
\cdot \\
\cdot \\
W & \text{or} & -W \\
-W & & W
\end{array}
$$

and proofs of the joint inconsistency of several schemata take the form

$$
\begin{array}{ll}
S_1 & \text{P} \\
S_2 & \text{P}
\end{array}
$$

$$
\begin{array}{c}
\vdots \\
\vdots
\end{array}
$$

S_n P

$$
\begin{array}{c}
\vdots \\
\vdots
\end{array}
$$

W		$-W$
$-W$	or	W

EXAMPLES

a.   Prove the inconsistency of '$(x)Fx \cdot -(\exists x)Fx$'.

Proof:

1	$(x)Fx \cdot - (\exists x)Fx$	P
2	$(x)Fx$	1, S
3	Fx	2, UI
4	$(\exists x)Fx$	3, EG
5	$-(\exists x)Fx$	1, S

b.   Prove the inconsistency of '$(x)(Fxy \equiv -Fxx)$'.

Proof:

1	$(x)(Fxy \equiv -Fxx)$	P
2	$Fyy \equiv -Fyy$	1, UI
3	Fyy	A
4	$-Fyy$	2, 3, MP
5	$-Fyy$	3-4, IP
6	Fyy	5, 2, MPB

c.   Prove the joint inconsistency of '$(x)Fxx$' and '$(x)(y)(Fxy \supset -Fyx)$'.

Proof:

1	$(x)Fxx$	P
2	$(x)(y)(Fxy \supset -Fyx)$	P
3	$(y)(Fxy \supset -Fyx)$	2, UI
4	$Fxx \supset -Fxx$	3, UI
5	Fxx	1, UI
6	$-Fxx$	4, 5, MP

d.   Prove the joint inconsistency of '$(x)(y)(Fxy \supset -Gxy)$', '$(x)(y)(Fxy \supset Gxy)$', and '$(\exists x)(\exists y)Fxy$'.

Proof: (Partially worked out)

1	$(x)(y)(Fxy \supset -Gxy)$	P
2	$(x)(y)(Fxy \supset Gxy)$	P
3	$(\exists x)(\exists y)Fxy$	P
4	$x\mid$ $(\exists y)Fxy$	A

5	y	Fxy	A
6		$(y)(Fxy \supset Gxy)$	2, UI
7		$Fxy \supset Gxy$	6, UI
8		$(y)(Fxy \supset -Gxy)$	1, UI
9		$Fxy \supset -Gxy$	8, UI
10		$-Gxy$	5, 8, MP

$$p \cdot \bar{p} \qquad \text{EI}$$

$$p$$
$$\bar{p}$$

(*Exercise:* Complete this proof of inconsistency.)

EXERCISES FOR SECS. 3.3.3 TO 3.3.5

A. Prove these QS.

1. $(x)Fx \supset (x)Fz$
2. $(x)(y)Gxy \supset (y)(x)Gxy$
3. $(z)(w)Hzw \supset (w)(z)Hwz$
4. $(x)(y)(z)Gxyz \supset (z)Gzzz$
5. $(\exists y)Fy \supset (\exists z)Fz$
6. $(\exists x)(\exists y)(\exists z)Hxyz \supset (\exists z)(\exists x)(\exists y)Hxyz$
7. $(\exists z)(\exists w)Fzw \supset (\exists z)(\exists w)Fwz$
8. $(\exists x)Gxxx \supset (\exists y)(\exists z)(\exists x)Gyxz$
9. $(x)(y)(Fxy \supset -Fyx) \supset (y)-Fyy$
10. $(x)(y)(Fxy \supset Fyx) \cdot (x)(y)(z)(Fxy \cdot Fyz \supset Fxz) \supset (x)(y)(Fxy \supset Fxx)$
11. $(x)(y)(Gxy \equiv (z)(Hxz \equiv Hyz)) \supset (x)Gxx$
12. $(x)(y)(Gxy \equiv (z)(Hxz \equiv Hyz)) \supset (x)(y)(Gxy \supset Gyx)$
13. $(x)(y)(Gxy \equiv (z)(Hxz \equiv Hyz)) \supset (x)(y)(z)(Gxy \cdot Gyz \supset Gxz)$
14. $(x)(Fx \supset Gx) \supset (z)((\exists y)(Fy \cdot Hzy) \supset (\exists y)(Gy \cdot Hzy))$
15. $-(\exists y)(x)(Fxy \equiv -Fxx)$
16. $(x)Gx \supset -(\exists y)(x)(Fxy \equiv Gx \cdot -Fxx)$
17. $(x)(y)-Fxy \supset -(\exists x)(\exists y)Fxy$
18. $-(x)(y)Fxy \supset (\exists x)(\exists y)-Fxy$
19. $(\exists x)-Fxx \supset -(x)(y)Fxy$
20. $(\exists y)(x)(Fx \supset Gyx) \supset (x)(Fx \supset (\exists y)Gyx)$
21. $(x)(\exists y)(Fxy \supset Gx) \supset (x)((y)Fxy \supset Gx)$

22. $(\exists y)(Fy \supset (x)Fx)$
23. $(\exists y)((\exists x)Fx \supset Fy)$
24. $((x)Fx \supset (\exists y)Gy) \supset (\exists x)(\exists y)(Fx \supset Gy)$
25. $(x)(\exists y)(z)(Hx \cdot (Gy \supset Fz)) \supset (x)Hx \cdot ((y)Gy \supset (z)Fz)$

B. Prove the joint inconsistency of the QS in these lists.

1. $(\exists y)Fy, \qquad (x) - Fx$
2. $(x)(Fx \supset Gx), \qquad (x)(Fx \supset -Gx), \qquad (\exists y)Fy$
3. $(x)(y)(Fxy \supset -Fyx), \qquad (x)(y)(Fxy \supset Fyx), \qquad (\exists x)(\exists y)Fxy$
4. $(\exists y)(x)Fxy, \qquad -(x)(\exists y)Fxy$
5. $(x)(y)(z)(Fxy \cdot Fyz \supset -Fxz), \qquad (\exists x)Fxx$
6. $(z)(\exists y)(x)(Fxy \equiv -Fxx \cdot Gxz), \qquad (\exists z)(x)Gxz$

3.4   APPLICATIONS TO ORDINARY LANGUAGE

Most of the problems that arise in the application of full quantification theory to statements expressed in ordinary language have already been encountered in our previous discussions of one-variable quantification theory. To be sure, we can now handle statements whose logical complexity used to elude adequate description, and if the occasion demands it, we can also subject some statements previously treated to an even deeper analysis. For these reasons, a brief survey of some typical new problems and examples is now appropriate.

3.4.1   BRINGING OUT RELATIONSHIPS

Often an adequate logical analysis of a statement will depend upon recasting it so that one or more relationships which were implicit in its original form become explicit. Words such as 'mother', 'driver', 'uncle', 'shot', 'killed', and 'observed' may be used either to attribute properties — as in 'Mary is a mother' — or relations — as in 'Mary is the mother of John'. But even when such words are used in statements to attribute properties, the attribution of a relationship is implicit, so that we can always recast these statements to make this explicit. This happens when

Mary is a mother
John was struck
The robber was caught

are transformed to

Mary is the mother of someone.
John was struck by something.
The robber was caught by someone.

When an argument, which is so phrased that relationships such as these are left implicit, actually hinges upon these relationships, then its logical analysis will require transformations such as those given above. For example, consider the valid argument

All bus drivers must wash every bus they drive.
Wilson is a bus driver.
Hence Wilson must wash some bus.

To establish its validity, 'bus driver' must be expanded to make explicit the relationship between driver and bus; that is, the whole argument should be rephrased as

$(x)(y)(y$ is a bus $\cdot$ x drives $y \supset x$ must wash $y)$
$(\exists y)($Wilson drives $y \cdot y$ is a bus$)$
$\therefore (\exists y)(y$ is a bus $\cdot$ Wilson must wash $y)$

Again consider the valid argument

All robbers must compensate their victims.
John is a robber.
Hence John must compensate someone.

Its validity is established by first paraphrasing it as

$(x)(y)(x$ robs $y \supset x$ must compensate $y)$
$(\exists y)($John robs $y)$
$\therefore (\exists y)($John must compensate $y)$

(Here we have limited the universe of discourse to persons.)

The cases we have just considered have involved adjectival forms of verbs. Although this is usually a good clue to "concealed" relationships, there are even more subtle cases. Thus, consider the statement

(1)   All monetary contributions to churches are tax-deductible.

This says that anyone who contributes a given amount of money to a church may take that amount as a tax deduction. These fairly complex relationships become explicit when (1) is paraphrased as

$(x)(y)(z)(y$ is an amount of money $\cdot$ z is a church $\cdot$ x contributes y to $z \supset x$ may take y as a tax deduction$)$

Moreover, this expansion of (1) would be required to validate, for example, the argument

All monetary contributions to churches are tax-deductible.

Jones contributed some money to a church.
Therefore Jones has a tax deduction.

Naturally, not every problem requires us to bring out implicit relationships, whether expressed by verbal adjectives or in more subtle ways.
The argument

All mothers must prepare supper
Mary is a mother
Thus Mary must prepare supper

may be validated by simply paraphrasing it as

$(x)(x$ is a mother $\supset x$ must prepare supper)
Mary is a mother.
$\therefore$ Mary must prepare supper.

This example does not require a deeper analysis. Since a simpler analysis
will, if it is adequate, lead to a simpler derivation or proof, the maxim in this
and all other cases of paraphrasing is: reveal no more structure than the
problem at hand requires.

Terms such as 'mother' and 'child', 'speaker' and 'audience', 'killer' and
'victim', characterizing the objects between which a given relation holds,
are *correlative terms*. Often, in ordinary language, corelative terms take over
some of the functions assigned to quantifiers and variables in a formal
language. For example, the statement

(2) Every mother loves her children

can be paraphrased as

(3) Every mother loves all those she is the mother of

and finally as

(4) $(x)(y)(x$ is the mother of $y \supset x$ loves $y)$

Notice how in the passage from (2) to (4) part of the role of 'her children' in
(2) has been adsorbed by 'x is a mother of y' and part by the quantifier '(y)'.
Some simplification has also been achieved in passing from (2) to (4) because we have dispensed with the term 'children'. Since every mother is a
mother of her children and her children only, every killer *kills* his victims and
his victims only, etc., one or both of corelative terms will usually become
redundant when "concealed" relationships are made explicit in a quantificational paraphrase. Consequently, it is usually possible to simplify such paraphrases by dropping the corelative terms in favor of the relational term from

which they derive. In applying this technique, however, it is important to choose consistently the same relational term in favor of the corelative terms. For example, the valid argument

Every parent loves his children
Hence there are no children not loved by their parents

may be paraphrased as

$(x)(y)(x$ is a parent of $y \supset x$ loves $y)$
$\therefore -(\exists x)(\exists y)(x$ is a parent of $y \cdot -(x$ loves $y))$

or as

$(x)(y)(y$ is a child of $x \supset x$ loves $y)$
$\therefore -(\exists x)(\exists y)(y$ is a child of $x \cdot -(x$ loves $y))$

In the first case, the corelative terms 'parent' and 'child' have been dispensed with in favor of the relational term 'parent of'; in the second case, in favor of 'child of'. The argument remains valid under either transformation. However, if the argument is paraphrased as

$(x)(y)(x$ is a parent of $y \supset x$ loves $y)$
$\therefore -(\exists x)(\exists y)(y$ is a child of $x \cdot -(x$ loves $y))$

then it is not valid, as it stands, and requires the additional premisse

$(x)(y)(y$ is a child of $x \supset x$ is a parent of $y)$

EXERCISES FOR SEC. 3.4.1

Symbolize these statements, using logical symbols and the suggested notation. Reveal as much structure as possible.

1. Everyone who is related to Johnson is related to someone. (*Notation: R,j*)
2. Not every pencil on a desk is on a wooden desk. (*P,D,O,W*)
3. All mothers will watch all and only their own children. (*M,W*)
4. On each of Jane's fingers there is a ring (*j,F,O,R*)
5. If Smith is observed, he will bribe Jones. (*s,O,B,j*)
6. Whenever a child is in trouble, he summons his mother. (*C,T,S*)
7. Dogs which have owners are more expensive than those which do not. (*D,O,M*)
8. All horses buck sometimes. (*H,B,T*)
9. Some horses buck whenever a rider is on them. (*H,B,T,R*)
10. Whoever owns a car drives it on some bad roads. (*C,O,D,R,B*)
11. Whatever is a cause is caused by something in turn. (*C*)

12. There is a market which sells some things to some people but does not sell any-thing to some (other) people. (M,P,S)
13. No market has every person as customer, although there is a market that makes all its sales to one person. (M,P,S)
14. Every man that weds a girl loves her. (M,G,W)
15. Every observer photographed whatever he observed. (O,P)

3.4.2 SUPERLATIVES

The superlative forms of adjectives, such as 'best', 'greatest', 'least', and 'most evil', also require special attention when paraphrasing. Again, it may be necessary to bring out hidden relationships, but in this case, usually, something more is required. Consider, for example, the statement

(5) There is no greatest number.

This implicitly involves the relation 'greater than', and so at least this much should be brought out in its paraphrase. But (5) says more; it says that there is no number greater than every other number, and so it may be paraphrased as

(6) $-(\exists x)(x$ is a number $\cdot (y)(y$ is a number $\cdot -(x = y) \supset x > y))$

or by restricting the universe to numbers, as

(7) $-(\exists x)(y)(-(x = y) \supset x > y)$

Although (5) appears at first sight to have merely the form '$-(\exists x)Fx$', the superlative 'greatest' conceals a more complex form. All statements which begin with 'There is no _____est' may be subject to a similar analysis Thus

(8) There is no shortest man

(9) There is no funniest clown

may be paraphrased (restricting the universe appropriately) as

(10) $-(\exists x)(y)(-(x = y) \supset x$ is shorter than $y)$

(11) $-(\exists x)(y)(-(x = y) \supset x$ is funnier than $y)$

Superlatives occur, of course, in other contexts, but these occurrences can usually be handled by the technique just illustrated. Thus, consider the following examples:

The shortest member of the class heads the line.
The fastest runner will win if he is in good condition.

They may be paraphrased as

$(x)(x$ is in the class $\cdot$ $(y)(y$ is in the class $\cdot$ $-(x = y) \supset x$ is shorter than $y) \supset x$ heads the line)

$(x)(x$ is a runner $\cdot$ $(y)(y$ is a runner $\cdot$ $-(x = y) \supset x$ runs faster than $y) \supset (x$ is in good condition $\supset x$ will win))

Naturally, there are exceptions to practically any rule of paraphrasing, and in the case of superlative terms, two types of exceptions deserve mention. The first may arise when a superlative is combined with a definite article, as in 'the tallest man'. Such phrases usually purport to identify a unique object and function more or less as names. Thus many sentences in which they occur are simple-subject–predicate or relational sentences, such as the following examples:

The tallest man in the room hit his head on the door frame.
The smallest whole nonnegative number is zero.
The last chairman was better than the present one.

Consequently, given our present techniques, these examples must be treated as simple-subject–predicate and relational sentences, and the superlative phrases in question replaced by individual constants. Later, we shall introduce additional techniques which will permit an even deeper analysis of these sentences.

By the way, ordinary language is so intricate that even these exceptions have exceptions! The statement

(12) The tallest man does not exist

is *not* a simple-subject–predicate sentence, but rather means

(13) There is no tallest man.

Consequently, (12) may be treated in the same way as the nonexceptional superlatives are.

The second type of exception that arises in connection with superlatives occurs when they are combined with plural nouns, as in 'the smartest men'. These exceptions are encountered in such sentences as

(14) The smartest men save at Brooks

in which reference is not made to *the* smartest *man*, but rather to those men who are smarter than average. It is possible to paraphrase (14) as

(15) $(x)(x$ is a man $\cdot$ x is smarter than average $\supset x$ saves at Brooks)

but such a paraphrase does not bring out all the structure necessary to validate many arguments in which (14) can occur. In this book we shall not develop the techniques necessary to give a full analysis to statements such as these. Their treatment would plunge us into a rather unsettled area of logic. Some logicians think that special and as yet unperfected purely logical techniques suffice for dealing with these statements. Others believe that they are best treated by means of mathematical methods used in statistical reasoning.

3.4.3   COMPLEX PRONOMINAL CROSS REFERENCES

The greatest number of problems encountered in paraphrasing statements into logical notation are due to the complexities of pronominal cross reference present in ordinary language. Unfortunately, it is difficult even to begin to set down rules of thumb for treating these problems. Generally, the best procedure consists in first carefully thinking through the sentence at hand, being sure, of course, to consider the context in which it occurs. Once this step of analysis has been carried out, it is often advisable to try out an intermediate paraphrase which may combine both logical and ordinary notation. This step will usually lead one to further paraphrases, and finally to a complete quantificational paraphrase of the original sentence. In carrying out these paraphrases, it is generally useful to paraphrase inward, since this tends to resolve problems into simpler components. Often several tentative paraphrases will have to be examined and tested against the original sentence before a final paraphrase can be obtained. These suggestions are so general that they are of little practical value. The student will find that in these matters experience is the best teacher. To help the student gain some experience, several rather different but complex examples will be worked out in the remainder of this section.

Let us start with

(16) Everyone who loves has his love returned.

This means

(17) Everyone who loves someone is loved in return by that person

or

(18) If one person loves another, that person loves him, too.

This leads us to

(19) $(x)(y)(x \text{ loves } y \supset y \text{ loves } x)$

restricting the universe to persons.

Next, let us try

(20) Everybody loves those his loved ones love.

This says that everyone loves a certain type of person. And who are these people? — The people his loved ones love. So this much leads to

(21) $(x)(x$ loves those whom x's loved ones love)

and this in turn to

(22) $(x)(y)(y$ is loved by one of x's loved ones $\supset x$ loves $y)$

Now a person's loved ones are those he loves; so 'z is one of x's loved ones' means 'x loves z'. Thus 'y is loved by one of x's loved ones' means '$(\exists z)(x$ loves $z \cdot z$ loves $y)$'. So (22) may be paraphrased as

(23) $(x)(y)[(\exists z)(x$ loves $z \cdot z$ loves $y] \supset x$ loves $y)$

or equivalently by

(24) $(x)(y)(z)(x$ loves $z \cdot z$ loves $y \supset x$ loves $y)$

Next let us consider an example in which pronouns play an even greater role:

(25) If two instances of time are distinct, then one is before the other.

Notice first that (25) is a statement about all instances of time; it says of *any* two of them that if they are distinct, then one is before the other. This much leads to

(26) $(x)(y)[-(x = y) \supset$ one of x and y is before the other]

provided that we restrict the universe to instants of time. The remaining problem is the expression

One of x and y is before the other.

It is a tempting move to paraphrase this as 'x is before y'. However, this leads to

(27) $(x)(y)[-(x = y) \supset x$ is before $y]$

which is incorrect, because it states that of two distinct instants of time, the first is before the second. This is too strong. To say that one of two instants of time is before the other is *not* to say which one is. Thus, what we want is

$(x$ is before $y) \vee (y$ is before $x)$

Consequently, the appropriate paraphrase of (25) is

(28) $(x)(y)[-(x = y) \supset ((x$ is before $y) \vee (y$ is before $x))]$

Our next example is

(29) Everyone who is admitted is examined beforehand.

As a start, let us transform this to

(30) $(x)(x$ is admitted $\supset x$ is examined beforehand)

This is not an adequate analysis of (29) if we are to bring out the relation between the time of admittance and the time of examination. Thus let us rewrite (30) as

(31) $(x)(x$ is a person admitted at a given time $\supset x$ is examined before that time)

If we let the given time be represented by 'y', then the consequent clause expands as

$(\exists z)(x$ is examined at time $z \cdot z$ is before $y)$

and the antecedent as

x is a person admitted at time y.

Although the component clauses have been analyzed, the problem of how they are put together still remains. If we try

(32) $(\exists y)(x$ is a person admitted at time $y) \supset (\exists z)(x$ is examined at time $z \cdot z$ is before $y)$

we find that the 'y' in the antecedent and the one in the consequent are not linked. Thus we might try

(33) $(\exists y)(x$ is a person admitted at time $y \supset (\exists z)(x$ is examined at time $z \cdot z$ is before $y))$

But this says only that there is *some* time such that those admitted then are examined beforehand at that time. This could be true if no one was examined who was admitted, so long as no one was admitted at this time. Obviously, (29) means that everyone admitted at *any* time is examined beforehand. This leads to

(34) $(x)(y)(x$ is a person admitted at time $y \supset (\exists z)(x$ is examined at time $z \cdot z$ is before $y))$

EXERCISES FOR SECS. 3.4.2 AND 3.4.3

Paraphrase the following, using logical symbols and the suggested notation.

1. No positive number is less than zero. (P,L,z)

2. There is no tallest man, although every man is taller than Jane. ($M,T,j,=$)
3. Whoever is the fastest member of the team will go to Italy. ($F,M,=,G,i$)
4. A horse faster than all dogs does not exist. (H,F,D)
5. Whoever kills everyone kills himself. (K)
6. Whoever kills Adam's killer is a killer who will not be killed. (K,a)
7. Everyone who loves someone but does not have his love returned will love everybody. (L)
8. One of Joe and Claire is older than the other. (O,j,c)
9. Given any two numbers, one is less than or equal to the other. (N,L)
10. If one number is less than another, the latter is not less than the former. (N,L)
11. Every man who weds a girl dates her beforehand. (M,W,G,D,B)
12. All houses on A Street are north of every house on B Street. (H,O,N,a,b)
13. There are at least two different cities on Kauai, and one is west of the other. (C,D,O,K,W)
14. John would always visit Mary before visiting Edith. (V,B,j,m,e)
15. A dog that comes to every whistler will come to no one who does not whistle for him. (D,C,W)

3.4.4 FROM PARAPHRASES TO SCHEMATA

Once a statement has been paraphrased into quantificational notation, it is a simple matter to find a schema diagramming it. Since this has been discussed in previous chapters, it is not necessary to go into the details of the procedure once again. However, it is convenient to accompany each schematic diagram of a statement with some indication of what each constant, predicate, or statement letter is supposed to represent. This may be accomplished by supplementing each diagram with a table in which each constant, statement, or predicate letter is followed by the name, sentence, or predicate it represents. Thus suppose, for example, that we are given the statement

(35) Edith dates only those who date her or I do not know what I am talking about.

Suppose, further, that we analyze the first disjunct completely and leave the second one alone, so that our paraphrase is

(36) (x)(Edith dates $x \supset x$ dates Edith) $\lor$ I do not know what I am talking about

Then a schema diagramming (36) and (35) is '$(x)(Fex \supset Fxe) \lor p$'

and the table accompanying it is

p : I do not know what I am talking about

e : Edith

F : ① dates ②

EXERCISES FOR SEC. 3.4.4

A. Obtain schemata diagramming the statements given in the exercises for Secs. 3.2.1 to 3.2.3. Reveal as much structure as possible.

B. Establish the validity of each of the following arguments by means of a derivation.

1. Each of Edith's brothers attends Dartmouth. So if Edith has any brothers, then someone attends Dartmouth.

2. Every person who buys at least one gallon will receive a ticket. Hence if no one receives a ticket, then no one buys a gallon.

3. Some of John's brothers are friends of Adam. All friends of Adam are friends of Charles. Hence some of John's brothers are friends of Charles.

4. Everyone loves all those who love him. Everyone loves everybody those he loves also love. So anyone who loves anybody loves himself.

5. All trucks are motor vehicles. Hence every truck driver is a motor-vehicle driver.

6. Some teachers are admired by all students who admire any teacher. Every student admires at least one teacher. Hence there are teachers who are admired by all their students.

7. No number is smaller than itself. Hence there is no number that is smaller than *all* numbers.

8. If one number is less than another, then the numbers are different. If one number is less than a second and the second is less than a third, then the first is less than the third. So if every number is less than some number, then every number is less than two different numbers.

9. Every event is caused by only an earlier event, and if one event is earlier than another, the latter is not earlier than the former. Hence there is no event which causes every event.

10. No student of a logician is a student of an artist. Hence if some logicians have students, then no artist has everyone for a student.

11. Every number greater than 1 is also greater than 0. One number is greater than another just in case the latter is less than the former. Hence every number which 1 is less than 1 is also a number which 0 is less than.

12. Every mother loves her children. Jane does not love any children. So Jane is not a mother.

13. Every parent loves his children. So if everyone has a parent, then everyone is loved.

14. Whoever is the fastest runner on the team will compete in the meet. No one on the team can run faster than Adam. Adam is on the team. So if someone is faster than another, just in case the latter is not faster than the former, then Adam will compete in the meet.

15. No one likes a person who does not like himself. No one will befriend a person he does not like. Hence someone who likes no one will not be befriended by anyone.

PART FOUR: EXTENSIONS OF QUANTIFICATION THEORY AND OTHER ADVANCED TOPICS

4.1 FUNCTIONAL TERMS

Quantification theory, as it now stands, is capable of treating all inferences in mathematics and practically all deductive inferences in the other sciences. Nonetheless, there are several types of inference that it can treat only in a very cumbersome manner, and to achieve a convenient treatment of these inferences, it is usual to extend quantification theory in several ways. The next few sections will be devoted to these extensions. Because the extensions in question are theoretically dispensable, their treatment here will be less rigorous than that given to full quantification theory. The student interested in fully rigorous treatment of these subjects should consult one of the more advanced treatises on mathematical logic.

Since most of the examples to be considered from now on will be drawn from mathematics and expressed in its own precise and symbolic language, the economy gained by carrying out derivations by means of schemata will no longer be significant. Indeed, our derivations will be more perspicuous on the whole if we stick with mathematical sentences, and so for the most part this will be our practice. Thus, for example, to show that '$(x)(y)(x < y \supset -(y < x))$' implies '$(x) - (x < x)$', we construct the following derivation:

$$
\begin{array}{lll}
1 & (x)(y)(x < y \supset -(y < x)) & \text{P} \\
2 & \quad x \quad \triangle & \text{A} \\
3 & \quad\quad x < x & \text{A} \\
4 & \quad\quad (y)(x < y \supset -(y < x)) & \text{1, UI} \\
5 & \quad\quad x < x \supset -(x < x) & \text{4, UI} \\
6 & \quad\quad -(x < x) & \text{3, 5, MP} \\
7 & \quad -(x < x) & \text{3-6, IP} \\
8 & (x) - (x < x) & \text{2-7, UG} \\
\end{array}
$$

An examination of mathematical arguments quickly reveals that many seemingly simple logical inferences may be handled only with difficulty in the context of full quantification theory. Thus consider the next two examples:

EXAMPLE A
(1) $(x)(y)(x + y = y + x)$ P

   Let z be any number. Then by (1)

(2) $(y)[(z + 1) + y = y + (z + 1)]$

So, since z is arbitrary,

(3) $(x)(y)[(x + 1) + y = y + (x + 1)]$

EXAMPLE B
(1) $(x)(x < x + 1)$ P
(2) $(x)(\exists y)(x < y)$ by (1)

The reason why these arguments appear so elementary is that they differ from arguments we have previously encountered only by containing applications of *extended* forms of universal instantiation and existential generalization. (Terms other than variables and constants replace α in the S_α of UI and EG.) This may be seen by formalizing them as follows:

EXAMPLE A.
$$
\begin{array}{lll}
1 & (x)(y)(x + y = y + x) & \text{P} \\
2 & z\ \triangle & \text{A} \\
3 & \quad (y)((z + 1) + y = y + (z + 1)) & \text{1, UI (extended)} \\
4 & (x)(y)((x + 1) + y = y + (x + 1)) & \text{2-3, UG}
\end{array}
$$

EXAMPLE B.
$$
\begin{array}{lll}
1 & (x)(x < x + 1) & \text{P} \\
2 & x\ \triangle & \text{A} \\
3 & \quad x < x + 1 & \text{1, UI} \\
4 & \quad (\exists y)(x < y) & \text{3, EG (extended)} \\
5 & (x)(\exists y)(x < y) & \text{2-4, UG}
\end{array}
$$

It is possible to handle these examples by means of quantification theory as it now stands, but only by first reformulating the language of mathematics itself so as to dispense with *functional terms* such as '$x + 1$'. Later, we shall indicate how this may be done. Right now it suffices to say that the dispensability of functional terms is a theoretical dispensability, not a practical one. No one would recommend that mathematicians actually *use* a language without functional terms, but for certain investigations into the nature of mathematics itself, it is important to know that such languages are possible.

   Theoretical dispensability aside, it is fairly easy to extend universal instantiation and existential generalization to allow for their use in connection with functional terms. But first we must indicate what functional terms are. Let us give some examples:

$$x + y, \qquad xy, \qquad x - y, \qquad \sqrt{x}, \qquad x^y$$
$$(x + y) - z, \qquad (x + 0)y, \qquad (0 + 1), \qquad 1^2, \qquad \sqrt{4}$$

The last three examples are names of particular objects; so they may be viewed as individual constants, and dealing with them poses no new problems. The other examples are not names, however, and become names only when their variables are replaced by the names of appropriate objects. These are the functional terms that pose the new problems. More generally, functional terms are composed of variables, individual constants, and expressions known as *functors*, in much the same way that compound sentences are composed of sentences and statement connectives. *A functor is a pattern of symbols and blanks which becomes a name when the blanks are filled by names.* The number of blanks determines the *degree* of the functor. Thus, '_____ + 1' is a functor of degree 1; '_____ + _____', of degree 2; '_____ (_____ + _____)', of degree 3; and so on. Functional terms are gotten from functors by filling their blanks by variables or individual constants (names) and iterating this process. More precisely, if a number of functors and individual constants are listed, then the functional terms composed of them are determined by means of the following rules:

1   If ϕ is a functor of degree n and $\alpha_1, \alpha_2, \cdots, \alpha_n$ are variables or individual constants, then $\phi(\alpha_1, \alpha_2, \cdots, \alpha_n)$ is a functional term.

2   If ϕ is a functor of degree n and $\beta_1, \beta_2, \cdots, \beta_n$ are functional terms, then so is $\phi(\beta_1, \beta_2, \cdots, \beta_n)$.

(In order to achieve generality, the symbol 'ϕ' has been placed initially, but as '_____ + _____' and '_____ + _____' illustrate, not all functors behave in this way.)

EXAMPLE. Given the individual constants '0' and '1' and the functor '_____ + _____', the functional terms composed from them are generated by the following rules:

a.   If α and β are variables or the individual constants '0' or '1', $(\alpha + \beta)$ is a functional term.

b.   If α and β are functional terms, so is $(\alpha + \beta)$.

Thus some of the functional terms so generated are

$$(x + 1), \qquad (x + y), \qquad (0 + 1), \qquad ((0 + 1) + x)$$

Now that functional terms have been characterized, it is a simple matter to make the appropriate extensions of universal instantiation and existential generalization. In the case of universal instantiation, we now permit the universally quantified variable to be replaced by functional terms. And in the case of existential generalization, we permit the replacement of functional terms by variables and the existential quantifications of these variables. Examples of extended UI are

1	$(x)(x + 0 = x)$	P
2	$(x + 1) + 0 = x + 1$	1, UI
3	$(x + y) + 0 = x + y$	1, UI
4	$(5 + y) + 0 = 5 + y$	2, UI

EXAMPLES OF EXTENDED EG

1	$(x + 1) - 1 = x + 0$	P
2	$(\exists y)(y - 1 = x + 0)$	1, EG
3	$(\exists y)((x + 1) - 1 = y)$	1, EG
4	$(\exists x)(\exists y)(x - 1 = y)$	3, EG

Notice that the following are merely applications of the old UI and EG:

1	$(x)(x + 0 = x)$	P
2	$1 + 0 = 1$	1, UI
3	$(2 + 2) + 0 = 2 + 2$	1, UI

1	$(x + 1) - 1 = x + 0$	P
2	$(\exists y)((x + 1) - y = x + 0)$	1, EG
3	$(\exists z)(\exists y)((x + z) - y = x + 0)$	2, EG
4	$(\exists w)(\exists z)(\exists y)((x + z) - y = x + w)$	3, EG

   Because of the additional variables introduced by the functional terms, we must be extra wary of capturing.† Unless capturing is avoided, incorrect inferences such as the following are possible:

| 1 | $(x)(\exists y)(x < y)$ |
| 2 | $(\exists y)((w - w) + y < y)$ |

[Step 1 is a true statement of number theory. Since step 2 reduces to '$(\exists y)$ $(y < y)$' because $w - w = 0$ and $0 + y < y$, it is false.]

EXAMPLES

a. To derive '$(x)(y)(x + (y + 1) = (y + 1) + x)$' from '$(x)(y)(x + y = y + x)$'.

---

†Let S_α and S_β be as in the statement of UI and EG, but in this case let β be a functional term. Then the condition on UI and EG that no occurrence of α within the scope of an occurrence of (β) or $(\exists\beta)$ be replaced in obtaining S_β from S_α is changed to: no occurrence of α within the scope of an occurrence of (γ) or $(\exists\gamma)$ may be replaced in obtaining S_β from S_α, where γ is any variable that has a free occurrence within β. This will avoid capturing when the extended forms of x UI and EG are used.

Derivation:

1	$(x)(y)(x + y = y + x)$	P
2	x △	A
3	y △	A
4	$(y)(x + y = y + x)$	1, UI
5	$x + (y + 1) = (y + 1) + x$	4, UI
6	$(y)(x + (y + 1) = (y + 1) + x)$	3-5, UG
7	$(x)(y)(x + (y + 1) = (y + 1) + x)$	2-6, UG

b. To derive '$(x)(\exists y)(x + 1 < y + 1)$' from '$(x)(x < x + 1)$'.

Derivation:

1	$(x)(x < x + 1)$	P
2	x △	A
3	$x + 1 < (x + 1) + 1$	1, UI
4	$(\exists y)(x + 1 < y + 1)$	3, EG
5	$(x)(\exists y)(x + 1 < y + 1)$	2-4, UG

c. To derive '$(x)(y)(x < y \supset x < y + 1)$' from '$(x)(x < x + 1)$' and '$(x)(y)(z)$ $(x < y \cdot y < z \supset x < z)$'.

Derivation: (Partially worked out)

	$(x)(x < x + 1)$	P
	$(x)(y)(z)(x < y \cdot y < z \supset x < z)$	P
x	△	A
y	△	A
	$x < y$	A
	$y < y + 1$	
	?	
	$x < y + 1$	
	$x < y \supset x < y + 1$	CP
	$(y)(x < y \supset x < y + 1)$	UG
	$(x)(y)(x < y \supset x < y + 1)$	UG

(*Exercise:* Complete this derivation.)

d. To derive '$(x)(0 + x = x)$' from '$(x)(x + 0 = x)$' and '$(x)(y)(x + y = y + x)$' and '$(x)(y)(z)(x - y \cdot y - z \supset x - z)$'.

Derivation: (Partially worked out)

	$(x)(x + 0 = x)$	P
	$(x)(y)(x + y = y + x)$	P
	$(x)(y)(z)(x = y \cdot y = z \supset x = z)$	P

$$
\begin{array}{ll}
x \mid \triangle & \\
\quad x + 0 = x & 1, \text{UI} \\
\quad (y) \, 0 + y = y + 0 & 2, \text{UI} \\
\quad 0 + x = x + 0 & 6, \text{UI} \\
\quad ? & \\
\quad 0 + x = x & \\
(x)(0 + x = x) & \text{UG}
\end{array}
$$

(*Exercise:*   Complete this derivation.)

e.   To derive '$(x)(\exists y)(x + 1 = y)$' from '$(x)(x = x)$'.

Derivation: (Partially worked out)

$$
\begin{array}{ll}
(x)(x = x) & \text{P} \\
x \mid \triangle & \text{A} \\
\quad x + 1 = x + 1 & 1, \text{UI} \\
\quad ? & \\
(x)(\exists y)(x + 1 = y) & \text{UG}
\end{array}
$$

(*Exercise:*   Complete this derivation.)

EXERCISES FOR SEC. 4.1

Derivations

Derive	From
1. $(x)(y)(x < y \supset x < y + 1)$	$(x)(x < x + 1)$, $(x)(y)(z)(x < y \cdot y < z \supset x < z)$
2. $(x)(0 + x = x)$	$(x)(x + 0 = x)$, $(x)(y)(x + y = y + x)$,
	$(x)(y)(z)(x = y \cdot y = z \supset x = z)$
3. $(x)(\exists y)(x + 1 = y)$	$(x)(x = x)$
4. $(x)(\exists y)(x < x + y)$	$(x)(x < x + 1)$
5. $(x)(y)(x - x \leqslant y)$	$(x)(0 \leqslant x)$, $(x)(x - x = 0)$,
	$(x)(y)(z)(x = y \cdot y \leqslant z \supset x \leqslant z)$
6. $(x)(\exists z)(z \leqslant x)$	$(\exists y)(x)(y + y \leqslant x)$
7. $(x)(y)(\exists z)(x + z = (y + 1) + x)$	$(x)(y)(x + y = y + x)$

4.2   IDENTITY
4.2.1   IDENTITY STATEMENTS
By means of the equals sign, '$=$', a familiar symbol to students of mathematics, we affirm *identities*. When objects are identical, they are one and the same object. They are not merely very similar or partially identical; they are completely the same. No difference between them exists; they are one, not

two. This basic characteristic of identity tends to be obscured by the use of the equals sign in many geometry textbooks, where statements such as the following appear:

'Since triangles ABC and $A'B'C'$ are congruent, $AB = A'B''$.

Such statements are usually made only in the interesting case where triangle ABC is *not identical* with triangle $A'B'C'$ and AB is not identical with $A'B'$. Consequently, here '$AB = A'B'$' cannot be interpreted as stating that AB and $A'B'$ are identical. Indeed, as any student of geometry knows, the proper interpretation of this statement is that the *lengths* of AB and $A'B'$ are the same. Expressed by using '=' to mean *identity*, the statement becomes

The length of $AB =$ the length of $A'B'$

Fortunately, '=' does mean identity in all other branches of mathematics. This is how the sign will be used in this book.

Because every theory has occasion to declare that some of its objects are the same or distinct, the sign of identity appears in the vocabulary of every theory. It is thus as pervasive and independent of subject matter as the truth-functions and quantifiers. For this reason, the deductive arguments that turn upon the characteristics of identity merit the attention of the logician.

To assert that

$1 + 1 = 2$
Shakespeare $=$ Bacon
$\sqrt{64} = 8$

is to assert that $1 + 1$ and 2 are identical numbers, that Shakespeare and Bacon are the same person, and that $\sqrt{64}$ and 8 are the same number. More generally,

$a = b$

is true if and only if a and b are the same object. It is obvious, then, that every object is identical with itself and with no other object. This causes one to wonder how identity can be a useful relation or a relation at all.

The first question may be answered by pointing out that one and the same object may be known to us in different ways or may have more than one name. The identity sign is then needed to state that an object known or names in one way is the same as an object known or named in another way. This is done in the statements

The morning star $=$ the evening star
Miss Jane Smith $=$ Mrs. Jane Smith Jones
The author of $Hamlet =$ the author of the *Novum Organum*

All these statements are nontrivial. The first was verified by careful astronomical observations; the second, perhaps, by checking society columns or marriage records; and the truth-value of the third is still unknown and of interest to some Shakespearean scholars. Of course, the statements

The morning star = the morning star
Miss Jane Smith = Miss Jane Smith
The author of *Hamlet* = the author of *Hamlet*

are trivially true. But their triviality need not preclude us from making other nontrivial or even false identity statements. The second question may be answered by recalling that, although identity truly holds only between an object and itself, it is grammatically possible to express false identities between two objects, and this grammatical fact is what determines its relational character. Some philosophers, perhaps because they were unable to fathom this last point, have argued that identity is a relation that holds between *names*. Such a view runs into serious difficulties when we come to consider statements in which the identity sign is flanked by variables — and we must account for these statements since they abound in mathematics and science. Then it is impossible to give a coherent account of identity as a relation between names. How, for example, could we interpret

$(x)(y)(x$ is a real number and y is a real number$) \supset x + y = y + x)$

when it is known that the real numbers outnumber all possible names for them? No, identity is a relation between things, not their names, and it is the relation that holds between each thing and itself only.

Identity also owes its usefulness to its opposite — distinctness. Two objects are *distinct* if and only if they are not identical; that is, x and y are distinct if and only if $-(x = y)$. [From now on we shall follow custom and abbreviate '$-(a = b)$' by '$a \neq b$.'] Thus, to assert that there are at least two, three, or four things, we write

(1) $(\exists x)(\exists y)(x \neq y)$
(2) $(\exists x)(\exists y)(\exists z)(x \neq y \cdot y \neq z \cdot x \neq z)$
(3) $(\exists x)(\exists y)(\exists z)(\exists w)(x \neq y \cdot y \neq z \cdot z \neq w \cdot x \neq w \cdot y \neq w)$

Or to state that there are at least two F's, we write

(4) $(\exists x)(\exists y)(x \neq y \cdot Fx \cdot Fy)$

Identity is also used to assert that, at most, a given number of things exists. Thus, to say that at most two, three, or four things exist is to say

(5) $(x)(y)(z)(x = z \lor y = z)$
(6) $(x)(y)(z)(w)(x = w \lor y = w \lor z = w)$

(7) $(x)(y)(z)(w)(u)(x = u \lor y = u \lor z = u \lor w = u)$

In other words, to say that at most two things exist is to say that every thing is identical with one of two (not necessarily distinct) things.

Ordinarily, "at most" statements do not imply "at least" statements. Thus none of (5), (6), (7) imply any of (1), (2), (3); for (5), (6), (7) would be true if even *no objects*, nothing, existed. Conversely, (1), (2), (3) do not imply (5), (6), (7); for (1), (2), (3) will be true even if more than two, three, or four things existed, but under these respective conditions (5), (6), and (7) are false. The only case in which an "at most" statement implies an "at least" statement is that of

(8) $(x)(y)(x = y)$

the statement that at most one thing exists. The implication is a direct consequence of our definition of validity. This makes valid

$(x)(y)Fxy \supset (\exists x)Fxx$

from which it follows that (8) implies

(9) $(\exists x)(x = x)$

that is, there is at least one thing.

That at most one F exists is expressed by

(10) $(x)(y)(Fx \cdot Fy \supset x = y)$

and notice, this does not imply that at least one F exists. Nor do the statements that at most two or three F's exist imply it; that is, these do not:

(11) $(x)(y)(z)(Fx \cdot Fy \cdot Fz \supset (x = z \lor y = z))$

(12) $(x)(y)(z)(w)(Fx \cdot Fy \cdot Fz \cdot Fw \supset (x = w \lor y = w \lor z = w))$

By combining "at most" statements with "at least" statements one arrives at "exactly" statements. To say that exactly one thing exists is to say that at least and at most one thing exists; that is,

(13) $(\exists x)(y)(x = y)$

⌊We need not write '$(\exists x)(x = x) \cdot (x)(y)(x = y)$' because (13) is equivalent to it. (*Exercise.*) Because of similar equivalences the other "exactly" statements can also be simplified.⌋ On the other hand, to say that exactly one or a *unique* F exists is to say

(14) $(\exists x)(Fx \cdot (y)(Fy \supset x = y))$

In mathematics, uniqueness statements play important roles. Mathematicians often have to prove carefully that limits, least upper bounds, derivatives, etc., exist and are unique—a fact which sometimes bothers beginners of calculus. The famous parallel postulate of Euclidean geometry, for example, is also a uniqueness statement. Using 'P' for 'point', 'L' for 'line', '$\parallel$' for 'parallel', and 'O' for 'on', it may be expressed as

(15) $(x)(y)(Px \cdot Ly \cdot -Oxy \supset$
$\qquad (\exists z)(Lz \cdot z \parallel y \cdot Oxz \cdot (w)(Lw \cdot w \parallel y \cdot Oxw \supset w = z)))$

Since uniqueness statements are so common, it is convenient to have an abbreviation for them. Accordingly, (14) may be shortened to

(16) $(\exists ! x)Fx$

where '$(\exists ! x)$' is read as 'there is exactly one x' or 'there is a unique x'. Applying the abbreviation, (15) becomes shortened to

(17) $(x)(y)(Px \cdot Ly \cdot -Oxy \supset (\exists ! z)(Lz \cdot z \parallel y \cdot Oxz))$

Of course, we can go beyond "exactly one" statements to "exactly two", "exactly three" statements by analogously combining the appropriate "at most" and "at least" statement. Thus, that there are exactly two, exactly three, F's is rendered

(18) $(\exists x)(\exists y)(x \neq y \cdot Fx \cdot Fy \cdot (z)(Fz \supset (x = z \lor y = z)))$

(19) $(\exists x)(\exists y)(\exists z)(x \neq y \cdot y \neq z \cdot x \neq z \cdot Fx \cdot Fy \cdot Fz \cdot$
$\qquad (w)(Fw \supset (x = w \lor y = w \lor z = w)))$

4.2.2 IDENTITY SCHEMATA
The logic of identity is an extension of quantification theory. Identity schemata and sentences are constructed from statement letters; that is, 'p', 'q', 'r', etc., predicate letters appended with variables or individual constants, that is, 'Fx', 'Gax', '$Hxyz$', etc., and identity signs flanked by variables or individual constants, that is, '$x = y$', '$a = x$', '$a = b$', etc. The construction uses truth-functions and quantifiers in the usual way. Notice that for the first time sentences make an appearance along with schemata, for this method of construction produces sentences such as '$(x)(x = x)$', '$x = y$', and '$(\exists x)(\exists y)(x = y)$'. Validity can be defined in the usual way as truth under every interpretation in every universe. Because no new schematic letters have been introduced, it is not necessary to extend the concept of interpretation. Identity *sentences* pose a problem because they are not susceptible of interpretation (that technical concept is appropriate only to schemata). On the other hand, their validity can be simply characterized as truth in every non-

empty universe. Then '$(x)(x = x)$', '$(\exists x)(x = x)$', '$(y)(\exists x)(x = y)$' are all valid, since they are true in all universes. On the other hand, '$(x)(y)(x = y)$' and '$(\exists x)(y)(x = y)$' are not valid, since they are false in universes of more than one object. As these examples indicate, there are identity sentences which are valid although not quantificationally valid alone. Thus, for example, '$(x)(x = x)$', although valid in identity theory, has the form '$(x)Fxx$', and so is not logically true *by the lights of quantification theory alone*. This is true not only of some identity sentences, it is also true of certain identity schemata. The schema

(20) $(x)(y)(Fx \cdot x = y \supset Fy)$

for example, is valid. Given any nonempty universe and interpretation of 'F', (20) must come out true, for given any objects such that 'Fx' and '$x = y$' are true, 'Fy' must be true, too, since x and y are identical. On the other hand, the purely quantification structure of (20) comes to

(21) $(x)(y)(Fx \cdot Gxy \supset Fy)$

which is not a valid quantificational schema.

4.2.3   RULES FOR IDENTITY

We need not explore identity schemata and sentences and their validity any further. For the purposes of this book it suffices to state two rules of inference for identity. These are enough to handle all applications of the logic of identity we shall make. The first rule permits us to write the sentence '$(x)(x = x)$' at any stage of any derivation or proof. It is called the *axiom of identity*, and may be stated:

> At any stage in any derivation or proof, the identity sentence '$(x)(x = x)$' may be written as a step.

Reason: AI.

Notice that this rule is unlike the rule of assumption in that it *does not* require the initiation of new vertical lines.

EXAMPLES

a.   To prove: $(\exists y)(y = y)$.

Proof: 1 | $(x)(x = x)$ AI
            2 | $y = y$ 1, UI
            3 | $(\exists y)(y = y)$ 2, EG

b.   To prove: $(x)(\exists y)(x = y)$.

Proof: 1 | $(x)(x = x)$ AI
2 | x △   A
3 | | $x = x$ 1, UI
4 | | $(\exists y)(x = y)$ 3, EG
5 | $(x)(\exists y)(x = y)$ 2-4, UG

Because no difference exists between identical objects, anything true of one must be true of the other. In other words, if, for example, Shakespeare = Bacon, then anything that can be truly said of Shakespeare can be truly said of Bacon. This property of identity accounts for the validity of (20) above and motivates the next rule of identity. The rule is called *substitutivity of identity*, and may be stated as follows:

If S_β comes from S_α by replacing one or more occurrences of α in S_α by β, and no capturing results from this, and the replaced occurrences of α neither are nor contain bound occurrences of variables, then from S_α and $\alpha = \beta$ we may infer S_β.

Reason: Numerals referring to S_α and $\alpha = \beta$, followed by 'SI'. (Here S_α and S_β are sentences or schemata, and α and β are individual constants, variables, or functional terms.) The restrictions are essential, for without them invalid inferences would be possible. Here are two examples of such invalid inferences:

a.   1 | $(x)(\exists y)(x \neq y)$ P
2 | $(x)(\exists y)(x = y)$ P
3 | $(\exists y)(x = y)$ 2, UI
4 | y | $x = y$ A
5 | | $(\exists y)(x \neq y)$ 1, UI
6 | | $(\exists y)(y \neq y)$ 4, 5, SI   (incorrect: 'y' has
7 | $(\exists y)(y \neq y)$ 3, 4-6, EI   been captured.)

(Step 1 is true because more than one thing exists, step 2 because it is a valid identity sentence.)

b.   1 | $(x)((\exists y)(x = y) \cdot (\exists y)(x \neq y))$ P
2 | $(\exists y)(x = y) \cdot (\exists y)(x \neq y)$ 1, UI
3 | $(\exists y)(x = y)$ 2, S
4 | y | $x = y$ A
5 | | $(x)((\exists y)(x = y) \cdot (\exists y)(y \neq y))$ 1, 4, SI (incorrect: The
6 | $(x)((\exists y)(x = y) \cdot (\exists y)(y \neq y))$ 3, 4-5, EI occurrence of 'x'
7 | $(\exists y)(x = y) \cdot (\exists y)(y \neq y)$ 6, UI   replaced is bound.)
8 | $(\exists y)(y \neq y)$ 7, S

EXAMPLES

a.   To derive '$y = x$' from '$x = y$'.

Derivation: 1 | $x = y$ P
                 2 | $(x)(x = x)$ AI
                 3 | $x = x$ 2, UI
                 4 | $y = x$ 1, 3, SI

b.   To derive '$x = z$' from '$x = y$' and '$y = z$'.

Derivation: 1 | $x = y$ P
                 2 | $y = z$ P
                 3 | $x = z$ 1, 2, SI

(Notice that, in applying substitutivity of identity in this case, step 1 is S_y and step 3 is S_z.)

From derivations (a) and (b) we see that we can easily prove

(22) $(x)(y)(x = y \supset y = x)$

(23) $(x)(y)(z)(x = y \cdot y = z \supset x = z)$

The axiom of identity formulated the *reflexivity of identity*, (22) formulates the *symmetry of identity*, and (23) formulates the *transitivity of identity*. A relation such as identity, which is reflexive, symmetrical, and transitive, is called an *equivalence relation*.

c.   To derive 'Fy' from '$(\exists x)(x = y \cdot Fx)$'.

Derivation: 1 | $(\exists y)(x = y \cdot Fx)$ P
                 2 | x | $x = y \cdot Fx$ A
                 3 | | $x = y$ 2, S
                 4 | | Fx 2, S
                 5 | | Fy 3, 4, SI
                 6 | Fy 1, 2-5, EI

d.   To prove the joint inconsistency of '$(x)(y)(x + y = y + x)$', '$(x)(y)(x + y = y)$', and '$(x)(\exists y)(x \neq y)$'.

Proof of Inconsistency:

1 | $(x)(y)(x + y = y + x)$ P
2 | $(x)(y)(x + y = y)$ P
3 | $(x)(\exists y)(x \neq y)$ P
4 | $(\exists y)(x \neq y)$ 3, UI
5 | z | $x \neq z$ A
6 | | $(y)(x + y = y)$ 2, UI

7	$x + z = z$	6, UI
8	$(y)(x + y = y + x)$	1, UI
9	$x + z = z + x$	8, UI
10	$(y)(z + y = y)$	2, UI
11	$z + x = x$	10, UI
12	$x + z = x$	9, 11, SI
13	$x = z$	7, 12, SI
14	$x = z \lor -(\exists y)(x = y)$	13, add
15	$-(\exists y)(x = y)$	5, 14, DS
16	$-(\exists y)(x = y)$	4, 5-15, EI

e.   To prove: $x = y \supset x + z = y + z.$

Proof:

1	$x = y$	A
2	$(x)(x = x)$	AI
3	$x + z = x + z$	2, UI
4	$x + z = y + z$	1, 3, SI
5	$x = y \supset x + z = y + z$	1-4, CP

f.   To show that 'Only Andrew and Charles had keys to the locker' and 'Anyone who stole the coats had to have a key to the locker' imply 'If someone stole the coats, either Andrew or Charles did it'.

Proof of the Implication

Schemata: $(x)(Kx \supset (x = a \lor x = c))$ *(first sentence)*
$K :$ ① has a key to the locker; a : Andrew c : Charles
$(x)(Fx \supset Kx)$ *(second sentence)*
$F :$ ① steals the coats
$(\exists x)Fx \supset (Fa \lor Fc)$ *(third sentence)*

Derivation: (Partially worked out)

1	$(x)(Kx \supset (x = a \lor x = c))$	P
2	$(x)(Fx \supset Kx)$	P
3	$(\exists x)Fx$	A
4	x Fx	A
5	$Fx \supset Kx$	2, UI
6	Kx	4, 5, MP
7	$Kx \supset (x = a \lor x = c)$	1, UI
8	$x = a \lor x = c$	6, 7, MP
9	$x = a$	A
10	Fa	6, 9, SI
11	$Fa \lor Fc$	10, add

12 | | | $x = a \supset (Fa \lor Fc)$ 9-11, CP
| | | ?
| | | $x = c \supset (Fa \lor Fc)$
| | | $Fa \lor Fc$ SD
| | $Fa \lor Fc$ EI
| $(\exists x)Fx \supset (Fa \lor Fc)$ CP

(*Exercise:*   Complete this derivation.)

EXERCISES FOR SEC. 4.2

A.   Symbolize the following statements, using the notation of identity theory.
1.   There is at least one person, but everyone has at most one father.
2.   At most two robbers held up the store.
3.   Exactly one man is the president of the club.
4.   One and only one man issued the invitation.
5.   One and only one man issued an invitation to at most two women.
6.   At most two women stopped at the shop.
7.   No one but John or Bob has the key.
8.   Exactly two people have keys, and they are John and Bob.
9.   Whoever has the key is the one and only one robber.
10.   There are exactly two chiefs and at most three assistants.
11.   Distinct men have distinct wives.
12.   Some people marry each other, but not one marries himself.
13.   At least three of the horses in the pasture are jumpers.
14.   On each of my shelves there is a different book.
15.   No one owes anything to anyone but himself.
16.   Everyone has a unique father.
17.   A function always has a unique value for each argument.
18.   A function is one-one just in case each of its values is the value for a unique argument.
19.   If the directions do not specify a unique method, then there are at least three methods.
20.   Nobody here is unique in having problems.

B.   Prove these identity schemata and sentences.
1. $(x)(y)(x = y \supset y = x)$
2. $(x)(\exists y)((x = y) \cdot (z)(x = z \supset y = z))$
3. $(x)(y)(x = y \supset (Fx \equiv Fy))$
4. $Fy \equiv (\exists z)(y = z \cdot Fz)$
5. $Fy \equiv (z)(y = z \supset Fz)$
6. $(\exists ! x)Fx \supset (Fx \cdot Fy \supset x = y)$
7. $(\exists x)(y)(Fy \equiv x = y) \supset (\exists ! x)Fx$
8. $-(\exists ! x)Fx \cdot (\exists x)Fx$
     $\supset (\exists x)(\exists y)(x \neq y \cdot Fx \cdot Fy)$

C.   Establish the validity of the following arguments by means of a derivation in identity theory.

1. Jones has exactly one child. Hence, if Bill and Don are children of Jones, then Bill and Don are the same person.

2. Mary Smith is Mrs. W. B. Smith. So whoever lives with Mary Smith also lives with Mrs. W. B. Smith.

3. At most two dogs crossed the yard. A dog that had long ears crossed the yard; so did one with a short tail; and so did one with long hair. Hence some dog has long hair and either a short tail or long ears.

4. Any goat can jump higher than a smaller one. Hence, if there is a largest goat, then there is a highest-jumping one.

5. There is exactly one chair in my bedroom, and there are exactly two chairs in my office. Although nothing is in both my bedroom and in my office, everything in either one is in my house. There are no chairs in my house except those in my office and my bedroom. Hence there are exactly three chairs in my house.

6. There is a unique mayor, that is, Mr. Jackson. Hence, whoever is a friend of the mayor is a friend of Mr. Jackson.

7. There is a unique president and a unique vice president. Hence, if anyone is both the president and vice president, then only one person is.

8. The women's club has a unique officer. Mrs. W. C. Smith is an officer of the women's club. Therefore, if Mary Smith is an officer of the women's club, then she is Mrs. W. C. Smith.

4.3 DESCRIPTIONS

4.3.1 DEFINITE DESCRIPTIONS

Phrases beginning with the definite article 'the' and which purport to name one and only one object are known in logic as *definite descriptions*. Some examples of definite descriptions are

the capital of France · the oldest man in my family
the square root of 4 · the author of *Hamlet*
the first President of the United States · the smallest prime number

Also counted are many other phrases which purport to name one and only one object, but do not begin with 'the', for such phrases can usually be paraphrased as definite descriptions. Thus we can usually paraphrase

'Jones' boss' as 'the boss of Jones'
'his heart's desire' as 'the thing his heart desired'
'where he was born' as 'the place where he was born'

Thus, in general, any phrase (other than a proper name) which *purports* to name one and only one object can usually be easily converted into a definite description.

The emphasis here is on the word "purports", for many expressions which logicians wish to treat as definite descriptions fail to name unique objects either by naming none at all, such as 'the present Emperor of Russia', or by naming more than one, such as 'the author of the U.S. Constitution'. Of course, because of their lack of specificity, many definite descriptions, such as

the oldest brother of Paul   the next gas station
the left door   the longest night

will fail to name a unique object when taken in isolation. But in such cases the full context usually successfully determines the identity of the object described. In treating arguments containing these unspecific descriptions, one can, if confusion might arise, paraphrase them so that they are more specific. Thus 'the oldest brother of Paul' could be expanded to

the oldest brother of Paul Jones

or even to

the oldest brother of the Paul Jones born in Elmville July 1, 1881

if necessary.

Logicians use the symbol '$(\imath x)$' to express 'the thing x such that', or simply, 'the x such that'. Of course, '$(\imath y)$', '$(\imath z)$', and '$(\imath w)$' are read similarly. Using these symbols — call them *descriptors* — some of the previous definite descriptions may be symbolized as

$(\imath x)(x$ is the next gas station) $(\imath y)(y$ is the left door)
$(\imath z)(z$ wrote the U.S. Constitution) $(\imath w)(w$ is a boss of Jones)

Notice that *descriptors* are prefixed to open sentences, and convert open sentences into definite descriptions. Descriptors bind variables just as quantifiers do, and one may extend the notion of scope, freedom, and bondage to apply to them. Since we shall not take the trouble here to give precise definitions of these terms, let us consider an example:

$(x)(x = (\imath y)(y$ loves Jones) $\supset (\exists z)(z$ loves $x)$
$(w)(w$ loves $(\imath w)(w$ loves Jones $\cdot (\exists y)(y$ loves $w))$

Here the arrows indicate the bounds between the various quantifiers, descriptors, and variables. As the example shows, in determining whether an occurrence of a variable is free or bound, it is now necessary to pay attention to both the descriptors and quantifiers in whose scope it occurs.

So far, all the definite descriptions considered have been closed, but open definite descriptions which contain free variables are also possible. For example,

$(\imath x)(x \text{ loves } y)$ $(\imath y)(y \text{ is a child of } w)$
$(\imath z)(x + z = 7)$ $(\imath x)(y - x = 0)$

are open definite descriptions. Open definite descriptions do not purport to name unique objects by themselves, but when their free variables are replaced by names or closed definite descriptions, they do purport to name unique objects. Thus open definite descriptions may be viewed as a species of functional term. Indeed, given any open functional term, an open definite description of the same behavior can be easily found. Thus, answering to '$x + y$', we have '$(\imath z)(x + y = z)$'; answering to 'xy', we have '$(\imath z)(xy = z)$'; and answering to '$x + 1$' we have '$(\imath y)(x + 1 = y)$'. In general, answering to $f(x_1, x_2, \cdots, x_n)$, we have

$$(\imath y)(f(x_1, x_2, \cdots, x_n) = y)$$

Moreover, these terms have the same behavior in the sense that the following statements are true:

$(x)(y)(x + y = (\imath z)(x + y = z))$
$(x)(y)(xy = (\imath z)(xy = z))$
$(x)(x + 1 = (\imath y)(x + 1 = y))$
$(x_1)(x_2) \cdots (x_n)(f(x_1, x_2, \cdots, x_n) = (\imath y)(f(x_1, x_2, \cdots, x_n) = y))$

Moreover, since these statements are true, it follows by identity theory that every functional term and the definite description answering to it may be interchanged in any statement without affecting the statement's truth-value.

The replacements of functional terms by definite descriptions presented above may not appear very interesting, because the functional terms all reappear in the definite descriptions. However, these may easily be eliminated in favor of relational predicates. Thus '$x + y = z$' may be replaced by 'Σxyz', which is true just in case the sum of x and y is z. The expression '$xy = z$' may be likewise replaced by 'Πxyz', which is true if and only if the product of x and y is z. In general,

$$f(x_1, x_2, \cdots, x_n) = y$$

may be replaced by

$$Fx_1, x_2, \cdots, x_n y$$

which is true if and only if $f(x_1, x_2, \cdots, x_n)$ is y. Thus, by introducing special relational predicates, every functional term may be replaced by a definite description which contains no functional terms. Consequently, all functional terms which are not descriptions may be eliminated in favor of definite description. In a later chapter we shall see how to eliminate definite descriptions themselves, and thus how to eliminate all functional terms.

Proper names may also be eliminated in favor of definite descriptions. Usually, for any proper name, a definite description naming the same object can be found. Thus the truth of

Paris $= (\imath x)(x$ is the capital of France$)$
George Washington $= (\imath x)(x$ is the first U.S. President$)$
Venus $= (\imath x)(x$ is the morning star and the evening star$)$
$O = (\imath x)(x + x = x)$

show that 'Paris', 'George Washington', 'Venus', and 'O' may be replaced by definite descriptions. In general, if 'F' is a predicate which characterizes the object a and that object alone, then 'a' may be eliminated in favor of '$(\imath x)Fx$'. By means of a slight 'trick', it is also possible, given any object a, to introduce a predicate 'F' such that '$a = (\imath x)Fx$' is true. We merely introduce a new predicate symbol 'F' and interpret it so that 'Fx' is true if and only if x is a. Thus we see that in theory all proper names, functional terms, and descriptions can be eliminated from the language of every theory. This means that the language of every theory may be reformulated so that its basic apparatus consists merely of variables, predicates, quantifiers, and statement connectives. For certain investigations in the foundations of mathematics and science, this information is very important. However, languages without descriptions, proper names, and functional terms are extremely cumbersome, and no one would recommend that they be used in practice.

4.3.2 DESCRIPTIONS AND ARGUMENTS

The logic of descriptions is best approached by first considering a few examples of arguments whose correctness turns upon the presence of definite descriptions. Here are three:

(1)   The author of *Tom Sawyer* is the author of *Huckleberry Finn*. Hence someone wrote both *Tom Sawyer* and *Huckleberry Finn*.

(2)   John is the president of the class.
Someone is both president of the class and captain of the football team. Thus John is captain of the football team.

(3)   The man who hired John hires only honor graduates.
So John is an honor graduate.

Let us now symbolize these as follows:

(4) $(\imath x)(x$ wrote *Tom Sawyer*$) = (\imath x)(x$ wrote *Huckleberry Finn*$)$
∴ $(\exists x)(x$ wrote *Tom Sawyer* $\cdot$ x wrote *Huckleberry Finn*$)$

(5)   John $= (\imath x)(x$ is president of the class)
      $(\exists x)(x$ is president of the class $\cdot x$ is captain of the football team)
      $\therefore$ John is captain of the football team.

(6) $(x)((\imath y)(y$ hired John) hires $x \supset x$ is an honor graduate)
      $\therefore$ John is an honor graduate.

It is not hard to see that these arguments are not valid *as they stand*, either
in quantification theory or identity theory. However, they can be made valid
by the addition of further premisses. To (4) we need only add

(7) $(y)(y$ wrote *Tom Sawyer* $\equiv y = (\imath x)(x$ wrote *Tom Sawyer*))

(8) $(y)(y$ wrote *Huckleberry Finn* $\equiv y = (\imath x)(x$ wrote *Huckleberry Finn*))

to (5) we add

(9) $(y)(y$ is president of the class $\equiv y = (\imath x)(x$ is president of the class))

and to (6) we add

(10) $(z)(z$ hires John $\equiv z = (\imath y)(y$ hires John))

The extra premisses (7) to (10), all have the form

(11) $(y)(Fy \equiv y = (\imath x)Fx)$

and are called *descriptional premisses*. If there is a unique F, then the descriptional premiss must be true; for it states that $(\imath x)Fx$ and $(\imath x)Fx$ only is an F.
  Once the descriptional premisses are added to (4), (5), and (6), their
validity is easily established. To see this, let us diagram the statements
involved, using the following predicate letters and individual constants:

$T : \textcircled{1}$ wrote *Tom Sawyer* $F : \textcircled{1}$ wrote *Huckleberry Finn*
$j :$ John $P : \textcircled{1}$ is president of the class
$C : \textcircled{1}$ is captain of the football team $H : \textcircled{1}$ hires $\textcircled{2}$
$G : \textcircled{1}$ is an honor graduate

Then the schemata corresponding to each argument are

For (4): $(\imath x)Tx = (\imath x)Fx$
           $(y)(Ty \equiv y = (\imath x)Tx)$
           $(y)(Fy \equiv y = (\imath x)Fx)$
           $\therefore (\exists x)(Tx \cdot Fx)$

For (5): $j = (\imath x)Px$
           $(\exists x)(Px \cdot Cx)$
           $(y)(Py \equiv y = (\imath x)Px)$
           $\therefore Cj$

For (6): $(x)(H[(\imath y)Hyj]x \supset Gx)$
$(z)(Hzj \equiv z = (\imath y)Hyj)$
$\therefore Gj$

Then the derivations to validate each argument are the following:

For (4):

1	$(\imath x)Tx = (\imath x)Fx$	P
2	$(y)(Ty \equiv y = (\imath x)Tx)$	P
3	$(y)(Fy \equiv y = (\imath x)Fx)$	P
4	$(x)(x = x)$	AI
5	$(\imath y)Tx = (\imath x)Tx$	4, UI
6	$(\imath x)Fx = (\imath x)Fx$	4, UI
7	$T(\imath x)Tx \equiv (\imath x)Tx = (\imath x)Tx$	2, UI
8	$T(\imath x)Tx$	5, 7, MPB
9	$F(\imath x)Fx \equiv (\imath x)Fx = (\imath x)Fx$	3, UI
10	$F(\imath x)Fx$	6, 9, MPB
11	$T(\imath x)Fy$	8, 1, SI
12	$T(\imath y)Fx \cdot F(\imath x)Fx$	10, 11, PC
13	$(\exists x)(Tx \cdot Fx)$	12, EG

For (5):

1	$j = (\imath x)Px$	P
2	$(y)(Py \equiv y = (\imath x)Px)$	P
3	$(\exists x)Px \cdot Cx$	P
4	$x\|\ Px \cdot Cx$	A
5	Px	4, S
6	$Px \equiv x = (\imath x)Px$	2, UI
7	$x = (\imath x)Px$	5, 6, MPB
8	$(x)(x = x)$	AI
9	$j = j$	8, UI
10	$(\imath x)Px = j$	9, 1, SI
11	$x = j$	7, 10, SI
12	Cx	4, S
13	Cj	12, 11, SI
14	Cj	3, 4-13, EI

(Note that steps 8 to 10 are needed to convert step 1 into a form appropriate for the use of substitutivity of identity in step 11.)

For (6):

1	$(x)(H((\imath y)Hyj)\,x \supset Gx)$	P
2	$(z)(Hzj \equiv z = (\imath y)Hyj)$	P
3	$(x)(x = x)$	AI
4	$(\imath y)Hyj = (\imath y)Hyj$	3, UI
5	$H((\imath y)Hyj)j \equiv (\imath y)Hyj = (\imath y)Hyj$	2, UI
6	$H((\imath y)Hyj)j$	4, 5, MPB

$$\begin{array}{c|ll}
7 & H((\imath y)Hyj)j \supset Gj & \quad 1, \text{UI} \\
8 & Gj & \quad 6, 7, \text{MP}
\end{array}$$

We can now summarize the technique applied in these examples. Given an argument involving definite descriptions, one first symbolizes it, using descriptors to symbolize the descriptions upon which the argument hinges. It is useful here to apply the principle of revealing no unnecessary structure, for often only a few of the descriptions will be relevant to the structure of the argument in question. For example, it is completely superfluous to treat 'John' in the arguments above as a description. In the next step, one adds descriptional premisses corresponding to each description symbolized by means of descriptors. Finally, the argument is validated in the context of identity theory.

A notational simplification may be achieved by dispensing with definite descriptions in the actual derivations. Once the descriptional premisses have been supplied, they play no essential role, and may be replaced by individual constants (if closed) or functional terms containing their free variables (if open). (One may easily check that the derivations given above remain correct if the descriptions in them are replaced by individual constants.) These replacements eliminate such complicated expressions as

$$H((\imath y)Hyj)x$$

in favor of, simply,

$$Hdx$$

EXAMPLES

a. To derive from an appropriate descriptional premiss

$$(x)(f(x) = (\imath y)(f(x) = y))$$

Solution: The descriptional premiss is

$$(x)(z)(f(x) = z \equiv z = (y)(f(x) = y))$$

but '$(\imath y)(f(x) = y)$' may be abbreviated by '$d(x)$'; so the derivation becomes

$$\begin{array}{c|c|l}
1 & (x)(z)(f(x) = z \equiv z = d(x)) & \text{P} \\
2 & x\ \triangle & \text{A} \\
3 & (x)(x = x) & \text{AI} \\
4 & d(x) = d(x) & 3, \text{UI} \\
5 & (z)(f(x) = z \equiv z = d(x)) & 1, \text{UI} \\
6 & f(x) = d(x) \equiv d(x) = d(x) & 5, \text{UI}
\end{array}$$

$$\begin{array}{lll}
7 & | \quad f(x) = d(x) & \text{4, 6, MPB} \\
8 & | \quad (x)(f(x) = d(x)) & \text{2-7, UG}
\end{array}$$

b. To derive '$(x)(y)(x + y = y + x)$' from '$(x)(y)(x + y = (\imath z)\Sigma xyz)$', '$(x)(y)(z)$
$(w)(\Sigma xyz \cdot \Sigma yxw \supset z = w)$', and the descriptional premiss '$(x)(y)(z)(\Sigma xyz \equiv z = d(x,y))$', where '$d(x,y)$' replaces '$(\imath z)\Sigma xyz$'.

Derivation: (Partially worked out)

$$\begin{array}{lll}
1 & (x)(y)(x + y = d(x, y)) & \text{P} \\
2 & (x)(y)(z)(w)(\Sigma xyz \cdot \Sigma yxw \supset z = w) & \text{P} \\
3 & (x)(y)(z)(\Sigma xyz \equiv z = d(x, y)) & \text{P} \\
4 \quad u & \triangle & \text{A} \\
5 \quad\quad v & \triangle & \text{A} \\
6 & \quad (y)(u + y = d(u, y)) & \text{1, UI} \\
7 & \quad u + v = d(u, v) & \text{6, UI} \\
8 & \quad (y)(v + y = d(v, y)) & \text{1, UI} \\
9 & \quad v + u = d(v, u) & \text{8, UI} \\
10 & \quad (y)(z)(\Sigma uyz \equiv z = d(u, y)) & \text{3, UI} \\
11 & \quad (z)(\Sigma uvz \equiv z = d(u, v)) & \text{10, UI} \\
12 & \quad \Sigma uvd(u, v) \equiv d(u, v) = d(u, v) & \text{11, UI} \\
13 & \quad (x)(x = x) & \text{AI} \\
14 & \quad d(u, v) = d(u, v) & \text{13, UI} \\
15 & \quad \Sigma uvd(u, v) & \text{12, 14, MPB} \\
& \quad \cdot \\
& \quad \cdot \\
& \quad \cdot \\
& \quad \Sigma vud(v, u) & \text{MPB} \\
& \quad \cdot \\
& \quad \cdot \\
& \quad \cdot \\
& \quad d(u, v) = d(v, u) & \text{MP} \\
& \quad \cdot \\
& \quad \cdot \\
& \quad \cdot \\
& \quad u + v = v + u & \text{SI} \\
& \quad (y)(u + y = y + u) & \text{UG} \\
& (x)(y)(x + y = y + x) & \text{UG}
\end{array}$$

(*Exercise:* Complete this derivation.)

The last two examples should give the reader some indication of why functional terms may be eliminated in favor of descriptions. Needless to say, they also indicate some of the practical problems engendered by this elimination.

EXERCISES FOR SEC. 4.3

A.   Symbolize the following, using descriptors and the suggested notation.

1.   The U.S. President (P,u)
2.   The man who lives on the hill (ML,h)
3.   The tallest mountain $(M,=)$
4.   John's father (F,j)
5.   John's eldest brother $(B,j,E,=)$
6.   What James wants (W,j)
7.   When John married (T,M,j)
8.   When John married his wife (T,j,MW)
9.   Where the road to Rome crosses the road to Paris (P,R,r,p,G,C)
10.   The one who introduced the speaker (I,S)

B.   Eliminate all functional terms from the following, except for descriptions. Use descriptions to carry out the elimination. Use the suggested predicates.

1. $(x)(x + y = y + x)$ (Use 'Σxyz' for '$x + y = z$'.)
2. $(x)(x + 0 = x)$ (Use 'Σxyz' again and 'Zy' for '$y = 0$'.)
3.   New York's mayor is a woman.   (Use 'Nx' for 'x is New York'.)
4. $(x)(x \cdot 1 = x)$ (Use 'Πxyz' for '$x \cdot y = z$' and 'Ox' for '$x = 1$'.)
5. $(x)(y)(z)(x \cdot (y + z) = x \cdot y + x \cdot z)$ (Use 'Σxyz' and '$\Pi\ xyz$'.)

C.   Using descriptional premises, establish the validity of each of the following arguments by means of a derivation.

1.   Honolulu's mayor is a native of Hawaii. Hence some mayor is a native of Hawaii.
2.   The sole survivor of the battle is an American. Thus all survivors of the battle are Americans.
3.   The fastest horse in the race is a thoroughbred. Thus, if at least two horses are in the race, then some thoroughbred is faster than some other horse.
4.   John's father is a painter. Bill's father is a doctor. John and Bill have the same father. Therefore someone who is a doctor also fathered both Bill and John.
5.   The man who teaches this class teaches only logic classes. Hence this class is a logic class.

4.4   THE LOGIC OF RELATIONS

Quantification theory and identity theory find important applications in the study of the logical properties of relations. These properties are of special interest because they are possessed by several crucial relations in science and mathematics. By using logic, they can be studied in the abstract, and thus it becomes possible to gain information about many particular relations in one single blow. This approach, which is so characteristic of abstract algebra and topology in modern mathematics, forms one of the chief bonds between modern mathematical logic and contemporary mathematics. Nevertheless, much of the information gained in this chapter is applicable outside of mathematics, as some of the examples will show. The relations to be considered here will be, for the most part, dyadic.

4.4.1 REFLEXIVE, SYMMETRICAL, AND TRANSITIVE RELATIONS

A few dyadic relations have the property of holding between anything and itself, provided that the thing bears the relation (or has the relation borne to it) at all. These are *reflexive relations*. In other words, R is a reflexive relation if and only if

$$(x)(y)(Rxy \supset Rxx \cdot Ryy)$$

The relation of being *the same size as* is reflexive; for if a thing is the same size as anything, it is the same size as itself. Another reflexive relation is *less than or equal to*; if an object is less than or equal to anything or has anything less than or equal to it, then it is less than or equal to itself.

It is not only of interest to know that a given relation has a given logical property, it is also important to know the consequences of having such properties. For example, a relation R is reflexive if and only if it is such that both

(1) $(x)[(\exists y)Rxy \supset Rxx]$

(2) $(y)[(\exists x)Rxy \supset Ryy]$

That reflexivity implies (1) may be shown by the following derivation:

1			$(x)(y)(Rxy \supset Rxx \cdot Ryy)$	P
2	x	$\triangle$		A
3			$(\exists y)Rxy$	A
4		y	Rxy	A
5			$(y)(Rxy \supset Rxx \cdot Ryy)$	1, UI
6			$Rxy \supset Rxx \cdot Ryy$	5, UI
7			$Rxx \cdot Ryy$	4, 6, MP
8			Rxx	7, S
9			Rxx	3, 4-8, EI
10			$(\exists y)Rxy \supset Rxx$	3-9, CP
11			$(x)(\exists y)Rxy \supset Rxx$	2-10, UG

That reflexivity implies (2) and is jointly implied by (1) and (2) is left to be demonstrated by the reader.

Reflexive relations are rare, but even rarer are *totally reflexive relations.* These are relations which hold between anything and itself (unconditionally); that is, a relation R is totally reflexive if and only if

$(x)Rxx$

Identity is an example par excellence of a totally reflexive relation, since $(x)(x = x)$. Similarity is another totally reflexive relation, for everything is similar to itself. Totally reflexive relations are of course reflexive, but the converse is not always true. To take an example from economics, anything that belongs to the same income group as anything else of course belongs to the same income group as itself. Thus, belonging to the same income group is reflexive. On the other hand, not everything belongs to an income group — mountains do not — so it is not the case that everything belongs to the same income group as itself.

Reflexive relations are much more common than totally reflexive ones, because they need not relate everything to something. A totally reflexive relation must relate everything to something — at least to itself — while a reflexive relation need only relate those things to themselves which it relates to anything at all. Thus a relation which relates nothing to anything — as the relation between x and y such that $x \neq x$ and $y \neq y$ — will be reflexive (trivially and uninterestingly), but not totally reflexive. Indeed, the reader may easily verify that

$(x)(y) - Rxy$

implies reflexivity and is inconsistent with total reflexivity.

Sometimes it is convenient to consider a relation as restricted to a particular class. Then it makes sense to say, for example, that R is reflexive or totally reflexive in a class F. More precisely, *R is reflexive in F* if and only if

$(x)(y)(Fx \cdot Fy \supset (Rxy \supset Rxx \cdot Ryy))$

and *R is totally reflexive in F* if and only if

$(x)(Fx \supset Rxx)$

All relations which are simply reflexive will be totally reflexive in some class F. Thus the reflexive relation of belonging to the same income group is totally reflexive in the class of wage earners; that is,

$(x)(x$ is a wage earner $\supset x$ belongs to the same income group as $x)$

The class of things which bear a relation R or have R borne to them is called the *field of R*, symbolized 'F_R'. In other words, x is in the field of R if and only if

$(\exists y)(Rxy \lor Ryx)$

A reflexive relation is totally reflexive in its field; that is,

$(x)(F_R x \supset Rxx)$

may be derived from the two premisses

$(x)(y)(Rxy \supset Rxx \cdot Ryy)$
$(x)(F_R x \equiv (\exists y)(Rxy \lor Ryx))$

(This is left as an exercise.) This shows that if one restricts one's universe to the field of a reflexive relation, one may treat it as if it were totally reflexive.

When mathematicians write, for example,

Less than or equal to is reflexive; that is, for all numbers x, $x \le x$

it appears as if they have confused total reflexivity with simple reflexivity. In fact, however, they have merely restricted their universe of discourse to the field of this relation and have taken advantage of its being totally reflexive in its field.

If the relation R is always reversible, that is, if

$(x)(y)(Rxy \supset Ryx)$

then it is a *symmetrical relation*. *Identity, of the same size, belonging to the same income group* are all symmetrical relations. So are *married to, sibling of*, and *compatriot of*. The relation *less than or equal to* is not symmetrical, however, for $1 \le 2$ but $-(2 \le 1)$.

The last example also shows that not all reflexive relations are symmetrical. Examples of totally reflexive relations which are not symmetrical are hard to find, but the rather artificial relation of x to y such that $x \ne x$ and $y \ne y$ furnishes one example. For

$(x)(y)(x \ne x \cdot y \ne y \supset y \ne y \cdot x \ne x)$

is a logical truth; so the relation is symmetrical; while

$(x)(x \ne x \cdot x \ne x)$

is a falsehood of identity theory; so the relation is not totally reflexive.

A relation R is symmetrical in the class F if and only if

$(x)(y)(Fx \cdot Fy \supset (Rxy \supset Ryx))$

It is easy to show that every symmetrical relation is symmetrical in any class F. However, the converse is not necessarily true. In a given class of people, everyone who loves a person may have that love returned by that person, yet *love* (in general) is not a symmetrical relation, as many a bitter lesson has taught us.

Relations which "pass on" from one thing to the next are called *transitive*. Metaphors aside, the relation R is transitive if and only if

$(x)(y)(z)(Rxy \cdot Ryz \supset Rxz)$

Less than or equal to, shorter than, less than, greater than, ancestor of, belonging to a lower social class than are all examples of transitive relations. *Less than*, moreover, is a transitive relation which is neither reflexive nor symmetrical. Identity, however, is (totally) reflexive, symmetrical, and transitive.

Relations which are reflexive, transitive, and symmetrical are called *equivalence relations* and are very important in mathematics. If R is an equivalence relation, then its field may be partitioned into mutually exclusive classes such that every member of each class bears R to every other member in the class, but to no member of any other class. These classes are known as *equivalence classes* with respect to the relation R. To give an example of how this may be applied, let us consider the problem of determining what an income group is. First we consider all the wage earners and determine their annual wages. The relation *makes the same annual wage* is reflexive, symmetrical, and transitive. Thus it divides its field into equivalence classes such that two wage earners belong to the same equivalence class if and only if they make the same annual wage. Thus we can define income groups as equivalence classes with respect to this relation. This way of defining income groups generates too many income groups to be very useful in social science. This is because a man who makes $8,000 per annum will be in a different income group from one who makes $8,001, and both from one who makes $7,999. Thus social scientists find it more useful to divide annual wages into ranges, for example, 0–$2,000; $2,001–$5,000; etc. Then income groups are defined as equivalence classes with respect to the equivalence relation *falls within the same annual-wage range*. Of course, the social scientist must determine the best way (for his purposes) to set the limits of his annual-wage ranges. This, however, is a problem falling outside of the domain of logic and cannot be solved by it.

Reflexive, symmetrical, and transitive relations have their opposites in irreflexive, asymmetrical, and intransitive relations. A relation R is *irreflexive* if and only if

$(x) - Rxx$

Distinctness and dissimilarity are irreflexive. A relation may also be irreflexive in a class F; that is,

$(x)(Fx \supset -Rxx)$

Less than is irreflexive in the class of numbers. The opposite of symmetry is *asymmetry*. A relation R is asymmetrical if and only if

$(x)(y)(Rxy \supset -Ryx)$

Less than is also asymmetrical. Moreover, R is asymmetrical in the class F if and only if

$(x)(y)(Fx \cdot Fy \supset (Rxy \supset -Ryx))$

If there is a class of people who do not love those in the class who love them, then *loves* is asymmetrical in that class. But *loves* is not in general asymmetrical because there are people who love each other. Indeed, *loves* could not be asymmetrical if everyone loved himself, for no asymmetrical relation is either reflexive or totally reflexive. A property related to asymmetry is *antisymmetry*. R is antisymmetrical if and only if

$(x)(y)(Rxy \cdot Ryx \supset x = y)$

This is a kind of weak asymmetry, for if two or more things belong to the field of the antisymmetrical relation R, then R will be asymmetrical with respect to distinct things and symmetrical only with respect to identical things. This follows because the antisymmetry of R is equivalent to

$(x)(y)(Rxy \cdot x \neq y \supset -Ryx)$

Less than or equal to is an antisymmetrical relation:

$(x)(y)(x \leq y \cdot x \neq y \supset -(y \leq x))$

Some relations, such as the prosaic *loves*, are neither symmetrical, asymmetrical, nor antisymmetrical. The antisymmetry of a relation R in a class F may be defined in the usual way.

A relation R is *intransitive* if and only if

$(x)(y)(z)(Rxy \cdot Ryz \supset -Rxz)$

and it is *intransitive in the class F* if and only if

$(x)(y)(z)(Fx \cdot Fy \cdot Fz \supset (Rxy \cdot Ryz \supset -Rxz))$

The relation *son of* is intransitive; no one is the son of his grandfather. In mathematics the relation between a square and its root is intransitive: $(x)(y)(z)(y = \sqrt{x} \cdot z = \sqrt{y} \supset z \neq \sqrt{x})$. Anthropologists have studied certain primitive societies which are divided into two groups, called moieties. Each member of such a society belongs to one of the two moieties and must choose his mate from the other. Since there are only two moieties, the relation *belong to a different moiety* must be intransitive in the class of people belonging to this society. For if a, b, and c belong to the society and a belongs to a different moiety from b and b belongs to a different moiety from c, then a and c belong to the same moiety.

It should be noticed that intransitivity, asymmetry, and antisymmetry are rather strong properties, and are not just negations of transitivity and symmetry. A relation such as *loves* is neither intransitive nor asymmetrical nor antisymmetrical. But, on the other hand, it is also not symmetrical or transitive. All these properties fail to apply to it. It is natural to confuse nonsymmetry with asymmetry and nontransitivity with intransitivity, but the confusion is as mistaken as confusing nonwhite with black.

The next two properties take us out of the reflexive, symmetrical, and transitive families. The first is the property of being *connected*. A relation R is connected if and only if it relates any two things in its field, that is, if and only if

$$(x)(y)(F_R x \cdot F_R y \supset (x \neq y \supset (Rxy \lor Ryx)))$$

Older than is an example of a connected relation, for of any two things that are older than or younger than something, one is older than the other. *The same size as* is not connected, because two things can be the same size as some other things and not both be of the same size. Being connected in a class is a useful notion. A relation R is connected in a class F just in case

$$(x)(y)(Fx \cdot Fy \supset (x \neq y \supset (Rxy \lor Ryx)))$$

The relation *less than* is connected in the class of whole numbers. Finally, a relation which is connected in every class is called *totally connected*. Thus R is totally connected if and only if

$$(x)(y)(x \neq y \supset (Rxy \lor Ryx))$$

The relation of distinctness is totally connected.

A relation may not only be connected; it may also be *strongly connected* in the sense that it not only relates any two distinct x and y in its field but also relates any x and y in its field, distinct or not. More precisely, R is strongly connected if and only if

$$(x)(y)(F_R x \cdot F_R y \supset (Rxy \lor Ryx))$$

The relation *older than or equal in age* is a strongly connected relation. Strong connectivity in a class F and total strong connectivity of R mean, respectively,

$$(x)(y)(Fx \cdot Fy \supset (Rxy \lor Ryx))$$
$$(x)(y)(Rxy \lor Ryx)$$

Less than or equal to is a ready example of a relation strongly connected in the class of whole numbers, but examples of totally strongly connected relations are hard to come by. An artificial one is the relation of x to y such that $x = y \cdot y = y$. Observe that strong connectivity (in F) implies reflexivity (in F). The same goes for the total versions of these relations.

At this point it is useful to summarize the properties of relations studied so far:

Reflexivity:	$(x)(y)(Rxy \supset Rxx \cdot Ryy)$
Total reflexivity:	$(x)Rxx$
Irreflexivity:	$(x) - Rxx$
Symmetry:	$(x)(y)(Rxy \supset Ryx)$
Asymmetry:	$(x)(y)(Rxy \supset -Ryx)$
Antisymmetry:	$(x)(y)(Rxy \cdot Ryx \supset x = y)$
Transitivity:	$(x)(y)(z)(Rxy \cdot Ryz \supset Rxz)$
Intransitivity:	$(x)(y)(z)(Rxy \cdot Ryz \supset -Rxz)$
Connectivity:	$(x)(y)(F_R x \cdot F_R y \supset (x \neq y \supset (Rxy \lor Ryx)))$
Total connectivity:	$(x)(y)(x \neq y \supset (Rxy \lor Ryx))$
Strong connectivity:	$(x)(y)(F_R x \cdot F_R y \supset (Rxy \lor Ryx))$
Total strong connectivity:	$(x)(y)(Rxy \lor Ryx)$
Equivalence relation:	Reflexive, symmetrical, and transitive
The field of R:	$F_R x \equiv (\exists y)(Rxy \lor Ryx)$

EXERCISES FOR SEC. 4.4.1

A. Give examples of relations which in the class of humans are

1. Symmetric
2. Reflexive
3. Transitive
4. Symmetric but not reflexive
5. Transitive but not symmetric
6. Transitive and irreflexive
7. Asymmetric and irreflexive
8. Antisymmetric
9. Connected
10. Strongly connected

B. Establish the following:

1. The reflexivity of R implies
   a. $(x)((\exists y)Rxy \supset Rxx)$
   b. $(y)((\exists x)Rxy \supset Ryy)$
   and is jointly implied by them.
2. '$(x)(y)-Rxy$' implies the reflexivity of R but is inconsistent with its total reflexivity.
3. Every reflexive relation is totally reflexive in its field.
4. Transitivity and symmetry imply reflexivity.
5. Transitivity, symmetry, and '$(x)(\exists y)Rxy$' imply total reflexivity.

6. Intransitivity implies irreflexivity.
7. A relation is both symmetric and asymmetric in a class only if the class is empty.
8. If R and S are equivalence relations, then so is the relation (R/S), where $(R/S)xy \equiv (\exists z)(Rxz \cdot Szy)$

4.4.2   ORDERING RELATIONS

Among the most useful relations in mathematics and science are those which determine orderings of classes of objects. The relation *less than*, for example, orders numbers in terms of greater and less; *taller than* orders people and other objects in terms of heights; *preferable to* orders choices in terms of their consequences. There are, however, several types of ordering. In one class no two students may have the same height; in this case they can be ordered so that, after the first student, each will be taller than the one before him. In another class, however, several students may have the same height, and then, though they can be ordered in terms of height, the ordering will be of a different kind from that of the first class. These various types of ordering may be characterized and studied in terms of the properties of relations introduced above.

The first types of orderings to be considered go under the name of orderings, but they need not impose any genuine order on the class they order. *Quasi-orderings* impose the least order, for a relation *quasi-orders a class F* if and only if it is transitive and reflexive in F. Some genuine ordering relations such as *less than or equal to*, which is transitive and reflexive in the class of whole numbers, are quasi-orderings. But identity quasi-orders every class, and this relation would hardly be said to impose "order". By requiring the ordering relations to satisfy a further condition, namely, antisymmetry, we get partial orderings. In other words, a relation *partially-orders a class F* if and only if it is transitive, reflexive, and antisymmetric in F. A class of things which are all related to at least one different member in the class by means of a partial ordering will be "lined up" by means of it. But a class can contain such subclasses and also "isolated" members and still be partially-ordered by the relation. In this case, it will be impossible to "line up" all its members. To take an example, let us consider a class A of the classes $\{1\}$, $\{1,2\}$, $\{1,2,3\}$, $\{1,2,3,4\}$, $\{6\}$, $\{7\}$. Then the subclass relation $\subseteq$ partially-orders A, for $\subseteq$ is transitive, (totally) reflexive, and antisymmetrical in A. Moreover, part of A can be "lined up" by the subclass relation, namely, $\{1\} \subseteq \{1,2\} \subseteq \{1,2,3\} \subseteq \{1,2,3,4\}$; but $\{6\}$ and $\{7\}$ are isolated, since they are not subclasses of any other members of A nor do they have other members of A as subclasses.

A little reflection reveals that the reason that part of A can be "lined up" by means of $\subset$ is that $\subseteq$ is (strongly) connected in this part. This leads us to the next kind of orderings, *simple orderings*. A relation is a *simple ordering of a class F* if and only if it is reflexive, antisymmetric, transitive, and connected in *F*. *Less than or equal to* is a simple ordering of the class of whole numbers. Identity which quasi- and partially-orders every class is not a simple ordering of any class, because it is not connected in any class. The subclass relation is a simple ordering of the class *B:* $\{1\}$, $\{1,2\}$, $\{1,2,3\}$, $\{1,2,3,4\}$.

By starting with irreflexive and transitive relations we shall obtain the *strict partial orderings* and *strict simple orderings*. (These are not types of partial and simple orderings.) A relation is *a strict partial ordering of a class* if and only if it is transitive and asymmetric in the class. *Less than*, for example, is a strict partial ordering of the whole numbers. Just as a simple ordering determines a "lineup" of the class it orders, so does a connected strict partial ordering. This type of ordering is called a strict simple ordering. Again, *less than* is a strict simple ordering of the whole numbers. Of course, not every strict partial ordering is a strict simple ordering, and here is an example in point: Suppose that the Smiths and Jones are two families that have no relatives in common. Suppose, further, that each family has exactly one male child in each generation, who in turn fathers a male child in the next generation. Then the relation *male descendant of* is a strict simple ordering of the males of the Smith family and also of the males of the Jones family, but it is not a strict simple ordering of the males who belong to either family. For the relation is not connected in the last class: no Smith is a male descendant of a Jones, and conversely.

The various ordering relations may now be summarized:

R is a quasi-ordering of *F* $\equiv$ *R* is transitive and reflexive in *F*.
R is a partial ordering of *F* $\equiv$ *R* is transitive, reflexive, and antisymmetric in *F*.
R Is a simple ordering of *F* $\equiv$ *R* is transitive, reflexive, antisymmetric, and connected in *F*.
R is a strict partial ordering of *F* $\equiv$ *R* is asymmetric and transitive in *F*.
R is a strict simple ordering of *F* $\equiv$ *R* is asymmetric, transitive, and connected in *F*.

Since a simple ordering is always a partial ordering, and a partial ordering is always a quasi-ordering, and since a strict simple ordering is always a strict partial ordering, the following tree diagram helps to picture the relative strength of the type of orderings considered:

Strict simple ordering	Simple ordering
	Partial ordering
Strict partial ordering	Quasi-ordering

Transitive

Often, mathematicians say that a given relation is a certain kind of ordering, without referring to the class it orders. In terms of the concepts developed here, these statements are best interpreted as to the effect that such relations are orderings (of the appropriate type) of their fields. Thus the statement

Less than is a strict simple ordering

means

Less than is a strict simple ordering of its field.

An ordering relation, however, does not order its field alone. It is not hard to show that if R orders its field in one of the ways considered here, then it orders every subclass of its field in the same way.† For example, *less than* is a simple ordering of the class of real numbers, which in most treatments of the real numbers is its field. Yet *less than* is also a simple ordering of the rational real numbers, the integral real numbers, and the odd and even real numbers.

EXERCISES FOR SEC. 4.4.2

A. Give examples of the following types of orderings of the class of humans:

1. Quasi-ordering
2. Partial ordering
3. Simple orderings

4. A quasi-ordering which is not a simple ordering
5. Strict partial orderings
6. Strict simple orderings

B. Establish the following:

1. If R is a partial ordering and A is a subclass of the field of R, then R partially-orders A.

2. If R and S are partial orderings, then so is the relation $(R \cap S)$, where $(R \cap S)xy \equiv Rxy \cdot Sxy$

3. If R is a strict simple ordering, then if A is a subclass of its field, then R is a strict simple ordering of A.

4. If R is a simple ordering, then the relation of x to y such that $Rxy \cdot x \neq y$ is a strict simple ordering.

4.4.3   CORRELATING RELATIONS

We turn now from ordering relations to correlating relations; these are the one-many, many-one, and one-one relations. A relation R *is a one-many relation* if and only if

---

†This remark does not apply to all types of orderings, in particular *dense* orderings R, that is, those such that $(x)(y)(Rxy \supset (\exists z)(Rxz \cdot Rzy))$. *Less than* is a dense ordering of the real numbers, but not of the integral real numbers.

$(x)(y)(z)(Rxy \cdot Rzy \supset x = z)$

A relation R *is one-many in the class F* if and only if

$(x)(y)(z)(Fx \cdot Fy \cdot Fz \supset (Rxy \cdot Rzy \supset x = z))$

In order words, a one-many relation is a relation which relates at most one thing to each thing.

This point can be better understood with the aid of a diagram. An arrow from one point to another will be used to indicate that the object at the tail of the arrow is related by the relation R to the one at the head of the arrow. Thus, for example, Rab, Rbd, Rca, Rbe may be represented by

In the case of a one-many relation, no two arrows lead to the same point; that is, we have no three distinct points x, y, and z such that

For if such a configuration were possible, we should have Rxy and Rzy, and hence $x = z$. But $x \neq z$ by assumption. On the other hand, *this* configuration is possible in the case of a one-many relation:

Notice that, given $x \neq y$, in this picture we cannot have Rxx. (Why?)

Some examples of one-many relations are *biological father of* and *square of*, for a person has one and only one biological father and a number has one and only one square. On the other hand, a man may father several children, and a number may be the square of two numbers; for example, $4 = 2^2 = (-2)^2$; so *child of* and *square root of* are not one-many relations. Identity is also a one-many relation, since every object has only one object identical with it.

Many-one relations are just the reverse of one-many relations. A relation R is many-one if and only if

$(x)(y)(z)(Ryx \cdot Ryz \supset x = z)$

In a many-one relation several things may be related to one thing; we can have

However, one thing cannot be related to several things by a many-one relation; we cannot have

as we can have in the case of a one-many relation.

Some examples of many-one relations are *square root of*, *citizen of*, and identity. A number can be the square root of at most one number, although numbers can have two square roots. A man can be a citizen of at most one country, although countries have many citizens.

A relation which is both a one-many and many-one is called a *one-one* relation. *Double of* is a one-one relation among numbers, since for all numbers x, y, z,

$$(x = 2y \cdot x = 2z \supset y = z) \cdot (y = 2x \cdot y = 2z \supset x = z)$$

Married to is a one-one relation among the populations of contemporary Europe. A final example is the relation *state governor of*, for every state has at most one governor, and one can be the governor of at most one state.

The *domain* of a relation R is the class of things which are related to something by R. The domain of R is denoted by the expression 'D_R'; thus

(1) $(x)(D_R x \equiv (\exists y)Rxy)$

The *range* of a relation R, denoted by 'R_R', is the class of things which have R borne to them. Thus

(2) $(x)(R_R x \equiv (\exists y)Ryx)$

From (1) and (2) it follows that

(3) $(x)(F_R x \equiv (D_R x \lor R_R x))$

that is, something belongs to the field of a relation if and only if it belongs to its domain or range. A many-one relation correlates a unique object in its range, with each object in its domain. (Distinct or identical objects may be correlated with distinct members of the domain.) A one-many relation, on the other hand, correlates a unique object in its domain with each object in its range. Finally, a one-one relation uniquely matches to objects in its domain and range. In contemporary European populations the relation *husband of* is one-one and matches each member of its domain—each husband—with a unique member of its image—his wife. The U.S. government is rapidly setting up a one-one relation between its citizens and a certain subclass of the nonnegative numbers by matching people one-to-one with social-security numbers.

Functions in mathematics may be construed as many-one relations. A mathematical function from the class A into the class B assigns each member A—its domain of arguments—a unique object in B—its range of values. In other words, a mathematical *function* from A into B is a many-one relation whose domain is A and whose range is B. When a function is a relation which is one-one, the function is called a one-one function. The function x^2 from the positive and negative integers into the positive integers is a many-one relation, but it is not a one-one function. The function $x + 1$ from the integers into the integers, however, is a one-one function.

Functions need not be confined to mathematics, nor need they be expressed algebraically. Thus the socioeconomic index is a function from the class of people into the class of numbers which assigns a unique number to each person according to his social and economic class. Similarly, the *freshman-class rank* is a function which assigns a unique positive integer to each member of the freshman class of a college. These and the other examples given in this chapter clearly indicate that the properties of relations which we have examined are not merely of purely logical interest, but also help to clarify the concepts of mathematics and the physical and social sciences.

EXERCISES FOR SEC. 4.4.3

A. Give examples of the following kinds of relations:
    1. A one-many relation whose field is the class of positive integers
    2. A one-one relation whose domain is the class of positive integers and whose range is the class of even positive integers
    3. A many-one relation which is asymmetric
    4. An equivalence relation which is one-one
    5. A function whose domain is the class of positive integers and whose range is the class of negative integers
B. Establish the following:
    1. Where $\breve{R}$ is the relation between x and y such that
        $\breve{R}xy \equiv Ryx$
        show that
        a. If R is one-many, $\breve{R}$ is many-one.
        b. R is a function if R is a one-one function.
    2. If R is transitive, connected in its field, and also one-many or many-one, then its field must contain less than three objects

3. If R is an equivalence relation and one-many, then everything in its field bears R only to itself.

4.5 FORMAL DEDUCTIVE THEORIES

When the structure of a scientific or mathematical theory is specified in a rather exact and rigid way, it is known as a *formal deductive theory*. Most scientific theories are not specified with enough exactness to count as formal, but several mathematical theories have been formalized, with surprisingly fruitful results. Not only have the theories been greatly clarified and simplified in the process, but formalization has also produced important information about the theories themselves which would have been otherwise unavailable. Other theories, especially in the social sciences, are still so undeveloped that their formalization is practically impossible, and probably inappropriate at this time. Yet formalizing them will depend upon clearing up some of their basic conceptual difficulties, and so here, at least, formalization functions as an important methodological goal. Thus, as both an ideal and a reality, formalization constitutes an important application of logic to science and mathematics.

4.5.1 THE ELEMENTS OF A FORMAL DEDUCTIVE THEORY

There are two parts to every formal deductive theory: a *formal language* and a class of expressions in this language called *theorems*. A formal language is one whose *well-formed formulas* (abbreviated wffs) can be recognized by a (mechanical) decision procedure. Intuitively, the wffs of a formal language are its sentences. Yet some formal languages have schemata for wffs; so the term 'wff' does not completely correspond to the term 'sentence'. The theorems of formal deductive theory are certain wffs of its language. There need be no decision procedure for recognizing them, but there must be a proof procedure for proving them. Thus quantification theory may be construed as a formal deductive theory, since there is a decision procedure for its wffs (schemata) and a proof procedure for its theorems (valid schemata). It is clear, then, that the deductive apparatus of a formal deductive theory is always completely and exactly specified.

The two requirements on formal deductive theories are not as easily satisfied as one might think. English, for example, is not a formal language. It is so constantly and rapidly changing that it is impossible to specify it completely. Furthermore, even if we avoid this difficulty by dealing with only the portions of English which are pretty stable, it is very doubtful that it can be mechanically determined whether or not something is a sentence of English.

On the other hand, the language of physics approximates a formal language, but the class of theorems of physics is undetermined, and no proof procedure for them is in the offing. Of course, certain parts of physics can be formalized, but this is because they are relatively clear and settled. Susceptibility to formalization is a mark of a mature theory.

There are several ways in which the language and theorems of a formal theory may be specified. But typically, the method is as follows: First, a class of symbols called the *alphabet* of the theory is given. An alphabet is usually finite, but may also be infinite. The wffs of theory are certain strings of symbols in its alphabet. Consequently, one must be able to determine mechanically whether a symbol belongs to the alphabet of a theory; otherwise one could not do the same for the wffs. If the alphabet is finite, then it can be simply listed, as is done when giving the alphabet of English. If it is infinite, then rules must be given for generating it, such as were given in an earlier chapter for generating infinitely many variables. Once the alphabet is given, the wffs may be specified directly as certain strings of symbols in the alphabet. Usually, however, it is more convenient to specify, first, other strings, such as statement letters, terms, or predicates, and then give rules for constructing wffs from these. In any case, since there must be a mechanical procedure for recognizing wffs, there will also have to be mechanical procedures for recognizing statement letters, terms, or predicates (if these are employed at all).

EXAMPLE: A formal language for the theory of densely ordered sets with neither first nor last elements (Theory A)

1. Alphabet
    a. Logical symbols: $-$, $\cdot$, $\vee$, $\supset$, $\equiv$, $\exists$, x, y, z, w, $=$
    b. Nonlogical predicate: $<$
    c. Punctuation symbols: (,),'
2. Terms
    a. Variables
        (1) 'x,' 'y,' 'z,' and 'w' are variables.
        (2) If α is a variable, so is α'.
        (3) An expression is a variable if and only if its being so follows from (1) and (2).
    b   All and only variables are terms.
3. Wffs
    a. If α and β are terms, then $(\alpha < \beta)$ and $(\alpha = \beta)$ are wffs.
    b. If S and W are wffs and α is a variable, $-S$, $(S \cdot W)$, $(S \vee W)$, $(S \supset W)$, $(S \equiv W)$, $(\alpha)S$, and $(\exists\alpha)S$ are wffs.
    c. An expression is a wff if and only if its being so follows from (1) and (2).

It is easily seen that one can mechanically decide whether any expression is in the alphabet, a term, a predicate, or a wff of this formal language.

After the wffs of a formal deductive theory have been specified, the theorems must be specified, too. There are several ways to do this any of which will produce a proof procedure. Most often, however, one first specifies a class of wffs called *axioms*. There may be finitely or infinitely many axioms, but one must be able to decide mechanically whether or not a wff is an axiom. Thus, because identity theory has one axiom, '$(x)(x = x)$', one can always mechanically determine whether a wff of identity theory is an axiom. On the other hand, identity theory could have been formulated so as to have infinitely many axioms by making every wff of the form $v = v$, where v is a variable, an axiom. Again, one could mechanically decide whether something is an axiom.

After the axioms have been specified, it is usual to lay down rules of inference or generating further wffs from the axioms. Although there are some exceptions, it is customary to take only logical rules of inference as the rules of inference of a formal deductive theory. Whatever rules of inference are used, it must be possible to decide mechanically whether a given wff follows from others by means of a given rule. A *proof* in a formal deductive theory then consists of a finite sequence of wffs, each of which is either an axiom or follows from previous wffs in the sequence by one of the rules of inference. Consequently, given any sequence of wffs, one can mechanically determine whether or not it is a proof. The *theorems* of a formal theory are the last wffs in any proof. Since one cannot in general determine mechanically whether a given wff has a proof, there need not be a decision procedure for the theorems of a formal deductive theory. On the other hand, every formal deductive theory whose theorems are specified in terms of axioms and rules of inference will have a proof procedure. One very inefficient proof procedure consists in systematically enumerating all sequences of wffs and checking each to see if they are proofs of the wff to be proved. If the wff is a theorem, its proof will eventually turn up. On the other hand, if the wff is not a theorem, we shall not be able at any given moment to distinguish it mechanically from a theorem whose proof has not yet turned up. Thus a proof procedure need not yield a decision procedure. Of course, there are more refined and efficient proof procedures for formal deductive theories than the one just described, and some formal deductive theories, such as truth-function theory, even have decision procedures for their theorems.

EXAMPLES. Three versions of truth-function theory.

Version 1: Formal language: The wffs are TFS.

Theorems: All and only valid TFS are theorems.

Version 2: Formal language: same as version 1.

Theorems: Every wff which can be proved by means of the rules of inference stated earlier in this book.

Version 3: Formal language: same as version 1.

Theorems:
a. Axioms. All wffs of the forms

$S \supset (W \supset S)$
$(S \supset (W \supset E)) \supset ((S \supset W) \supset (S \supset E))$
$(-S \supset -W) \supset (W \supset S)$

b. Rules of inference
   1 Modus ponens
   2 Every wff $(S \lor W)$ may be interchanged with $(-S \supset W)$, and conversely.
   3 Every wff $(S \cdot W)$ may be interchanged with $-(S \supset -W)$, and conversely.
   4 Every wff $(S = W)$ may be interchanged with $((S \supset W) \cdot (W \supset S))$, and conversely.

Comments: First, notice that all three versions have a formal language, because there is a decision procedure for recognizing TFS. Second, there is a decision procedure for recognizing the theorems of version 1, and this also furnishes a proof procedure. Third, since one can always enumerate and check the proofs of versions 2 and 3, there are proof procedures for these versions. Fourth, only version 3 specifies its theorems in terms of axioms (of which there are infinitely many) and rules of inference. Finally — and the proof of this is beyond the scope of this book — all three versions have the same class of theorems, namely, the class of valid TFS. Thus there is a decision procedure for the theorems of all three versions.

Although truth-function theory, quantification theory, and identity theory can be presented as formal deductive theories, most formal deductive theories are not purely logical and deal with some nonlogical concepts and have some nonlogical theorems. It is usual to specify the theorems of these theories by merely listing their nonlogical axioms and letting their logical rules of inference be understood. The understood rules are known as the *underlying logic* of the theory in question. In most theories the underlying logic is quantification theory, in many others it is identity theory (which includes quantification theory).

EXAMPLE. Theory A (continued)

4. Underlying logic: identity theory

5.   Nonlogical axioms

Axiom 1. $(x)(y)(z)(x < y \cdot y < z \supset x < z)$

Axiom 2. $(x)(y)(x < y \supset -(y < x))$

Axiom 3. $(x)(y)(x \neq y \supset (x < y \vee y < z))$

Axiom 4. $(x)(y)(x < y \supset (\exists x)(x < z \cdot z < y))$

Axiom 5. $(x)(\exists y)(\exists x)(x < y \cdot z < x)$

Since identity theory is the underlying logic of this theory, proofs in it may be written as derivations in identity theory in which Axioms 1 to 4 may be written at will. Only one example proof will be given now, since we shall study this theory later in some detail.

EXAMPLE: Proof of '$x < y \supset x \neq y$'.

Proof:

1	$x < y$	A
2	$x = y$	A
3	$(x)(y)(x < y \supset -(y < x))$	Axiom 2
4	$(y)(x < y \supset -(y < x)$	3, UI
5	$x < y \supset -(y < x)$	4, UI
6	$-(y < x)$	1, 5, MP
7	$-(y < y)$	2, 6, SI
8	$y < y$	1, 2, SI
9	$x \neq y$	2-8, IP
10	$x < y \supset x \neq y$	1-9, CP

EXERCISES FOR SEC. 4.5.1

A.   Formalize the theory of the betweenness relation (for points on a line). The theory is based upon one three-place nonlogical predicate 'B', which means ① is between ② and ③'. Its formal language will consist of the set of statements that can be formed from 'B', using the notation of identity theory. Its underlying logic is identity theory, and its axioms are formalizations of the following statements:

1.   If x is between y and z, then all three are distinct for all x, y, and z.

2.   If x is between y and z, and z is between y and w, then x is between y and w, for all x, y, z, and w.

3.   Between any distinct x and y there is a z.

4.   Every x is between some y and z.

5.   For any distinct x and y, there is a z such that z is between x and y or between y and x.

B.   Using version 3 of truth-function theory, prove

1. $(p \supset (q \supset p)) \supset ((p \supset q) \supset (p \supset p))$

2. $(p \supset q) \supset (p \supset p)$
3. $(p \supset (q \supset p)) \supset (p \supset p)$
4. $\bar{p} \supset \bar{p}$
5. $p \vee \bar{p}$

4.5.2 PROPERTIES OF FORMAL DEDUCTIVE THEORIES

After a theory has been formalized, several interesting and important questions can be asked about it. Three of the most important of these are the questions of its *consistency, completeness,* and *decidability*. Let us discuss consistency first. A formal deductive theory is said to be consistent if and only if for no wff W are both W and $-W$ theorems. If a theory is not consistent and contains a modicum of truth-function theory in its underlying logic, then every wff of its language is a theorem. Most scientific theories are designed as instruments for determining the truth about a given subject matter, and their theorems are supposed to be true statements about this subject. However, in an inconsistent theory, at least one false statement — since one of W or $-W$ is false — will be a theorem. It may be even worse, for in most inconsistent theories, every true and false statement of its language will be a theorem, with the result that the theory will be incapable of segregating truth from falsity. Thus consistency is the *sine qua non* of an acceptable scientific or mathematical theory.

Completeness and decidability are not as important as consistency. A formal deductive theory is *complete* if and only if, for every closed wff W, either W or $-W$ is a theorem. An inconsistent theory (with a little logic) is trivially complete because all its wffs are theorems. This type of complete theory is uninteresting; the interesting ones are those which are both consistent and complete. Such theories have such a large stock of theorems that no more can be added without engendering inconsistency. Intuitively, a consistent and complete theory contains every truth that can be expressed in its language.

When a theory contains schemata, then the concept of completeness just introduced is not really appropriate. Truth-function theory is not complete in this sense because neither 'p' nor '$\bar{p}$' is a theorem. Indeed, no invalid and consistent TFS nor its negation is a theorem. On the other hand, it was pointed out earlier that both quantification theory and truth-function theory are complete *in the sense that* all valid TFS and QS are theorems. (The same holds for identity theory.) This sort of completeness is known as semantical completeness.

Many very important theories are incomplete, although they do not contain schemata. This important discovery is due to Kurt Gödel. In 1931, Gödel proved that elementary-number theory — and any theory which contains it—is incomplete if it is consistent. Moreover, such a theory is *incompletable* in the following sense: it is impossible to enlarge its class of theorems so as to obtain a consistent and complete formal deductive theory. If a formal deductive theory is consistent and incomplete, then there will be a wff W such that neither W nor $-W$ is a theorem. Thus one of them may be added as a new axiom without destroying the consistency of the theory. Gödel showed that for a very important class of theories this process can be extended indefinitely. The import of this result should not be underestimated. As most branches of science and mathematics use elementary-number theory, it is impossible to construct consistent and complete formal deductive theories for most branches of science and mathematics.

Some theories are complete, but their scope is usually rather limited. Elementary-number theory *without* multiplication, for example, is complete. Since most consistent and important theories will be incomplete, completeness is not a necessary condition of an adequate theory.

The last property in our list is decidability. A formal deductive theory is decidable just in case there is a decision procedure for recognizing its theorems. Many important formal deductive theories are not decidable. Quantification theory and elementary-number theory are two outstanding examples. Moreover, decidability and completeness are closely related. As long as a theory contains quantification theory in its underlying logic, it is complete only if it is decidable. This may be seen as follows: We may restrict ourselves to closed wffs, since an open wff is a theorem if and only if its universal closure is, provided that the theory contains quantification theory in its underlying logic. Every formal deductive theory has a proof procedure; so, to decide whether a closed wff W is a theorem, we apply the proof procedure to both W and $-W$. Since the theory is complete, a proof of one of them will eventually turn up, and this decides one question. (Here it is assumed that the theory is consistent, so that W is a theorem if and only if $-W$ is not. If the theory is not consistent, the decision procedure is simply: when asked whether a wff is a theory, answer 'yes'!)

Some decidable formal deductive theories are not complete. Truth-function theory is an example, although the present concept of completeness is not fully appropriate here. A more interesting example is the following Theory T. The formal language of Theory T is simply the formal language of Theory A, given in Sec. 4.5.1. The theorems of Theory T, however, are just those which may be obtained by substitution in valid TFS. Thus, among the theorems of Theory T, we have

$x < y \supset (x < y \lor x = y)$
$x < y \lor -(x < y)$

Yet the following are not theorems of Theory T:

$x < y \supset -(y < x)$
$x < y \supset x \neq y$

Since one can mechanically determine whether a wff of Theory T can be obtained by substitution in a valid TFS, Theory T is decidable. Yet Theory T is not complete. Of course, some theories are both complete and decidable — Theory A is an example, although proving this takes us beyond this book.

We have, then, some indication of the important things that can be discovered about the consistency, completeness, and decidability of formal deductive theories. Unfortunately, the proofs of these results lie byond the scope of this book. Yet it should be clear that the study of formal deductive theories and their properties is one of the very exciting fields of logic. Not only has it yielded several outstanding results about mathematics, such as Gödel's theorem on the incompleteness of elementary-number theory, but it still contains many interesting and unresolved problems.

EXERCISES FOR SEC. 4.5.2

A. The theory of the betweenness relation can be "translated" into Theory A by replacing all occurrences of 'B ①②③' by '②$<$①$\cdot$①$<$③'. This translation converts the axioms of the theory into theorems of Theory A. Since the theories have the same underlying logic, this translation also converts the theorems of the former into theorems of the latter. Establish the following:

1. If Theory A is consistent, then so is the theory of the betweennesss relation.

2. The following is not a theorem of the theory of the betweenness relation: $(x)(y)(z)(Bxyz \supset Bxzy)$.

3. The theory of the betweenness relation is decidable. [*Hint:* Theory A is decidable.]

B. The theory of the betweenness relation can be extended by adding as a new axiom $(x)(y)(z)(Bxyz \supset Bxzy)$

Then, however, a new "translation" into Theory A is needed. In this instance 'B' is translated as

②$<$①$\cdot$①$<$③$\lor$③$<$①$\cdot$①$<$②.

Establish the following:

1. The translation converts theorems of the extended theory into theorems of Theory A.

2. If Theory A is consistent, so is the extended theory.

3. Given the consistency of Theory A, the original theory of the betweenness relation is not complete because

$(x)(y)(z)(Bxyz \supset Bxzy)$
$-(x)(y)(z)(Bxyz \supset Bxzy)$

both fail to be theorems.

4.5.3 THREE FORMAL DEDUCTIVE THEORIES

In this section we shall consider three examples of formal deductive theories. Two are drawn from mathematics, and one from social science. We shall not only describe these theories but also prove several of the theorems of each. For this reason, it is first convenient to consider a few ways for "speeding up" these proofs.

Theorems are proved in a sequential order, many of the earlier theorems being applied in the proofs of later ones. As matters stand, every time a theorem is applied in the proof of another, it is necessary to prove it within this proof. Yet if the theorem in question has already been proved, this is surely a waste of time, energy, and paper. It is much simpler just to write the theorem in question as a step in the proof and give as its reason a reference to the place in which its proof may be found. To be exact, each theorem is assigned a number when it is proved. Then a theorem may be written as a step in the proof of a later theorem, and its number given as its reason. Thus Theorem 7, for example, may be written as a step in the proof of Theorem 8, and 'Theorem 7' written as its reason.

The next simplification concerns universal instantiation. Let us spare ourselves those tedious portions of derivations, such as

1	$(x)(y)(z)(w)Fxyzw$	P
2	$(y)(z)(w)Fxyzw$	1, UI
3	$(z)(w)Fxyzw$	2, UI
4	$(w)Fxyzw$	3, UI
5	$Fxyzw$	4, UI

which involve repeated applications of universal instantiations to wffs originating from the same universal quantification. To avoid such repetitions, we can carry out the whole sequence of applications of universal instantiation at once. This condenses the previous derivation to, simply,

1	$(x)(y)(z)(w)Fxyzw$	P
2	$Fxyzw$	1, UI

A quite similar situation occurs with universal generalization. Here we have the problem of repetitious sequences of applications of universal generalization, as in the derivation

1	$(x)(y)(z)(w)Fxyzw$				P
2	w	$\triangle$			A
3		z	$\triangle$		A
4			y	$\triangle$	A
5				x	$\triangle$	A
6					$Fxyzw$	1, UI

7	$\mid$ $\mid$ $\mid$ $(x)Fxyzw$	5-6, UG
8	$\mid$ $\mid$ $(y)(x)Fxyzw$	4-7, UG
9	$\mid$ $(z)(y)(x)Fxyzw$	3-8, UG
10	$(w)(z)(y)(x)Fxyzw$	2-9, UG

Again, the simplest way is to carry out all these applications at once, thus telescoping the last derivation to

1	$(x)(y)(z)(w)Fxyzw$	P
2	w, z, y, x $\mid$ $\triangle$	A
3	$\mid$ $Fxyzw$	1, UI
4	$(w)(z)(y)(x)Fxyzw$	2-3, UG

These three conventions, using previously proved theorems and condensing applications of universal instantiation and generalization, will help simplify markedly our proofs of theorems in formal deductive theories. Of course, further conventions for shortening proofs are possible, and anyone making a pastime of proving theorems in formal deductive theories will want to invent and use them. It is essential, however, that whatever conventions one uses, completely unabbreviated proofs be suppliable upon demand.

4.5.3.1   THE THEORY OF DENSELY ORDERED SETS
WITH NEITHER FIRST NOR LAST ELEMENT

The first example of formal deductive theory which will be considered is the theory of densely ordered sets with neither first nor last (Theory A, for short). The theory is applicable to the fields of strict simple orderings which are dense and which have no first or last element (with respect to the ordering). The field of an ordering is dense if and only if, between any two of its members, there is a third. The theory is applicable to the ordering of the rational numbers, for example, since it is strict, simple, and dense, and there is no greatest or least rational number. The theory does not apply to the integers, however, because they are not densely ordered.

The formal language of Theory A has already been specified. It involves the predicates '$=$' (for identity) and '$<$' (for 'less than') and composes its statements from these and variables, quantifiers, and truth-functions. Its underlying logic is identity theory. Although its axioms have already been listed, it will not hurt to recall them here:

Axiom 1. $(x)(y)(x < y \supset -(y < x))$

Axiom 2. $(x)(y)(z)(x < y \cdot y < z \supset x < z)$

Axiom 3. $(x)(y)(x \neq y \supset (x < y \lor y < x))$

Axiom 4. $(x)(y)(x < y \supset (\exists z)(x < z \cdot z < y))$

Axiom 5. $(x)(\exists y)(\exists z)(x < y \cdot z < x)$

These may be written as steps in proofs at will. Now let us prove some theorems.

THEOREM 1. $(x)(y)(x < y \supset x \neq y)$

Proof:

1	x, y	$\triangle$	A
2		$x < y$	A
3		$x = y$	A
4		$(x)(y)(x < y \supset -(y < x))$	Axiom 1
5		$x < y \supset -(y < x)$	4, UI
6		$-(y < x)$	2, 5, MP
7		$-(y < y)$	3, 6, SI
8		$y < y$	2, 3, SI
9		$x \neq y$	3-8, IP
10		$x < y \supset x \neq y$	2-9, CP
11		$(x)(y)(x < y \supset x \neq y)$	1-10, UG

THEOREM 2. $(x) - (x < x)$ Exercise

THEOREM 3. $(\exists x)(\exists y)(x < y)$

Proof:

1		$(x)(\exists y)(\exists z)(x < y \cdot z < x)$	Axiom 5
2		$(\exists y)(\exists z)(x < y \cdot z < x)$	1, UI
3	y	$(\exists z)(x < y \cdot z < x)$	A
4	z	$x < y \cdot z < x$	A
5		$x < y$	4, S
6		$(\exists y)(x < y)$	5, EG
7		$(\exists x)(\exists y)(x < y)$	6, EG
8		$(\exists x)(\exists y)(x < y)$	3, 4-7, EI
9		$(\exists x)(\exists y)(x < y)$	2, 3-8, EI

THEOREM 4. $(\exists x)(\exists y)(x \neq y)$ Exercise

THEOREM 5. $(x)(\exists y)(x < y)$ Exercise

THEOREM 6. $(x)(\exists y)(y < x)$ Exercise

THEOREM 7. $-(\exists x)(y)(x \neq y \supset y < x)$

Proof:

1		$(\exists x)(y)(x \neq y \supset y < x)$	A
2	x	$(y)(x \neq y \supset y < x)$	A
3		$(x)(\exists y)(x < y)$	Theorem 5
4		$(\exists y)(x < y)$	3, UI
5	y	$x < y$	A

6	$(x)(y)(x < y \supset x \neq y)$	Theorem 1
7	$x < y \supset x \neq y$	6, UI
8	$x \neq y$	5, 7, MP
9	$x \neq y \supset y < x$	2, UI
10	$y < x$	8, 9, MP
11	$(x)(y)(x < y \supset -(y < x))$	Axiom 1
12	$x < y \supset -(y < x)$	11, UI
13	$-(y < x)$	5, 12, MP
14	$y < x \lor -(\exists x)(\exists y)(x \neq y)$	10, add
15	$-(\exists x)(\exists y)(x \neq y)$	13, 14, DS
16	$-(\exists x)(\exists y)(x \neq y)$	4, 5-15, EI
17	$-(\exists x)(\exists y)(x \neq y)$	1, 2-16, EI
18	$(\exists x)(\exists y)(x \neq y)$	Theorem 4
19	$-(\exists x)(y)(x \neq y \supset y < x)$	1-18, IP

THEOREM 8. $-(\exists x)(y)(x \neq y \supset x < y)$ Exercise

THEOREM 9. $(x)(\exists y)(\exists z)(x < y \cdot y < z)$ Exercise

THEOREM 10. $(x)(\exists y)(\exists z)(z < y \cdot y < x)$ Exercise

THEOREM 11. $(x) - (\exists ! \, y)(x < y)$ Exercise

THEOREM 12. $(x)(y)[(z)(z < x \equiv z < y) \supset x = y]$

Proof:

1	x, y $\triangle$	A
2	$(z)(z < x \equiv z < y)$	A
3	$x \neq y$	A
4	$(x)(y)(x \neq y \supset (x < y \lor y < x))$	Axiom 3
5	$x \neq y \supset (x < y \lor y < x)$	4, UI
6	$x < y \lor y < x$	3, 5, MP
7	$x < y$	A
8	$x < x \equiv x < y$	2, UI
9	$x < x$	7, 8, MPB
10	$(x) - (x < x)$	Theorem 2
11	$-(x < x)$	10, UI
12	$-(x < y)$	7-11, IP
13	$y < x$	6, 12, DS
14	$y < x \equiv y < y$	2, UI
15	$y < y$	13, 14, MPB
16	$(x) - (x < x)$	Theorem 2
17	$-(y < y)$	16, UI
18	$-(x \neq y)$	3-17, IP
19	$x = y$	18, DNE
20	$(z)(z < x \equiv z < y) \supset x = y$	2-19, CP
21	$(x)(y)[(z)(z < x \equiv z < y) \supset x - y]$	1-20, UG

THEOREM 13. $(x)(y)[(z)(z < x \supset z < y) \supset (x = y \lor x < y)]$ Exercise

THEOREM 14. $(x)(y)[x \neq y \supset (\exists z)((x < z \cdot z < y) \lor (y < z \cdot z < x))]$ Exercise

THEOREM 15. $(\exists x)(\exists y)(\exists z)(x \neq y \cdot y \neq z \cdot x \neq z)$ Exercise

THEOREM 16. $(x)(y)(x < y \supset -(\exists ! z)(x < z \cdot z < y))$ Exercise

THEOREM 17. $(x)(y)(z)(x < z \cdot y < z \supset (\exists w)(x < w \cdot y < w \cdot w < z))$ Exercise

THEOREM 18. $(x)(y)(x = y \supset -(\exists z)(x < z \cdot z < y))$ Exercise

4.5.3.2 THE THEORY OF GROUPS (THEORY B)

A group consists of four things: a class of objects (the members of the group); a function which assigns a member of the class to every ordered pair of members of the class (symbolized here by '+'); a function, called the *inverse function*, whose domain and range are the class in question (symbolized here by '*'); and a member of the class, called the *unit* (symbolized here by 'u'). Furthermore, for all x, y, and z in the group, the following must be true:

(1) $(x + y) + z = x + (y + z)$ (associativity of '+')
(2) $x + u = x$ (existence of a unit)
(3) $x + x^* = u$ (existence of an inverse)

The positive and negative integers form a group with respect to addition. For if '$x + y$' is interpreted as the sum of x and y, 'u' as 0, and 'x^*' as $-x$, then (1), (2), and (3) are true for all integers. The positive integers are not a group with respect to addition, however, for there is no interpretation of '*' which will make (3) true in this universe; or as mathematicians say, inverses do not exist for each positive integer.

    A formal language for the theory of groups may be specified as follows:

1. Alphabet:
    a. Logical symbols: $x, y, z, w, -, \cdot, \lor, \supset, =, \exists, =$
    b. Nonlogical symbols: $*, +, u$
    c. Punctuation symbols: $(,),'$
2. Terms
    a. Variables
        (1) 'x', 'v', 'z', and 'w' are variables.
        (2) If α is a variable, so is α'.
        (3) An expression is variable if and only if its being so follows from (1) and (2).
    b. Terms
        (1) Every variable is a term.
        (2) 'u' is a term.

    (3)   If α and β are terms, so are α^* and $(\alpha + \beta)$.

    (4)   An expression is a term if and only if its being so follows from (1), (2), and (3).

3. Wffs

    a. If α and β are terms, then $(\alpha = \beta)$ is a wff.

    b. If S and W are wffs and α is a variable, then $-S$, $(S \cdot W)$, $(S \lor W)$, $(S \supset W)$, $(S \equiv W)$, $(\alpha)S$, and $(\exists \alpha)S$ are wffs.

    c. An expression is a wff if and only if its being so follows from (a) and (b).

When no unclarity will arise, some parentheses will be omitted from wffs; thus '$x = y + z$' will be written in place of '$(x = (y + z))$'.

    The theorems of the theory of groups may now be characterized.

4. Underlying logic: identity theory

5. Axioms

    Axiom 1. $(x)(y)(z)((x + y) + z = x + (y + z))$

    Axiom 2. $(x)(x + u = x)$

    Axiom 3. $(x)(x + x^* = u)$

Unlike Theory A, the theory of groups is not decidable. Moreover, the proofs of some of its theorems are far from easy. The reader may verify this by trying to prove them before looking at the proofs given below.

THEOREM 1. $(x)(y)(z)(x + z = y + z \supset x = y)$

Proof:	1	x, y', w	$\triangle$	A
	2		$x + w = y' + w$	A
	3		$(x)(x = x)$	AI
	4		$(x + w) + w^* = (x + w) + w^*$	3, UI
	5		$(x + w) + w^* = (y' + w) + w^*$	2, 4, SI
	6		$(x)(y)(z)((x + y) + z = x + (y + z))$	Axiom 1
	7		$(x + w) + w^* = x + (w + w^*)$	6, UI
	8		$x + (w + w^*) = (y' + w) + w^*$	5, 7, SI
	9		$(x)(x + x^* = u)$	Axiom 3
	10		$w + w^* = u$	9, UI
	11		$x + u = (y' + w) + w^*$	8, 10, SI
	12		$(x)(x + u = x)$	Axiom 2
	13		$x + u = x$	12, UI
	14		$x = (y' + w) + w^*$	11, 13, SI
	15		$(y' + w) + w^* = y' + (w + w^*)$	6, UI
	16		$x = y' + (w + w^*)$	14, 15, SI
	17		$x = y' + u$	16, 10, SI
	18		$y' + u = y'$	12, UI

19	$\quad\vert\quad\vert\quad x = y'$	17, 18, SI
20	$\quad\vert\quad x + w = y' + w \supset x = y'$	2-19, CP
21	$(x)(y)(z)(x + z = y + z \supset x = y)$	1-20, UG

THEOREM 2. $(x)(u + x = x)$

Proof:

1 $\vert w$	$\triangle$	A
2	$(x)(y)(z)((x + y) + z = x + (y + z))$	Axiom
3	$(u + w) + w^* = u + (w + w^*)$	2, UI
4	$(x)(x + x^* = u)$	Axiom 3
5	$w + w^* = u$	4, UI
6	$(u + w) + w^* = u + u$	3, 5, SI
7	$(x)(x + u = x)$	Axiom 2
8	$u + u = u$	7, UI
9	$(u + w) + w^* = u$	6, 8, SI
10	$(x)(x = x)$	AI
11	$w + w^* = w + w^*$	10, UI
12	$u = w + w^*$	11, 5, SI
13	$(u + w) + w^* = w + w^*$	9, 12, SI
14	$(x)(y)(z)(x + z = y + z \supset x = y)$	Theorem 1
15	$(u + w) + w^* = w + w^* \supset u + w = w$	14, UI
16	$u + w = w$	15, 13, MP
17	$(x)(u + x = x)$	1-16, UG

THEOREM 3. $(x)(x + u = u + x)$ Exercise

THEOREM 4. $(y)[(x)(x + y = x) \supset y = u]$ Exercise

THEOREM 5. $(x)(x^* + x = u)$

Proof:

1 $\vert w$	$\triangle$	A
2	$(x)(y)(z)((x + y) + z = x + (y + z))$	Axiom 1
3	$(w^* + w) + w^* = w^* + (w + w^*)$	2, UI
4	$(x)(x + x^* = u)$	Axiom 3
5	$w + w^* = u$	4, UI
6	$(w^* + w) + w^* = w^* + u$	5, 3, SI
7	$(x)(x + u = u + x)$	Theorem 3
8	$w^* + u = u + w^*$	7, UI
9	$(w^* + w) + w^* = u + w^*$	6, 8, SI
10	$(x)(y)(z)(x + z = y + z \supset x = y)$	Theorem 1
11	$(w^* + w) + w^* = u + w^* \supset w^* + w = u$	10, UI
12	$w^* + w = u$	11, 9, MP
13	$(x)(x^* + x = u)$	1-12, UG

THEOREM 6. $(x)(x + x^* = x^* + x)$ Exercise

THEOREM 7. $(x)(y)(z)(z + x = z + y \supset x = y)$ Exercise

THEOREM 8. $(x)(\exists ! y)(x + y = x)$ Exercise

THEOREM 9. $(\exists ! y)(x)(x + y = x)$ Exercise

THEOREM 10. $(x)(\exists ! y)(x + y = u)$ Exercise

THEOREM 11. $(x)[(x^{*})^{*} = x]$ Exercise

THEOREM 12. $(x)(y)(\exists ! z)(x = y + z)$ Exercise

THEOREM 13. $(x)(y)(\exists ! z)(x = z + y)$ Exercise

THEOREM 14. $(x)(y)[x \neq y \supset (\exists z)(x = y + z \cdot -(y)(y + z = y))]$ Exercise

THEOREM 15. $(x)(y)[(\exists z)(z \neq u \cdot x = y + z) \supset x \neq y]$ Exercise

4.5.3.3 KINSHIP THEORY (THEORY C)

The next theory is not one which scientists have actually developed. It is just an artificially constructed theory which is supposed to illustrate how formal deductive theories might be used in the social sciences. The theory is called *kinship theory* because it is supposed to be a systematization of some of the truths about the European and American kinship system. The language of the theory is constructed from logical symbols, variables, quantifiers, '=', and the two nonlogical symbols 'P' and 'M'. The symbol 'P' is short for 'parent of', and 'M' is short for 'male'. Thus '$Pxy \cdot Mx$' means 'x is a parent of y and x is a male'. The actual construction of the language of kinship theory is left as an exercise.

Kinship theory has identity theory as its underlying logic. In addition to its underlying logic, kinship theory also has the following axioms:

Axiom 1. $(x)(y)(Pxy \supset -Pyx)$

Axiom 2. $(x)(y)(z)(Pxy \cdot Pyz \supset -Pxz)$

Axiom 3. $(x)(\exists ! y)(Pyx \cdot My)$

Axiom 4. $(x)(\exists ! y)(Pyx \cdot -My)$

The theorems of kinship theory to be given now are all quite simple. The theory's power and usefulness will become apparent later, when it is supplemented with definitions of other kinship terms.

THEOREM 1. $(x) - Pxx$ Exercise

THEOREM 2. $(x)(y)(Pxy \supset x \neq y)$ Exercise

THEOREM 3. $(x)(y)(Pxy \supset -(\exists z)(Pxz \cdot Pzy))$ Exercise

THEOREM 4. $(x)(y)Mx \cdot My \cdot x \neq y \supset -(\exists z)(Pxz \cdot Pyz)$

Proof:					
1	x,y		$\triangle$		A
2				$Mx \cdot My \cdot x \neq y$	A
3				$(\exists z)(Pxz \cdot Pyz)$	A
4			z	$Pxz \cdot Pyz$	A
5				$(x)(\exists ! y)(Pyx \cdot My)$	Axiom 3
6				$(\exists ! y)(Pyz \cdot My)$	5, UI
7				$(\exists y)[Pyz \cdot My \cdot (x)(Pxz \cdot Mx \supset y = x)]$	unabbreviation
8			w	$Pwz \cdot Mw \cdot (x)(Pxz \cdot Mx \supset w = x)$	A
9				$(x)(Pxz \cdot Mx \supset w = x)$	8, S
10				$Pxz \cdot Mx \supset w = x$	9, UI
11				$Mx \cdot My$	2, S
12				Mx	11, S
13				Pxz	4, S
14				$Pxz \cdot Mx$	12, 13, PC
15				$w = x$	14, 10, MP
16				$Pyz \cdot My \supset w = y$	9, UI
17				Pyz	4, S
18				My	11, S
19				$Pyz \cdot My$	17, 18, PC
20				$w = y$	19, 16, MP
21				$x = y$	20, 15, SI
22				$x = y$	7, 8-21, EI
23				$x = y$	3, 4-22, EI
24				$x \neq y$	2, S
25				$-(\exists z)(Pxz \cdot Pyz)$	3-24, IP
26				$Mx \cdot My \cdot x \neq y \supset -(\exists z)Pxz \cdot Pyz)$	2-25, CP
27				$(x)(y)Mx \cdot My \cdot x \neq y \supset -(\exists z)(Pxz \cdot Pyz)$	1-26, UG

THEOREM 5. $(x)(y)[-Mx \cdot -My \cdot x \neq y \supset -(\exists z)(Pxz \cdot Pyz)]$ Exercise

THEOREM 6. $(x)(y)(z)(Pxz \cdot Pyz \supset (x = y \lor Mx \cdot -My \lor -Mx \cdot My))$

        Exercise

THEOREM 7. $(x)(\exists y)(\exists z)(Pyx \cdot Pzx \cdot y \neq z)$ Exercise

THEOREM 8. $(\exists x)(\exists y)(x \neq y)$ Exercise

THEOREM 9. $(\exists x)(\exists y)Pxy$ Exercise

THEOREM 10. $(\exists x)(\exists y)(\exists z)(x \neq y \cdot y \neq z \cdot x \neq z)$ Exercise

EXERCISES FOR SEC. 4.5.3
Prove all the unproved theorems of this section.

4.6 DEFINITIONS AND FORMAL DEDUCTIVE THEORIES

4.6.1 INTRODUCTION

In the most general sense of the term a definition is an explanation of the meaning of an expression. In this sense, definitions appear in almost every intellectual endeavor. Such a variety of cases fit this characterization of definitions as to render it unsatisfactory for the purpose of logic. Thus 'car' can be "defined" by pointing to cars; 'mathematics' by describing the techniques and concepts of that science; 'psychology' by saying that it is the science of human behavior. In short, for the layman, there are many legitimate ways of defining words.

In science and mathematics the methods of defining have been pared down a bit, and there are even commonly recognized rules of definition. Thus circularity would rule out this sequence of definitions:

Definition 1: 'Language' means 'a system of communication used in a human society'.

Definition 2: 'Human society' means 'a group of humans who speak the same language'.

Obviously, a word cannot end up being explained in terms of itself; so these definitions are not proper. Yet even general scientific practice is not all that precise. For this reason, formal deductive theories present an ideal vehicle for the study of definitions.

4.6.2 RULES OF DEFINITION

A definition explains one expression in terms of another. The expression explained is called the *definiendum*, while the expression doing the explaining, so to speak, is called the *definiens*. For example, in the definition

'IQ' means 'mental age divided by chronological age'

the definiendum is 'IQ' and the definiens is 'mental age divided by chronological age'. If the definiendum of a definition has been properly defined, then the definiendum and its definiens should be interchangeable in any sentence without affecting the meaning of the sentence. For this reason, formal deductive theories which contain definitions also provide for definitional interchanges, that is, permit inferences which depend upon interchanging a definiendum with a definiens, and vice versa.

4.6.2.1 CRITERIA FOR PROPER DEFINITIONS

When a definition is added to a formal deductive theory, it introduces a new expression into the language of the theory. This, of course, also adds many new wffs. Moreover, the definitional-interchange rule will make it possible to prove some of these new wffs as new theorems. For example, if we add the following definition to Theory A,

'$x \leq y$' means '$x < y \lor x = y$'

then we can prove the new theorem '$x < y \supset x \leq y$' as follows:

1		$x < y$	A
2		$x < y \lor x = y$	1, add
3		$x \leq y$	2, definitional interchange
4	$x < y \supset x \leq y$		1-3, CP

On the other hand, we could already prove '$x < y \supset (x < y \lor x = y)$', which, given the correctness of our definition, says the same thing as '$x < y \supset x \leq y$'. The point is this: Proper definitions increase the notation of a theory, but they do not permit the theory to say anything new; they increase the theorems of a theory, but they do not permit the proofs of anything that could not be proved in some other (perhaps more cumbersome) form. As a consequence, a consistent theory will remain consistent when proper definitions are added to it. Just what a proper definition is will emerge shortly.

Clearly, every expression of a theory cannot be defined; otherwise, some expressions would have to be defined circularly. Thus, in every theory, some expressions are taken as the basis for defining others. These basic expressions are known as *primitive*, or *undefined*, expressions. Although no definitions are offered for them, their meanings are not inscrutable. For there are other ways to learn to understand expressions than by using definitions. No definitions taught us to use 'stop', 'hot', 'yes', 'no', 'mother', for example.

Defined expressions must also be introduced sequentially. The first defined expression introduced must be defined solely in terms of primitive expressions. The second, however, may be defined in terms of the first and primitive expressions, and similarly for successive defined expressions. In this way, each defined expression boils down to primitive ones.

So far the notion of meaning has been used to gain some understanding of definitions. Now let us cast meaning aside. Otherwise, we shall find ourselves asking whether a given definition really does capture the meaning of its definiendum. Although there are ways to give sense and answers to such questions, dealing with them in general would take us into the theory of meaning, and dealing with them in particular, into the special sciences. Fortunately, the *deductive role* of definitions can be understood by viewing them as *abbreviatory conventions*. This shall be our stance from now on.

Where definitions are viewed in this light, the legitimacy of a rule of definitional interchange is obvious, for one is only interchanging expressions and their abbreviations. Of course, this presupposes that, from the deductive point of view, definitions be abbreviations, and just that. This means that every wff containing defined expressions must be construable as a wff in primitive notation and that every theorem which contains defined notation must be construable as a theorem in primitive notation which can be proved without the use of any definitions. The last clause is necessary lest definitions give rise to the proofs of primitive wffs which could not be proved prior to the introduction of definitions. This leads to the two following criteria for the propriety of definitions:

Criterion of eliminability: *A definition D introducing an expression E into Theory T satisfies the criterion of eliminability if and only if, given with wff S in which E appears, D and the previous definitions of Theory T determine a wff W in primitive notation such that $S = W$ can be derived from D, the previous definitions, and axioms of Theory T and the definitional interchange rule.*

Criterion of noncreativity: *A definition D introducing an expression E into Theory T satisfies the criterion of noncreativity if and only if there is no wff W in primitive notation which can be derived from D, the previous definitions, and axioms of Theory T and the definitional-interchange rule, but which cannot be derived from the axioms of Theory T alone.*

If a definition satisfies the first criterion, we can be certain that it will not permit us to construct wffs that are not abbreviations of wffs in primitive notation. If it also satisfies the second criterion, it will not create any new theorems; that is, any theorems we can prove using it will be (at worst) notational variants of what can be proved without the use of definitions.

The need for the criterion of noncreativity may not appear obvious; so let us consider an example of a creative definition. Introducing the symbol '*e*' into identity theory as an abbreviation of '*x*' will suffice. Then we can construct the following "proof":

1	x	$\triangle$	A
2		$(x)(x = x)$	AI
3		$x = x$	2, UI
4		$x = e$	3, definitional interchange
5		$(x)(x = e)$	1-4, UG
6		$(\exists y)(x)(x = y)$	5, EG

Not only is step 6 a new theorem in primitive notation, it is not even a truth of identity theory, since it asserts that there is exactly one thing. Step 4 is incorrect because the definition of '*e*' is improper.

4.6.2.2 THE FORMS OF DEFINITIONS

Whether or not a proposed definition satisfies the two criteria of proper definitions may not be obvious at a glance. Indeed, it may take quite a bit of proving, since the criteria refer to infinitely many wffs. For this reason it is convenient to give definitional forms which are known to produce definitions satisfying the two criteria. Basically, there are three types of definitions: those which introduce individual constants, those which introduce functional symbols (or functors), and those which introduce predicate symbols. This gives rise to three different forms of definition.

The form of definitions introducing individual constants is

Definition: $\alpha = \beta$

where α is the definiendum, β the definiens, and β is a *closed* functional term or individual constant composed of previously defined or primitive notation. 'Definition' is written to the left of '$\alpha = \beta$' to mark it as a definition and to distinguish it from identities which are theorems. The whole definition 'Definition: $\alpha = \beta$' is itself best understood as meaning 'α is an abbreviation of β'.

EXAMPLES

Proper Definitions (in the Theory of Groups):

Definition: $a = u + u$

Definition: $b = u + a$

Improper Definitions:

Definition: $a = x + x$ ['$x + x$' is open.]

Definition: $b = u + b$ ['b' occurs in the definiens.]

To introduce a functor ϕ, we introduce an open functional term composed of it and variables. If ϕ is a functor of degree n, then the open term is $\phi(\alpha_1, \alpha_2, \cdots, \alpha_n)$, where $\alpha_1, \alpha_2, \cdots, \alpha_n$ are distinct variables. The definition has the form

Definition: $\phi(\alpha_1, \alpha_2, \cdots, \alpha_n) = \beta$

where the definiens is also a functional term which contains no free occurrences of variables other than $\alpha_1, \alpha_2, \cdots, \alpha_n$ and need not contain free occurrences of all or any of these. Naturally, it contains only primitive and previously defined notation.

EXAMPLES

Proper Definitions (in the Theory of Groups):

Definition: $i(x) = x + u$

Definition: $3(x) = (x + x) + x$

Definition: $h(x,y) = (x + y) + (y + x)$

Definition: $g(x,y) = 3(x) + (3(y))^*$

Definition: $k(x,y) = x + 3\ (u)$

Improper Definitions:

Definition: $l(x,y) = x + z$ ['$l(x,y)$' does not contain a free
                                          occurrence of 'z'.]

Definition: $a(x) = a(u)$ ['a' is defined in terms of itself.]

The form of definitions of predicates is the last to be considered. To introduce a predicate ϕ, we introduce an open wff. If the predicate ϕ is an n-place
predicate, then the open wff has the form

$$\phi\alpha_1\alpha_2 \cdots \alpha_n$$

where α_1, α_2, $\cdots$, α_n are distinct variables. The definition has the form

Definition: $\phi\alpha_1\alpha_2 \cdots \alpha_n \equiv S$

where S is a wff which contains no free occurrences of variables other than
α_1, α_2, $\cdots$, α_n and need not contain free occurrences of all or any of these.

EXAMPLES

Proper Definitions (in Theories A and C):

Definition: $x \le y \equiv (x < y \lor x = y)$

Definition: $x > y \equiv y < x$

Definition: $Lx = (y)(x \ne y \supset x < y)$

Definition: $MOxy \equiv Pxy \cdot -Mx$

Definition: $FAxy = Pxy \cdot Mx$

Improper Definitions:

Definition: $Fx \equiv Pxy$ ['y' has no free occurrence in 'Fx'.]

Definition: $Au \equiv u = u + u$ ['Au' contains no free occurrence of
                                          variables.]

In the case of all three forms it is assumed that the individual constant,
functional term, or open sentence which is the definiendum is a new symbol.
Thus the definiendum of a definition must not contain primitive or previously

defined symbols (other than variables and punctuation symbols). For this reason, the following definitions are improper:

Definition: $a + u = u + u$ ['a' is new; '+' and 'u' are old.]

Definition: $x < s(x) \equiv (\exists z)(x < z)$ ['$s(x)$' is new; '<' is old.]

Later, we shall relax this requirement somewhat.

None of the examples considered here has contained a definite description in the definiens. Definite descriptions have very important applications in definitions, but because using them involves several complications, we shall postpone this until the next section.

EXERCISES FOR SECS. 4.6.1 TO 4.6.2.2

A. The following are *improper* definitions in Theories A, B, and C. In each case explain what is wrong with the *form* of the definition. Then show that the definition will fail to satisfy both the criteria of proper definitions.

  1. Definition: $Lxy \equiv (x < y \lor Lyx)$ (in Theory A)
  2. Definition: $a = x + y$ (in Theory B)
  3. Definition: $MOx \equiv Pxy \cdot -Mx$ (in Theory C)
  4. Definition: $x \cdot (y + (u + u)) = x \cdot y + x$ (in Theory B)

B. Give examples of improper and creative definitions which will render each of Theories A, B, and C inconsistent.

4.6.2.3   THE DEFINITIONAL-REPLACEMENT RULE

Since every definition takes the form of an identity or a biconditional, it could be added as an extra axiom, so to speak. The substitutivity of identity and the interchangeability of the biconditional would then guarantee the interchangeability of every definiendum with its definiens. It is simpler, however, to introduce a definitional-replacement rule which permits these interchanges outright. The rule is stated as follows.

Rule of definitional interchange: *If S_d and $S_d{}'$ are wffs of a formal deductive theory, Theory T, which contains a definition defining d as d', then if S_d results from $S_d{}'$ by interchange one or more occurrences of d with d', S_d may be inferred from $S_d{}'$ (in proofs in Theory T) and conversely.*

Reason: A numeral referring to the step from which the inference is made, followed by 'def.'. In applying this rule, it is understood that other expressions may replace the free variables in the definitions of functors and predicates and that the interchanges in question leave these expressions unchanged. *Also, no capturing is allowed.*

EXAMPLES. (The definitions used are those given in examples above.)

a.
1 | $(x)(x + u = x)$ — Axiom 2
2 | $(x)(i(x) = x)$ — 1, def.

b.
1 | $(x)(x + u = x)$ — Axiom 2
2 | $u + u = u$ — 1, UI
3 | $a = u$ — 2, def.
4 | $(\exists x)(a = x)$ — 3, EG

c.
1 | $(x)(x = x)$ — AI
2 | $g(u,u) = g(u,u)$ — 1, UI
3 | $g(u,u) = 3(u) + (3(u))^*$ — 2, def.
4 | $g(u,u) = (u + u) + u + ((u + u) + u)^*$ — 3, def.
5 | $(x)(x + u = x)$ — Axiom 2
6 | $u + u = u$ — 5, UI
7 | $g(u,u) = u + u + (u + u)^*$ — 4, 6, SI
8 | $g(u,u) = u + u^*$ — 7, 6, SI
9 | $(x)(x + x^* = u)$ — Axiom 3
10 | $u + u^* = u$ — 9, UI
11 | $g(u,u) = u$ — 8, 10, SI

d.
1 | $(x)(x = x)$ — AI
2 | $h(x,u) = h(x,u)$ — 1, UI
3 | $h(x,u) = (x + u) + (u + x)$ — 2, def.
4 | $(x)(x + u = x)$ — Axiom 2
5 | $(x)(u + x = x)$ — Theorem 2
6 | $x + u = x$ — 4, UI
7 | $u + x = x$ — 5, UI
8 | $h(x,u) = x + (u + x)$ — 3, 6, SI
9 | $h(x,u) = x + x$ — 8, 7, SI
10 | $h(x,u) + x = h(x,u) + x$ — 1, UI
11 | $h(x,u) + x = (x + x) + x$ — 10, 9, SI
12 | $h(x,u) + x = 3(x)$ — 11, def.

4.6.2.4 DEFINITIONS AND THEORY A

Several new theorems can be proved in Theory A by adding definitions to it. Let us forget the definitions in this theory given as examples above and start again. This time each definition will be numbered when it is given. Then we can refer to a definition by its number.

Definition 1: $x \le y \equiv (x < y \lor x = y)$

THEOREM 19. $(x)(y)(x < y \supset x \le y)$ — Exercise

THEOREM 20. $(x)(y)(x \neq y \cdot x \leq y \supset x < y)$ Exercise

THEOREM 21. $(x)(y)(x \leq y \lor y \leq x)$

Proof: (Partially worked out)

1	x,y	$\triangle$	A
2		$-(x < y)$	A
3		$-(x = y \lor x < y)$	2, Def. 1
		?	
		$x \neq y$	
		$-(x < y)$	
		$(x)(y)(x \neq y \supset (x < y \lor y < x))$	Axiom 3
		$x \neq y \supset (x < y \lor y < x)$	UI
		$x < y \lor y < x$	MP
		$y < x$	DS
		$y < x \lor y = x$	add
		$y \leq x$	Def. 1
		$-(x \leq y) \supset y \leq x$	CP
		?	
		$x \leq y \lor y \leq x$	
	$(x)(y)(x \leq y \lor y \leq x)$		UG

(*Exercise:* Complete this proof.)

THEOREM 22. $(x)(y)(x \leq y \cdot y \leq x \supset x = y)$ Exercise

THEOREM 23. $(x)(y)(z)(x \leq y \cdot y \leq z \supset x \leq z)$ Exercise

Definition 2: $Bzxy \equiv x < z \cdot z < y$

THEOREM 24. $(x)(y)(z)(Bzxy \supset x \neq y \cdot y \neq z \cdot x \neq z)$ Exercise

THEOREM 25. $(x)(y)(z)(Bzxy \supset -Bxzy \cdot -Byxz)$ Exercise

THEOREM 26. $(x) - Bxxx$ Exercise

THEOREM 27. $(x)(y)(z)(w)(Bzxy \cdot Byzw \supset Byxw \cdot Bzxw)$ Exercise

Definition 3: $Lx \equiv (y)(x \neq y \supset x < y)$

THEOREM 28. $-(\exists x)Lx$

THEOREM 29. $(x)(Lx \supset x < x)$ Exercise

THEOREM 30. $(x)(Lx \supset (y)(x < y))$ Exercise

A REFORMULATION OF THEORY A. Theorem 12 of Theory A is

$(x)(y)[(z)(z < x \equiv z < y) \supset x = y]$

Given this, we can easily prove

(1) $(x)(y)[(x = y) \equiv (z)(z < x \equiv z < y)]$

which suggests that '$x = y$' can be defined as '$(z)(z < x \equiv z < y)$', for (1) is the universal closure of a possible definition of '='. Of course, '=' cannot be defined in Theory A as it now stands, since '=' is a primitive symbol. Nonetheless, it is possible to reformulate the theory in such a way that '=' is not a primitive symbol.

How it is done will now be sketched.

The formal language of the new Theory A, let us call it Theory A′, contains all wffs of Theory A which do not contain the symbol '='. Its underlying logic no longer contains identity theory, of course, but instead contains quantification theory. We can use the axioms of Theory A again, except for Axiom 3, which contains '='. This will be replaced by a "translation" of it which does not contain '='. This produces the following axioms for Theory A′.

Axiom 1. $(x)(y)(x < y \supset -(y < x))$

Axiom 2. $(x)(y)(z)(x < y \cdot y < z \supset x < z)$

Axiom 3. $(x)(y)[-(z)(z < x \equiv z < y) \supset (x < y \lor y < x)]$

Axiom 4. $(x)(y)(x < y \supset (\exists z)(x < z \cdot z < y))$

Axiom 5. $(x)(\exists y)(\exists z)(x < y \cdot z < x)$

Next we add the following definition:

Definition 1′: $x = y \equiv (z)(z < x \equiv z < y)$

(In interchanging the definiens and definiendum of this definition, it is sometimes necessary to change the bound variable 'z' to avoid capturing, for example, in a proof of '$z = z$'. There are detours to avoid this problem, but we shall take the license of making such changes tacitly.)

THEOREM 1. $(x)(x = x)$

Proof:

1	x	$\triangle$	A
2		z $\triangle$	A
3		$\quad z < x$	A
4		$\quad z < x \supset z < x$	3-3, CP
5		$\quad z < x \equiv z < x$	4, PB
6		$(z)(z < x \equiv z < x)$	2-5, UG
7		$x = x$	6, Def. 1
8	$(x)(x = x)$		1-7, UG

THEOREM 2. $(x)(y)(x = y \supset y = x)$ Exercise

THEOREM 3. $(x)(y)(z)(x = y \cdot y = z \supset x = z)$ Exercise

THEOREM 4. $(x)(y)(x \neq y \supset (x < y \lor y < x))$ Exercise

The reader will notice that with Theorem 4 all the *axioms* of Theory A become *theorems* of Theory A', at least in defined notation. Can the same be said about the other theorems of Theory A? Not until we know that we can get the *effect* of identity theory in Theory A'. Since we have the axioms of Theory A as theorems of Theory A', we know that we can obtain all the theorems of Theory A which follow from its axioms by *quantification theory alone*. For we can carry out the same proofs except for writing 'Theorem 4' in place of 'Axiom 3'. Indeed, since '$(x)(x = x)$' is Theorem 1, we can even carry out all the proofs in which the axioms of identity are used. Only proofs in which the substitutivity of identity is used remain a problem.

Suppose that we can show that, whenever we have as steps in a proof in Theory A'

$(z)(z < x \equiv z < y)$
(_____ x _____)

then we can also obtain

(_____ y _____)

and as a further step, where (_____ y _____) comes from (_____ x _____) by replacing one or more free occurrences of 'x' by free occurrences of 'y'. Then we could get the effect of the substitutivity of identity in Theory A'. With a little effort this can be shown.

First, note that we have the following theorem in Theory A':

THEOREM 5. $(z)(z < x \equiv z < y) \supset (z)(x < z \equiv y < z)$ Exercise

Second, notice that, given the language of A', the occurrences of 'x' and 'y' in (_____ x _____) and (_____ y _____) occur only on the sides of '$<$' (or can be made to occur there by translating the wffs into primitive notation). Now suppose that (_____ x _____) and (_____ y _____) are among the shortest possible wffs. They must be both '$\alpha < x$' and '$\alpha < y$' or '$x < \alpha$' and '$y < \alpha$', where α is a variable. In this case, the effect of substitutivity of identity is readily forthcoming:

1	$x < \alpha$	P
2	$(z)(z < x \equiv z < y)$	P
3	$(z)(z < x \equiv z < y) \supset (z)(x < z \equiv y < z)$	Theorem 5
4	$(z)(x < z \equiv y < z)$	1, 3, MP
5	$x < \alpha \equiv y < \alpha$	4, UI
6	$y < \alpha$	1, 5, MPB

1	$\alpha < x$	P
2	$(z)(z < x \equiv z < y)$	P
3	$\alpha < x \equiv \alpha < y$	2, UI
4	$\alpha < y$	1, 3, MPB

Next suppose that we can get the effect of the substitutivity of identity in all wffs up to a given length. Then we can show that we can get its effect for all wffs of that length. To this we must consider the forms that (_____ x _____) and (_____ y _____) can take. There are seven cases corresponding to each of the truth-functions and quantifiers.

CASE I. (_____ x _____) is $-(\cdots x \cdots)$. Then (_____ y _____) is $-(\cdots y \cdots)$, and the derivation proceeds as follows:

1	$-(\cdots x \cdots)$	P
2	$(z)(z < x \equiv z < y)$	P
3	$(x)(y)(x = y \supset y = x)$	Theorem 2
4	$x = y \supset y = x$	3, UI
5	$(z)(z < x \equiv z < y) \supset (z)(y < z \equiv x < z)$	4, Def. 1
6	$(z)(y < z \equiv x < z)$	2, 5, MP
7	$\quad (\cdots y \cdots)$	A
8	$\quad (\cdots x \cdots)$	6, 7, SI (for shorter wffs)
9	$\quad -(\cdots x \cdots)$	1, R
10	$-(\cdots y \cdots)$	1-9, IP

CASE II. (_____ x _____) is $(\cdots x \cdots) \cdot (--- x ---))$. Then (_____ y _____) is $(\cdots y \cdots) \cdot (--- y ---)$. [One, or both, of $(\cdots x \cdots)$ and $(--- x ---)$ may not contain 'x' free.] The derivation proceeds as follows:

1	$(\cdots x \cdots) \cdot (--- x ---)$	P
2	$(z)(z < x \equiv z < y)$	P
3	$(\cdots x \cdot \cdot)$	1, S
4	$(\cdots y \cdots)$	2, 3, SI (for shorter wffs)
5	$(--- x ---)$	1, S
6	$(--- y ---)$	2, 5, SI (for shorter wffs)
7	$(\cdots y \cdots) \cdot (--- y ---)$	4, 6, PC

CASE III. (_____ x _____) is $(\cdots x \cdots) \lor (--- x ---)$

Exercise

CASE IV. (_____ x _____) is $(\cdots x \cdots) \supset (--- x ---)$

Exercise

CASE V. (_____ x _____) is $(\cdots x \cdots) \equiv (--- x ---)$

Exercise

CASE VI.   (_____ x _____) is $(\alpha)(\cdots x \cdots \alpha \cdots)$

α is distinct from both 'x' and 'y'. Then (_____ y _____) is $(\cdots y \cdots \alpha \cdots)$, and the derivation proceeds as follows:

1	$(\alpha)(\cdots x \cdots \alpha \cdots)$	P
2	$(z)(z < x \equiv z < y)$	P
3 α	$\triangle$	A
4	$(\cdots x \cdots \alpha \cdots)$	1, UI
5	$(\cdots y \cdots \alpha \cdots)$	2, 4, SI (for shorter wffs)
6	$(\alpha)(\cdots y \cdots \alpha \cdots)$	3-5, UG

CASE VII.   (_____ x _____) is $(\exists\alpha)(\cdots x \cdots \alpha \cdots)$ Exercise

We have shown that the effect of the substitutivity of identity can be gotten when (_____ x _____) is one of the shortest wffs. We have also just shown that the effect of the substitutivity of identity can also be gotten for (_____ x _____) of any length if it can be gotten for all shorter wffs. It then follows that the effect of the substitutivity of identity can be gotten for all wffs. For suppose, to the contrary, that there is a wff (_____ x _____) for which it cannot be gotten. Then there must be a shortest such (_____ x _____). This (_____ x _____) cannot be the very shortest of wffs. Thus there are wffs shorter than (_____ x _____) for which the effect of substitutivity of identity can be gotten. But then its effect can be gotten for (_____ x _____). And this contradicts our assumption.

We have shown that, for Theory A, the logic of identity can be reduced to quantification theory by means of a reformulation. This type of reduction can be carried out for all other formal deductive theories. Sometimes, however, it is necessary to replace '=' by an additional primitive predicate. Thus, in the case of group theory, we can replace '=' by 'I' and definite '=' by

Definition: $x = y \equiv Ixy$

The new axioms of group theory would then be

Axiom 1. $(x)Ixx$

Axiom 2. $(x)(y)(Ixy \supset Iyx)$

Axiom 3. $(x)(y)(Ixy \cdot Iyz \supset Ixz)$

Axiom 4. $(x)(y)(Ixy \supset Ix^*y^*)$

Axiom 5. $(x)(y)(z)(Ixy \supset I(x+z)(y+z) \cdot I(z+x)(z+y))$

Axiom 6. $(x)(y)(z)(I((x+y)+z)(x+(y+z)))$

Axiom 7. $(x)I(x+u)x$

Axiom 8. $(x)I(x+x^*)u$

The first five axioms will provide the effect of the substitutivity of identity, while the last three are "translations" of the original three axioms of group theory. When a theory contains other primitive predicates besides '=', then it usually is not necessary to add 'I' as a new predicate in carrying out this reduction. For in such cases '=' can usually be defined in terms of the other primitive predicates, as we did for Theory A.

4.6.2.5 DEFINITIONS AND THEORY C

Theory C obtains its main interest in connection with definitions, for they show that many other kinship relations can be defined in terms of *parent* and *male*.

Definition 1: $FEx \equiv -Mx$ (x is a female)

Definition 2: $Fxy \equiv Pxy \cdot Mx$ (x is a father of y)

Definition 3: $MOxy \equiv Pxy \cdot FEx$ (x is a mother of y)

Definition 4: $SBxy \equiv (z)(Pzx \supset Pzy)$ (x is a sibling of y)

Definition 5: $BRxy \equiv SBxy \cdot Mx$ (x is a brother of y)

Definition 6: $SIxy \equiv SBxy \cdot FEx$ (x is a sister of y)

Definition 7: $GRxy \equiv (\exists z)(Pxz \cdot Pzy)$ (x is a grandparent of y)

Definition 8: $GFxy \equiv GPxy \cdot Mx$ (x is a grandfather of y)

Definition 9: $GMxy \equiv GPxy \cdot FEx$ (x is a grandmother of y)

Definition 10: $Axy \equiv (\exists z)(Pzy \cdot SIxz)$ (x is a (blood) aunt of y)

Definition 11: $Uxy \equiv (\exists z)(Pzy \cdot BRxz)$ (x is a (blood) uncle of y)

Definition 12: $Cxy \equiv (\exists z)((Azy \lor Uzy) \cdot Pzx)$ (x is a cousin of y)

These definitions naturally introduce new theorems. Some are listed now:

THEOREM 11. $(x)(Mx \lor FEx)$ Exercise

THEOREM 12. $(x)(\exists ! y)Fyz$ Exercise

THEOREM 13. $(x)(\exists ! y)MOyx$ Exercise

THEOREM 14. $(x)(y)(MOxy \supset -Fxy$ Exercise

THEOREM 15. $(x)(y)(z)(w)(Fxy \cdot Fxz \cdot MOwy \cdot MOwz \supset SByz)$ Exercise

THEOREM 16. $FBxy \supset (\exists z)(MOzx \cdot MOzy)$ Exercise

THEOREM 17. $(x)SBxx$ Exercise†

---

†It may be objected that *sibling* is not reflexive and '$(x)SBxx$' should not be a theorem. That it is a theorem is a simple consequence of the definition of 'SB' given. One could revise this definition, or one could even revise the reading of 'SB' to 'sibling or oneself'. The first choice would excise the objectionable theorem; the second would give it a less objectionable reading.

THEOREM 18. $(x)(y)(z)(SBxy \cdot SByz \supset SBxz)$ Exercise

THEOREM 19. $(x)(y)(SBxy \supset SByx)$ Exercise

THEOREM 20. $(z)(\exists x)(\exists y)(x \neq y \cdot GFxz \cdot GFyz)$ Exercise

THEOREM 21. $(x)(y)(Cxy \supset Cyx)$ Exercise

THEOREM 22. $(x)(y)[(\exists z)(\exists w)(GFzx \cdot GFzy \cdot GMwx \cdot GMwy)$
  $\supset (-SBxy \supset Cxy)]$ Exercise

THEOREM 23. $(x)(y)(Cxy \supset (\exists z)(\exists w)(GFzx \cdot GFzy \cdot GMwx \cdot GMwy))$
  Exercise

THEOREM 24. $(x)(y)((\exists z)(Fzx \cdot BRyz) \supset Uyz)$ Exercise

THEOREM 25. $(x)(\exists y)(\exists z)(y \neq z \cdot GFyx \cdot GFzx \cdot (w)(GFwx$
  $\supset (w = y \lor w = z)))$ Exercise

EXERCISES FOR SECS. 4.6.2.3 TO 4.6.2.5

A. Prove all the theorems left unproved in these sections.
B. Reformulate Theory C so that its underlying logic is no longer identity theory but simply quantification theory.

4.7 THE CONTEXTUAL DEFINITION OF DEFINITE DESCRIPTIONS

4.7.1 CONTEXTUAL DEFINITIONS

We had no need for a separate logic of description in the chapter on definite description, for there we saw that arguments involving definite description can be treated within identity theory, provided that descriptional premises are used. Now we shall go one step further and show that definite descriptions need never appear in the primitive notation of a theory because they can always be introduced via definitions.

Definite descriptions are singular terms formed from open sentences with the aid of descriptors. Unless the notation of a theory contains expressions like descriptors, which produce singular terms from open sentences, the usual forms of definition will not be suitable for defining definite descriptions. The usual definitions correlate open sentences with other open sentences, and singular terms with other singular terms. To bridge the gap between open sentences and singular terms we must turn to *contextual definitions*.

A contextual definition of a singular term introduces the term in a *particular* context. Although the definition may be employed to eliminate the term from that context, it differs from other definitions by failing to eliminate the term from all contexts in which it may appear. For example, suppose we use the contextual definition

Definition: $(\imath x)(x = x) < y \equiv (\exists x)(x = x \cdot (w)(w = w \supset w = x) \cdot x < y)$

to introduce '$(\imath x)(x = x)$'. Then we can eliminate '$(\imath x)(x = x)$' from the left side of '$<$', but not from the right side. Thus contextual definitions may not satisfy the criterion of eliminability. Later, we shall find that they may not satisfy the criterion of noncreativity, either.

4.7.2 THE CONTEXTUAL DEFINITION OF DESCRIPTIONS

Because of their failure to satisfy the two criteria for proper definitions, contextual definitions must be approached with caution. To simplify matters, they will be treated here only in connection with definite description. (This has been their chief and most important use, anyhow.) We shall also limit our attention to theories which contain no primitive functors or descriptor-like expressions. (This again reflects custom, and simplifies things considerably.) As a consequence, our exposition will fail to cover Theory B given above. But this is really no drawback, as we shall see later. Finally, we shall assume that the theories we are dealing with also already contain '$=$' as a primitive or defined symbol. Again, this is not much of a restriction.

As singular terms, definite descriptions can occur only where variables can occur. Thus, if definite descriptions can be eliminated from the smallest contexts in which variables can appear, they can be eliminated from all larger contexts which contain these smallest contexts. For example, by applying the definition given above,

$x = y \lor (\imath x)(x = x) < y$

becomes

$x = y \lor (\exists x)(x = x \cdot (w)(w = w \supset w = x) \cdot x < y)$

Moreover, in eliminating definite descriptions, we need only consider their occurrences in *primitive* contexts, since defined contexts can be converted to primitive ones by applying definitions. Thus the general problem of eliminating a definite description from all wffs in which it appears reduces to the problem of eliminating it from the smallest primitive contexts in which it can appear. If there are several of these contexts, then several contextual definitions will be necessary. Taken individually, none will satisfy the criterion of eliminability, although taken together they will. This is why it is still possible to use contextual definitions.

Once descriptors have been added to a formal language, one can usually construct infinitely many definite descriptions. This is because most formal languages contain infinitely many open sentences. Thus infinitely many contextual definitions will be required to define definite descriptions. This problem can be met by using *definition schemata*. These are devices which are used to postulate that a description of given form occurring in a context of a given form is to be eliminated in favor of an expression of a given form. Every definite description has the form

$(\imath \alpha)\phi\alpha$

where α is a variable, and $\phi\alpha$ an open sentence. Thus the following is a definition schema which indicates how definite descriptions are to be eliminated from the left side of '$<$':

Definition: $(\imath\alpha)\phi\alpha < \beta \equiv (\exists\alpha)(\phi\alpha \cdot (\gamma)(\phi\gamma \supset \gamma = \alpha) \cdot \alpha < \beta)$

where β is a singular term or a variable, and γ is not α. By applying this, we can convert

$(\imath x)(x < x) < (\imath y)(y = y)$

to

$(\exists x)(x < x \cdot (z)(z < z \supset z = x) \cdot x < (\imath y)(y = y))$

[We still have not given a definition schema for eliminating the occurrence of '$(\imath y)(y = y)$'.] The definition schema leaves the choice of the variable γ open. This leeway is necessary to avoid capturing when unabbreviating defined expressions. To eliminate descriptions from the right side of '$<$', we can introduce the definition schema

Definition: $\beta < (\imath\alpha)\phi\alpha \equiv (\exists\alpha)(\phi\alpha \cdot (\gamma)(\phi\gamma \supset \gamma = \alpha) \cdot \beta < \alpha)$

By applying this, the last sentence converts to

$(\exists x)(x < x \cdot (z)(z < z \supset z = x) \cdot (\exists y)(y = y \cdot (w)(w = w \supset w = y) \cdot x < y))$

   A different definition schema will be needed for each smallest primitive context in which descriptives can occur. Nonetheless, it is possible to indicate the general form which these schemata must take. This will determine the form of all contextual definitions of description. The description has been represented by $(\imath\alpha)\phi\alpha$. Let us now represent the context by ψ. Thus the description in the context is represented by

$\psi(\imath\alpha)\phi\alpha$

Given this, the general schema for contextual definition is, simply,

(1)   Definition: $\psi(\imath\alpha)\phi\alpha \equiv (\exists\alpha)(\phi\alpha \cdot (\gamma)(\phi\gamma \supset \gamma = \alpha) \cdot \psi\alpha)$

Here again, the variable γ must be different from α. Notice that all definitions of definite descriptions are essentially alike and really differ only in the context ψ and the open sentence $\phi\alpha$.

4.7.3 JUSTIFICATION

Schema (1) above presents the form of all contextual definitions of definite descriptions. Clearly, however, it needs some justification as a form of a definition and as an analysis of definite description. Will schema (1) provide an adequate logic of descriptions? Will it provide formally satisfactory definitions? These are questions which must be faced now.

It turns out that the second question is the better one to consider first. This question divides into two parts, schema (1) and the criterion of eliminability and schema (1) and the criterion of noncreativity. We have already noticed that single contextual definitions can fail to satisfy the criterion of eliminability. Indeed they must, if the theory containing them has more than one smallest primitive context open to variables. But when a contextual definition (schema) is given for each primitive context, it will be possible to eliminate descriptions from every wff. Thus, schema (1) produces definitions which satisfy the spirit, if not the letter, of the criterion of eliminability. When the proper number of contextual definitions is given, expressions containing descriptions are construable as abbreviations of expressions which do not contain them. Consequently, whether or not contextual definitions are to be called definitions is a terminological matter. Proper contextual definitions function as abbreviatory conventions, at least from the point of view of eliminability.

Such a glib approach is not possible, however, with respect to the criterion of noncreativity. Once definite descriptions have been introduced into a theory, they count as singular terms of that theory. These singular terms can then figure in applications of universal instantiation and existential generalization. But sometimes the results are disastrous! Thus, suppose that definite descriptions are introduced into identity theory by means of the two definition schemta.

Definition 1: $(\imath\alpha)\phi\alpha = \beta \equiv (\exists\alpha)(\phi\alpha \cdot (\gamma)(\phi\gamma \supset \gamma = \alpha) \cdot \alpha = \beta)$

Definition 2: $\beta = (\imath\alpha)\phi\alpha \equiv (\exists\alpha)(\phi\alpha \cdot (\gamma)(\phi\gamma \supset \gamma = \alpha) \cdot \beta = \alpha)$

Then we can construct the following "proof":

1	$(x)(x = x)$	AI
2	$(\imath y)(y \neq y) = (\imath y)(y \neq y)$	1, UI
3	$(\exists x)(x = (\imath y)(y \neq y))$	2, EG

where step 3 is certainly false, since it says that there is something that is the thing which is not identical with itself. But how can there be such a thing? Everything *is* identical with itself! Furthermore, we can continue this proof to arrive at an outright contradiction. Here is how:

4	$(\exists x)(\exists y)(y \neq y \cdot (z)(z \neq z \supset z = y) \cdot x = y)$	3, Def. 2
5	$x \mid (\exists y)(y \neq y \cdot (z)(z + z \supset z = y) \cdot x = y)$	A
6	$y \mid y \neq y \cdot (z)(z \neq z \supset z = y) \cdot x = y$	A
7	$y \neq y$	6, S
8	$y = y$	1, UI
9	$y = y \lor -(x)(x = x)$	8, add
10	$-(x)(x = x)$	7, 9, DS
11	$-(x)(x = x)$	5, 6-10, EI
12	$-(x)(x = x)$	4, 5-11, EI

These definitions are creative in the worst way—they create contradictions in consistent theories!

Before we abandon our program of defining descriptions, let us see what happens if they are taken as primitive; and the descriptional-premiss approach is used. In this case, the descriptional premisses would take the form of additional axioms. In other words, we should need the axiom schema

(4) $(\beta)(\phi\beta \equiv (\imath\alpha)\phi\alpha = \beta)$

The same trouble arises, however, for we can now construct the following "proof":

1	$(y)(y \neq y \equiv (\imath x)(x \neq x) = y)$	Axiom 4
2	$(x)(x = x)$	AI
3	$(\imath x)(x \neq x) = (\imath x)(x \neq x)$	2, UI
4	$(\imath x)(x \neq x) \neq (\imath x)(x \neq y) \equiv (\imath x)(x \neq x) = (\imath x)(x \neq x)$	1, UI
5	$(\imath x)(x \neq x) \neq (\imath x)(x \neq x)$	3, 4, MP

Again we have arrived at a contradiction; so *defining* descriptions cannot be the source of our troubles.

Actually, these difficulties are not entirely new, because they can already occur with respect to ordinary proper names. This has been swept under the carpet before, but now it must be faced in the open. Thus, consider the following "proof":

1.	$(x)(x = x)$	AI
2.	Hamlet $=$ Hamlet	1, UI
3.	$(\exists x)(x = \text{Hamlet})$	2, EG

While step 1 is clearly true, step 3 is just as clearly false; for '$(\exists x)(x = \text{Hamlet})$' is true if and only if some *actual* object is Hamlet. To make matters worse, given any singular term α, one can easily prove in identity theory that

$(\exists ! x)(x = \alpha)$

which is certainly anomalous if α does not name a unique object. Thus our difficulties do not really hinge upon descriptions at all. In fact, they are traceable to a presupposition on the application of quantification theory which we have passed over until now. The presupposition in question comes to this: a singular term may replace a variable, and conversely, if and only if the singular term in question designates a unique object. Before descriptions were introduced, one hardly had to worry about this presupposition, for most applications of logic are concerned with arguments whose singular terms do designate unique objects, or at least do so when the argument is paraphrased properly. Once descriptions enter the scene, singular terms which do not designate unique objects become extremely plentiful. For given any condition F, if there are no F or more than one F, '$(\imath x)Fx$' fails to designate a unique object. Yet, by means of identity theory and our contextual definitions (or descriptional premisses), it is quite easy to prove—once '$(\imath x)Fx$' is present—that there is a unique F. Moreover, by choosing F appropriately, it becomes quite easy to prove contradictions. Thus some restriction on the application of quantification theory to definite descriptions is clearly necessary.

The required restriction for the contextual-definition approach to descriptions is this:

> *No variable may replace a definite description* $(\imath\alpha)\phi\alpha$ *in the application of* EG *and no definite description* $(\imath\alpha)\phi\alpha$ *may replace a variable in an application of* UI *unless* $(\exists\,!\,\alpha)\phi\alpha$ *is a previous step of the derivation in question.*

The condition $(\exists\,!\,\alpha)\phi\alpha$ is called the uniqueness condition. (This condition can always be established in the descriptional-premiss approach, even when there is no unique ϕ. Consequently, its truth is an informal presupposition of every application of this approach.) Notice that this restriction makes UI and EG rules of inference which refer back to two previous steps where descriptions introduced by contextual definitions are concerned. Also, since descriptions are functional terms, UI and EG are being used in their extended forms.

EXAMPLE.   To derive '$(\exists x)(x = (\imath x)Fx)$' from '$(\exists\,!\,x)Fx$', given that '$(\imath x)Fx$' has been introduced by contextual definitions.

Derivation:

1	$(\exists\,!\,x)Fx$	P
2	$(x)(x = x)$	AI
3	$(\imath x)Fx = (\imath x)Fx$	1, 2, UI
4	$(\exists x)(x = (\imath x)Fx)$	1, 3, EG

The two rules UI and EG may be applied without any dire consequences to any description which satisfies the uniqueness condition. To see this we shall show that whenever these rules are applied to descriptions satisfying the condition, the same steps can be carried out without applying these rules to the descriptions in question. Naturally, in carrying this out, we have to use the uniqueness condition itself, contextual definitions, and other rules of identity theory. (For the sake of simplicity we shall assume that '=' is a primitive predicate of every formal deductive theory into which the descriptions have been introduced, and that these theories contain identity theory in their underlying logic. This assumption can be dispensed with, but then the argument to follow would be rather complicated.)

Let us suppose that in a formal deductive theory T, the following inferences occur:

(A) $(\exists ! \alpha)\phi\alpha$
       $(\beta)(\underline{\hspace{2cm}} \beta \underline{\hspace{2cm}})$
       $\therefore \underline{\hspace{2cm}} (\imath\alpha)\phi\alpha \underline{\hspace{2cm}}$ UI

(B) $(\exists ! \alpha)\phi\alpha$
       $\underline{\hspace{2cm}} (\imath\alpha)\phi\alpha \underline{\hspace{2cm}}$
       $\therefore (\exists\beta)(\underline{\hspace{2cm}} \beta \underline{\hspace{2cm}})$ EG

We now want to show that the effect of (A) and (B) can be gotten without applying UI or EG to $(\imath\alpha)\phi\alpha$. To do this we must first show that, from the uniqueness condition, we can derive

(C) $(\exists\beta)(\beta = (\imath\alpha)\phi\alpha)$

where β does not occur free in $(\imath\alpha)\phi\alpha$.

The following derivation accomplishes this:

1		$(\exists\alpha)(\phi\alpha \cdot (\beta)(\phi\beta \supset \beta = \alpha)$	uniqueness condition
2	α	$\phi\alpha \cdot (\beta)(\phi\beta \supset \beta = \alpha)$	A
3		$(x)(x = x)$	AI
4		$\beta = \beta$	3, UI
5		$\phi\alpha \cdot (\beta)(\phi\beta \supset \beta = \alpha) \cdot \beta = \beta$	2, 4, PC
6		$(\exists\alpha)(\phi\alpha \cdot (\beta)(\phi\beta \supset \beta = \alpha) \cdot \beta = \alpha)$	5, EG
7		$\beta = (\imath\alpha)\phi\alpha$	6, def.
8		$\beta = (\imath\alpha)\phi\alpha$	1, 2-7, EI
9		$(\exists\beta)(\beta = (\imath\alpha)\phi\alpha)$	8, EG

Then, to carry out inferences of the form (A), we proceed as follows:

(A')	1		$(\beta)(\underline{\hspace{1.5cm}} \beta \underline{\hspace{1.5cm}})$	P
	2		$(\exists ! \alpha)\phi\alpha$	P
	3		$(\exists\beta)(\beta = (\imath\alpha)\phi\alpha)$	(C)
	4	β	$\beta = (\imath\alpha)\phi\alpha$	A
	5		$\underline{\hspace{1.5cm}} \beta \underline{\hspace{1.5cm}}$	1, UI

$$
\begin{array}{lll}
6 & \underline{\qquad\qquad} (\imath\alpha)\phi\alpha \underline{\qquad\qquad} & 4, 5, \text{SI} \\
7 & \underline{\qquad\qquad} (\imath\alpha)\phi\alpha \underline{\qquad\qquad} & 3, 4\text{-}6, \text{EI}
\end{array}
$$

On the other hand, to carry out an inference of the form (B) we proceed in this way:

$$
\begin{array}{clll}
(\text{B}') & 1 & \underline{\qquad\qquad} (\imath\alpha)\phi\alpha \underline{\qquad\qquad} & \text{P} \\
& 2 & (\exists\,!\,\alpha)\phi\alpha & \text{P} \\
& 3 & (\exists\beta)(\beta = (\imath\alpha)\phi\alpha) & \text{(C)} \\
& 4 & \beta\mid\ \beta = (\imath\alpha)\phi\alpha & \text{A} \\
& 5 & \quad (x)(x = x) & \text{AI} \\
& 6 & \quad \beta = \beta & 5, \text{UI} \\
& 7 & \quad (\imath\alpha)\phi\alpha = \beta & 6, 4, \text{SI} \\
& 8 & \quad \underline{\qquad} \beta \underline{\qquad} & 1, 7, \text{SI} \\
& 9 & (\exists\beta)(\underline{\qquad} \beta \underline{\qquad}\ ) & 8, \text{EG} \\
& 10 & (\exists\beta)(\underline{\qquad} \beta \underline{\qquad}) & 3, 4\text{-}9, \text{EI}
\end{array}
$$

Notice that neither (A'), (B'), nor (C) contains applications of UI or EG with respect to $(\imath\alpha)\phi\alpha$. This establishes that any derivation which contains applications of these rules to descriptions can be reconstructed without these applications, so long as the uniqueness condition has been established for the descriptions in question. To carry out the reconstruction one need only follow the patterns of (A'), (B'), and (C).

If the reader returns to the contradictions presented above, he will see that they were generated by applying EG and UI to descriptions which cannot satisfy the uniqueness condition. Now something stronger can be proved, namely, that so long as we abide by the restrictions on the application of quantification theory to descriptions, the contextual definitions of definite descriptions will not be creative. The essential ideas of the proof of this are contained in (A'), (B'), and (C'), but the full proof belongs in a more advanced text.

We must turn now to the adequacy of our analysis of description. This problem will be approached from two directions. First, we shall show that on our account $(\imath x)Fx$ is the object it is supposed to be. Second, we shall show that anything that can properly be done by means of the descriptional-premiss method can also be done with the contextual-definition method.

Turning to the object $(\imath x)Fx$, we see that it is supposed to be the unique F if there is one. In other words, given anything, if it and only it is an F, then it is identical with $(\imath x)Fx$. Formally, this comes to

(1) $(y)(Fy \cdot (z)(Fz \supset z = y) \supset y = (\imath x)Fx)$

The contextual-definition approach to descriptions *does* satisfy this measure of adequacy. For one can prove (1) using identity theory and contextual definitions. The proof is simple though lengthy, and the uniqueness condition is not required in it. It is left as an exercise for the reader. [*Hint:* After (1) has been unabbreviated, the proof is a lot like the proof of (C).] Given (1) and identity theory, anything that can be proved about an object which is the unique F can also be proved about $(\imath x)Fx$.

Next, let us compare the contextual-definition approach with the descriptional-premiss approach. The descriptional-premiss approach must be modified somewhat, for it, too, can generate contradictions if used unrestrictedly. In this case, the required restriction is:

> *No descriptional premiss may be adopted for a given description unless that description satisfies the uniqueness condition.*†

Let us suppose, then, that we are given an argument involving the description, say, '$(\imath x)(x = 0)$'. Let us further suppose that the uniqueness condition has been established for '$(\imath x)(x = 0)$' and that the argument in question can be validated by adding the relevant descriptional premiss. Can the same argument be validated under the contextual approach? Yes; for by using contextual definitions, the descriptional premiss for '$(\imath x)(x = 0)$' can be derived from the uniqueness condition. We already know that (1) can be derived under the contextual-definition approach; so we may obtain the descriptional premiss for '$(\imath x)(x = 0)$' as follows:

1		$(\exists y)(y = 0) \cdot (z)(z = 0 \supset z = y))$	uniqueness condition
2	y	$y = 0 \cdot (z)(z = 0 \supset z = y)$	A
3		$(y)[y = 0 \cdot (z)(z = 0 \supset z = y) \supset y = (\imath x)(x = 0)]$	(1)
4		$y = 0 \cdot (z)(z = 0 \supset z = y) \supset y = (\imath x)(x = 0)$	3, UI
5		$y = (\imath x)(x = 0)$	2, 4, MP
6		$(z)(z = 0 \supset z = y)$	2, S
7		$y = 0$	2, S
		$\cdot$	
		$\cdot$	
		$\cdot$	
		$(z)(z = 0 \equiv z = y)$	UG
		$(z)(z = 0 \equiv z = (\imath x)(x = 0))$	SI
		$(z)(z = 0 \equiv z = (\imath x)(x = 0))$	EI

(*Exercise:* Complete this derivation.)

Yet once we obtain a descriptional premiss for '$(\imath x)(x = 0)$', the argument in question can be treated in the same way as it would be treated under the descriptional-premiss approach.

†In the case of the validation of arguments, it is usually an implicit assumption that this condition is met.

The contextual-definition approach to descriptions is thus as adequate as the descriptional-premiss approach. The latter, which treats descriptions as genuine singular terms, is more efficient, and should be used when simply validating arguments involving descriptions. The former, which does not treat descriptions on a par with genuine singular terms, is of considerable theoretical interest, and should be used when one's aim is the construction of a theory without *primitive* singular terms.

EXERCISES FOR SEC. 4.7

Introduce definite descriptions, by means of contextual definitions, into Theories A and C.

4.8   DEFINITE DESCRIPTIONS AND DEFINITIONS

4.8.1   THE FORM OF DEFINITIONS VIA DEFINITE DESCRIPTIONS

A theory whose notation includes definite descriptions (whether as primitive or defined) may use them in its definitions. In fact, they are often very useful for defining other singular terms. For example, Theory C contains no primitive singular terms. But we can introduce definite descriptions into this theory by means of contextual definitions. Then we can use definite descriptions to define other singular terms. The terms '$f(x)$', meaning 'the father of x', and '$m(x)$', meaning 'the mother of x', can be defined by

Definition: $f(x) = (\imath y)Fyx$

Definition: $m(x) = (\imath y)MOyx$

Indeed, given any formal language containing primitive singular terms, one can always construct another formal language which is a "translation" of the first, containing no primitive singular terms. This is done by defining definite description in the new language and then defining the old singular terms via definite descriptions. Shortly, we shall see how this can be done for the theory of groups.

When a definiens of a definition is a definite description, the definition must be subject to a restriction in order to prevent it from being creative. To illustrate the need for this, suppose that we define '$p(x)$', or 'the parent of x', in Theory C by

Definition: $p(x) = (\imath y)Pyx$

Then we can prove

(1) $(w)(z)(Pwx \cdot Pzx \supset w = z)$

as follows:

1	$(x)(x = x)$	AI
2	$p(x) = p(x)$	1, UI
3	$(\imath y)Pyx = (\imath y)Pyx$	2, def.
4	$(\exists y)(Pyx \cdot (z)(Pzx \supset z = y) \cdot (\imath y)Pyx = y)$	3, def.
5	$y\lvert Pyx \cdot (z)(Pzx \supset z = y) \cdot (\imath y)Pyx = y$	A
6	$Pyx \cdot (z)(Pzx \supset z = y)$	5, S
7	$w,z\lvert \quad \triangle$	A
8	$Pwx \cdot Pzx$	A
9	$(z)(Pzx \supset z = y)$	6, S
10	$Pwx \supset w = y$	9, UI
11	$Pzx \supset z = y$	9, UI
12	Pwx	8, S
13	Pzx	8, S
14	$w = y$	12, 10, MP
15	$z = y$	13, 11, MP
16	$z = z$	1, UI
17	$y = z$	16, 15, SI
18	$w = z$	14, 17, SI
19	$Pwx \cdot Pzx \supset w = z$	8-18, CP
20	$(w)(z)(Pwx \cdot Pzx \supset w = z)$	7-19, UG
21	$(w)(z)(Pwx \cdot Pzx \supset w = z)$	4, 5-20, EI

On the other hand, we can also prove

(2) $(\exists z)(\exists w)(Pzx \cdot Pwx \cdot z \neq w)$

and (1) and (2) yield a contradiction.

The steps which are to blame here are steps 2 and 3. The definite description '$(\imath y)Pyx$' does not satisfy the uniqueness condition, but by applying universal instantiation to '$p(x)$' and then unabbreviating, we have in effect applied universal instantiation to '$(\imath y)Pyx$'. There are two ways to avoid this problem. One is to prohibit applications of universal instantiation and existential generalization to singular terms defined as descriptions, unless the descriptions satisfy the uniqueness condition. The other is to prohibit definitions of singular terms as definite descriptions which do not satisfy the uniqueness condition. The latter way accords with mathematical practice much better. In mathematics, a definition of an object as the object satisfying a certain condition is always justified by proofs that the condition determines a unique object. (That is why mathematicians are always proving that limits exist and are unique.) We shall follow mathematical practice and adopt the second method. This amounts to adopting the following uniqueness restriction.

Uniqueness restriction: *Definitions of individual constants c and functors f of the form*

Definition: $c = (\imath v)Pv$

Definition: $f(v_1, v_2, \cdots, v_n) = (\imath v)Rv_1, v_2, \cdots, v_n v$

are proper if and only if

$(\exists ! \alpha)\phi\alpha$

$(\beta_1)(\beta_2) \cdots (\beta_n)(\exists ! \alpha)\phi\beta_1\beta_2 \cdots \beta_n\alpha$

can be derived from the previous definitions and axioms of the theory in question.

The definitions of '$f(x)$' and '$m(x)$' given above do satisfy this requirement, while the definition of '$p(x)$' does not.

4.8.2 AN APPLICATION OF CONTEXTUAL DEFINITIONS TO THE THEORY OF GROUPS

In this section, contextual definitions of definite descriptions will be applied to reformulate the theory of groups in a language without primitive singular terms. Theory B has three kinds of primitive singular terms: 'u', those containing '+', and those containing '*'. Thus, in reformulating the theory of groups, we must eliminate 'u', '+', and '*' as primitive symbols. This may be accomplished by replacing '+' by the predicate symbol 'Σ', where 'Σxyz' can be construed as '$x + y = z$'. The symbol '*' is replaceable by 'S', where 'Sxy' can be construed as '$x^* = y$'. We need not introduce a primitive symbol to replace 'u', because of special properties of the theory of groups. (Indeed, we need not even introduce one to replace '*', but the exposition will be a little easier if we do.) Thus our new theory, call it Theory B', will compose its wffs from variables, quantifiers, truth-functions, '=', 'Σ', and 'S'.

Identity theory is the underlying logic of Theory B', and in addition it has the following axioms:

Axiom 1 $(x)(y)(\exists ! z)\Sigma xyz$

Axiom 2 $(x)(\exists ! y)Sxy$

Axiom 3 $(\exists ! w)(x)(\Sigma xwx \cdot (y)(Sxy \supset \Sigma xyw))$

Axiom 4 $(x)(y)(z)(w_1)(w_2)(w_3)(\Sigma xyw_1 \cdot \Sigma w_1 zw_2 \cdot \Sigma yzw_3 \supset \Sigma xw_3w_2)$

The first two axioms are the uniqueness conditions for '$(\imath z)\Sigma xyz$' and '$(\imath y)Sxy$', respectively. The third is a combined "translation" of '$(x)(x + u = x)$' and '$(x)(x + x^* = u)$', and the fourth is a "translation" of '$(x)(y)(z)((x + y) + z = z + (y + z))$'.

Our problem is that of defining '+', '*', and 'u' in Theory B' and proving the axioms of Theory B as Theory B'. To do this, we first introduce definite descriptions into Theory B' by means of contextual definitions. The theory has seven relevant, primitive contexts: two for '=', three for 'Σ', and two for 'S'. Thus our method calls for seven contextual-definition schemata. These will not be given completely here, and are left as an exercise. Two are given now as examples.

Definition: $S\beta(\imath\alpha)\phi\alpha \equiv (\exists\alpha)(\phi\alpha \cdot (\gamma)(\phi\gamma \supset \gamma = \alpha) \cdot S\beta\alpha)$

Definition: $\Sigma(\imath\alpha)\phi\alpha\beta_1\beta_2 \equiv (\exists\alpha)(\phi\alpha \cdot (\gamma)(\phi\gamma \supset \gamma = \alpha) \cdot \Sigma\alpha\beta_1\beta_2)$

Once definite description is available, '+', '*', and 'u' are easily defined. By Axioms 1 to 3, the following definitions are proper:

Definition 8: $x + y = (\imath z)\Sigma xyz$

Definition 9: $x^* = (\imath y)Sxy$

Definition 10: $u = (\imath w)(x)(\Sigma xwx \cdot (y)(Sxy \supset \Sigma xyw))$

All that remains, then, is to derive the previous axioms of group theory as theorems of Theory B'. In order to do this, we must first develop several theorems which are consequences of our definitions of '+', '*', and 'u' in terms of definite descriptions. The next three theorems are all special cases of the schema

$(x)[Fx \cdot (y)(Fy \supset y = x) \supset x = (\imath z)Fz]$

mentioned in the last section.

THEOREM   1. $(z)(x)[Sxz \cdot (w)(Sxw \supset w = z) \supset z = (\imath y)Sxy]$

THEOREM   2. $(w)(x)(y)[\Sigma xyw \cdot (w_1)(\Sigma xyw_1 \supset w_1 = w) \supset w = (\imath z)\Sigma xyz]$

THEOREM   3. $(z)[(x)(\Sigma xzx \cdot (y)(Sxy \supset \Sigma xyz)) \cdot (w_1)[(x)(\Sigma xw_1x \\ \cdot (y)(Sxy \supset \Sigma xyw_1)) \supset w_1 = z] \supset z = (\imath w)(x)(\Sigma xwx \\ \cdot (y)(Sxy \supset \Sigma xyw))]$

Next we may obtain

THEOREM   4. $(x)(y)(\Sigma xy(x + y))$

THEOREM   5. $(x)Sxx^*$

THEOREM   6. $(x)(\Sigma xux \cdot (y)(Sxy \supset \Sigma xyu))$

(*Exercise:*   Prove these three theorems. *Hint:*   Use Axioms 1 to 3, Definitions 8 to 10, and Theorems 1 to 3.)

It is then easy to prove (in the order given)

THEOREM   7. $(x)(y)(z)(\Sigma xyz \equiv x + y = z)$ Exercise

THEOREM   8. $(x)(y)(Sxy \equiv x^* = y)$ Exercise

THEOREM   9. $(x)(x + u = x)$ Exercise

THEOREM 10. $(x)(y)(x^* = y \supset x + y = u)$ Exercise

THEOREM 11. $(x)(x + x^* = u)$ Exercise

We now have only

$$(x)(y)(z)((x + y) \neq z = x + (y + z))$$

to prove, and this may be accomplished as follows:

1	x,y,z	$\triangle$	A
2		$(x)(y)(z)(w_1)(w_2)(w_3)(\Sigma xyw_1 \cdot \Sigma w_1 zw_2 \cdot \Sigma yzw_3$	
		$\qquad\qquad\qquad\qquad \supset \Sigma xw_3w_2)$	Axiom 4
3		$\Sigma xy(x + y) \cdot \Sigma(x + y)z((x + y) + z) \cdot \Sigma yz(y + z) \supset$	
		$\qquad\qquad\qquad\qquad \Sigma x(y + z)((x + y) + z)$	3, UI
4		$(x)(y)\Sigma xy(x + y)$	Theorem 5

$\Sigma xy(x + y)$
?
$(w)(w_1)\Sigma ww_1(w + w_1)$
?
$\Sigma(x + y)z((x + y) + z)$
$\Sigma yz(y + z)$
?
$\Sigma x(y + z)((x + y) + z)$
?
$(x)(y)(w)(\Sigma xyw \equiv (x + y) = w)$
$\Sigma x(y + z)((x + y) + z) = x + (y + z) = (x + y) + z$
$x + (y + z) = (x + y) + z$
?
$(x + y) + z = x + (y + z)$
$(x)(y)(z)((x + y) + z = x + (y + z))$ UG

(*Exercise:*   Complete this proof.)

We have shown that Theory B has a definitional translation in Theory B'. The two theories are really equivalent, but showing that would take us beyond the scope of this book. The general method illustrated here is applicable to a rather wide class of formal deductive theories. Given any one of them, we can find a new theory which contains no primitive singular terms but into which the first can be translated by means of definitions.

EXERCISES FOR SEC. 4.8

A. Prove the unproved theorems of this section.

B. Define in Theory C the term 'x's maternal grandfather'. Show that the definition is proper.

C. Why cannot 'x's grandfather' be defined via a definite description?

APPENDIX

This appendix is devoted to demonstrating the soundness and completeness of the rules of inference used in this book.

A system of rules of inference is sound just in case the following conditions are satisfied:

1 If a schema is derivable (by means of the rules) from one or more schemata, then it is implied by them.
2 If a schema is provable (by means of the rules), then it is valid.

On the other hand, a system of rules of inference is complete (with respect to a class of schemata) if and only if these conditions are met:

1 If a schema (in the class) is implied by one or more schemata (in the class), then it is derivable from them (by means of the rules).
2 If a schema (in the class) is valid, then it is provable (by means of the rules).

It will be shown, first, that the truth-functional rules are sound and complete with respect to the class of TFS. Afterward, it will be shown that the truth-functional and quantificational rules are sound and complete with respect to the class of QS.

1 THE SOUNDNESS OF THE TRUTH-FUNCTIONAL RULES
In the demonstration of the soundness of the truth-functional rules, several simple laws of implication will be needed. They will be stated now and their proofs are left as exercises.

LAW A   A conjunction of one or more schemata implies each of its components; it also implies every conjunction of one or more of its components.

LAW B   If S comes from W, E, or N by one of the rules of inference, MP, MT, DNI, DNE, S, PC, add, DS, SD, PB, or MPB, then S is implied by the schemata W, E, or N from which it is obtained.

LAW C   If a schema implies each of several schemata, then it implies their conjunction.

LAW D   If the conjunction $S \cdot W$ implies E, then S implies the conditional $W \supset E$.

LAW E   If the conjunction $S \cdot W$ implies E and it also implies $-E$, then S implies $-W$.

The *premisses of a step* in a derivation (or proof) are the premisses of the derivation (if any) plus all the schemata which are assumptions heading up the vertical lines that pass by the step.

EXAMPLE.   In the following derivation the premisses of step 6 are '$p \supset (q \lor r)$', '$\bar{\bar{p}}$', and 'q'.

1	$p \supset (q \lor r)$	P
2	$\bar{\bar{p}}$	A
3	p	2, DNE
4	$q \lor r$	1, 3, MP
5	$\bar{q}$	A
6	r	5, 4, DS
7	$\bar{q} \supset r$	5-6, CP
8	$\bar{\bar{p}} \supset (\bar{q} \supset r)$	2-7, CP

A derivation (or proof) is *sound in a given step* just in case the step is valid or implied by the conjunction of its premisses. The example is a derivation which is sound in all its steps.

In order to establish that the truth-functional rules are sound, it will be shown that every derivation (or proof) constructed by means of them is *sound in all its steps*. Since the conclusion of a derivation has as its premisses the premisses of the derivation, it will follow that the conclusion of every derivation is implied by the premisses of the derivation. (Notice that there is a difference between the premisses of a derivation — these are the steps whose reason is 'P' — and the premisses of a given step.) Moreover, since the conclusion of a proof has no premisses, it will also follow that every provable schema is valid.

In order to prove that every derivation (or proof) is sound in all its steps, it suffices to show that

1   Every derivation (or proof) is sound in its first step.

2   If a derivation is sound in all steps up to a step (*n*), *then* it is also sound in step (*n*).

For suppose that (1) and (2) hold. Suppose, further, that a derivation (or proof) is not sound in some step. Since it is not sound in some step, there must be first step (*m*) at which it fails to be sound. This cannot be the first step by (1); so the derivation (or proof) must have earlier steps in which it is sound. But by (2), since it is sound in all steps earlier than step (*m*), step (*m*) should also be sound. This contradiction follows from the assumption that the derivation was not sound in some step; so that assumption must be false if (1) and (2) hold. This shows that our problem reduces to establishing (1) and (2).

It is easy to see that (1) must hold. For the first step of a derivation is either a premiss of the derivation or else an assumption. In either case this step is one of its own premisses; so by Law A the conjunction of its premisses implies it.

Before passing to (2), let us introduce the notation '$P(n)$' to stand for the conjunction of the premisses (if any) of step (*n*). '$P(i)$' stands for the conjunction of the premisses (if any) of step (*i*), and so on.

To establish (2), let us *assume that we are given an arbitrary derivation and that it is sound in all its steps up to step (n)*. We want to show that the derivation is also sound in step (*n*). To do this we distinguish a variety of cases, each answering to a possible way in which step (*n*) could have been introduced into the derivation. It will be shown that, in each case, the derivation is sound.

Case 1:   Step (*n*) is a premiss of the derivation. Then step (*n*) is one of its own premisses and implied by $P(n)$ by Law A.

Case 2:   Step (*n*) is an assumption.   (Exercise.)

Case 3:   Step (*n*) is a reiteration of an earlier step (*i*). Suppose that (*n*) and (*i*) have premisses. Then all the premisses of step (*i*) are also premisses of (*n*). So $P(n)$ implies $P(i)$. But since (*i*) is an earlier step, it follows by our assumption that $P(i)$ implies (*i*). So $P(n)$ implies (*i*). If (*n*) has no premisses, neither does (*i*). But then (*i*) must be valid; so (*n*) is also valid. If (*n*) has premisses and (*i*) does not, then both (*i*) and (*n*) are valid, and $P(n)$ implies (*n*).

Case 4:   Step (*n*) comes from one or more steps (*i*), (*j*), (*k*) by means of one of the rules MP, MT, . . . , MPB, and PB. Then, by Law B, the conjunction of (*i*), (*j*), and (*k*) implies (*n*). Suppose that (*n*), (*i*), (*j*), and (*k*) have premisses. Then every premiss of (*i*), (*j*), or (*k*) is also a premiss of (*n*). So by Law A, $P(n)$ implies each of $P(i)$, $P(j)$, and $P(k)$. So by Law C, it implies their conjunction. But as earlier steps, $P(i)$ implies (*i*), $P(j)$ implies (*j*), and $P(k)$ implies (k). Hence the conjunction $P(i) \cdot P(j) \cdot P(k)$ implies the conjunction $(i) \cdot (j) \cdot (k)$. (Why?) Therefore $P(n)$ implies (n). Suppose that (n) has no premisses. Then neither does (i), (j), or (k). So (i), (j), and (k) are all valid. Hence their conjunction is also valid. But since this conjunction implies (n), (n) is valid too. [*Exercise:* Handle the case in which (n) has premisses but one or more of (i), (j), or (k) does not.]

Case 5: Step (n) has been introduced via the rule of conditional proof. Then step (n) is a conditional whose antecedent is a step (i) and whose consequent is step $(n - 1)$. And as an earlier step, $(n - 1)$ is implied by $P(n - 1)$; that is, $P(n) \cdot (i)$ implies $(n - 1)$. But by Law D, $P(n)$ implies $(i) \supset (n - 1)$; that is, $P(n)$ implies (n). If (n) has no premisses, then (i) must imply $(n - 1)$. But then $(i) \supset (n - 1)$; that is, (n) is valid.

Case 6: Step (n) has been introduced via the rule of indirect proof. Then step (n) is the negation $-(i)$ of a step (i), which is itself an assumption from which two steps, (j) and $-(j)$, have been derived. [One of (j) and $-(j)$ is step $(n - 1)$.] Suppose that (n) has premisses. Then the conjunction of the premisses of (i), (j), and $-(j)$ is $P(n) \cdot (i)$. Since (j) and $-(j)$ are earlier than (n), they are both implied by $P(n) \cdot (i)$. So by Law E, $P(n)$ implies $-(i)$, that is, (n). [*Exercise:* Handle the case in which (n) has no premisses.]

Thus, in each of the five possible cases, the derivation is sound in step (n). Consequently, the derivation will be sound in step (n) provided that it is sound in all its earlier steps, and (2) must hold. This completes the proof of the soundness or the truth-functional rules of inference.

2. THE COMPLETENESS OF THE TRUTH-FUNCTIONAL RULES OF INFERENCE

Just as some auxiliary concepts were needed in the soundness proof of the preceding section, an auxiliary concept is needed for the proof of the completeness of the truth-functional rules. This is the concept of the *consistency as to derivability of a class of schemata*, or simply, the *D-consistency of a class of schemata*. We shall say that a class of schemata is *D-consistent* just in case no two schemata S and $-S$ may be derived (by means of the truth-functional rules) from any finite number of members of the class. (The class itself may be infinite in size.)

The key to the completeness proof will consist in tying D-consistency with interpretational consistency, that is, consistency in the sense of having a true interpretation. Let us say that a class of schemata is *I*-consistent if and only if there is a simultaneous interpretation of all its members under which they all come out true.

EXAMPLES

a. The class $\{p, q, p \lor q, q = p\}$ is I-consistent, since all its members come out true when 'p' and 'q' are both made T.

b. The class $\{p, q, p \lor q\}$ is not I-consistent; nor is it D-consistent, since 'p' and '$\bar{p}$' can be derived from its members.

The soundness of the truth-functional rules establishes that every non-empty I-consistent class of TFS is also D-consistent. For suppose that there is an I-consistent class of TFS which is not D-consistent. Then, for some TFS S, both S and $-S$ may be derived from some finite number of members of the class. But then S and $-S$ can also be derived from the conjunction of these members. Thus the negation of this conjunction can be proved by IP. And therefore it must be valid, since the rules are sound. But then the conjunction is inconsistent, and its components have no simultaneous interpretation under which they are all true. This contradicts the assumption that the class is I-consistent.

Next it will be shown that

1   Every nonempty D-consistent class of TFS is I-consistent.

From (1) the completeness of truth-functional rules follows. To see this, let us suppose that (1) holds and that S is a valid TFS. We want to show that S is provable. Since S is valid, $-S$ is inconsistent. So the class which contains just $-S$ alone is not I-consistent. Hence, by (1), this class is not D-consistent, and so, for some TFS W, both W and $-W$ may be derived from S (using the truth-functional rules). Thus we can construct a proof of S as follows: First assume $-S$; then derive W and $-W$ from it. Next apply IP to obtain $--S$, and then DNE to obtain S.

[*Exercise:*   Assuming that (1) holds, show that if a TFS S is implied by one or more TFS, then it can be derived from them. *Hint:*   The class containing $-S$ and the TFS implying S is not I-consistent.]

To prove (1), we shall show that every D-consistent class of TFS can be extended until it becomes a D-consistent class which contains every TFS or its negation. The idea behind the proof is that we start with a class and keep adding to it, making sure that at each step we preserve D-consistency. It will be necessary to make this more precise, however.

Let us assume that all TFS have been arranged in some sequence. For example, this can be done by placing the shorter ones before the longer ones, and those of the same length can be arranged "alphabetically". For example, taking the alphabet as $-, \cdot, \lor, \supset, \equiv, (,), ', q, r, s$, the TFS '$(p \lor q)$' would come after '$(p \cdot q)$' and before '$(p \supset q)$'. (For purposes of ordering TFS, it is convenient to replace the statement letters p_1', q_1', r_1', s_1', p_2', q_2', r_2', s_2', etc., by 'p''', 'q''', 'r''', 's''', 'p'''', 'q'''', 'r'''', 's'''', etc. In this way 'p'''', for example, can be construed as a TFS of length 3, that is, of the same length as '$--p'$'.)

Let us suppose that Γ is a D-consistent class of TFS. We shall now define a sequence $\Gamma_0, \Gamma_1, \Gamma_2, \ldots$ of D-consistent extensions of Γ.

Γ_0 is Γ

Γ_{n+1} is $\begin{cases} \Gamma_n \cup \{S_{n+1}\} & \text{if this class is } D\text{-consistent} \\ \Gamma_n & \text{otherwise} \end{cases}$

Here S_{n+1} is the $(n + 1)$st TFS in the sequence of all TFS. Next let Γ^* be the union of all the Γ_n in the sequence. Since each Γ_n is a subclass of Γ^*, Γ is a subclass of Γ^*. Also, Γ_{n+1} is D-consistent provided that Γ_n is. For $\Gamma_{n+1} = \Gamma_n$, or else Γ_{n+1} is the D-consistent class $\Gamma_n \cup \{S_{n+1}\}$. It follows that Γ^* is D-consistent if Γ is. For if Γ is D-consistent, then so are $\Gamma_0, \Gamma_1, \Gamma_2, \ldots$. Now suppose that Γ^* is not D-consistent. Then for some S, S and $-S$ are derivable from some finite number of members of Γ^*. But these members of Γ^* must also belong to some Γ_n, and thus this Γ_n would not be D-consistent. This contradicts the D-consistency of all the Γ_n.

The next stage in the proof of (1) consists in establishing several facts about Γ^*. These will be listed now:

a. If S is derivable from some finite number of members of Γ^*, then S belongs to Γ^*.
b. S belongs to Γ^* just in case $-S$ does not.
c. S and W both belong to Γ^* just in case $S \cdot W$ does.
c. S or W belongs to Γ^* just in case $S \vee W$ does.
e. Either S does not belong or W does belong to Γ^* just in case $S \supset W$ belongs to Γ^*.
f. Either both S and W belong to Γ^* or both $-S$ and $-W$ belong to Γ^* just in case $S \equiv W$ belongs.

These facts will be established one at a time. (Several will be left as exercises.)

(a) Suppose that S is derivable from some finite number of members of Γ^*. Now S is S_n for some n. So consider Γ_n. If S_n belongs to Γ_n, then Γ_n is $\Gamma_{n-1} \cup \{S_n\}$, and S_n belongs to Γ^*. On the other hand, suppose that S_n does not belong to Γ_n. Then Γ_n is Γ_{n-1} and $\Gamma_{n-1} \cup \{S_n\}$ is not D-consistent. Since S is derivable from members of Γ^*, it will be derivable from members of a Γ_m to which all these members of Γ^* belong. But then $\Gamma_{n-1} \cup \Gamma_m$ is not D-consistent. For from members of Γ_m, S can be derived, and from S and members of Γ_{n-1}, W and $-W$ can be derived for some W. Thus W and $-W$ can be derived from $\Gamma_{n-1} \cup \Gamma_m$. But then Γ^* (since it contains $\Gamma_{n-1} \cup \Gamma_m$) is not D-consistent, and this is a contradiction. So in either case S_n is a member of Γ_n. So it is a member of Γ^*.

(b) If S belongs to Γ^*, then $-S$ does not, since Γ^* would not be D-consistent if it did. Suppose that S does not belong to Γ^*. S is S_n for some n, and since S does not belong to Γ^*, it also does not belong to Γ_n. But then $\Gamma_{n-1} \cup \{S_n\}$ is not D-consistent. That is, W and $-W$ for some W can be derived from some members of Γ_{n-1} and S_n. But then we can construct a derivation with these members of Γ_{n-1} as premises, with S_n as an assumption, and with W and $-W$ in the subproof headed by S_n. Thus, by IP, we can derive $-S_n$ from these members of Γ_{n-1}. But then we can derive $-S_n$, that is, $-S$ from members of Γ^*; so by (a), $-S$ belongs to Γ^*.

(c) If either S or W belongs to Γ^*, then $S \vee W$ must also belong to Γ^*, since it is derivable from each of S and W. If neither S nor W belongs to Γ^*, then by (b) both $-S$ and $-W$ belong. But then $-(S \vee W)$ also belongs, since it is derivable from $-S$ and $-W$. (*Exercise:* Show that.) So $S \vee W$ does not belong to Γ^*.

[*Exercise:* Establish (c), (e), and (f).]

Next we shall give a simultaneous interpretation of all the members of Γ^* which makes them all true. This will show that both Γ and Γ^* are I-consistent.

Every statement letter or its negation belongs to Γ^*. This is a consequence of (b). So let us assign a statement letter the value T if it belongs to Γ^*; otherwise let us assign it F. It will be shown that this assignment makes all the members of Γ^* come out true by showing that

2   S comes out true for the assignment just in case it belongs to Γ^*

The proof of (2) can be reduced in the manner of the soundness proof of the last section to the proof of:

3   If S has no connectives, then S comes out true if and only if it belongs to Γ^*.

4   If (2) holds for all TFS with fewer connectives than S, then it also holds for S.

It is easy to see that (3) holds, since TFS with no connectives are statement letters.

Thus the proof has reduced to showing that (4) holds. Hence let us suppose that S is any TFS with one or more connectives and that (2) holds for TFS with fewer connectives than S. Five cases arise according to the main connective of S.

Case 1: S is $-W$. Then (2) holds for W. But $-W$ comes out true if and only if W comes out false. W comes out false if and only if it does not belong to Γ^*. But by (b), W does not belong to Γ^* if and only if $-W$ does. So $-W$ comes out true if and only if it belongs to Γ^*.

Case 2: S is $W \cdot E$. Then (2) holds for both W and E. $W \cdot E$ comes out true just in case both W and E come out true. But these come out true if and only if both belong to Γ^*. Moreover, both belong to Γ^*, by (c), just in case $W \cdot E$ belongs to Γ^*. So $W \cdot E$ comes out true if and only if it belongs to Γ^*.

Case 3: S is $W \vee E$. (Exercise.)

Case 4: S is $W \supset E$. (Exercise.)

Case 5: S is $W \equiv E$. (Exercise.)

Thus, in each case, S comes out true if and only if it belongs to Γ^*. This shows that (2) holds for S. Thus (4) holds.

Since (3) and (4) hold, (2) holds for all TFS. Hence Γ^* is I-consistent, and so is Γ. Thus, if Γ is a D-consistent class of TFS, then it is I-consistent too. This concludes the proof of the completeness of the truth-functional rules.

3. THE SOUNDNESS OF THE QUANTIFICATIONAL RULES

The proof of the soundness of the quantificational rules is simply an extension of the one used to prove the soundness of the truth-functional rules. However, before embarking on this proof, we must modify our terminology slightly, consider a minor variation on the quantificational rules, and establish some additional laws of validity and implication.

First let us turn to a modification in our terminology. By the soundness of a derivation in a step we shall now mean that the step is '$\triangle$', valid, or is implied by the conjunction of all its premises except '$\triangle$' (if that is one of its premises).

The variation on the rules comes to this: In initiating a UG or EI subproof, we shall now assume that the restricted variable is chosen so that it has never appeared before in the derivation. This imposes no limitations on what can be proved or derived by means of the rules, since at the end of a UG subproof we can always change the restricted variable while applying UG, and to end an EI subproof, we must obtain something that does not contain free occurrences of the restricted variable. Moreover, since the subproofs are restricted, using these new variables will not prevent us from using steps which could be used before. Thus these rules, with the additional restrictions on UG AND EI subproofs, are sound and complete if and only if the original ones are.

The laws needed are these:

a. If S comes from W by UI or EG, then W implies S.
b. If S is valid, then $(\alpha)S$ is valid.
c. If α does not occur free in W, then $(\alpha)(W \supset S)$ and $W \supset (\alpha)S$ are equivalent.
d. If α does not occur free in W, then $(\alpha)(S \supset W)$ and $(\exists\alpha)S \supset W$ are equivalent.

The proofs of some of them now follow.

(a)   The UI case. Suppose that S comes from W by UI. Then W is $(\alpha)S$. Let U be any universe, and I any simultaneous interpretation of S and $(\alpha)S$ in U. Suppose that I makes $(\alpha)S$ true in U. Then for all choices of α in U, S is made true in U by I. Thus if α occurs free in S, I makes S true in U. If α does not occur free in S, then $(\alpha)S$ and S have the same truth-value; so again I makes S true in U. (*Exercise:* Establish the EG case.)

(c)   Assume that α does not occur free in W. Let U be any universe, and let I be any simultaneous interpretation of $(\alpha)(W \supset S)$ and $W \supset (\alpha)S$ in U. Two cases arise. Case 1: I makes W false in U. Then I makes both $W \supset (\alpha)S$ and $(\alpha)(W \supset S)$ true in U. Case 2: I makes W true in U. Then I makes $W \supset (\alpha)S$ true in U if and only if it makes $(\alpha)S$ true in U. Also, I makes $(\alpha)(W \supset S)$ true in U if and only if it makes S true in U for all choices of α. So I makes both $(\alpha)(W \supset S)$ and $W \supset (\alpha)S$ true in U if and only if it makes $(\alpha)S$ true in U. Thus $(\alpha)(W \supset S)$ and $W \supset (\alpha)S$ are both made true in U or both are made false in U. Thus in either case 1 or case 2, I makes the two schemata have the same truth-value in U.

[*Exercise:*   Establish (b) and (d).]

The soundness proof will proceed as in the case of the truth-functional rules; that is, we shall show that

1   Every derivation (proof) is sound in its first step.
2   If a derivation (proof) is sound in all its steps up to a step (n), then it is also sound in step (n).

The proof of (1) runs as before, except that now we must consider assumptions that begin UG subproofs. (No first step can be an assumption of an EI subproof.) These assumptions are always '$\triangle$' and sound by definition; so every derivation is sound in such a step.

The proof of (2) also runs as before, but now we must consider steps that are introduced by the quantificational clauses of the rule of assumption, by UI, EG, UG, or EI. So let us consider each case anew.

Case 1:   Step (n) is a premiss of the derivation. This case is the same as before.

Case 2:   Step (n) is an assumption. Then (n) is 'Δ' or a schema. If it is 'Δ', then the derivation is sound in step (n) by definition. If it is a schema, then it is a component of $P(n)$, and so implied by it.

Cases 3–6:   These are as before.

Case 7:   Step (n) comes from an earlier step (i) by UI. Then by Law A, (i) implies (n). But every premiss of (n) is a premiss of (i) (if both have premisses). So $P(n)$ implies $P(i)$. But $P(i)$ implies (i), since (i) is earlier than (n). So $P(n)$ implies (n). If (n) has no premisses, then neither does (i). So (i) is valid, and thus (n) must be too. If (n) has premisses and (i) does not, $P(n)$ implies (i), since (i) is valid. But then $P(n)$ implies (n).

Case 8:   Step (n) comes from step (i) by EG.   (Exercise.)

Case 9:   Step (n) comes from steps (i) to $(n-1)$ by UG. Then step (n) is of the form $(\alpha)S$, and step $(n-1)$ is of the form S. Steps (1) to $(n-1)$ belong to a restricted UG subproof whose restricted variable β occurs nowhere in the derivation before it occurs in this subproof. If step (n) has no premisses, then step $(n-1)$ has no premiss besides 'Δ'. Thus, as an earlier step, step $(n-1)$ is valid. So, by Law B, $(\alpha)S$, that is, (n), is valid. Next suppose that (n) has premisses. Then the premisses of $(n-1)$ are the premisses of (n) plus 'Δ'. As an earlier step, $(n-1)$ is implied by all its premisses except 'Δ'; that is, $P(n)$ implies S. Hence $P(n) \supset S$ is valid. But then $(\beta)(P(n) \supset S)$ is valid. However, β does not occur free in $P(n)$; so $(\beta)(P(n) \supset S)$ is equivalent to $P(n) \supset (\beta)S$, which is also valid. But by a change of a bound variable, $P(n) \supset (\alpha)S$ is also valid, and this means that $P(n)$ implies (n).

Case 10:   Step (n) comes from steps (i), (j)-$(n-1)$ by EI. Then step (i) is of the form $(\exists\alpha)S$, step (j) is of the form S, and steps $(n-1)$ and (n) are both of the form W. Moreover, the restricted variable β of the EI subproof ending in $(n-1)$ does not occur before step (j) nor free in W. The premisses of (i) and (n) are the same, while the premisses of (j) and $(n-1)$ are those of (n) plus S. Suppose that (n) has no premisses. Then step $(n-1)$ is implied by S. That is, $S \supset W$ is valid. But then $(\beta)(S \supset W)$ is valid, and hence $(\exists\beta)S \supset W$ is valid. Yet, by a change of a bound variable, $(\exists\alpha)S \supset W$ is also valid. But then W, that is, (n), is also valid, since the earlier step $(\exists\alpha)S$ must be valid. Next suppose that (n) has premisses. Then $P(n) \cdot S$ implies W. But then $P(n)$ implies $S \supset W$; that is, $P(n) \supset (S \supset W)$ is valid. But then $(\beta)(P(n) \supset (S \supset W))$ is also valid and equivalent to $P(n) \supset (\beta)(S \supset W)$. This valid schema is in turn equivalent to $P(n) \supset ((\exists\beta)S \supset W)$, which is in turn equivalent to $P(n) \supset ((\exists\alpha)S \supset W)$. But then $P(n)$ implies $(\exists\alpha)S \supset W$. Yet $P(i)$ implies $(\exists\alpha)S$, and

$P(i)$ and $P(n)$ are the same; so $P(n)$ implies $(\exists\alpha)S$. From this it follows that $P(n)$ implies W. This concludes the extension of the soundness proof from the truth-functional to the quantificational case.

4. THE COMPLETENESS OF THE QUANTIFICATIONAL RULES

The quantificational rules include the truth-functional rules plus UI, EG, UG, and EI. Accordingly, to extend the previous completeness proof, we must redefine the notion of D-consistency to read

> *A class of QS is D-consistent just in case for no QS W are both W and $-W$ derivable (by means of the quantificational rules) from a finite number of members of the class.*

Also, I-consistency must be redefined to take account of universes of discourse. The definition now reads

> *A class of QS is I-consistent if and only if all its members have a simultaneously true interpretation in some universe.*

Finally, in this proof our attention will be restricted to *closed* QS. This is no limitation, since every universal closure of an open schema, that is, the result of prefixing universal quantifiers to bind all free occurrences of variables in the open schema, is valid just in case the open schema is. Moreover, an open schema is provable just in case its universal closures are.

EXAMPLE. '$Fxy \vee -Fxy$' is an open schema. One of its universal closures is $(x)(y)(Fxy \vee -Fxy)$. From a proof of the latter, we can obtain a proof of the former by two applications of UI. Moreover, given the proof of the first,

$$\left|\begin{array}{l} \cdot \\ \cdot \\ \cdot \\ Fxy \vee -Fxy \end{array}\right.$$

we can construct a new proof of the second:

$$\left|\begin{array}{ll} x\left|\begin{array}{l}\triangle \\ y\left|\begin{array}{l}\triangle \\ \cdot \\ \cdot \\ \cdot \\ Fxy \vee -Fxy \\ (y)(Fxy \vee -Fxy) \\ (x)(y)(Fxy \vee -Fxy) \end{array}\right. \end{array}\right. & \begin{array}{l} A \\ A \\ \\ \\ \\ \\ UG \\ UG \end{array} \end{array}\right.$$

(*Exercise:* Show that every nonempty *I*-consistent class of closed QS is also *D*-consistent.)

As before, the completeness of the rules will follow from

1   Every nonempty *D*-consistent class of closed QS is also *I*-consistent. Thus our main effort will center on demonstrating (1).

Before proving (1), we must consider a simple extension of the class of all QS obtained by adding a new sequence $i_1, i_2, i_3, \ldots$ of individual constants to our original list of individual constants and building QS as before with these new constants and the old ones. QS which contain such constants will be called *extended* QS. The quantificational rules can be easily extended to these new QS without affecting their soundness. The class of all closed QS and closed extended QS can easily be arranged in a sequence, and we shall assume that this has been done. The same will be assumed with respect to the class of all closed existential quantifications in this class. We can now turn to the proof of (1).

Suppose that Γ is a *D*-consistent class of closed QS. Let us define a sequence $\Gamma^0, \Gamma^1, \Gamma^2, \ldots$ of classes of closed QS and extended QS as follows:

Γ^0 is
Γ^{n+1} is $\Gamma^n \cup \{(\exists\alpha)S_\alpha \supset S_\beta\}$

where $(\exists\alpha)S_\alpha$ is the $(n+1)$st member of the sequence of closed existential quantifications of QS or extended QS and where S_β comes from S_α by replacing all free occurrences of α by the first constant in the sequence $i_1, i_2, \ldots$ not to occur in any member of Γ^n nor in $(\exists\alpha)S_\alpha$. (If α has no free occurrences in S_α, then S_β is simply S_α.) Next let Γ^+ be the union of all the Γ^n.

We can show that Γ^+ is *D*-consistent. For Γ^0 is *D*-consistent since it is Γ. Next suppose that Γ^n is *D*-consistent. If Γ^{n+1} is not *D*-consistent, then some W and $-W$ are derivable from members of Γ^n and $(\exists\alpha)S_\alpha \supset S_\beta$, where this extended QS is determined as in the definition of Γ^{n+1}. Thus, by IP, $-((\exists\alpha)S_\alpha \supset S_\beta)$ is derivable from members of Γ^n. But then both $(\exists\alpha)S_\alpha$ and $-S_\beta$ are also derivable from these members of Γ^n. Now consider the following derivation: The premises are the members of Γ^n in question. From these we derive $(\exists\alpha)S_\alpha$. Then we start an EI subproof whose restricted "variable" is β. Since β does not appear in the premises, they can all be reiterated into this subproof. Then we derive $-S_\beta$ from them. Now our subproof contains both S_β (its assumption) and $-S_\beta$. Thus we can derive '$p \cdot \bar{p}$' in the subproof and then remove it by EI. But then we can derive both 'p' and '$\bar{p}$' from our premises. But this means that Γ^n is not *D*-consistent—a contradiction. So Γ^{n+1} is *D*-consistent if Γ^n is. But then all the Γ^n are *D*-consistent, and so must be

Γ^+, since any derivation from its members is a derivation from members of Γ^n for some n.

Starting with Γ^+, we define a new sequence of classes $\Gamma_0, \Gamma_1, \Gamma_2, \ldots$, where

Γ_0 is Γ^+

Γ_{n+1} is $\begin{cases} \Gamma_n \cup \{S_{n+1}\} & \text{if this class is } D\text{-consistent} \\ \Gamma_n & \text{otherwise} \end{cases}$

Here S_{n+1} is the $(n+1)$st member of the sequence of closed QS and extended QS. Then Γ^* is defined as the union of the Γ_n. Virtually the same argument as we used in the truth-functional case may be used to show that Γ^* is D-consistent.

The next stage in the proof consists in establishing some facts about Γ^*. They are the old facts (a) to (f), except that they now apply to a new Γ^*, whose proofs are the same. In addition, there are two new facts:

g. S_β belongs to Γ^* for each individual constant β if and only if $(\alpha)S_\beta$ belongs to Γ^*.

h. S_β belongs to Γ^* for some individual constant β if and only if $(\exists\alpha)S_\alpha$ belongs.

Here is the proof of (g). Suppose that $(\alpha)S_\alpha$ belongs to Γ^*. Then S_β for each individual constant β is derivable from a member of Γ^* by UI. So, by (a), S_β belongs to Γ^* for each individual constant β. If $(\alpha)S$ does not belong to Γ^*, then, by (b), $-(\alpha)S_\alpha$ does. But $(\exists\alpha)-S_\alpha$ is derivable from this; so it also belongs to Γ^*. But then so does $-S_\beta$ for some constant β, because $(\exists\alpha)-S_\alpha \supset -S_\beta$ belongs to Γ^*. But then S_β does not belong to Γ^*.

[*Exercise:* Establish (h).]

Now we are ready to give a simultaneous interpretation of Γ^*. Our universe U will be the class of all individual constants (both new and old). Individual constants will be assigned themselves. Statement letters will be assigned T if they belong to Γ^*; otherwise they are assigned F. A monadic occurrence of a predicate letter Φ is assigned the one-place predicate:

Φ *with the individual constant* '①' *appended to it belongs to* Γ^*.

A dyadic occurrence of a predicate letter Ψ is assigned the two-place predicate:

Ψ *with the individual constants* '①' *and* '②' *appended to it (in that order) belongs to* Γ^*.

Other occurrences of predicate letters are interpreted similarly.

EXAMPLE: The QS 'Fa' is interpreted by assigning 'a' to 'a' and by assigning the predicate " 'F' with the individual constant '①' appended to it belongs to Γ^*'' to 'F'. Then 'Fa' is interpreted as true just in case 'F' with the individual constant 'a' appended to it belongs to Γ^*. In other words, 'Fa' is true under this interpretation just in case it belongs to Γ^*.

Next it will be shown that

2   S comes out true in U for the interpretation just in case S belongs to Γ^*.

This again reduces to showing:

3   If S has no connectives or quantifiers, then (2) holds for S.

4   If (2) holds for all QS or extended QS with fewer connectives and quantifiers than S, then it also holds for S.

The proof of (3) follows immediately from the interpretation chosen.
To show that (4) holds, we must again distinguish cases.

Cases 1 to 5:   The same as the truth-functional cases 1 to 5.

Case 6: S is $(\alpha)W_\alpha$. Then $(\alpha)W_\alpha$ is true in U just in case W_β is for each individual constant β. But since W_β has one less quantifier, this holds just in case W_β belongs to Γ^* for each individual constant β. And this holds just in case $(\alpha)W_\alpha$ belongs to Γ^*. Thus $(\alpha)W_\alpha$ comes out true in U just in case it belongs to Γ^*.

Case 7: S is $(\exists\alpha)W_\alpha$. (Exercise.)

This concludes the proof of the completeness of the quantificational proof. Since the universe U used in the proof is what mathematicians call a countable universe, an important corollary of the proof is the Löwenheim-Skolem Theorem:

> *Every D- (or I-) consistent class of* QS *has a simultaneously true interpretation in a countable universe.*

BIBLIOGRAPHY

1   GENERAL INTRODUCTIONS TO SYMBOLIC LOGIC
   Carnap, Rudolf: *Introduction to Symbolic Logic and Its Applications*, Dover Publications, Inc., New York, 1958.
   Copi, Irving M.: *Symbolic Logic*, The Macmillan Company, New York, 1954.
   Fitch, Frederic Benton: *Symbolic Logic*, The Ronald Press Company, New York, 1952.

Quine, Willard Van Orman: *Methods of Logic*, Holt, Rinehart and Winston, Inc., New York, 1950; rev. ed., 1956.

Suppes, Patrick: *Introduction to Logic*, D. Van Nostrand Company, Inc., New York, 1957.

2 ADVANCED TEXTS

Church, Alonzo: *Introduction to Mathematical Logic*, Princeton University Press, Princeton, N.J., 1956.

Kleene, S. C.: *Introduction to Metamathematics*, D. Van Nostrand Company, Inc., New York, 1952.

Mendelson, Elliott: *Introduction to Mathematical Logic*, D. Van Nostrand Company, Inc., New York, 1964.

Shoenfield, Joseph R.: *Mathematical Logic*, Addison-Wesley Publishing Company, Inc., Reading, Mass., 1967.

3 CLASS THEORY AND RELATION THEORY

Halmos, Paul R.: *Naïve Set Theory*, D. Van Nostrand Company, Inc., New York, 1960.

Quine, Willard Van Orman: *Set Theory and Its Logic*, Harvard University Press, Cambridge, Mass., 1963.

Suppes, Patrick: *Introduction to Logic*, D. Van Nostrand Company, Inc., New York, 1957.

4 THEORY OF DEFINITIONS

Suppes, Patrick: *Introduction to Logic*, D. Van Nostrand Company, Inc., New York, 1957.

5 FORMAL DEDUCTIVE THEORIES

Tarski, Alfred: *Introduction to Logic and to the Methodology of the Deductive Sciences*, Oxford University Press, Fair Lawn, N.J., 1941.

6 CIRCUIT THEORY

Hohn, Franz E.: *Applied Boolean Algebra*, 2d ed., The Macmillan Company, New York, 1966.

Whitesitt, J. Eldon: *Boolean Algebra and Its Applications*, Addison-Wesley Publishing Company, Inc., Reading, Mass., 1961.

7 PHILOSOPHY OF SCIENCE

Hempel, Carl G.: *Philosophy of Natural Science*, Prentice-Hall, Inc., Englewood Cliffs, N.J., 1966.

INDEX

INDEX

This book was set in Helvetica by The Poole Clarinda Company, and printed on permanent paper and bound by The Maple Press Company. The designer was J. Paul Kirouac; the drawings were done by Engineering-Drafting Company. The editors were James Mirrielees and Andrea Stryker-Rodda. William P. Weiss supervised the production.